Landscape Construction

North Carolina Landscape Contractors' Licensing Board

Manual of Practice

Special Edition

David Sauter

CENGAGE Learning™

Australia • Brazil • Japan • Korea • Mexico • Singapore • Spain • United Kingdom • United States

CENGAGE Learning

Landscape Construction: North Carolina Landscape Contractors' Licensing Board, Manual of Practice, Special Edition
David Sauter

Landscape Construction, 3rd Edition, David Sauter

This book contains select works from existing Cengage Learning resources and was produced by Cengage Learning Custom Solutions for collegiate use. As such, those adopting and/or contributing to this work are responsible for editorial content accuracy, continuity and completeness.

ISBN-13: 978-1-305-75540-6

Cengage Learning
20 Channel Center Street
Boston, MA 02210
USA

Cengage Learning is a leading provider of customized learning solutions with office locations around the globe, including Singapore, the United Kingdom, Australia, Mexico, Brazil, and Japan. Locate your local office at **www.international.cengage.com/region.**

Cengage Learning products are represented in Canada by Nelson Education, Ltd.

For your lifelong learning solutions, visit **www.cengage.com/custom.**

Visit our corporate website at **www.cengage.com**

TABLE OF CONTENTS

SECTION 6 LANDSCAPE PAVING

PREFACE

To change a site from an underdeveloped space to an attractive, functional, outdoor area, sound design and a skilled landscape contractor are needed. Just as the designer must perceive the visual potential and practical concerns that a site offers, the landscape contractor must possess creativity and a wide range of tangible skills to develop, interpret and implement the plan. Because Landscape Contracting in North Carolina requires knowledge of a broad range of construction techniques, the State licenses those qualified individuals who have the proper education, training and experience and can demonstrate that knowledge through the testing process.

This manual is intended for individuals readying themselves for the NCLCLB licensing exam and practicing professionals seeking to expand their expertise. The sections of this manual present that information according to the logical steps of landscape construction. The first section provides information regarding preconstruction activities, including design, safety, legal issues, interpreting construction documents, basic construction math, bidding and estimating, and other basic skills. Following this initial unit are sections dedicated to the work typically associated with landscape construction: site preparation; grading, site drainage, and erosion protection; site utilities; landscape retaining walls and stairs; landscape paving; freestanding walls; landscape amenities; and planting. Chapters within each section detail the steps necessary to install materials covered under the section's title. Fundamental data related to construction techniques and materials are provided.

CAUTION

Construction of any of the elements presented in this manual should not be attempted by those with little or no experience. If lacking in hands-on experience with any of these methods and techniques discussed herein, additional education, perhaps in the form of an apprenticeship, is highly recommended.

OTHER SUPPLEMENTARY TEXTS

A primary aspect of landscape construction is planting. This manual deals primarily with construction and installation techniques. The Landscape Contractor should have a working knowledge of horticulture as well. For this reason, The North Carolina Landscape Contractor's Licensing Board has prepared a companion text, North Carolina Manual of Horticultural Practice. This manual includes sections on basic botany, nomenclature, plant materials, horticultural site considerations, planting techniques and landscape management.

Another text, prepared by NASCLA and NCLCLB, North Carolina Contractors' Guide to Business, Law and Project Management presents an overview of the legal and business aspects of Landscape Contracting in North Carolina. The combination of these three manuals offers a base of knowledge for those preparing for the North Carolina Landscape Contractors' licensing exam as well as a reference for practitioners.

THE PROFESSION OF LANDSCAPE CONTRACTORS

When considering the importance of landscape contracting in the design and construction process, one should remember the significance of how the site is experienced. Judgments often begin with the first impression a visitor has of a site. People may not even enter a home, yet they develop an opinion of the occupant by how well the exterior environment is presented. People make decisions about whether to shop at a store without ever seeing the merchandise, but by judging the exterior of the business. Landscaping determines the economic or social success of many projects, and the work of the landscape contractor plays a significant role in determining that success.

As the importance of exterior image and environment has increased, so has the importance of the landscape contracting profession. Public appreciation of a well functioning and attractive site has been credited with increasing business in certain markets. What once may have been a sideline to a retail plant sale operation or a small contracting firm has now evolved into a variety of business types and service providers known as *landscape contractors.*

Environmental issues have also widened the role the landscape contractor must play. Concepts such as sustainable landscaping require that contractors think beyond altering the environment and consider the impacts their work has on the environment. Altering sites with sensitivity, reducing needless consumption of resources, selecting ecologically sound materials, and choosing low-impact construction methods are among the concerns facing today's contractor. To concurrently address both the alteration and preservation of the environment, the industry must incorporate new and old philosophies and attitudes.

An increase in the number of landscape contractors and the amount of work available in North Carolina have sparked significant changes in the industry. Basic among the types of landscape companies are the general practitioners who provide their clients a full range of landscape construction services. The growth of the industry has also led to a variety of specialists who concentrate on a single aspect of the process. Specialists are common in irrigation, grading, water feature construction, and planting. Depending on the size of the market, contractors who specialize in wall construction, decorative paving, and amenity installation can also be found.

The separation of design from construction has been reduced with the growth of design/build firms. Design/build companies prepare a design for the client and follow up with installation of the design. Many design/build firms can also provide separate services, if required, by a bidding situation. In recognition of the value of maintenance contracts for installed landscapes, a growing number of businesses offer a "full-service" approach that includes design, installation and maintenance of a project.

Many landscape contracts incorporate areas of the design and build process that involve allied professions and trades such as landscape architects, plumbing and irrigation contractors, electrical contractors and other trades, all while being ultimately responsible to the owner via the contract between the owner and the Landscape Contractor. As such, building relationships with the owners and allied team members is a critical part of being a landscape contractor. Working together as a team benefits the process and the results.

With the landscape contracting industry filling a variety of roles, it is necessary to prepare professionals who can address many aspects of the trade. This manual covers these diverse technical requirements in an attempt to improve the quality of work within the profession of landscape construction. Depending on their choice of specialization, landscape contractors may be required to master one, two, or possibly all of these skills.

The varied opportunities available for practicing in the field of landscape contracting and the specific career choice may determine what education and experience are required to be successful. This manual can be used in preparation for the NCLCLB licensing exam, and to improve the skills of a student or contracting professional in two ways. When used as a comprehensive manual, the entire process of landscape contracting can be viewed. Each section can also be used as a stand-alone teaching unit for introducing specialized construction techniques when appropriate. The NCLCLB strongly urges you to both read and practice. When addressing a technical topic such as this, few educational techniques work better than the combination of reading, seeing, and doing.

THE NORTH CAROLINA LICENSED LANDSCAPE CONTRACTOR

North Carolina has a rich history of landscape contracting. From large scale projects such as Asheville's Biltmore Estate, to our tree lined towns and cities, to the most intimate of private gardens, landscape contractors have played a large role in helping make North Carolina such a wonderful place to live in and visit.

The profession has grown from humble beginnings to be an important aspect of the state's economy. Realizing this importance and the impact it has on the state's economy and the public's health, safety, and welfare, the NC General Assembly, in 2014, revised the existing NC Contractors' registration process, making landscape contracting a licensed trade. The law, GS 89D, is a **practice act** requiring licensure for any landscape contracting project with a single-year value of $30,000.00 or more.

The law defines landscape contractor as:

Any person who, for compensation or other consideration, does any of the following:

a. *Engages in the business requiring the art, experience, ability, knowledge, science, and skill to prepare contracts and bid for the performance of landscape services, including installing, planting, repairing, and managing gardens, lawns, shrubs, vines, trees, or other decorative vegetation, including the finish grading and preparation of plots and areas of land for decorative utilitarian treatment and arrangement.*

b. *Practices the act of horticulture consultation or planting design for employment purposes.*

c. *Constructs, installs, or maintains landscape drainage systems and cisterns; provided the landscaping contractor makes no connection to pipes, fixtures, apparatus, or appurtenances installed upon the premises, or in a building, to supply water thereto or convey sewage or other waste therefrom as defined in G.S. 87-21.*

d. *Designs, installs, or maintains low-voltage landscape lighting systems, provided (i) the work does not exceed the scope of the exception set forth in G.S. 87-43.1(7) and (ii) the low-voltage lighting systems do not exceed 50 volts and constitute a Class II or Class III cord and plug connected power system.*

e. *Engages in the construction of garden pools, retaining walls, walks, patios, or other decorative landscape features.*

The law's definition of landscape contracting is a broad one that covers many activities. Licensed landscape contractors should only perform work in those areas that they are well educated in and have substantial experience in.

The law was created solely to protect the health safety, and welfare of the citizens of North Carolina. The legislation created the North Carolina Landscape Contractors' Licensing Board to work on behalf of the citizens to administer and enforce the law. The Board is self funded through licensing fees and has numerous powers and duties, all of which are in place to protect the public's interests. These duties include testing for licensure and the development and enforcement of minimum standards of practice. There are many aspects of the law, including multiple requirements and exemptions. Requirements include: yearly renewal, yearly continuing education, and upholding minimum standards. The full text of GS 89D is presented in Appendix H.

Allied North Carolina Professions, Trades, and Boards

A companion text prepared by NASCLA and NCLCLB, "Landscape Contracting in North Carolina (working title)" has a full overview of the GS 89D and other NC licenses and certifications associated with Landscape Contracting. The following are of particular interest to the NC Landscape Contractor in that the landscape contractor must not include in their services those of other licensed professions, unless an exemption exists for limited practice in these areas. Consult these licensing boards if you are uncertain of any aspects of the laws.

<u>GS 89A Landscape Architects North Carolina Board of Landscape Architects</u>

This practice act defines landscape architecture as "The performance of services in connection with the development of land areas where, and to the extent that the dominant purpose of the services is the preservation, enhancement or determination of proper land uses, natural land features, ground cover and planting, naturalistic and aesthetic values, the settings, approaches or environment for structures or other improvements, natural drainage and the consideration and determination of inherent problems of the land relating to the erosion, wear and tear, blight or other hazards. This practice shall include the preparation of plans and specifications and supervising the execution of projects involving the arranging of land and the elements set forth in this subsection used in connection with the land for public and private use and enjoyment, embracing the following, all in accordance with the accepted professional standards of public health, safety and welfare."

This law exempts the design of landscape elements for single family residences, sites one acre and less, and projects of any size that include the design of planting and mulching only. Contact the North Carolina Board of Landscape Architects for more information (www.ncbola.org).

GS 89G Irrigation Contractors North Carolina Irrigation Contractors' Licensing Board

Landscape Irrigation Contracting is now regulated in the State of North Carolina under GS 89G. The purpose of this **practice act** is to protect the public health, safety and welfare and to promote the efficient use of water. The North Carolina Irrigation Contractors' Licensing Board (NCICLB) oversees the licensing of Landscape Irrigation Contractors in North Carolina. According to this licensure law, no person shall engage in the practice of irrigation construction or contracting, use the designation 'irrigation contractor,' or advertise using any title or description that implies licensure as an irrigation contractor unless the person is licensed as an irrigation contractor.

This law has a number of exemptions that include any irrigation construction or contracting work where the price of all contracts for labor, material, and other items for a given jobsite is less than two thousand five hundred dollars for the life of the irrigation system. Contact the NCICLB (www.nciclb.org) for additional information.

NC Pesticide Law of 1971 - North Carolina Pesticide Board

Licensing is required for commercial applicators applying any type of pesticide for compensation, public operators working for a state or local government who apply pesticides in their course of work, dealers selling restricted use pesticides, or pest control consultants making recommendations for pesticide treatment of pest problems.

Pesticide Applicators

(A) Commercial Ground Applicators: The North Carolina Pesticide Law of 1971 requires licensing for individuals applying any pesticide for compensation.

(B) Public Ground Operators: Employees of federal, state, county, or municipal governments who apply pesticides in the course of their jobs are certified and licensed in the same manner as commercial applicators.

(C) Private Pesticide Applicators: Farmers, or their employees, who use restricted use pesticides in the production of an agricultural commodity, on land that they own or lease, are certified as Private Pesticide Applicators.

(D) Aerial Applicators: Pesticide applicators who apply pesticides with a plane or helicopter. The aerial applicator is required to pass two exams, one in aerial methods, and one in the specialty area in which he will work. The certification period for aerial applicators is two years, with an annual license renewal required.

Pesticide Dealers: Individuals who sell, distribute, hold, or make available for use restricted use pesticides to end users are required to have a Pesticide Dealer's License.

Pest Control Consultants: Anyone who, for a fee, offers or supplies technical advice, supervision, or recommends the use of pesticides is required to obtain a Pest Control Consultants License.

North Carolina Licensing Board for General Contractors

In 1925 the North Carolina General Assembly established the authority of the North Carolina Licensing Board for General Contractors, amending Chapter 318 of the Public Laws, designed for the purpose of safeguarding life, health and property and to promote public welfare. The Board issues several types of contractor licenses. Here are the types of contractor licenses the Board regulates:

- Building
- Residential
- Highway
- Public utilities
- Specialty: Water and sewer lines, Water purification and sewage disposal, Grading and excavating, Asbestos, Insulation, Roofing, Electrical (ahead of point of delivery), Boring and tunneling, Concrete construction, Interior construction, Marine construction, Masonry construction, Communications, Railroad construction, Metal erection, Swimming pools.

North Carolina licensed landscape contractors should familiarize themselves with these GC licenses to insure that their areas of practice are not considered solelyunder these laws.

Professional Associations

Many landscape contractors benefit from active membership in local and national contractors' and trade associations. These groups provide valuable support, education and information to those engaged in the practice of building landscapes. North Carolina's Green Industry is a diverse and vibrant sector of the economy and is represented by these associations:

- NC Nursery & Landscape Association
- NC Urban Forest Council
- Carolinas Irrigation Association
- Turfgrass Council of NC
- NC Sod Producers Association
- NC Commercial Flower Growers Assn.
- NC Pine Needle Producers Association
- NC Composting Council, Inc.

Similar national organizations include AmericanHort (the consolidation of the ANLA and OFA), The National Association of Landscape Professionals (formerly PLANET). The American Society of Landscape Architects, and the Association of Professional Landscape Designers.

Participation in one or more of these professional organizations has many benefits for the landscape contractor, such as broadening their knowledge through continuing education, staying current with regulatory issues, and widening their network. You may be competitors, but together, you build a stronger more professional industry.

REGARDING THE USE OF THIS MANUAL

- This manual is intended to provide an overview of the practice of licensed landscape contracting in North Carolina and to function as a study guide for the licensure exam. Additional supervised education provided by educational institutions and trade association is strongly advised.
- Practice of the profession of landscape construction is filled with safety and health hazards, and use of this book without proper experience or supervision will place the reader at risk. *The reader assumes all risk when engaging in unsupervised activities.*
- It is assumed that the readers of this manual possess basic skills necessary to safely perform landscape construction activities and operate construction equipment. Readers who lack skill in these tasks must obtain

instruction in these essential areas before attempting to undertake the activities described in this manual.

- It is important to understand what aspects of a project should be completed by the landscape contractor and when a professional from another trade should be called in. Throughout the manual, reference is made to work tasks that should be completed by related design and construction professionals.
- Design and construction references made within this manual do not supersede instructions provided by contract documents. Materials, methods, and performance required by plans and specifications must be followed.
- Historical restorations may require procedures different from those described in this manual.
- Manufacturer's instructions or manuals supersede the recommendations made in this manual.
- References made to proprietary materials or methods are not endorsements of those materials or methods.
- Verify with local building professionals the appropriateness of recommendations made in this manual. Local building officials should be contacted to verify legal requirements for the region in which any work is performed.

SECTION 1

BEFORE CONSTRUCTION BEGINS

INTRODUCTION

Before beginning any construction project, landscape contractors need to consider the safety, legality, sustainability, and process of the task they are about to undertake. Engaging in a project without knowing the risks involved may bring unnecessary dangers for the contractor, the crew, the public, and even on the site itself. Information presented in this section will detail many activities that landscape contractors should investigate before they begin any physical work.

Design, and steps undertaken to create the project you are about to build are covered in Chapter 1. The steps of the construction process, from preconstruction activities to cleanup, are covered in Chapter 2. Chapter 3 discusses legal complexities that may influence the project, including building codes, contracts, insurance requirements, and the relationship among the designer, client, and contractor. As an assist to those learning to implement design plans, a guide to interpreting construction documents is presented in Chapter 4. Landscape contractors must calculate material needs, estimate costs, and bid construction projects; to do so, they need basic math skills. The essential math formulas and examples presented in Chapter 5 will help students estimate costs of and bid on construction projects. As a corollary, Chapter 6 suggests methods for presenting project estimates and bids. Chapter 7 offers important advice to help a crew reduce its risk of injury during the construction process. Basic construction techniques, including equipment operation, are described in Chapter 8. Explaining the establishment of horizontal and vertical controls, Chapter 8 addresses accurate layout of proposed improvements.

Although they may be tempted to move quickly into the physical phase of a project, landscape contractors must examine the essential tasks that should precede actual construction. Planning and preparation can reduce the common risks found in, and minimize the potential hazards of, landscape contracting.

CHAPTER 1

BASICS OF LANDSCAPE DESIGN

OBJECTIVES

By reading and practicing the techniques described in this chapter, the reader should be able to successfully complete the following activities:

- Describe the design process
- Create exterior spaces using hardscape and softscape materials
- Arrange hardscape and softscape materials in esthetically pleasing forms
- Estimate the costs of a landscape design
- List the criteria for selecting plant material for a project

As with most aspects of the built environment, results are enhanced if the project is guided by a design or plan. The landscape is no exception to this axiom. When a creative and functional design is prepared that the landscape construction professional can use to guide installation the results typically far exceed a project installed in a haphazard and random fashion. The role of landscape design is to utilize a process that combines the conditions, restrictions, and opportunities of the site with the needs and desires of the client. When carried out under the direction of an experienced designer the final product blends function with esthetics to create an environment everyone can enjoy.

RELATED INFORMATION

Information in this chapter is supplemented by instruction provided elsewhere in this text and in other sources. Before undertaking the activities described in this chapter, read the related information in these sources:

- Legal Requirements, Chapter 3
- Interpreting Construction Documents, Chapter 4
- North Carolina Manual of Professional Horticultural Practice
- Construction Math, Chapter 5
- Project Pricing, Chapter 6
- Materials and Installation Techniques for Retaining Walls, Chapter 18
- Materials and Site Preparation for Paving, Chapter 24

DESIGNING THE LANDSCAPE

Design has many definitions, but when applied to the field of landscaping it can be said that landscape design is the creative arrangement of elements on a site in order to solve the problems of the site and serve the needs of the user. This approach involves following a process, or series of steps, and using traditional and invented methods to create a better environment. As a result of this process it is intended that any issues present on the site have been resolved and that improvements in the way the client wants to use the site have been addressed. While this is a very simplified description of landscape design, it serves as an introduction to the goal of designing the landscape.

The mystery and fear encountered when preparing a landscape design can be overcome when the designer learns the tools that have been used in the profession for centuries. Like any problem solving encounter, designing a landscape is a matter of having a set of steps (design process) to follow and techniques (design theories) to accomplish each step. The more complex the problem(s) being solved, the more steps and techniques involved. For the designer intending to take on simple basic issues, learning the steps of the design process and applying the techniques listed below should provide adequate results. The designer should remember that the process, whether the short or long method, is basic to all projects. The theories of design can be applied as necessary. In designs that involve creating spaces for the entire site and selecting plants and materials, it would involve, at a minimum, use of the theories on the creation of spaces, functional arrangement of spaces, and designing with plant material. For issues that are simpler, the short process with the designing with plant material theory may be adequate. In any project the design theory on esthetics may be beneficial to improve the look and function of the design.

As presented in this text, the topic is condensed to the very basics and is intended to serve as an primer for anyone attempting to design. A licensed landscape contractor who engages in design must remember that many designers have years of training and experience, and the practice of both the art and science of design benefit from extensive experience they possess. That should not, however, discourage licensed landscape contractors from engaging in the design process and learning the skills that lead to creation of functional and attractive environments. Even if the goal of the Construction Professional is not to design, understanding how the process works and choices are made will aid them in building projects. For licensed landscape contractors who wish to include design as a major component of their business, additional education from community colleges and universities with a proven landscape design curricula should be considered. In addition, there are many design related continuing education opportunities offered by professional trade associations.

Design Elements Beyond the Scope of the Landscape Construction Professional

There will be projects for which the Landscape Construction Professional is not qualified or legally allowed to design. It is the Landscape Construction Professional's responsibility to understand the limitations applied to their ability to design. In many states, design must be undertaken by a licensed Landscape Architect or other licensed Design Professional. This limitation includes most non-private projects, projects in which the public can be exposed to dangers from sub-standard design and projects which require significant engineering. The Landscape Construction Professional must also be aware of their design capabilities, and seek professional help when they are not sure about answers.

Presentation of Designs

Designs can be presented to clients in many forms, ranging from a photos of an idea similar to what is being proposed to elaborate three-dimensional drawings. Most typically the design is presented to the client in a two-dimensional graphic form call a plan (Figure 1-1) The plan shows a bird's eye view of proposed improvements that are drawn to scale using symbols and textures to illustrate the landscape elements. The plan illustrates the design showing the horizontal dimensions of length and width, but does not graphically show the vertical dimension. Using the plan a designer can use lines to show the limits of the project and structures, shapes to outline the boundaries of hardscape improvements, and rounded symbols representing plant material. When drawn to scale, full sized site reduced to the size of the paper on meaning the drawing is an exact replica of the which it is drawn, the plan serves as a tool to

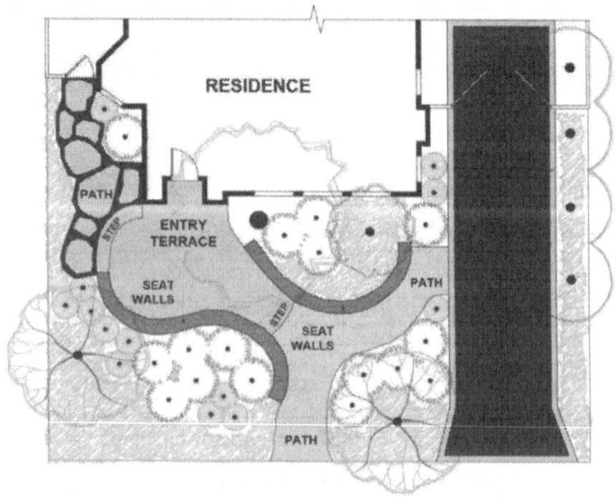

Figure 1-1. Example of a plan view drawing used to share designs with clients.

understand how the parts of the design will work together to address the needs of the client. A plan can be produced on almost any size of paper, with 18" x 24" and 24" x 36" being the most common, and can be black and white or rendered with color. Typically one of the first steps to be taken in the process of design, the plan often begins by drawing the existing conditions on a sheet of paper that will serve as a base map for continued work. This base map serves as the underlying guide for arranging landscape elements and eventually the parts of the base map that are to be retained are traced along with the elements proposed to create a graphic representation of the landscape design.

In addition to the plan, designers may use photographs of ideas or proposed plant materials or three-dimensional sketches to communicate to clients their recommendations for improvements (Figure 1-2). While these methods are good at illustrating the idea, the lack of two-dimensional measurements will required additional work be done to construct the project. To illustrate design ideas that have vertical elements (such as walls, fences and arbors) the designer may use sections or elevations to explain their ideas. The section and elevation are drawings that show the design using one of the horizontal dimensions, either length or width, and the vertical dimension. Like their plan counterpart, sections and elevations are drawn to scale to give the client and contractor a measureable drawing from which to build.

Figure 1-2. A three-dimensional sketch used to share design ideas with clients.

DESIGN PROCESS

Creating a landscape design is made easier by following a process that guides the transformation from existing to desired. Regardless of the size of the project, a thought process that asks questions and evaluates options in an orderly fashion will typically produce results that are more effective that randomly attacking the issues. To accomplish this orderly transition, the design process is one of the most effective tools used by the designer. While the actual number of steps and procedures used for each step may vary from designer to designer, they typically involve analyzing the problem, preparing alternative solutions, and then selecting and articulating the solution which best addresses the original problem. This process can be brief if the encounter with the client is to address a simple problem, such as picking a plant to shade a patio or deciding how to screen an unsightly view, or can be very extensive if the project involves a large site with many decisions to be made. For many landscapes the process will lie somewhere between these two extremes, with the designer needing to determine with an initial phone call or site visit whether the project requires a formal (lengthened version) process or the use of a consultation (a shortened version) process (Figure 1-3).

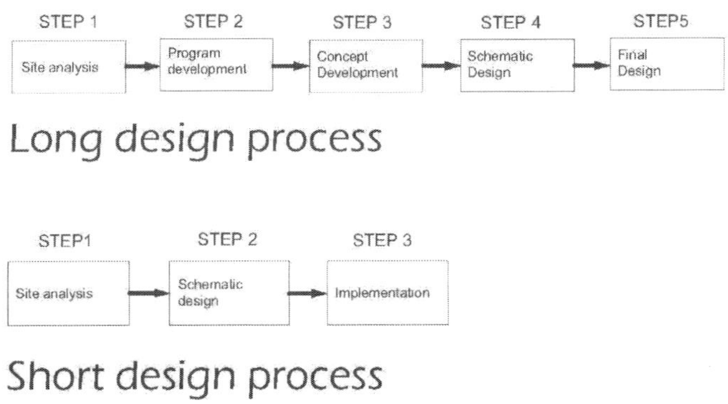

Figure 1-3. Flow chart of long and short versions of the design process.

Formal (Long) Process

The longer, formal process for design is appropriate when the designer is facing a large or complex project. This form of the design process includes specific steps in which various activities are performed to address the complexity of the project. Each step is sequential and can involve the investigation of a great number of topics, but when performed properly the designer can create solutions for projects that include a number of landscape elements woven together into an acceptable arrangement. The formal process will typically require multiple visits to the site as well as meetings with the clients. The designer will almost always prepare landscape graphics that illustrate their ideas to their clients and to contractors who will build the project. It is also possible that local jurisdictions will have codes and ordinances that must be considered as part of the process. The general steps of the formal process are identified below in their recommended order.

Site Analysis. The process begins with collection of data regarding the site. Typical information collected will be boundary information, topographic data, location of existing structures and site improvements, location of existing plant material on the site, and the routing of utilities that serve the site. The designer should also make notes regarding the conditions on and surrounding the site, such as good views, outstanding features, and problems such as drainage issues or intrusive elements. This information can be provided by a land surveyor with existing map provided by the owner, but is often collected by the designer visiting and measuring the site.

Preparation of a base map that notes the above information provides a beginning point for creating the design. Base maps should have important information such as the drawing scale, north direction, and notes about utilities and data collection placed directly on the drawing (Figure 1-4). Photos of the site can also aid in the recall of specific site conditions during later phases of the process.

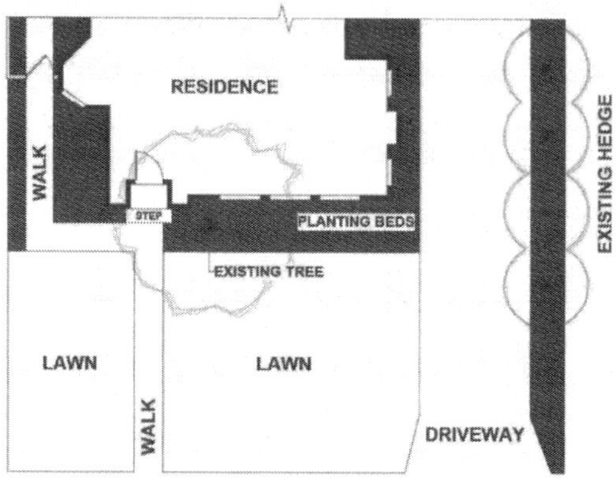

Figure 1-4. Example of a base map.

Program Development. In addition to gathering information about the site, the designer must spend time identifying the needs and desires of the client. An interview with all parties involved in using the site is a helpful tool to discuss what activities should be planned for the project, and to discuss items such as timeline, budget, construction, who will maintain the site, and what their future plans for the site include. Legal limitations on such items as fences, pools, water features, irrigation, lighting and vehicles should also be noted at this stage. Collect specific information regarding the size of patios and decks, where vehicles will park, access to the site, service areas, children's needs for play and client needs for gardening, relaxing and storage of items. This information is typically gathered in written form that will later be converted to spaces and plants on the design graphics.

Concept Development. Once a base map has been developed and program information sorted out regarding client needs, the physical design of the site begins. The designer removes from the base map all elements that will not be part of the final design. The program information is converted into "bubbles", or general shapes that represent the approximate size and configuration of the spaces desired by the client. Some spaces must be represented by shapes that are of particular dimensions and configuration, such as drives for vehicles must be of the appropriate width and dining areas must be large enough to contain a table and chairs. Other spaces may have variable dimensions and form, such as vegetable gardens, lawns, and water features. The designer then draws these "bubbles" on the base map in various patterns that create a functional and esthetic layout. When arranging the spaces it is important that the location of spaces match the function, such as drives connect roadways with a garage and access routes connect walkways to doors and use areas. Begin with the fixed shapes that require exact positions, then be creative in placing the spaces that have variable form requirements. A deck may need to be connected to a structure near the family room, but a planting bed may be placed in a variety of locations and configurations. Show in the concept how the arrangement of space will address items such as drainage from the site, and how grades will be traversed (using placement of stairs, walls and ramps). Continue placing spaces until all the required elements are located on the site. If not elements fit on the site a more creative solution must be found or the program scaled back, and if extra space is available spaces can be added or expanded. These conceptual options should be in graphic form and drawn to scale so they can be evaluated by others. Review with the client various arrangements to find out if one idea is more acceptable than others. When agreement is reached, that concept will move to the next step of the process.

Schematic Design. Using the concept that is the most appropriate solution for the site, create a more specific design by turning the conceptual "bubbles" into exterior "rooms" and landscape plantings. This design will also be in graphic form, with the layout more precise and detailed than the conceptual drawing. The loose "bubbles" from the concept should now be given hard edges that represent landscape components such as the edges of walks, railings on decks, edgers around lawns and borders around beds. These exterior "rooms" should fill up all open space of the site, with no open, unused area between them. If additional room exists, expand adjacent "rooms" until they abut each other. To enhance the quality of the design in this phase, try different form arrangements (such as rounded forms, square forms, see Form Composition below) to see if a single form or combination of forms creates a more pleasing composition. Recall that planting spaces can take on many forms, so in addition to using plants for their own program purposes, also use plants to fill between the hardscape areas on the design. The schematic design will be complete when all of the spaces have the correct size, configuration and location and are arranged in a pleasing manner on the site.

Final Design. The last step in creating the graphic design is to add all appropriate detail to the drawing. A final design is typically prepared in plan form after spending time with the client choosing desirable plants and materials for hardscape and reviewing budgets to verify that the project can be constructed. This detail can include such items as plant names, materials for paving, elevations and dimensions for hardscape improvements, and construction details for carpentry items. Most final designs will include a plant list that indicates the species of plants recommended as well as notations on the drawing that show the plant location. Notes and enlargement of detailed areas are also common additions to the design. This document, which may be a plan for a new patio or a master plan for an entire site, will serve as the reference for implementation of the project over the life of the construction period.

Construction Documents. Typically prepared by a Landscape Architect, the construction documents are the detailed drawings that specifically guide the building of the project.

Construction documents (see Chapter 4) typically include plans that show what elements of the existing site that are to be protected or removed, the placement of utilities, layout of new elements, grading of the site, placement of proposed plant material and details for specific improvements. Also included are specifications that dictate the methods and materials that are to be used in construction. Construction documents allow a project to be competitively bid by providing the contractors a uniform and specific set of instruction that allow their price to be compared to other contractors. While construction documents can be prepared for any size of project, it is possible that a contractor, when allowed by law, can build improvements using the final design document. In this instance the project is typically limited in scope, easily interpreted with no significant limitations and supervised by the designer during implementation.

Implementation. Once design and construction documents have been prepared, the project is implemented. This phase, which can run for a few days to several years, involves the installation of the elements identified in the design.

Maintenance. Following the completion of the project installation, caring for the plant material, hardscape and landscape systems installed must be considered. Often left to the client to implement, proper maintenance is essential to bring the design to its full recognition, and to keep the design functioning as planned over the life of the project. Failure to properly adjust systems, prune plants and maintain hardscape will shorten the useful life of a project significantly. To ensure the health of the project, the designer or the contractor should orient the client to proper maintenance techniques and guide them to a competent landscape gardener for the long-term care of the site. In sites with extensive improvements, a maintenance manual can be prepared that will document the activities and methods that provide the best care for a project.

Evaluation. Periodically, a designer should return to a project to evaluate how well the solutions devised addressed the original problems. Viewing a mature garden from the standpoint of function and esthetics can help the designer improve their techniques, process, approach to design theory and choices in materials and placement in future projects.

Consultation (short) Process

The consultation would be reserved for those projects where the problem is isolated, straightforward, and can be solved through consideration of ideas recommended while meeting with the client. Examples would include problems that involve the placement of no more than a small group of plants, typically only two or three species, or correction of some hardscape issue that does not require extensive work or permitting. While this process is condensed in time and effort, it is, none the less, a form of the design process. When consulting with a client the process steps are typically orally discussed and a plan, if any, is prepared on graph paper or described and agreed to by both parties. The phases of the design process outlined above that are typically involved in consulting are analysis, schematic design and implementation. If consultation is the proper approach to design, the designer will typically ask questions to identify the problem and the parameters in which a solution can be established. Discover what the client needs and what might allow or prevent a solution. The designer can then recommend a small number of solutions that the designer and client can discuss at that moment, evaluating each idea to determine if one or more will provide an adequate response to the problem. If one of the solutions presents itself as appropriate, the designer can then arrange for implementation of that idea.

Design Process and Budgeting

Throughout the process of designing a landscape it is advisable to track the estimated costs of improvements recommended for a site. The estimates do not need to be excessively detailed during the early phases of the design, but should be accurate enough to identify if the desired elements of the program are even possible to build with the client's budget. In is not unusual to find out early that the amount set aside for improvements by the client will not cover the cost of all that they desire. When faced with this dilemma the designer should discuss options with the client, including expanding the budget, phasing the project over several budget cycles or scaling the project back to match expectations and resources

DESIGN THEORY

Working in concert with the design process is design theory. While process is the road the designer travels down, design theory is the vehicle that carries them on the trip. Design theory is a collection of tools the designer uses to make decisions as they determine the size and placement of elements in the landscape. How do we know where the outdoor dining area should be located, how do we know if a hedge is a better choice than a fence, how do we know how many people can be entertained on a deck; each of these questions require answers generated by the extensive list of tools available to the designer engaging in design theory. While the approaches to design listed below are only a partial listing, they represent many of the basic ways a designer will turn an existing site and some scribbled notes into a functioning exterior.

Use of Existing Site Features

Evaluating the site for existing features that have value is a staple of the design process. The designer should not overlook the obvious elements that can help a design. Existing plant material that is healthy, structures that can be utilized, good views, outstanding architecture...these are all examples of what might already be on a site that can enhance the final product. While the designer should be responsible and remove that which is not working towards a solution to site problems, it is equally irresponsible to remove elements that are still valuable. With the concept of sustainability underpinning our work, items that can be recycled for other purposes in the design add a new dimension of reutilizing site features. Old paving materials that can be turned into walls, water that can be captured on site, plants that can be pruned into useable specimens are all examples of examining the site for "found" treasures.

Creation of Spaces

Many designers use the theory of creating "outdoor rooms" when designing the landscape. Like the architecture of a structure, one can view the use and arrangement of outdoor space like arranging rooms in a home. There are areas for entertainment, areas for recreation, eating spaces, work spaces, and service areas. When engaging in the conceptual layout of a design the outdoor room technique has the benefit of viewing a space for appropriate size and correct placement in the landscape. To further develop the concept of outdoor rooms, visualize each space as having walls created by fencing or plant material, with windows and doors in that room created by the openings through the plants. The floor is the paving or ground cover and if a roof is required a tree can be placed nearby or an arbor added over the space. Another technique for creating outdoor rooms is to draw the rooms needed (as identified in the program development) on a sheet of paper and tear them out along their boundaries. The pieces of paper can be set on the base map and rearranged like a puzzle to explore different placement options. Once a successful arrangement has been created a second sheet of paper can be laid on top of the pieces and traced for a concept (Figure 1-5). This technique is particularly helpful for the new designer, or one who is experiencing a mental block on how to arrange spaces. Experienced designers can often visualize these spaces without such tools, but do not hesitate to use any method available to improve your design.

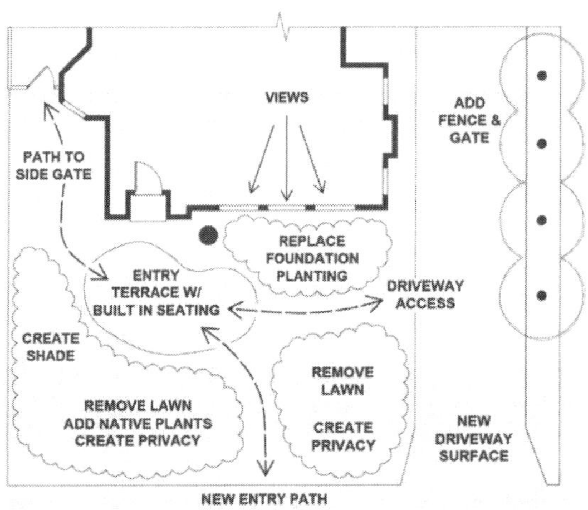

Figure 1-5. A concept drawing showing location of spaces.

Functional Layout of Spaces

An important aspect of design theory is the functional layout of the elements of a design. It does little good to place a windbreak away from the prevailing wind, or to locate a vegetable garden in an area with too much shade. Because each space designed must function properly it is not uncommon for a designer to list the functional criteria of a space as part of the conceptual design. This involves noting where a space should be located with regards to orientation, sun access, near water, near an interior space or other similar types of restrictions. Designers can do a separate diagram to plot the necessary layout of several related spaces. This diagram can be simple circles that are arranged so that the spaces which must be adjacent are identified, while those spaces that can or must be separated are placed accordingly. Engaging in this task before entering into the conceptual design phase will make that step of the work more effective.

Several types of spaces have specific requirements for placement within the landscape. When the need for these types of areas is identified in the program the designer must pay attention to the details required for addressing each area.

Service Areas. Spaces around the home or business that are dedicated to storage, work and other non-recreational tasks typically require isolation from spaces that are used for other purposes.

Service areas often require fences or hedges for screening, and may have specific access and utility requirements. Spaces along the sides of structures and behind garages are common placement areas, but with creativity many of the service areas can be incorporated into the unscreened areas of the design. Potting sheds and compost bins could be key design elements in any design.

Recreational Areas. Residential landscapes are commonly filled with areas for adults and children to play. Knowing the dimensions and physical requirements for such activities as play courts, swimming pools and play structures will help in determining the placement of such elements. In addition to the recreational activities with prescribed dimensions and grades, adding space for free play can often be accommodated using lawn and open space that also ties together other use areas.

Outdoor Living Areas. Almost every design includes some type of outdoor space that is to be used for the basic functions of life. Whether dining, cooking, entertaining or simply relaxing the outdoor living area is a staple of most landscape designs. To properly design such areas it is important to understand the activity to be performed and the number of people to be accommodated. Sizing the space can be based on the average number of users that will occupy the space. Most designs are based on this average to avoid under or over building a space.
Sources are available for determining sizes, but for a patio/deck the average of 40 square feet per person is a common minimum. More space will be required for the furniture used in the space and if cooking is involved the access to cooking and serving surfaces should be considered. If the client entertains often, the space may be made larger or access to overflow areas such as lawns and patios may be necessary. Certain activities will require that the space be located next to interior spaces for easy access, while others may require connection to gas, electric, or other utilities. Placement of outdoor living areas will be a critical component of the design, so beginning the conceptual process with placing these elements is recommended.

Garden Areas. Few landscape designs are complete without the inclusion of gardens. Whether the purpose is for food production or simply esthetics, the garden is a foundation element in landscape design. Fortunately, the variety of plant sizes and shapes makes the creation of gardens one of the more flexible spaces in the landscape. Gardens can be of almost any shape and size, and the placement can include every range of cultural conditions on a site. When choosing the location for a food production garden, keep in mind the need for sun to grow many of the typical garden plants and the need for water and soil amendments to keep plants healthy. Many also like to have these gardens near a kitchen for easy access, and the level of maintenance dedicated to the garden will determine whether it is a service activity to be screened or a well maintained garden that can add to the esthetic appeal of the landscape. Lacking space, many garden plants can also be established in containers that reduce the limitations of size. Gardens and plantings, including many planting beds and specimen plants should be located where they are seen or discovered. Such additions to the landscape are intended to be viewed and should be placed where they receive proper exposure.

Site Amenities. Features placed on the site to enhance the appearance or use of the project will typically require special design considerations. Water features, playgrounds, utility sheds, sculpture, lighting and other components that create special interest would fall under this category. Review the installation instructions for each amenity to discover if utility connection or special site preparation, such as concrete footings or special surfaces are necessary. Examine the directions to find out what types of dimensions should be allowed for the feature and for the safe/work zone around the feature. Include these findings in the program descriptions of each amenity to help in finding the proper location during conceptual design.

Grade Changes, Walls and Stairs. When working with a site that has significant grade changes, special attention must be paid to how those grades are managed. It may be possible to leave the grade unchanged and plant the slope with ground covers or turf, but if more useable area is desired or there is a fear of erosion it may be prudent to terrace the slope using retaining walls. Whether walls or a planted slope is used, if a circulation route traverses the slope the designer must determine if the pathway can be accomplished by following the existing grade, extending the length of the path across the grade to lower the slope, or installing stairs. When walls are used it will almost always involve stairs to connect levels. Understanding the physical parameters of stairs, including the proper rise and run, and what limitations on grade changes are necessary to accommodate the disabled will all be elements of designing with grade changes.

The Esthetics of Landscape Design

It would be foolhardy to spend the time arranging a landscape that served only functional needs and ignored the visual appeal. While the landscape must perform its functional roles, doing so in an attractive manner creates an additional dimension to the design. Esthetics are often considered to be personal and a matter of pleasing the person who is viewing or performing the design work. Even when allowing for a wide range of personal choice regarding what is considered attractive and what is considered oddly out of place, the esthetics of design are guided by various sets of principles that help the designer create and judge the appearance of their work.

Elements of Design. Four basic tenets of design that carry significant importance in the landscape are the elements of design: form, texture, line and color. The application of these elements provides interest and gives life to a design, and they can be applied to numerous parts of the design at any stage of the design process.

- Form refers to the shape of spaces and objects. The viewer of the landscape can see form in the shapes of the patios, decks and lawns of the landscape, and can also see form in the materials that are used. Forms can be of any composition (see Form Composition below) or can be very standard geometric shapes. Design theory ranges on the use of form in designs, but most suggest that a design have a single dominant form with the possibility of one or two subordinate/complimentary forms. An example would be a formal landscape laid out with primarily rectangular shapes for walks, lawns and plantings, but having a living area that is rounded in shape. This

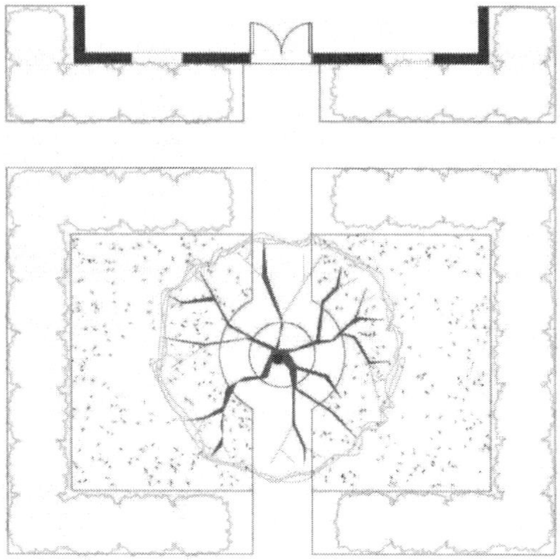

Figure 1-6. An example of form as a design element.

creates a single dominant form that is complemented by the limited use of a second form. There are, however, no stringent rules that would preclude a designer using several forms in a design as long as they are coherent and adhere to the design principles noted below (Figure 1-6).

- Texture refers to how smooth or rough a surface appears and is based on the visual perception of objects in a landscape. Most often texture is judged using the size of leaves on plants, with small leaves creating fine textures and large leaves creating coarse textures. The hardscape elements can also suggest texture, with smooth concrete creating a fine texture while intricate brick paving creates a busier, coarser texture. Texture can also be used in combination with form to suggest a fine texture in a manicured landscape (clipped hedges and trimmed lawns) or a rougher informal landscape (using natural shapes of plants and unmown ground covers). For interest, most landscapes attempt to provide a range of textures to keep the viewer interested. This means providing a diversity of plant material with different leaf sizes, and considering the placement and texture of hardscape elements Figure 1-7).

Figure 1-7. An example of texture as a design element.

- Line refers to the linear form created by the intersection of two distinctly different textural surfaces. Areas where lawns meet planting beds, trees meet the sky, where hardscape meets plant materials would be examples of line in the landscape. Line is one of the more difficult design elements to create, but is one of the most obvious to see when the design is viewed. Conscience attempts to created line in the landscape are typically done using form composition techniques that are used to create the spaces and outdoor rooms of the landscape. More subtle attempts at designing with line include the use of plants that will be silhouetted against skylines or walls. Line typically helps in evoking feelings through the landscape and moving the eye to desired locations within the site (Figure 1-8).

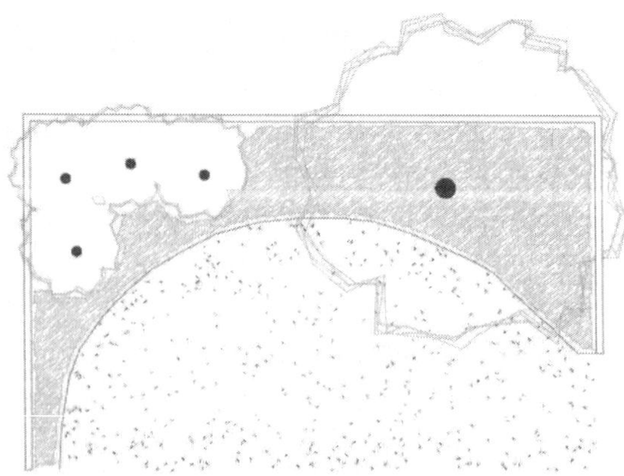

Figure 1-8. An example of line as a design element.

- Color in the landscape is an unavoidable element to design work. Each of the components of design, both plant material and hardscape, bring color in some form to the design. In some ways, the overwhelming presence of green in the landscape creates the need to work as hard at considering color as any of the design elements. Color evokes feelings, aides in depth perception, creates interest, provides the surprise and continuity of the design and when used correctly color is the strongest of the design elements. To successfully use color the designer must understand the basics of color theory and where and when the color is present in the landscape. Color theory suggests that colors be selected that follow one of a few schemes. These schemes would include:
    - monochromatic (all colors are shades and tints of a single color)
    - analogous (all colors are from adjacent spots on the color wheel)
    - complementary (colors are selected from opposite or triadic locations on the color wheel).

When colors are from a planned scheme the visual impact in coherent and orderly. Greens, whites, grays and variegated colors can be used to join and/or separate the colors. The designer must consider the sequencing of color from season to season, providing plants that offer interest in the spring, summer, fall and winter. Color is not only the show of the flower or bloom, color can also be obtained from subtle sources such as twigs, berries, buds and fall foliage color. The hardscape element also offers the opportunity to provide color, with vertical surfaces such as walls and fences being more prominent that horizontal surfaces.

Designers will use shapes of rooms, forms of ground cover and planting beds, placement of larger plant material, selection of hardscape, and, most commonly, the selection of plants to introduce the design elements. For a design to provide maximum visual impact all of the design elements should be considered as part of the design.

Form Composition. One of the most important aspects of the landscape design is the form given to the spaces used to create outdoor rooms. For many designers the choice is an unconscious collection of spaces created by the functional layout of the needed patios, gardens, lawns and other spaces dictated by the program. While this method to create form is not incorrect, a higher order design has given at least some consideration to converting these random spaces into a collection of spaces that are unified through geometry. Form composition involves refining these random edges into shapes that can be recognized and create particular moods and a unity among the design elements. The composition of form is based in adjusting or placing the visible edges, primarily horizontal but also vertical, in positions that create arcs, angles, and lines. Any geometric form can be used in landscape design, but the most common compositions are squares and rectangles, angular, diagonals, circles, arcs/tangents and combinations of these shapes. The generic forms are primarily used to create the edges of open spaces (including outdoor use areas, lawns, and planting beds) while the generic form or a complementary form is used to treat transition areas between spaces and detailed edges.

- Squares and Rectangles. Forms that have opposite sides of equal length that are parallel create a formal feel. Rectangles in particular give a landscape the look of a proper and elite space that is easy to view and traverse. The eye is drawn to the corners of such spaces is decorated, and to the centers of the sides if openings are created. Square and rectangles also have a strong focal point at the center of the space, and it is common to place art, water or specimen plant material at that location. Rectangles can be arranged with the centers of the sides aligned to create formal rooms

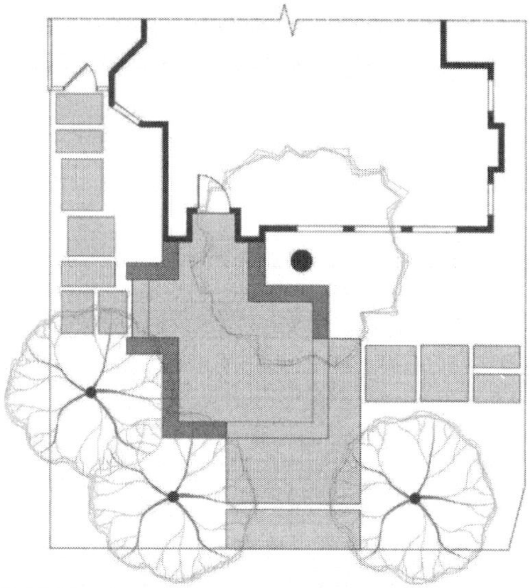

Figure 1-9. Form composition using squares and rectangles.

linked together, which squares can be arranged in the same type of patter or placed in rows and/or columns to create more informal gridded landscapes (Figure 1-9).

- Angles. Angular arrangement of lines energizes a landscape, creating a less formal yet hard edged spaces. To be successful with angular arrangements the designer should confine the angles to families of angles that work well together (such as 90 and 45 degrees or 30 and 60 degree angles). Mixing too many differing angles together will create an undecipherable arrangement that is uncomfortable and unattractive. Too many small angles, even when complementary, will also create a space difficult to identify. Angles should be broad and observable for most spaces, with smaller variations used for transition spaces. Care should be taken to minimize the use of acute angles where spaces intersect as they create difficult visual and maintenance issues (Figure 1-10).
- Diagonals. Diagonals are a variation of angular compositions that utilize 45

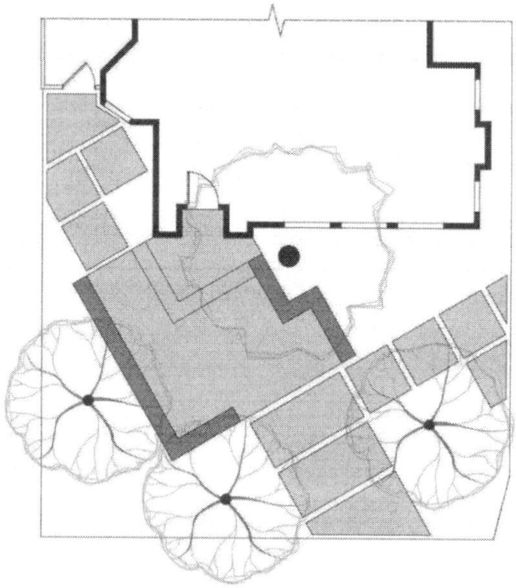

Figure 1-10. Form composition using angles.

degree angles to dissect large spaces. Diagonals can be very attractive when combined with other forms used for transitions. Use of diagonals also creates interesting and energetic spaces with dynamic shapes.

- Circles. Circular spaces create peaceful and tranquil spaces for most outdoor use areas. Placing circular spaces in the landscape ease the viewer into the space and create a strong focal point at the center of the space. Lacking any angled corners, the viewer's eye moves continuously until a break or focal point is provided to stop the pan. Use of multiple circular spaces creates a series of spaces that have an undulating edge considered softer to view than the harsher linear edge. Circles can be nested, overlapped, or repeated to create larger and more diverse spaces. When intersecting circles the extension of the circle1 - 25 should pass through the center of the adjacent circle in order to provide visual order (Figure 1-11).

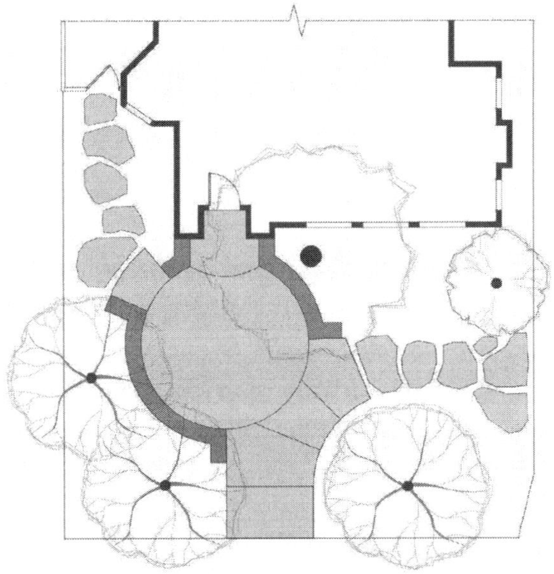

Figure 1-11. Form composition using circles.

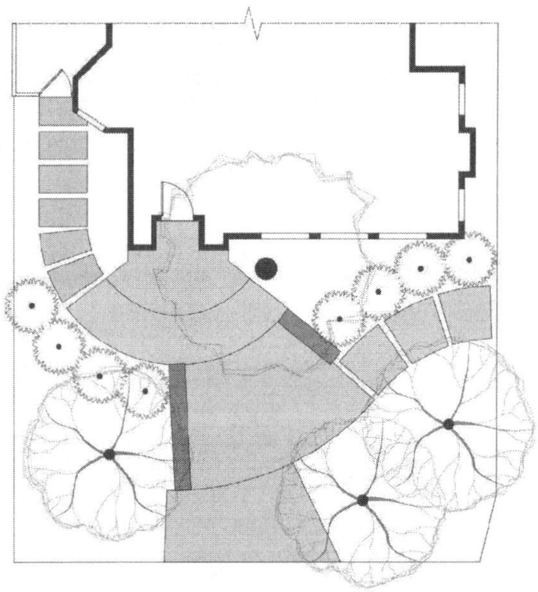

Figure 1-12. Form composition using arcs and tangents.

- Arc/tangents. The arc/tangent, or curvilinear design is a derivation of circles and is considered to be one of the most natural and distilling line available to the landscape designer. Lacking sharp corners and jointing concave and convex arcs, the curvilinear shape most closely mimics natures form composition. When creating arcs for this form, utilize no more than one-third of the full circle. Tangents (straight lines) do not need to be placed between arcs, but can be used to extend the form to match the size of a shape without necessitating a wavy line (Figure 1-12).
- Form combinations. Forms from the above list can be combined in many ways to create a variety of moods and feelings for a site, as well as to transition between site and architecture. When combining forms it is best to have a dominant form that makes up the majority of the edges, while a second subordinate form is used to complement or contrast the primary dominant form. Placing the transition from one form to another at a grade change, at a location where moving from hardscape to lawn/planting, or when going around a corner or through a vertical structure in the landscape will make the transition smoother (Figure 1-13).

Material Selection. Most designers jump immediately to the material selection in design. In addition to being a topic which most understand it is also one which most are exciting about performing. Material selection would include articulating the choices of hardscape materials and, in some cases, the plant material recommended to the client. When selecting materials it is important to place this step in the proper sequence as well as considering all aspects of materials selected.

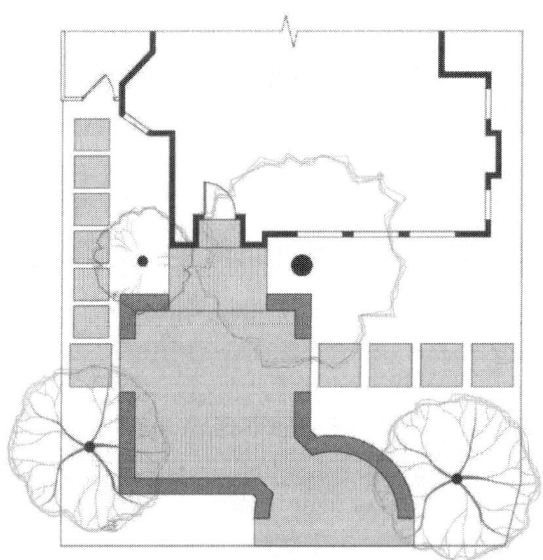

Figure 1-13. Form composition using a combination of basic geometric forms.

Material selection should be undertaken after the design reaches the Final Design stage of the process. Spending inordinate amounts of time deciding if a patio should be brick or stone will serve little purpose if the design process shows that a patio is not a necessary component of the design. Often the excitement of clients to have a designed space pushes the designer into making choices before the need has even been studied. Once the time reaches to choose materials, do so based on the time of space that has been recommended, and include consideration of characteristics such as maintenance, cost, esthetics, and installation methods.

The materials chosen for a design often remain with the design for the life of the project, so using the proper method for making such choices is critical.

Principles of Design. When preparing a design, the designer must have some method to judge if their work is conforming to basic artistic principles. Designers use the principles of design to make such judgments and also to guide their work as they assemble the components of their site.

While subjective and subject to interpretation depending on what design text you might read, the principles can be summarized by defining a few simple artistic concepts.

- Unity is a principle that demands a harmonious relationship between all aspects of the design. Design that exhibits unity creates a sense that everything used to create the design belongs there, whether it is the color for a wall to a plant with a particular form. It is achieved, in part, by successfully using the other design principles and by maintaining a consistency in the elements selected for the site. This common thread may be a color, form, design style, material or a unifying element in each of these components.
- Order is the overall organization of the design, including the selection of design elements as well as their function and placement in the design. For a garden that emphasizes an edible theme, order could be expressed as including an outdoor kitchen, dining area, garden and entertainment area with plants selected that provide food as well as esthetics. Order is typically lacks clutter and is a neat and tidy arrangement of spaces and selection of garden elements.
- Scale, or sometime called proportion, means the size of the elements relate to the site, and the elements of the site relate to the user. Scale is the human perception of space and design elements as they relate to the viewer. In most cases the landscape elements should not be too tall or short, or placed so close or far away that a person using the landscape feels uncomfortable. Creating overhead structures or shade trees with branches that create a roof to outdoor spaces is a common method of making patios feel more human scale, while using entry arbors can help scale entries to large landscapes.
- Balance is the equality of visual mass on either side of a particular sight line. It directs the eye of the viewer and helps to move people through a space. Balance is created by placing an equal amount of vertical object on either side of where a view is to be directed. If a designer wants the public to see the front entry to a residence, a balanced planting framing the entry will accomplish that task.
- Rhythm involves the relationship and linkage between landscape elements. Rhythm has several subcomponents that can be created with elements, such as repetition, contrast, and variety.
    - Repetition of elements creates a strong sense of calm, order and helps move the eye around the landscape. It the element is a plant movement it can be something that is repeated such as a hedge or vine planted on a wall that creates backdrop and is consistent across a wide area.

- Contrast is the use of an element to attract the eye, such as a plant with unique characteristics from the surrounding plants, plants with color or unique textures or other landscape elements such as sculpture or water features. Emphasis is used to draw a viewer's attention to a particular location in the landscape.
- Variety is the use of dissimilar items to create interest in the landscape. While not as intensified as contrast, variety refers to using plants of different textures and colors to create an interesting palate for the scenery or the use of two or three paving types to identify different areas of use.

The entire corps of design elements work together to create a design that both functions and looks attractive. To simplify your use of design principles, arrange the design first to meet the functional requirements of the site and program, then add or subtract elements based on whether the design meets the tests of the principles. Not every design will be able to satisfy each of the requirements of the principles, but pay particular attention to the concepts of Unity and Order. If any principles provide the most reliable guidance it would be creating order and unity from the elements selected. During the design process, unity and order are more closely associated with all phases of design, while scale, balance and rhythm are more associated with schematic and final design steps.

DESIGNING WITH PLANT MATERIAL

Of all the design elements that can be used for landscaping, plant material is the most important. Despite the heavy use of hardscape and the glamour of lighting, without plant material the design is merely an interior space without a roof. This level of importance dictates that plant material be addressed separately from general design theory.

Design using plants will follow the same process as the design of overall site, with special consideration given to when and where plants can function as the floors, walls and roofs of outdoor spaces. This relationship of planting design to the design process allows an ever progressing level of detail be determined, reducing the stress of trying to select from every available plant to perform a particular purpose.

- Analysis/program development. During analysis, several items related to plant material should be considered. Initially the designer should identify the location and condition of existing plant material. Decisions as to whether existing plants are to be kept and incorporated into the design or removed can be made based on this information. In addition, site conditions such as sun orientation, soil type and available water for plants will later influence the placement and selection of plants. Lastly, observing where plants can be used to block cold breezes, create shade, screen views and other environmental design issues should be documented during analysis.
- Conceptual design. Treating plant material during conceptual design is a matter of creating "bubbles" that represent the uses of plants to resolve issues identified in the analysis and to address needs/desires of the clients. While the "bubbles" do not contain a specific plant name, they do indicate if the type of plant to be used is evergreen or deciduous, tall or short, specimen or background. The shapes of the "bubbles" can be arranged to meet almost any dimensional criteria, with shapes of almost any size accommodating the future choice of plant.
- Schematic design. When moving into the schematic design phase, plant material "bubbles" should turn into plant movements shown by circles and textures representing plants and ground covers, respectively. Detailing the shapes of plant movements should follow the general rules identified in the form composition section above. Specific plant

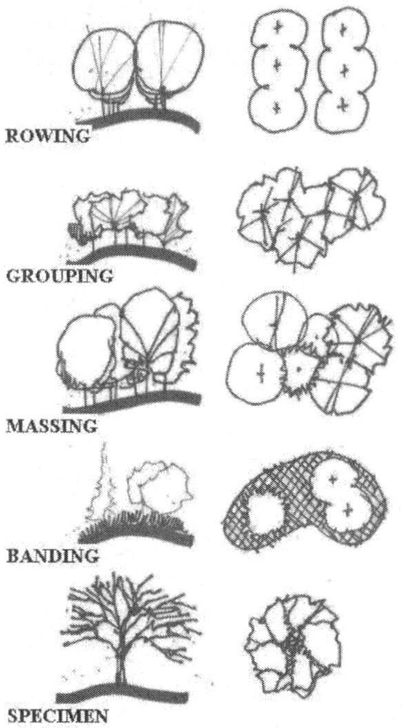

Figure 1-14. Planting techniques

movements can be created using the following techniques (Figure 1-14):

- Rowing. Placing several plants in a row to screen or emphasize a view.
- Grouping. Setting small groups, typically 3 to 9 plants, of the same species together for screening, space separation or as a focal point.
- Massing. Placing a large group of plants, typically 5 or more, or mixed species to create and separate space.
- Banding. Placing a low growing mass of ground cover or other low growing plants around other plant groupings and specimens in order to combine them into a single planting movement.
- Specimen. Placing a single, ornamental plant in a position to attract attention.

- Unless shading an entire area of the site, the circles should be confined to the space created by the "bubbles". These circles should indicate the category of plant material (as listed below) that will best serve the identified purpose of the plants and fit into the dimensions available. At this point it is also helpful to note if a particular hydrozone is desired for each plant grouping. This will help in later choosing plants appropriate to the water conditions of the planting location. Note that names for plants have still not been required, only the location and classification as noted below (Figure 1-15).

- Overstory (or shade trees). Deciduous, coniferous, evergreen broadleaf woody plants; woody over 40' in height.
- Understory (or ornamental trees). Deciduous, coniferous, evergreen broadleaf woody plants 15' to 40' in height
- Tall shrubs. Deciduous, coniferous, evergreen broadleaf woody plants 10' to 15' in height.
- Medium shrub. Deciduous, coniferous, evergreen broadleaf woody plants 10' to 15' in height
- Low shrubs. Deciduous, coniferous, evergreen broadleaf woody plants up to 5' in height.
- Perennial forbs.
- Perennial decorative grasses.
- Ground covers evergreen.
- Ground covers annual.
- Turf.

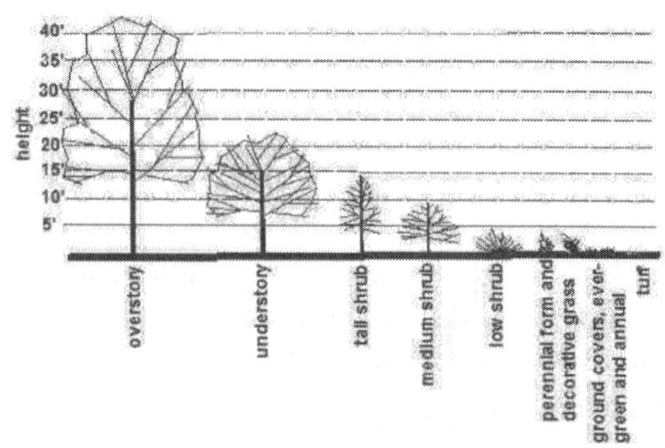

Figure 1-15. Classification of plants for the schematic phase of planting design.

Note: the designations in this list are the author's and may vary from designer to designer.

- Final design. At this step specific plant material area selected to complete the design. Consider plants in the following order: identify necessary turf areas, select overstory (shade) trees first, understory (ornamental) second, shrubs (all classes) third, then finish with perennials, decorative grasses, and ground covers. Considering the availability of plant material in regions throughout the country, this will allow you to select plants from the smallest pool (trees) first and the largest pools last giving you the maximum number of choices. Plants should be chosen so that they meet the required classification (as noted above), cultural requirements and esthetic characteristics desired for each location within the site. Specific criteria of each consideration is as follows:
    - Classification. The plant should fit within the circle identified in the schematic design phase when it reaches mature size. Some designers will recommend that the maximum size be slightly larger than the circle to create faster fill in and allowance for pruning.
    - Cultural requirements.

Water requirements. Plants require water to survive and the available water at the planting location must match the plants need for water. The concept of hydrozoning, or placing plants of similar irrigation needs together, is a widely accepted method for placing plants in the landscape.

- Sun exposure. Identify if the plant required full, partial, or very limited sun exposure. Placing a plant in the wrong exposure may deter growth, flowering, fruiting and development.
- Soil. Plant material derive their water and nutrients from the soil, as well as using soil for anchoring the root system of the plant. While many soils are suitable for planting any type of plant, certain plants may be sensitive to poor soils.
- Maintenance requirements. Selecting plants that are prone to specific predictable maintenance problems can lead to higher maintenance costs over the life of the plant. Severe problems can limit the length of the plants life.
- Pests. As with maintenance, certain plants may be susceptible to known pest problems that can cost the plant and client over the long term. Minimizing selection of these plants will help the overall sustainability of the project.
- Esthetic requirements. Choosing plants that add to the esthetic beauty of the site is a primary concern for the plant lover. Choices should be carefully planned to choose and arrange the plants based on the design elements noted above; line, form, color and texture. Consider all parts of the plant when looking for design elements. Beauty can come from foliage, branches, flower, fruit, fall color, form, size and virtually any component of a plant.

SUSTAINABILITY IN THE LANDSCAPE

Concerns regarding the quality of our environment have not escaped the field of landscaping. In many ways, the landscape profession has been a leader in identifying materials and developing processes that enhance our surroundings. Concepts such as preserving soil, composting waste, capturing rainwater, reducing irrigation, limiting pesticide use and similar types of common place activities in the landscape field have been placed under the heading of sustainable landscaping, or sustainability. A full list of considerations should be included at various points in the landscape design process that ensure the design is providing maximum consideration to sustainability. These considerations would include the following:

- use of drought tolerant plants to reduce irrigation
- use of native plants and locally adapted non-invasive plants to protect native plant communities
- selection of plant material that will attract wildlife and beneficial organisms
- creating a diversity of habitats with plant material, including varying height of plants
- preserving native soil and enhancing damaged soil with organic matter
- using Integrated Pest Management as best practices for controlling landscape pests
- adjusting irrigation equipment to provide efficient use and distribution of water

To assist the designer in preparing designs that are more environmentally friendly, many local governments have instituted ordinances or guidelines for creating sustainable landscapes. In addition, national organizations such as the Green Building Council and the American Society of Landscape Architects (in conjunction with other environmental groups) have created initiatives intended to improve sustainability in the build environment. The Green Building Council has established a rating system for construction and development entitled Leadership in Energy and Environmental Design (LEED) and the ASLA has created the Sustainable Sites Initiative to educate professionals on the techniques for creating sustainable landscapes.

ADDITIONAL CONSIDERATIONS

As mentioned in the introductory paragraphs, this section on landscape design can provide only an overview of everything that has to happen to create professional landscape designs. A few of the items that are condensed or not discussed in this section include the following:

- Maintenance requirements. Keeping the new landscape in good condition can often require more effort than the original design and construction. While the majority of the effort for maintenance is performed after construction, considering the maintenance load of various design options, hardscape selection and plant choices can reduce the long term costs of a project. Understanding which choices will lead to higher maintenance costs and fully explaining the options to a client during design is often a necessary step.
- Future development. Designs that are prepared for the needs of today may not serve clients in the future. Be certain to ask questions about expanding house plans, how long they intend to live at the residence, are more children planned and are there future desires they haven't shared yet through the program. While not all future considerations can be incorporated into design, creative planning may allow a lawn to be converted to a swimming pool, a play structure to a perennial garden or a garden to a gazebo when the need arises.
- Cost estimates. Throughout the design process it may be important to keep the client appraised of the anticipated costs of the project. Using the techniques described in Chapter 5- Estimating Costs the client can updated at the end of each phase as to whether the project is adhering to the budget defined in the analysis and program development.

CHAPTER 2

THE LANDSCAPE CONSTRUCTION PROCESS

OBJECTIVES

By reading and practicing the techniques described in this chapter, the reader should be able to successfully complete the following activities:

- Describe the steps of the construction process.
- Plan construction activities.

The process of landscape construction should be efficient yet complementary to other projects in progress at a site. Landscape work has many potential conflicts—e.g., delays in material delivery, tardiness or illness of crew members, periods of inclement weather, numerous contractors at work at the same time—and by being aware of such conflicts, as well as the activities required during construction, landscape contractors can better control the progress of their projects.

This chapter outlines the general process for landscape contracting improvements. Each major step is identified, along with the basic construction activities that will occur during the process, and an explanation is given for why such activities must be performed (Figure 2-1). Timeline alternatives that accommodate variations in the industry are also given. It should be noted that the process outlined in this chapter serves as a guideline; actual construction practices may vary from contractor to contractor, and from region to region, or may change as the size of the project increases or as the weather conditions fluctuate.

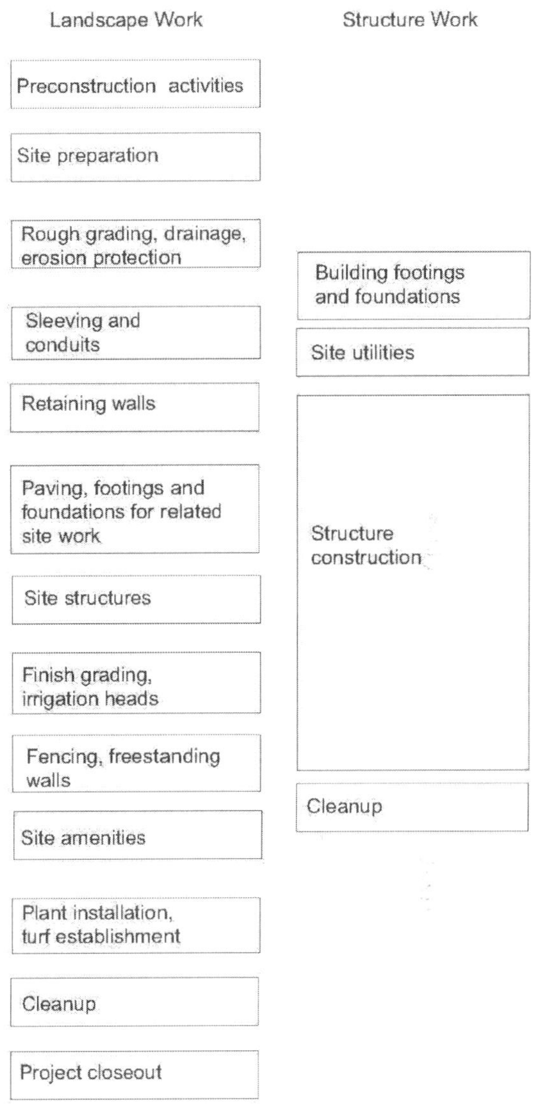

Figure 2-1 Flowchart of the landscape construction process. The right column shows how structure work relates to the landscape process.

The process outline provided in Chapter 2 corresponds chronologically to the numerical sections and chapters of this book. Some of the processes described in these chapters may be performed by specialty contractors or contractors licensed in other trades. Subsequent chapters will provide more detailed descriptions of what is summarized in this first chapter.

PRECONSTRUCTION ACTIVITIES

Before they can begin work, landscape contractors must first have a project. **Bidding**, or competing with other contractors for a job, is the one way in which contractors are authorized to work on a site. The general, or prime, contractor will sign a contract with the site owner to conclude the bidding process and to initiate the second phase of a project: preconstruction planning. If the project is large or within the public domain, the owner's representative will give written authorization to signal the beginning of work.

When working as subcontractors, landscape contractors will receive authorization or permission to work from the general contractor; and the two parties may or may not sign a contract. Scheduling of work is critical when landscape contractors operate as subcontractors for larger firms. It is important to verify that other construction activities will not disturb completed work. Restoration work typically does not qualify for additional pay, even if another contractor disturbs or destroys the work already completed. In situations where work has been negotiated directly with a client, signatures by both parties on a legally binding contract is adequate to begin construction.

Prior to beginning any work, landscape contractors should obtain required permits, insurance, and bonding. Orders should be placed in advance for materials that may require lead time for manufacturing, such as premanufactured bridges, amenities, lighting, special-dimensioned features, specialty paving, and wall materials. Before construction can proceed, layout of critical dimensions and grades will be required (Figure 2-2). Anyone who is not comfortable doing this work, or is not qualified because of the critical nature of the development, should contact a registered land surveyor to provide construction staking. Also, prior to construction, the contractor must consider what steps will be required during the construction phase to protect finished work already in place. On sites with multiple contractors, it is important that finished work be respected by all.

Figure 2-2 Using a surveyor's transit to stake grades at a landscape project.

EXISTING SITE ELEMENTS

Site preparation can vary significantly, but performing this step typically incorporates two basic tasks: protecting existing site features and demolishing or removing existing site elements that are no longer wanted. Protection and demolition activities are best performed before any other phase of the project begins.

Protection of site elements could include defining an access route to construction; fencing the perimeter; stabilizing benchmarks and baselines used to lay out the project; and protecting any plant material, structures, paving, or permanent improvements that will be part of the finished project. Proper protection of existing site features involves the time and effort necessary to reduce significant restoration as a result of construction damage. Construction documents will outline the items to be safeguarded as part of this step. For projects without construction documents, the contractor may have the responsibility of making those judgments.

Site demolition involves the removal of existing site improvements that are not part of the finished project. This work is often performed by a specialty contractor. Disposal of the removed elements is also the contractor's responsibility; and in many cases, recycling or reusing old materials can result in cost savings. Removing old structures, worn pavement, or damaged and misplaced plant material is a common activity before a contractor undertakes new construction. Unlike site protection, demolition is almost impossible to overlook. It can, however, do unnecessary damage to a site if not properly performed; and contractors will need to restore the damage at their own expense. Failing to consider how demolition materials can be recycled also creates a cost to the environment. Old paving, recycled concrete, chipped and composted plant material, and many other products once considered waste could have more productive uses; and the contractor can find ways to recycle these unwanted materials.

ROUGH GRADING, EROSION PROTECTION, AND SITE DRAINAGE

Rough grading to achieve the desired landform and drainage will follow the site preparation activities. A majority of the grading work must be completed before any further steps can be taken. Grading for large projects can be broken down into distinct steps that efficiently sculpt the site and preserve resources such as topsoil. Smaller projects often condense the steps because a small site does not lend itself well to the specialized grading activities of larger projects. In North Carolina, rough grading is not routinely performed by landscape contractors.

Initial steps in grading include the stripping of sod and vegetative cover from the areas where the grade will be changed. Once the plant material has been removed, the topsoil is scraped from the site and stockpiled for future use. Subgrade soils are then cut from areas where there is an excess and filled into areas where there are voids (Figure 2-3). Grades established during this phase will be below what is planned for finish grades because paving and topsoil will be placed on top of the subgrade. Grading to facilitate site drainage and to install drainage systems, such as tile or storm sewers, is also performed. Grading activities are then stopped until all utilities, structures, and paving are put into place. Temporary erosion protection is installed at this time to reduce damage to the site until finish grading can occur.

SITE UTILITIES

Depending on the size of the project, subcontractors who specialize in installation of water, sewer, gas, electric, phone, and other communication utilities will probably be assigned to complete most of the major utility work. Establishment of rough grade prior to beginning this phase is essential to maintain proper cover over utility rough-ins. Trenching and placement of major utility structures, such as manholes and shutoffs, should be performed and then back-filled to avoid disturbing finished elements of the landscape. Conduits and sleeves for future utility and irrigation installation may also be completed at this time.

Coordination and awareness of utility installation is critical to the landscape contractor. Documentation of utility locations also aids in future construction work that requires excavation. Utilities installed in improper or unknown locations may have a significant negative impact on placement of future plantings and landscape walls, as well as on future paving.

LANDSCAPE RETAINING WALLS AND STAIRS

Once rough grade has been established over a site, construction can begin on landscape walls

Figure 2-3 Rough grading an athletic field site.

(Figure 2-4). In areas where utilities must pass near or under a wall, the utility should be completed and the grade above the utility must be compacted prior to placing the wall. Walls that retain the subgrade for paved areas must be in place before the paving activity can begin.

LANDSCAPE PAVING

When all rough grades, utilities, and landscape walls that support paved areas are in place and heavy traffic across the site has stopped, landscape paving can begin. Exceptions to this timing occur when asphalt roadways are left unsurfaced, or surfaced only with a base layer, until all construction traffic has ceased. This step includes the installation of pedestrian concrete paving, brick and interlocking concrete paving block, stone, and granular paving used for walks, drives, patios, and other outdoor circulation and use areas (Figure 2-5). Paving edges provide elevation guidelines for lawns and planting beds, allowing topsoil to be redistributed over the site. Final grade should be established after all paving operations are complete. Timing of pavement projects should be coordinated with the completion of structures or paved areas near buildings. Any structure-related pavement should be completed before landscape paving is installed.

Provided future construction will not disturb it, concrete for any fencing or landscape amenities that require footings can also be poured at this time. This facilitates the efficient delivery of materials and reduces the potential for damage to a completed site structure by paving and building activities.

Figure 2-4 Building a dry-laid, limestone, landscape retaining wall.

SITE STRUCTURES AND WOOD CONSTRUCTION

Structures related to landscape use can be built at a variety of times during the construction process. Again, this work is often performed by a specialty contractor. Determining the proper time will depend on whether the structure is freestanding, such as a gazebo or trellis, or attached to a building, such as a deck. Once subgrade is established, foundations or slabs for freestanding landscape structures can be placed and erection of the structure can begin. Because structures may require utility connections and site walkways may have a paved connection, pouring of slabs could occur between utility construction and landscape paving.

However, a preferred alternative is to pour footings at the same time that landscape paving activities are underway and to finish the structures after paving and buildings are in place.

Although footings, subsurface work, and portions of the site structure that are not connected to a building may be undertaken after site utility work is complete, finish work and connection to the building may have to be delayed. Structures that are attached to buildings will need to have building exterior work underway before construction begins. Most connections for site structures are made to the exterior sheathing or surfacing material, or these connections are designed to integrate with building roofs. Also, because buildings may require a vehicle access route near to where they are planned, material delivery may also influence the timing of this phase. Delivery of materials should be timed to avoid damage to the finished landscape by vehicles traveling to and from a site.

FINISH GRADING

Following the completion of other hardscape construction activities, and prior to installation of turf areas and plantings, topsoil is removed from the stockpile and respread over the areas on which turf or plant material is placed. Finish, or fine, grading is performed after the topsoil is respread to achieve the final grades desired by the designer.

FREESTANDING WALLS

Timing of freestanding wall installation varies from project to project. Work in this area is often performed by a specialty contractor. Footings for freestanding walls should be installed when other footings are placed and when masonry work is completed before finish grading begins.

SITE AMENITIES

Amenity installation includes such work as placement of benches, flagpoles, trash

Figure 2-5 Preparing a site for landscape paving.

receptacles, bike racks, and site lighting. These elements are the finishing touches of the hardscape, and their placement should be postponed as late as possible to protect the finishes and delicate workings.

Portions of the work related to amenities, particularly footings and wiring, will need to be addressed during the landscape paving and utility phases of the project. However, final placement of the amenity should occur just before or after plant material is installed.

Water elements in the landscape should be completed and their proper operation verified prior to planting. Repairs to decorative pools and fountains require significant disturbance of the surrounding area.

PLANT MATERIAL AND TURF AREAS

Installation or preparation of plant material and turf areas is reserved until the end of a project. Plants and lawns are sensitive, and performing any other task after this step can seriously damage them. Plant installation should begin with large trees and plants in areas that are difficult to access. Smaller trees and shrubs should be installed next, followed by edgers and ground cover plantings. Post-planting care, including mulching, should be accomplished when each plant group is installed. Preparation and installation of turf areas typically begins after plants are installed. However, some landscape contractors practice an alternative method; they prepare all turf areas prior to planting trees and shrubs and then repair any damage to turf areas after they complete the planting.

Timing of plant material installation is important to the plants' survival and the owner's maintenance load. Maintenance of all plants and lawns, particularly watering, consumes a great deal of time. Fall installation of plantings and cool season lawns provides the best chance of survival and minimizes maintenance, but this timing does not always coordinate with the completion of building projects. Completion during the winter, spring, or summer will require a maintenance program that is instituted immediately to ensure plant survival until the owner accepts the project.

CLEANUP

After completing the landscape installation, contractors must clean and touch up exterior areas where work has been completed. The time invested to wash walkways, touch up paint on amenities, and make sure light bulbs are working is worth the effort. Cleanup can be more difficult when the general contractor requires that landscaping be completed before building exteriors or corrective work can be finished. Therefore, contractors should verify that all exterior work on the site is complete before they apply final aesthetic treatments.

PROJECT CLOSEOUT

When all work is substantially complete, a close out process is most important to insure that all parties agree that the work has been performed and installed as agreed upon. This process varies depending on the form of contract for the project. When the landscape contractor is the prime contractor, he/she first confirms that all work by all parties, including subcontractors, is complete and per all contract documents and agreements. Areas requiring remedial work are listed in a punchlist. When the landscape contractor determines that all punchiest items are complete, a review is scheduled with the owner or their representative. Again, the project is reviewed and, if all items are acceptable, accepted by the owner.

A similar process is followed when the landscape contractor is working as a subcontractor. The prime contractor reviews the work to insure it is complete. The prime contractor, an owner's representative such as a landscape architect, or the owner themselves will perform the punch list review.

It is important to establish the acceptance point of a project in that it usually defines the beginning of any warranties. It is also very important to determine and assign at the point of acceptance the responsibility of project maintenance. Most warranties are subject to proper maintenance. Especially with new plantings, a gap in maintenance of just a few days can be very detrimental to the project.

WARRANTY PERIOD

The contractor's responsibility may extend beyond completion of a project. Many owners require a warranty period in which the work performed may require replacement or repair.

Plant material usually falls under this requirement, but lighting, paving, and carpentry work may also have warranty periods. Most common in North Carolina is a one year warranty period that may or may not include lawns. As determined by contract or by mutual agreement between owner and contractor, a warranty typically requires the contractor to repair or replace defective improvements and/or dead plants for the duration of the warranty period.

SCHEDULING CONSTRUCTION ACTIVITIES

Successful management of a landscape business extends beyond recognizing the phases of construction activities. Contractors must also develop skill in effective scheduling of activities. Scheduling must be considered on two levels: individual project scheduling and the integration of schedules for proposed and existing projects. This section addresses in general the techniques for effective scheduling. A full explanation of scheduling techniques would require an in-depth analysis and presentation beyond this text's scope. Literature, coursework, software, and consultation with other contractors can elaborate more extensively on the details of the techniques introduced in this section. For further information, conduct web searches using the key words presented in boldface here, or contact a local educational institution with a business or construction management department.

The contractor must master the first level of scheduling: individual projects. One common approach to scheduling is performing the work in sequence from start to finish with little more than a starting date and an anticipated completion date. This method is most effective when the project is short in duration (two weeks or less), requires sequential installation (the project involves only one phase and each step of the phase must be completed before the next can begin), or the construction is completed using a small crew. When it exceeds these limits, a project typically requires formal scheduling. Scheduling of more complex construction projects can be accomplished by using a number of techniques, including bar charting and logical graphing.Bar Charts (Gantt Charts)

A common technique for scheduling construction activities is the bar chart, or **Gantt chart**. The bar chart lists the construction activities, or tasks, that need to be performed down a single column, typically in the order in which they are to be performed (Table 2-1). A second column, indicating the length of time to complete each activity, is often added. At the top of the chart, dates for the construction project are noted in a horizontal row. To the right of each activity, a line, or bar, is drawn from the starting date to the completion date for that activity. All activities in the first column are charted in this manner across the rows of the chart, with the bar for each activity beginning at the earliest possible starting date. Many activities must be completed in sequence, requiring the completion of one activity before the next can be started. Some activities may be completed independently and can be charted when scheduling the work is most convenient.

Table 2–1 Sample Gantt Chart

Phase	Task	Req days	May	June	July	Aug
1	obtain permits / prep work					
	-obtain construction permits	5				
	-order and deliver wall materials	5				
	-order and deliver paving materials	5				
2	rough grade					
	-remove and stockpile topsoil	2				
	-rough grade	5				
	-respread topsoil	2				
	-finish grade	3				
3	wall construction					
	-wall base installation	3				
	-wall material installation	8				
4	paving installation					
	-paving base preparation	4				
	-paving installation	10				
5	cleanup	2				

Although this is a simple bar chart, it represents how a contractor can plan construction activities, including ordering supplies, scheduling subcontractors, and even completing job related administrative tasks. Charting activities allows the contractor to identify critical points in the construction schedule and to adjust activities to meet schedule demands. Gantt charting is useful for small projects that must be completed in a linear manner, or one step after the other, and for contractors who have small crews and can engage in only one activity at a time.

A contractor can construct a simple Gantt chart by using a pencil and a sheet of graphing paper or can develop more complex charts by using the numerous templates and computer scheduling programs available. Templates list typical construction activities, and the contractor can easily choose from among those activities and then insert the duration of the work to produce a chart. Other scheduling programs can generate an entire chart once the contractor provides information about the duration and sequence of the activities.

Logical Network Scheduling (CPM)

Although the bar chart provides a useful tool for scheduling projects that can follow a general linear path from beginning to end, projects that have several interconnected activities or numerous simultaneous tasks may require a scheduling method that can accommodate these variables. Scheduling methods like **critical path method (CPM)**, or critical path analysis, use logic charts to diagram sequential, or interrelated, tasks and to determine the length of time required to complete a project.

CPM identifies each activity in a sequence. A flowchart is prepared with these activities graphically represented using nodes (circles) connected by arrows showing the logical sequence of completion (Figure 2-6). Times to complete the tasks are added to the chart. Some methods of CPM place the time on the connecting arrows (AOA, or assignment on arrows) or on the nodes (AON, or assignment on nodes). Either method is acceptable as long as it is applied consistently. When all activities and paths are represented, the diagram can be evaluated to find the critical, or longest, path through the project. This critical path identifies activities that, if postponed, will delay completion of the project. CPM not only identifies what activities are critical to the timely completion of the project, but it also improves the understanding of the relationships among various construction activities.

Additional Scheduling Methods

As projects become even more complex and unpredictable, more complex scheduling methods become more appropriate. Methods such as **program evaluation and review technique (PERT)** combine CPM with probability to identify completion dates that are optimistic, pessimistic, and most likely. Although not applicable to every project, PERT may be used in large construction

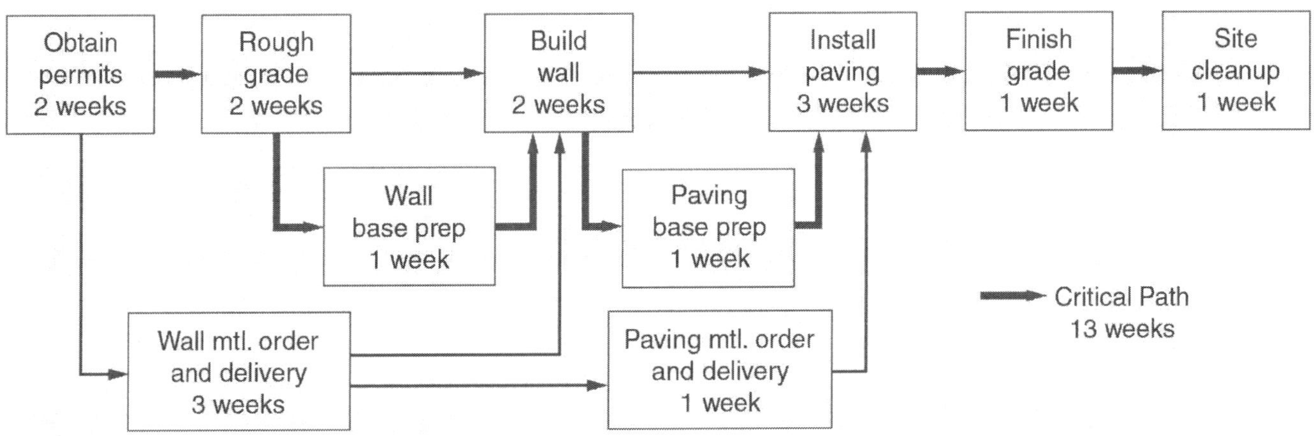

Figure 2-6 CPM charts identify activities in sequence.

projects that are likely to be influenced by nature or human factors. Examples include projects that are to be completed during unseasonable weather conditions or grading in an area that may be delayed because of unknown underground conditions. The second level of scheduling a contractor must master is integrating the schedules of the many projects being solicited and implemented. Success at this level depends on how well the contractor can plan individual projects without being overbooked with work or being without work for extended periods. Like many businesses, landscape contracting typically requires that multiple projects be contracted simultaneously to keep crews busy and to use equipment and labor efficiently. The activities of multiple projects must be simultaneously integrated to avoid conflicts. Staying in business also requires that new projects be sought while working on current projects. Scheduling at this level involves concurrent marketing of services, bidding on projects, and obtaining permits for future projects while engaging in the construction of existing projects.

CHAPTER 3

LEGAL REQUIREMENTS

OBJECTIVES

By reading and practicing the techniques described in this chapter, the reader should be able to successfully complete the following activities:

- Develop relationships with other contractors.
- List the potential legal implications of a construction project.
- Identify sources of information on construction restrictions.

Many legal controls can and often do influence landscape construction work. Few activities that the landscape contractor undertakes will be without some form of standard—either voluntary or involuntary. Although these standards influence the speed and efficiency of a landscape operation, the contractor's attitude toward controls should be tempered with the understanding that most legal requirements protect the health, safety, and welfare of the public and of the contractor.

This chapter covers typical relationships, rules, **contracts**, standards, and entities that govern the profession of landscape contracting in many parts of the nation. National standards, or **codes**, provide guidance in the form of construction standards. Local **ordinances** and building departments provide requirements for location, construction, and, occasionally, style of landscape improvements that can be installed. Local governments may also require that owners or contractors obtain permits and pay fees prior to construction. Contract documents, a legally binding set of instructions, guide projects by placing control over the materials and methods that may be used. In addition, insurance standards, usually expressed in limitations and restrictions incorporated into policies and contracts, also provide some level of control over landscape work.

Before beginning a construction project, the contractor must verify legal requirements. Failure to do so may mean paying fines or removing parts of a project that do not comply with regulations. To verify that the locale has regulations by which the contractor must abide, look in the government section of the phone book for county and city building departments or for a zoning administrator. In some areas, planning departments and forestry departments may be the local regulatory agencies. When you describe the work being done, these officials should be able to provide direction through the appropriate process. Ignorance of legal requirements will not relieve the contractor of liability.

> **CAUTION**
>
> Legal counsel should be obtained for the interpretation of any information described herein.

RELATED INFORMATION

Information in this chapter is supplemented by instruction provided elsewhere in this text and in other sources. Before undertaking the activities described in this chapter, read the related information in these sources:

- Interpreting Construction Documents, Chapter 4
- Project Pricing, Chapter 6
- North Carolina Landscape Contractors' Guide to Business, Law and Project Management

CONTRACTOR/CLIENT RELATIONSHIPS

Entering the world of business requires the contractor to be aware of the many methods for obtaining work, to understand relationships with clients and related parties, and to execute contractual relationships with clients. Because space is limited in this text, this chapter provides an overview of the most common contractor/client relationships. The author suggests supplemental reading to obtain additional information regarding design and construction contracts.

Obtaining Landscape Contracting Work

Obtaining work is essential for the contractor to maintain a business. Methods to obtain, or procure, work in the contracting field range from informal marketing efforts to formal contracting with owners and developers and formal subcontracting arrangements with major builders. Several aspects of the contractor's work may influence the success in obtaining contracts. These aspects include such factors as how the contractor's rates for performing services compare with others in the market area, how efficiently the contractor works, and how quickly the contractor can provide services. Experience in performing similar types of projects and the quality of the contractor's work are also crucial selling points. Depending on the type of procurement method, one or more of these factors may be critical. Three basic methods for obtaining work in the landscape contracting field can be identified: direct procurement, competitive negotiation, and competitive bidding. These opportunities may present themselves in various forms. Oftentimes, a request for pricing a project comes in the form of an RFQ (Request for Qualifications) or RFP (Request for Proposal). Chapter 5 explains specific techniques for calculating and presenting costs that these methods require.

Direct Procurement. Direct procurement involves the acquisition of contracts for landscape services directly from a client. The contractor may initiate direct procurement through advertising or marketing of services, by the client through referral from another client, or by what the industry terms "walk-in" business. In any instance, the contractor sells materials and services to the client without direct competition from other parties.

Competitive Negotiation. Many customers prefer to "shop" for landscape services and receive proposals from several service providers. This form of procurement often requires the contractor to submit detailed explanations and itemization to ensure the selection of services based on similar proposals. Competitive projects may be client-originated or solicited from **general contractors,** also known as **prime contractors** (contractors who hold the prime contract for completion of a large construction project) or from **design professionals** (landscape architects, architects, and engineers) who have projects with private clients. General contractors or specialized contractors, those who perform specific operations for a project, often use competitive negotiation to select subcontractors.

Although negotiation is standard practice, it is very important to understand the process and insure that all parties are negotiating the same or very similar products. This "apples per apples" approach can limit misunderstandings in the process. Slight differences between interpretations of client needs can lead to substantial differences in price and the client often ends up not knowing what they are really getting. The inconsistencies of this process underscore the importance of providing design services as a separate phase from installation services. With a set design, all bidders are pricing 'apples for apples.'

Competitive Bidding. Bidding is a formal process practiced by public clients for all but small projects and by private clients for most large projects. Competitive bidding requires that contractors offer, or bid, a sealed project cost based on a specific design. A client will open all proposals at a designated time and place. Selection of a contractor is typically based on the lowest bid submitted by a qualified contractor.

A design professional or the client's agent generally determines a qualified contractor. Certain contractors may be disqualified from bidding based on sound legal reasons such as lack of experience, financial insolvency, or government sanction.

Submission of bids is often restricted to prime contractors. In many projects, the landscape contractor will not be the entity submitting the bid. Landscape contractors may submit a bid or negotiated price to a prime contractor, who will add that total to the other subcontractor prices and submit it as part of that contractor's bid. It is not unusual for a landscape contractor to submit prices to several different prime contractors for the same project. Bidding opportunities can be obtained by reviewing public notices, contacting plan houses (such as Dodge Data and Analytics, a private publisher who tracks major invitations to bid), prime contractors, and design professionals. Prices prepared for bids may take different forms, as described in Chapter 6.

Relationships Between Contractor and Client

When work is secured, the contractor's relationship with the client is defined as either a prime contractor or a subcontractor. Whichever of these positions the contractor holds will have a significant impact on control of the project. Third parties, such as design professionals acting as owner's agents and consulting construction managers, also affect the relationship between contractor and client with revisions (Figure 3-1).

Prime Contractor Relationships. Responsible for completing all aspects of a project, a general contractor holds the prime construction contract with the client, who is typically the project owner or financier. This relationship is framed by the terms of a contract spelling out each party's lights and responsibilities. On complex projects, the prime contractor may be responsible for numerous suppliers and subcontractors, including those doing the landscape installation, as well as his or her own workforce (Figure 3-1 A). When subcontractors complete portions of a project, the prime contractor may or may not assume responsibility for the work. Protection from damage by others may be the responsibility of the subcontractor for that portion of work. Insure that this detail is understood and agreed to by all involved parties.

In projects that cover only landscape construction elements, the landscape contractor may serve as a prime contractor (Figure 3-1 B). The landscape contractor is then responsible for completion of all work, including those elements that are subcontracted to others.

Another arrangement under the contractual arrangements for a project is the concept of multiple general contractors (Figure 3-1 C). For reasons of timing, cost, or quality control, the client may choose to separate major work areas into separate contracts. Prime contracts will be offered for each of the work areas, with each general contractor being responsible for work within the appropriate trade. The general contractors, owner's agent, and other parties to the work must then coordinate activities among all the contracts.

Subcontractor Relationships. Subcontractors perform specialized work for a project; and although they seldom have a contractual relationship with the project owner or financier, subcontractors maintain a formal or informal relationship with the general contractor. Employing several subcontractors from many building trades for large building projects is a common practice, as is subcontracting landscape elements of a project. Specialization within the landscape contracting field has also increased the possibility of having several landscape-related subcontractors for a single project, such as those who specialize in irrigation, wall construction, plant installation, and turf establishment.

Third Parties to Contractor/Client Relationships. Communications between the prime contractor and owner will typically be referred to the owner's agent (Figure 3-1). In many projects, this will be the design professional.

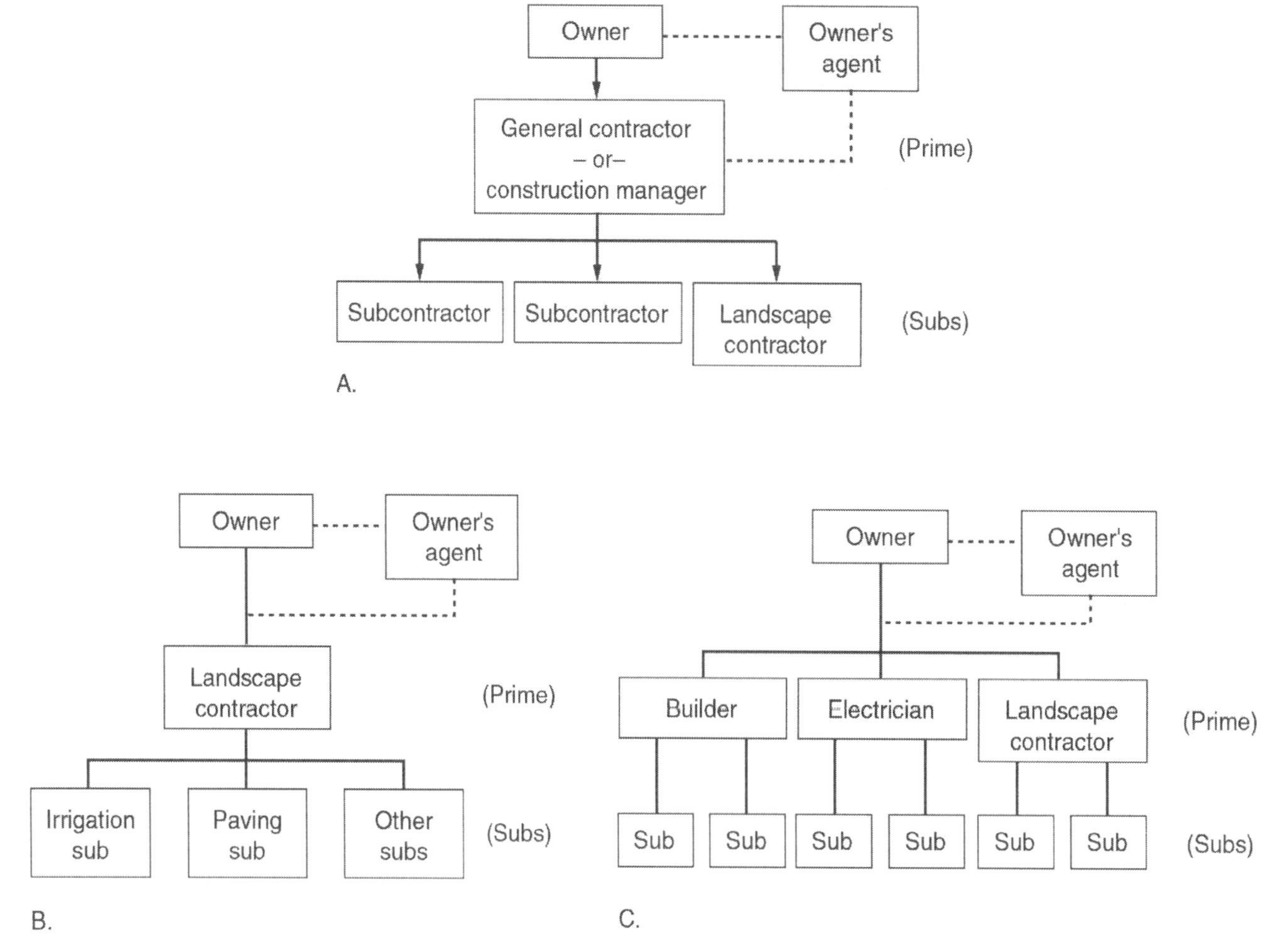

Figure 3-1 Relationship of owner and contractors in the landscape process. (A) Landscape contractor as a subcontractor. (B) Landscape contractor as a prime contractor. (C) Landscape contractor as one of several prime contractors.

The owner's agent will serve as the clearinghouse for all communications with the owner, accepting and approving submissions and providing instructions to the general contractor. Whether a general contractor performs landscaping work on a small project or a subcontractor performs landscaping work on a large project, any change or deviation from the plans and specifications will require approval from the owner's agent.

Construction Managers

An alternative to completing a project using the typical contractor/subcontractor relationship is to employ a project management firm. The project management firm bridges between design and construction by contracting with the project owner to advise on design and construction and by maintaining the integrity of the project by managing its installation.

The construction management model has three variations. First is the design-build firm, which project owners employ to complete both the design and implementation of a project. Another variation is the agency construction manager who, in exchange for a fee, assists the owner in employing both designers and contractors. Either of these two methods provides advantages to owners. For example, some owners may have too many projects or very complex projects and may need assistance to manage them. Other owners may be novices in the implementation of construction projects and may need an experienced manager. Additional advantages in the form of cost savings are often derived from integrating design and construction. Construction management reduces the adversarial roles often found between designers and contractors and maintains tighter control over the scheduling of activities. Yet a third form of construction management is the at-risk model, in which the manager acts as designer and general contractor for a project, providing the owner a guaranteed maximum price.

Forms of Contracts

A written contract should guide the execution of work in any form. Whether simple or extensive, the contract forms a basis for a relationship between parties and provides a mechanism whereby disputes can be resolved. As mentioned earlier, seek the advice of appropriate legal counsel before preparing and entering into any contract.

Required Conditions of a Contract. Certain conditions must be written into or contained within contracts. They must contain lawful subject matter, must include an offer and exchange (a fee for services rendered), must be negotiated between competent parties, and must not be signed under duress. Contracts must also include agreement and be in proper form for the jurisdiction in which the work will be performed. In addition, the following items should be included in a contract for landscape services:[1]

- Names and addresses of the parties involved
- Date of contract preparation
- Description of the work to be accomplished (also called the scope of services) and the materials or services to be provided, including the location where it is to be accomplished
- The terms of completion, including -inspection, the completion date, and the penalty for not completing on time
- The terms of payment
- The signatures of both parties or their legal representatives
- The date of signing

Contract Documents. The documents used to bid and construct large projects are collectively referred to as **contract documents** or **construction drawings**. Included in a full set of contract documents for a large project would be instructions for bidding, contracts for construction, general instructions, and specific technical instructions. These preceding elements are collectively referred to as **specifications**. Also included within the contract document definition would be the set of plans used to guide construction, provisions for change orders if construction is altered, and payment and completion documents to be used during construction. For suggestions on interpreting the drawings and specifications for construction - purposes, refer to Chapter 4. All elements of this project documentation are part of a legally binding contract, whether work is performed as a general contractor or as a subcontractor.

Subcontractor/Contractor Agreements. The relationship between a subcontractor and general contractor may be in the form of a contract, an informal letter agreement, or, inadvisably, through oral agreement. Formal and informal agreements should address issues such as recognition of the prime contract, work to be performed by the subcontractor, payments to the subcontractor, timing of the work, insurance and bonding required of the subcontractor, special conditions required by the project, and agreement by the parties.

[1]Jack Ingels, *Landscaping Principles and Practices,* 7th ed. (Clifton Park, NY: Delmar Cengage Learning, 2009).

Two-Party Contracts. Smaller projects may proceed without the benefit of an expansive set of contract documents. Contractors may work from written -proposals or landscape drawings that have been -presented to, and agreed upon by, the client. Although it varies according to where the contract is prepared and how the proposal is worded, most written -proposals are legally binding if both parties sign the document. Proposals lack the type of specific instructions for every element of the project that contract documents provide. Hence, a great deal of communication and understanding by the parties is required to avoid disputes.

BUILDING CODES

Codes are typically prepared by national institutes or organizations that have an interest in advancing the safe application of their trade. Two of the most prominent types of building codes are structure building codes and the National Electrical Code (NEC).

Structure Building Codes

When landscape projects involve the construction of decorative landscape features, the guidelines of the standardized building codes typically come into play. Building codes provide a wealth of information regarding the safe planning of structures. Information regarding material standards, connectors, area planning, dimensions, and other details of building construction are included in these codes. Building codes are adopted on a statewide as well as a locality-by-locality basis, so check with the city or county zoning administrator or building office to determine if the codes apply to work being performed.

ORDINANCES AND DEED RESTRICTIONS

Local control over construction projects is typically expressed through the use of ordinances that control zoning and building. These regulations place stipulations on the use of land and the construction of improvements on property that lies within a legal **jurisdiction**. In large communities, these regulations can be extensive and complex; in small communities, they may not exist at all. In absence of an ordinance and permit system, a governmental unit may require adherence to one or more of the codes mentioned in the previous section. Some local government controls are listed in the following section. Contact local building officials, zoning administrators, city foresters, or homeowner association officials to determine if any regulations apply to the work being done.

Zoning Ordinance

Zoning ordinances control how land within a government's jurisdiction may be used. This control may restrict the type of structure one may place on a property, the dimensions of that structure, and the uses of the structure. Also common in a zoning ordinance are requirements for **setbacks**, or distances between improvements and property lines. Elements of a zoning ordinance that may influence landscape construction include provisions that control fence requirements (such as around a swimming pool) and location, fence height and materials, deck location, deck materials and construction, and railing requirements.

Sign Ordinance

Signage controls may be located within a zoning ordinance, but some locales place regulations on signage in a separate ordinance. Controls on sign use, materials, location, lighting, and size are common in developed areas.

Parking Ordinance

Quantity and location of parking spaces, as well as control of access drives, can sometimes be found in an ordinance separate from the zoning ordinance.

Landscape Ordinances

Many municipalities and counties have landscape ordinances that prescribe planting requirements for certain conditions and uses. These requirements often include plant sizes at planting time, quantities required and the species of plants that may or may not be used. These ordinances

Figure 3-2 Street trees along a public boulevard.

can cover a broad range of situations, including street tree plantings, parking lot plantings, screening, and protection of existing plants and their critical root zones. These rules may be organized in one section of the zoning ordinance or may be spread throughout different portions of the ordinance.

Plant Pruning and Removal Regulations

In communities where plant material is protected from development, permission may be required before trees and shrubs are pruned or removed. In selected communities, trees that are of select species or of a certain age or size may be declared heritage or historic trees. Such a designation is intended to protect the plant from damage, particularly from maintenance and construction operations. In addition, the removal of smaller plants or pruning to allow construction may be regulated. Discuss any plans that require major plant pruning or removal of plants with the city forester, parks department, or zoning administrator.

Floodplain and Restricted Area Regulations

Protection of waterways and natural areas has proven beneficial to reducing pollution, enhancing wildlife, and improving overall environmental quality. Many waterways, water bodies, and natural areas are protected from construction activities by entities such as city ordinances, water quality boards, water districts, and the Army Corps of Engineers. Conducting construction operations within these areas may be prohibited, or at least restricted, and may require special permits. Typical restrictions include requirement of permits, limits on the amount and location of earthmoving, limits on plant material, design control over outfall and discharge structures, and requirement of installation of erosion control protection.

If contractors are not sure of, or are not notified of, work conducted in restricted areas, they should communicate with city or county officials. Indications that restricted areas may exist are the presence of standing or moving water bodies within 100 feet of the construction site or the existence of wetland plants (cattails, rushes, sedges) within your work area.

Disposal of Site Drainage

When construction plans require water to be collected and diverted away from improvements, verify that the planned outlet location is acceptable for dumping. Pollution or flooding regulations may restrict the emptying of drainage into storm sewers, streams, and other waterways. Changing the drainage of runoff in a manner that damages neighboring property could be considered trespassing (see "Tort Issues" later in this chapter). The local water district or city engineer should be able to provide information regarding legal outlets for tiles and drainage swales.

Deed Restrictions

Planned communities, condominium housing complexes, historic districts, and other communities may have restrictions that control what type of exterior improvements can be planned and built. These restrictions are intended to develop uniformity of development or to protect historical authenticity. Review plans with authorities in these situations to verify if construction work must follow established guidelines.

Historic Districts

Neighborhoods with unique and older homes could be designated as historic districts and the homes as historic properties. If the property is on the National Historic Register or within a National Historic District, work on the exterior of a site could be restricted. Even if there is no national historic designation, many jurisdictions have state and local equivalent designations to protect the site. Limitations often include the type and number of changes that can be made to building exteriors, dictation of specific materials, and possibly controls over a wide range of design materials. To verify if the site has such restrictions, contact city or county zoning officials, or check with a state historical society.

In addition to structures on them, sites may also have protection according to their archeological, Native American, or ancient graveyards status. Although the designer is often asked to verify if such restrictions apply, contractors should also be aware of the protected status of the site and be prepared to ask what conditions might apply to their work. During construction, contractors should be observant of any antiquity or artifact unearthed during their work and be prepared to suspend activity until the authorities can clear the site.

Building Permits and Site Plan Reviews

To verify compliance with ordinances, counties and communities often require that a building permit be obtained prior to beginning construction. The process of obtaining a permit may simply involve an official who reviews ideas, or it may require a series of committee meetings in a process called a site plan review. Either method will most likely require preparation of a plan that contains descriptions of the work, along with elevations and dimensions. Building and zoning officials typically supervise the issuance of building permits and submissions for a site plan review.

INSURANCE, BONDING, AND LICENSURE

Insurance, bonding, and licensure are means in which contractors can protect themselves and the business being operated.

Insurance

Considering the risks involved in construction, contractors are advised to obtain necessary insurance to cover the perils faced when building landscapes. Risk in the landscaping industry comes primarily in the form of comprehensive liability from accidental destruction of property, employee accidents, and vehicular accidents. Natural peril coverage and errors in workmanship are also risk areas for which protection may be sought. Other activities that may require insurance protection might include umbrella liability policies, equipment and materials coverage, and crime policies.

Contracted projects typically require that contractors have insurance coverage before work begins, and contractors should not begin any work without securing basic coverage. An insurance agent can best advise about the extent or amount of coverage needed for a particular job.

Bonding

Bonding is a surety tool in which a bonding agency guarantees payment in the event a contractor fails to complete a legal obligation. Common for large projects, bonding is required for landscape contractor licensing in North Carolina. Bonding protects the project owner from losses, damages, liens, and unpaid bills on the contractor's part. Common bonds used in construction are described in the following section. Bonding and insurance agents are typically contacted to obtain proper construction bonding.

Bid Bond. The bid bond protects the owner if a contractor withdraws a bid after opening. Most formal bids require that a bond in the amount of 5%–10% of the total bid be included with the bid. If the low bidder on a project withdraws, the owner may apply the bond against the expense of rebidding the project.

Performance and Payment Bonds. Successful bidders are often required to submit performance and payment bond(s) prior to beginning construction. Performance bonds provide protection to the owner in the event that the contractor fails to complete the conditions of the construction contract. Payment bonds (also known as labor and material payment bonds) guarantee payment of labor and material bills that the contractor incurs in the construction of the contracted project.

Performance and payment bonds that combine these two sureties are available, but many projects require submission of dual bonds—one covering each risk. Typically, bonding for performance and payment is 100% of the contract value. If either of these conditions for which the contractor is bonded occurs, the bonding company may be contacted for assistance in completing the project and/or payments.

Business Licensing

Several states, counties, and cities require that anyone providing products and services to the public obtain a business license to operate in their jurisdiction. The process for obtaining a license may be as simple as filling out an application and paying a fee, or it could include bonding and proof of insurance. The issuing agency may stipulate additional licensure requirements. In some cases, the contractor may be required to obtain a license for every jurisdiction in which the firm works. Contact state departments of commerce, county clerks, and city clerks for information regarding business licenses.

Contractor Licensing

North Carolina requires that landscape and irrigation contractors be licensed to practice their trade. By licensing the professions, states can provide some level of protection for the public's health, safety, and welfare by screening out unqualified practitioners. Licensure procedures vary from state to state and may include completing legal documents, taking exams, or providing evidence of capability to perform work. To determine whether a business will require licensure, contact the North Carolina Landscape Contractors' Licensing Board.

Bonding and verification of insurance may be additional requirements. If your company is planning to engage in design/ build operations, verify licensure requirements for contracting and designing. North Carolina requires the licensure of landscape architects and restricts the level of design work that can be performed by others. The North Carolina landscape architecture licensure law is a practice act. Practice laws limit the scope of work that an unlicensed professional may design. In some areas, work on public and commercial projects may legally require the design skills of a licensed landscape architect, rather than the -**landscape designer** or contractor. In North Carolina, landscape design by unlicensed individuals is limited to single family residential properties, sites under one acre and sites where only planting and mulching is designed.

TORT ISSUES

A contractor will be required to perform activities within the boundaries of the law. Although specific legal requirements vary from region to region, several general requirements are similar without regard to locality. Failure to abide by legal requirements resulting in damage to another's property is considered a **tort** and could result in payment of damages to the offended party. It is to the contractor's benefit to discuss common legal requirements with industry officials, association members, and insurance and legal advisors before beginning work in the landscaping field. The next section discusses common issues that could lead to legal action.

Trespass

Trespass is an offense committed against another's property. A charge of trespass requires physical entry without permission and the commission of damage. Trespassing is not limited to humans physically entering a site and committing damages. It involves anything under the contractor's control, including equipment, debris, drainage, or other entities, that enters someone else's property and causes damage.

Nuisance

A disruption that causes discomfort to another is considered a nuisance. Working in an unsafe manner or at odd hours may be considered a nuisance. If they meet the legal tests, excessive noise and dust or even disruption caused by construction activities may also be construed as a nuisance.

Negligence

Failure of a professional to act in a reasonable and prudent manner to safeguard the well-being of others leads to negligence. For example, failing to mark construction areas or performing overhead work without any safeguards could lead to legal action if a contractor does not engage in actions or protective measures that would be reasonably expected to protect the public.

Riparian Rights

Subject to state and federal laws, landowners have rights regarding access to and use of waterways that run through or abut their properties. Changing the conditions of that waterway, possibly through irrigation or damming, may create a legal violation of those laws.

Lateral and Subjacent Rights

Construction activities that affect the lateral support of neighboring properties may lead to legal action. Landowners are entitled to maintenance of the grade at their property line. For example, if excavation for a parking lot collapses the neighboring grade, lateral support has been denied. Grade change activities must be completed within the boundaries of a project, not outside those boundaries unless neighboring property owners have given prior approval.

CHAPTER 4

INTERPRETING CONSTRUCTION DOCUMENTS

OBJECTIVES

By reading and practicing the techniques described in this chapter, the reader should be able to successfully complete the following activities:

- Measure a construction drawing using a scale.
- Comprehend what construction activities are required from construction plans and specifications.
- Build a landscape project from a set of plans and specifications.

Large and/or complex projects require detailed instructions explaining how the project is to be built. These instructions, called plans and **specifications** (this term is often shortened to "specs"), are prepared by design professionals such as landscape architects, architects, and engineers. Plans and specifications provide the information necessary to ensure that the project is constructed exactly as the owner desires.

This chapter explains the types of construction documents that may be encountered on a project and explains how to interpret the content of key documents. Each plan and specification contains a different type of information, but all plans and specs work in concert to provide necessary information. Even if bidding only landscape work, the landscape contractor should obtain a complete set of construction drawings and specifications at the beginning of the project to verify that other project activities will not change or influence the bid. Because they often receive only their section of the plans and specs, subcontractors encounter problems when they later discover they must perform work that was described in sections they did not review.

RELATED INFORMATION

Information in this chapter is supplemented by instruction provided elsewhere in this text and in other sources. Before undertaking the activities described in this chapter, read the related information in these sources:

- Legal Requirements, Chapter 3
- Project Pricing, Chapter 6
- Construction Layout, Chapter 9

READING SPECIFICATIONS

Specifications provide written instructions about most aspects of project construction. Because they address a wide range of topics, specifications are typically organized into sections that cover the nontechnical aspects of the work, often called *general conditions,* and the specific construction procedures, often called *technical specifications.*

General Conditions

General project information is located in the front of the spec manual and includes a wide range of documents. Based on the scope of the project, this information can be quite detailed and extensive. The information contained in these sections pertains to all work, and contractors should familiarize themselves with the details before beginning construction. Special requirements necessitated by laws and regulations should be explained in this part of the specs. Typical documents found in the general conditions section include:

1. Bidding information
    - Invitation to bidders
    - Instructions for bidders

- Bid form
- Noncollusion affidavit
- Bid bond form
- Receipt of addenda acknowledgment

2. Sample contract and other forms to be submitted
3. Forms used during construction
    - Notice to proceed
    - Change order form
    - Certificate of payment
    - Certificate of substantial completion
    - Lien releases
4. General conditions
    - Definitions of roles and responsibilities for owner, design professional, contractor, and subcontractors
    - Clauses addressing contract time, payment, completion, retention of fees, changes in work, correction of deficient work, bonding, insurance, royalty payments, related contracts, protection of the work, resolution of disputes, termination of the contract, and miscellaneous provisions
5. Supplemental conditions
    - Government requirements that will govern work, such as anti-kickback regulations, prevailing wage rates, adherence to civil rights, nondiscrimination, and labor legislation
    - Warranties and guarantees
    - Subcontractor approvals
    - Temporary fixtures and utilities
    - Request for material submissions and approval of substitution requirements
    - Other requirements relating specifically to the project

Technical Specifications

Technical specifications include descriptions of the methods, materials, and performance of project components. A variation of technical specifications, typically more common in nonlandscape trade areas, may specify a particular product name or specify how the installation should perform after completion.

To keep the instructions manageable, technical specs are typically grouped according to trade. In large projects, several sections might contain building specifications that have limited impact on landscaping work. Although professionals will use an organizational style with which they are familiar, one standard is a numbering system known as Masterspec®, published by ARCOM. Under the Masterspec system, the work for a project is divided into 33 divisions (with nonconsecutive division numbers ranging from 1 to 33; certain sections are left blank for future expansion). Landscaping and sitework are typically found in division 32, but portions of a landscape contractor's work may also be found in divisions 12 (site furnishings), 26 (exterior lighting), 31 (earthmoving), and other sections within the specifications. In addition to Masterspec®, another set of standard specifications can be obtained from Masterformat by CSI (Construction Specifications Institute) and yet another called Construction Document Specifications, standard specs prepared by the American Institute of Architects (see Appendix B).

Two basic types of technical specifications are typical to the construction industry. Material and workmanship specifications and performance specifications vary widely in their approach to directing the type of construction used on a project. The wording and manner of the technical specification influence the choices a contractor must make.

Material and Workmanship Specifications. Material and workmanship specifications detail the materials and construction procedures to be used to complete each project component. This type of specification restricts the contractor to use only those elements that the designer has chosen. A typical format for material and workmanship specification begins with a section covering aspects such as warranties, material delivery, and reference standards. A second part indicates what materials are to be used for the project. This description can be written as a closed or an open specification.

- Closed Specifications. Closed specifications limit the contractor's choice of methods and materials. For example, choices may be limited to a single product brand/model (proprietary specification) or to a specific procedure. When closed specifications are used, substitutions are not common.
- Open Specifications. Giving the contractor more choice of materials and methods, open specifications may list two to three alternative brands/models or list a brand/model and the clause "or equal." The "or equal" clause allows the contractor to propose brands/models to the owner's agent for approval.

The last part of this type of specification describes the detailed installation methods to be used. An example of a material and workmanship specification is presented in Appendix A.

Performance Specifications. Without providing specific materials or methods, performance specifications prescribe the results that a component of construction must obtain. This type of specification limits the contractor only in producing a product that looks and performs as the designer intended. An example of a performance specification in landscaping is presented in Appendix A.

Reference Standards. Throughout specifications and construction material literature, references can be found to standards that testing agencies, associations, and organizations publish. Design professionals often refer to these specifications and incorporate their parameters as part of legally binding contracts. These organizations spend considerable time preparing standards for the performance and installation of materials, many of which are related to the landscaping industry. A common reference is the American Society for Testing Materials, which prepares standards used throughout all industries. References relating to landscape trade areas include American Association of Nurserymen standards for nursery stock (ANSI Z 60.1), Interlocking Concrete Paving Institute (ICPI), Brick Institute of America, Portland Cement Association, National Electrical Manufacturers Association (NEMA), Asphalt Institute, American Concrete Institute (ACI), Sustainable Forestry Institute (SFI) and American Institute of Timber Construction. When reference is made to one of these standards, contractors are responsible for obtaining the relevant information and verifying that their work conforms to the standard.

Additional Specification Documents

In addition to those provided by the specifications, other written instructions may be provided during the construction process. Two key documents that affect the process are addenda and change orders. **Addenda** are official notifications of changes in the project, typically revisions of the construction plans or specifications, that occur before the time of bid opening.

Addenda modify the project, and these modifications should be reflected in any bid submitted. **Change orders** are revisions to the project that occur after the contracts have been signed. The owner's agent initiates change orders, and the contractor responds by submitting price and/or project scope changes.

READING CONSTRUCTION DRAWINGS

Plans are the graphic communication tools that provide information regarding location, grade, and type of improvements to be placed on the site. To interpret construction plans, contractors need a basic understanding of engineering drafting elements. Following are descriptions for reading drawing scales, dimensions, abbreviations, symbols, and textures. This presentation is an overview and should not be interpreted as a comprehensive explanation of all aspects of engineering graphics. Interpretation of specific plans prepared for landscape construction follows the information for reading drawings.

Drawing Scale

To assist in the interpretation of construction plans, a discussion of the concept of **scale** should precede plan reading. Because most drawings cannot be drawn life-size, the site must be reduced to fit on a sheet of paper that is convenient to carry and read. To reduce the size in a manner that is consistent and measurable for all drawings, the concept of scale is used.

Simply put, scale means that a certain measurement on a drawing is equal to a distance on the actual site. Whenever that scaled distance is measured on a plan, the same actual distance should be obtainable on the site.

Scale in landscape construction drawings is typically a reference of 1 inch on the drawing that equals a certain number of feet on the site. Choice of scale depends on the size of the object/site being measured or the stated scale on a drawing. An example would be a scale stated as 1 inch = 20 feet, where 1 inch on a construction drawing equals 20 feet on the actual site. Two types of scales are used for construction drawings: an architect's scale that uses fractional divisions and an engineer's scale that uses multiples of 10 (Figure 4-1).

Special instruments, conveniently termed *scales,* are available for the measuring of plans.Contractors do not have to constantly measure the number of inches and multiply by a conversion number when they use scales. Rather, scales indicate the number of actual feet on the instrument. Although the reading of scales, particularly the architect's scales, takes some training and practice, they are useful tools for interpreting construction drawings. Landscape drawings and details relating to landscape work can be drawn in either type of scale. The reader should be able to locate a written scale and a graphic, or bar, scale on each drawing.

Measuring lines with the architect's scale first requires finding the scale that matches the drawing being interpreted. After locating the scale, identify the line to be measured. Set the scale next to the line being measured. Adjust the scale so that one end of the line is in the inch measurement area (this is the finely divided area behind the zero) and the other end rests directly on a foot mark. Read the foot reading and inch reading to obtain the measurement.

Use caution when reading both the foot and inch readings on the architect's scale. Architect's scales have two scales running in opposite directions along the same edge of the scale—one reading the top set of numbers and the other reading the bottom set of numbers. Inch markings on the architect's scale may represent inches or fractions of inches, depending on the accuracy of the scale.

Measuring lines with engineer's scales also requires determining drawing scale before measurement. Locate the line to be measured and place the zero mark from the correct scale at one end of the line. Count the marks along the scale to determine line length. Each mark on an engineer's scale represents 1 foot. Helpful numbers are placed to identify increments along the scale. Inches can only be estimated on an engineer's scale.

A warning is in order when using scales to obtain measurements from construction plans. Because the paper on which a drawing is printed can stretch and shrink, using a scale to determine the dimension of objects shown on a construction plan is not recommended when dimensions are provided. Look for a labeled dimension, which always take precedence over a scaled measurement. Plans that show plant locations may rely on the design professional's field staking or on the contractor's interpretation of the dimensions to accurately locate plants. In addition, plant spacing may be noted elsewhere on the plan. In the absence of labeled dimensions, call the designer for a written verification of missing dimensions or for instructions on interpreting site element locations.

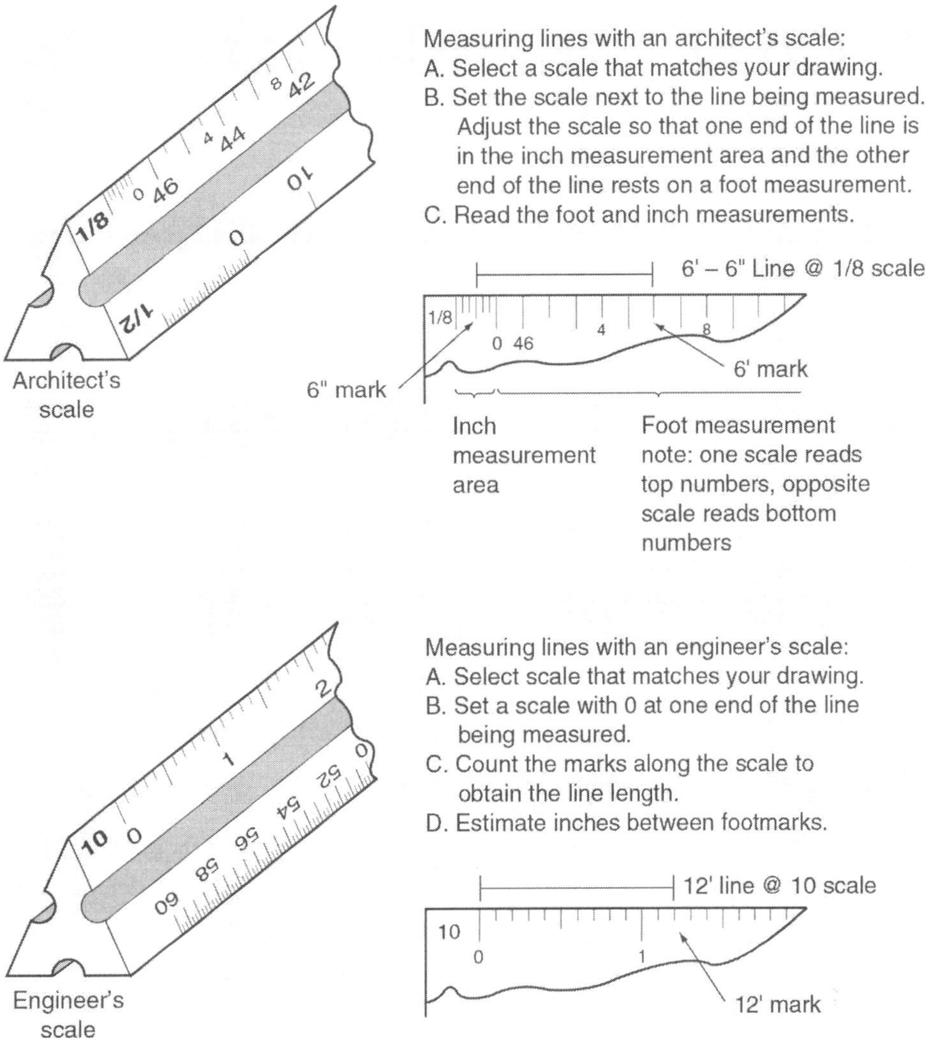

Figure 4-1 An architect's scale with fractional divisions (top) and an engineer's scale with divisions in multiples of 10.

Drawing Types

Three types of drawings are typically used to show improvements for a project—**plan view**, **cross sections**, and **elevations**. Plan view is the primary drawing type used for landscape improvements. Plans show a view looking straight down on the top of a project. Only two dimensions of site elements are visible in a plan view—the length and the width. Cross sections show a side view that cuts vertically through an object, whereas an elevation is a side view that shows the vertical surface of the object. Height and either length or width are the only two dimensions of site elements visible in cross sections and elevations. Cross sections and elevations used for landscape elements are typically used to show details of installations.

Line Types

Construction drawings use a hierarchy of line weights to identify the importance of drawing elements. Lines that are the darkest on the plans typically indicate structures. A second tier of line

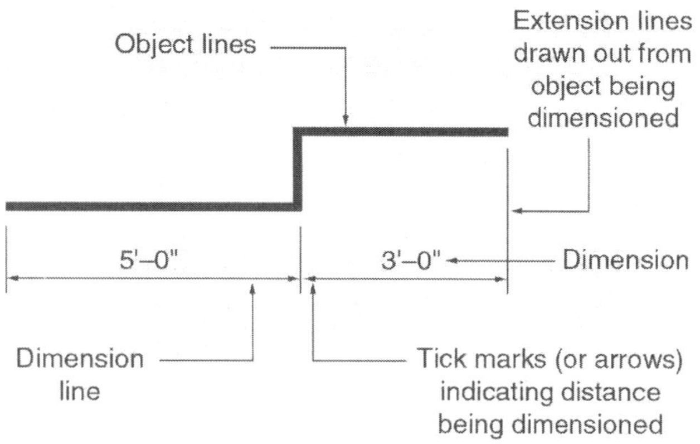

Figure 4-2 Typical line types on construction graphics.

weights is reserved for hardscape and items to be constructed (object lines). The next level of line width/darkness is used for dimensioning and notations (Figure 4-2). The variation in line weight is to improve readability of the plan and to underscore the importance of drawn elements. Dashed lines are often used to indicate existing contours, subsurface elements, hidden elements, or overhangs.

Dimensioning

Items shown on plans for which location is critical have dimensions shown using special lines and labels (Figure 4-2). A typical dimension is located on a line that is slightly separated from and parallel to the object being dimensioned. The object being dimensioned and the dimension line are connected by extension lines that are drawn perpendicular to the object being dimensioned. The extension lines should line up with each end of the object being measured. In instances where several short measurements are provided for an object, an overall dimension may be placed outside the short dimensions.

Dimensions are placed in or above the dimension line and are stated in feet and inches, or feet and tenths for metric measurements. When dimensioning several similarly spaced elements, the designer usually dimensions the first element and adds the abbreviation *typ.* This abbreviation indicates that all following elements along that dimension line have similar measurements. When the dimension line is too small to place the measurement directly on the dimension line, the dimension may be placed to the side with a leader to the dimension line (Figure 4-3).

Abbreviations, Symbols, and Textures Used on Construction Plans

Adding to the difficulty of interpreting construction plans is the variety of abbreviations (Table 4-1), symbols (Figure 4-4), and textures (Figure 4-5) used to represent construction measures and materials. Many of these items are standardized throughout all construction industries.

COMPUTER GENERATED (CADD) DRAWINGS

Drawings used for construction may be drafted by hand or drafted on a computer using **CADD (computer aided drafting and design)** technology. Drawings produced by either method should be treated in the same manner when reading and interpreting. Only rarely will a drawing be provided as a digital file (no paper drawings, but rather a file that a computer reads). Should you receive such a file, you will need the appropriate software to read it. This may necessitate a purchase of the same CADD program used to create the drawing. Because users can measure with drawing and area calculation tools, CADD drawing files offer the advantage of obtaining accurate project dimensions. Use caution that you do not alter the design when opening and interpreting the drawing.

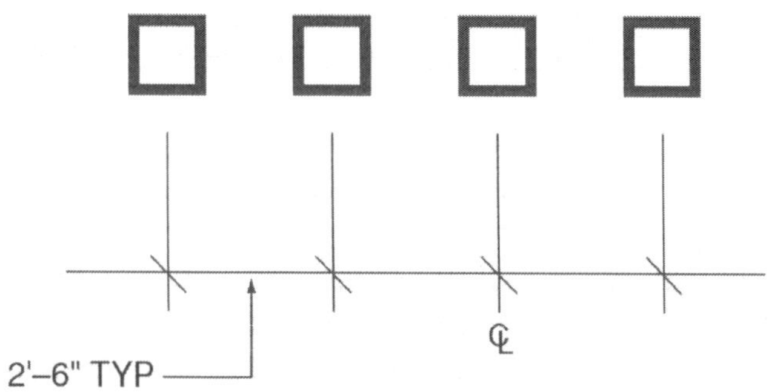

Figure 4-3 Dimensional notations.

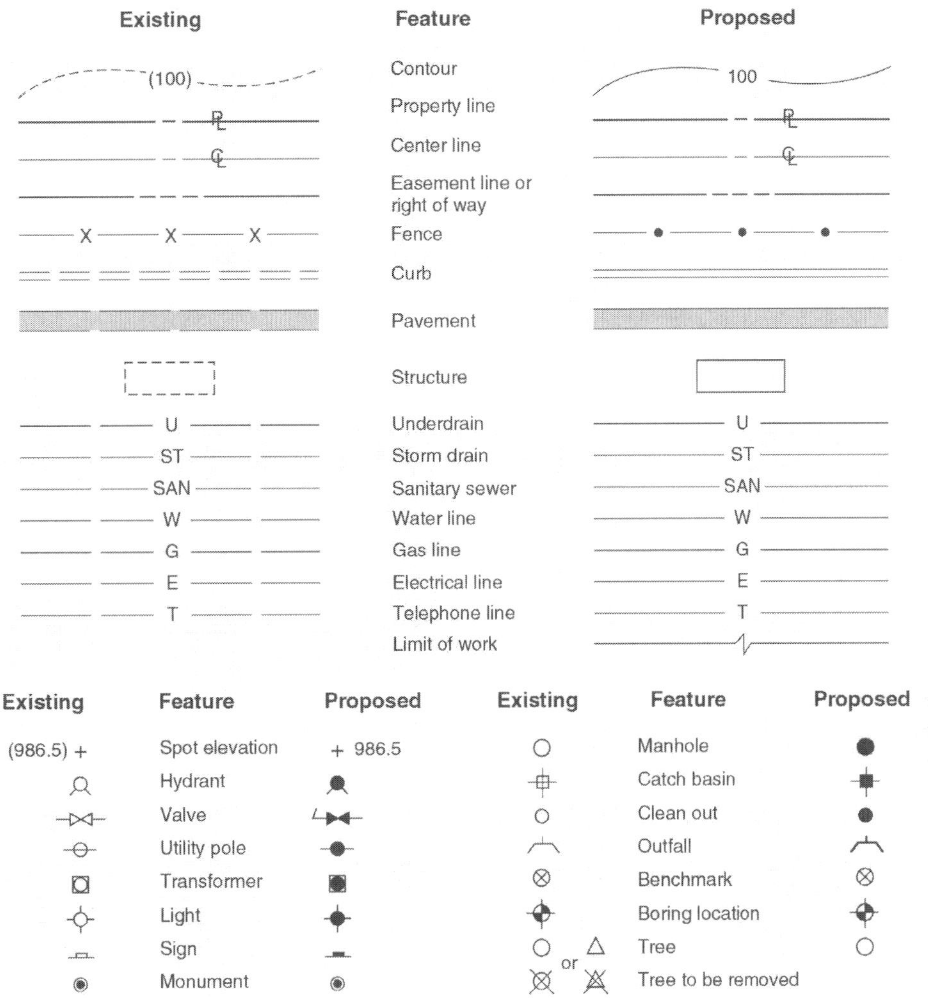

Figure 4-4 Typical symbols used on construction drawings.

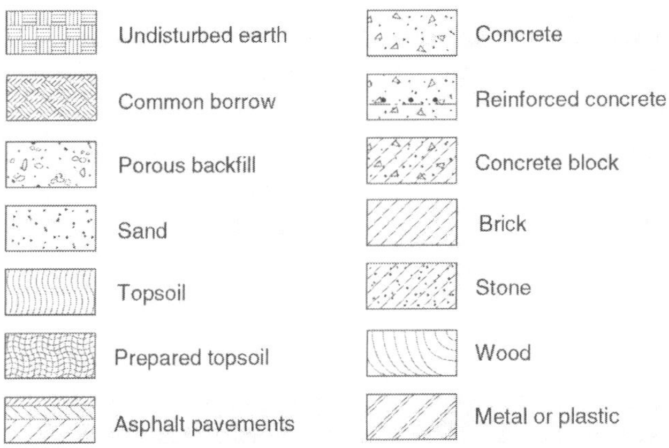

Figure 4-5 Typical plan and section/elevation textures used on construction drawings.

If the drawing is a pdf (portable document format) document, you will need to obtain software called Adobe® Reader® to view the drawing. You can obtain this software for free from Adobe's Web site http://www.adobe.com/products/. Pdf files can be opened and printed but not changed. Use caution when obtaining quantities from pdf files, as the scale of the drawing you are viewing may not be the original scale as prepared by the designer. Other file types may be available to contractors for estimating and installation purposes. Check with the designer providing the documents for instructions on opening and using such files.

Table 4-1 Typical construction drawing abbreviations

B&B	**Balled and burlap**
BC	Bottom of curb
BM	Benchmark
BS	Bottom of slope
Cal	Caliper
CB	Catch basin
CL	Center line
CLF	Chain-link fence
CMP	Corrugated metal pipe
Conc	Concrete
CF	Cubic feet
CY	Cubic yards
Dim	Dimension
Dia	Diameter
El	Elevation
Exist	Existing
Exp	Expansion
FFE	Finish floor elevation
FG	Finished gradee
FH	Fire hydrant
FL	Flow line
Ftg	Footing
FT	Foot or feet
Ga	Gauge
Gal	Gallon
HB	Hose bibb
HP	High point
ID	Inside diameter
Inv	Invert
LP	Low point
Lin	Linear
LF	Linear feet
Max	Maximum
MH	Manhole
NIC	Not in contract
NTS	Not to scale
Nom	Nominal dimension
OC	On center
OD	Outside diameter
PCP	Porous concrete pipe
ROW	Right-of-way
SI	Storm inlet
SF	Square feet
SY	Square yards
TC	Top of curb
TCP	Terra-cotta pipe
TW	Top of wall
TS	Top of slope
Typ	Typical
Var	Varies or variable
VCP	Vitrified clay pipe
WWM	Welded wire mesh
YD	Yard drain

SHOP DRAWINGS

Shop drawings are graphic documents provided to an owner by a contractor or material supplier that show the construction details of a project's particular prefabricated or custom fabricated element. Shop drawings represent the contractor's or supplier's interpretation of the designer's requirements from the construction documents. The owner's agent typically approves shop drawings before they are implemented.

RECORD DRAWINGS

Record Drawings, also referred to as **As-Built Drawings** show the way a project was actually built, including any adjustments made as a result of field conditions and change orders. Record drawings are essentially a set of original construction drawings marked up with the changes that were implemented during construction. As-Built Drawings are differentiated from Record Drawings as they are usually prepared by surveyors and certified for exactness.

INTERPRETING LANDSCAPE CONSTRUCTION PLANS

Typical landscape construction plans are based on divisions of the work. Without experience in working with construction plans, landscape contractors could misinterpret the information these documents present. Included with each plan description are the types of data it includes, an explanation of how the data are graphically presented, and recommendations for interpreting plan information.

Site Demolition

Site preparation plans show which parts of the existing site are to be removed and which are to be protected. Items that are to be protected or removed are indicated by notations and textures, with boundaries and work areas identified by symbols and lines. Although other contractors may do a majority of the work on this plan, the landscape contractor may occasionally have the responsibility of protecting existing site elements, particularly plant material.

To interpret the information on a site preparation plan, follow these steps:

- Obtain and read all plans and specifications related to site preparation for the project.
- Review the symbols, textures, and abbreviations used on the site preparation plan and locate and read any special notes placed on the plan.
- Become familiar with the drawing layout and locate major improvements such as buildings, roadways, parking lots, and natural features.
- Identify project boundaries and limits of work.
- Identify existing site elements to be preserved.
- Locate plant material to be fenced and the temporary erosion controls to be installed.
- Read notations regarding site elements to be removed.

Site Layout (Construction Staking)

Site construction staking plans show the horizontal location of all proposed improvements. Dimensions of walks, patios, drives, and any other landscape element for which location is critical are indicated on this plan. Design professionals use several formats for locating objects, including grids, **baselines**, and object dimensions. Grid format uses dimensions referenced from two baselines. Measurements are made down both baselines from a single beginning point to locate an object (Figure 4-6). Baseline format measures down a single reference line to provide one dimension for a point and makes a measurement at a right angle to that reference line to obtain the second dimension for a point. Using this format of two measurements, you can locate any point on a project (Figure 4-7). Object dimensioning format uses measurements along an existing object to locate new points. Buildings, roadways, or any other existing object can be used to dimension to new points (Figure 4-8). Dimensions should be carefully marked on a plan to avoid confusion with other numbers and lines.

Detail Keys. Details are identified on construction plans using a symbol termed a **detail key**. Although typically located on the construction staking plan, detail keys may be found on any of the plans. The detail key indicates the sheet number on which the detail is located and the detail number (Figure 4-9). Two numbers are placed inside a circle, with the detail number located on top and the number of the sheet where the detail is located on the bottom. A line that divides the circle will have an arrow, indicating which way the detail is facing.

To interpret the information on a construction staking plan, follow these steps:

- Obtain and read all plans and specifications related to construction staking for the project.
- Review the symbols, textures, and abbreviations used on the construction staking plan and locate and read any special notes placed on the plan.
- Become familiar with the drawing layout and locate major improvements such as buildings, roadways, parking lots, and natural features.
- Determine the layout method used.
- Find the reference point or beginning point used for layout.
- Read and mark overall dimensions for improvements.
- Locate specific dimensions for improvement.
- Identify which improvements have details, and use the keys to locate the details on the appropriate sheet.

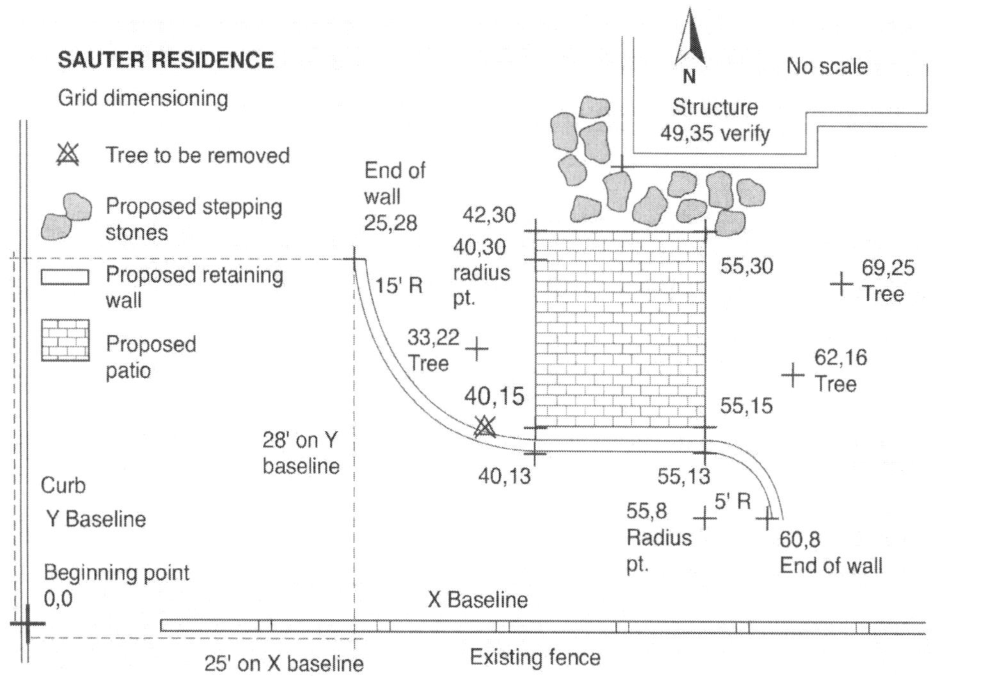

Figure 4-6 Layout plan using grid dimensioning. All points are located using *X* and *Y* coordinates laid out in reference to the beginning point. Dashed lines show example measurements to the first point located at 25 feet down the *X* baseline and 28 feet down the *Y* baseline.

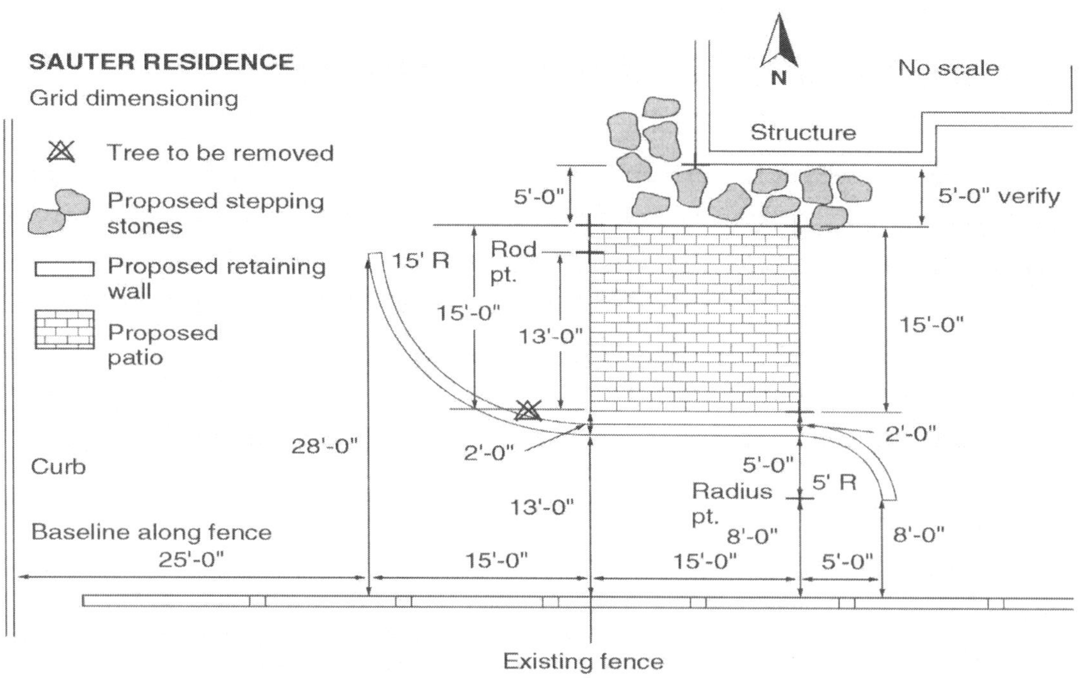

Figure 4-7 Layout plan using baseline dimensions. Points are located measuring off a project baseline.

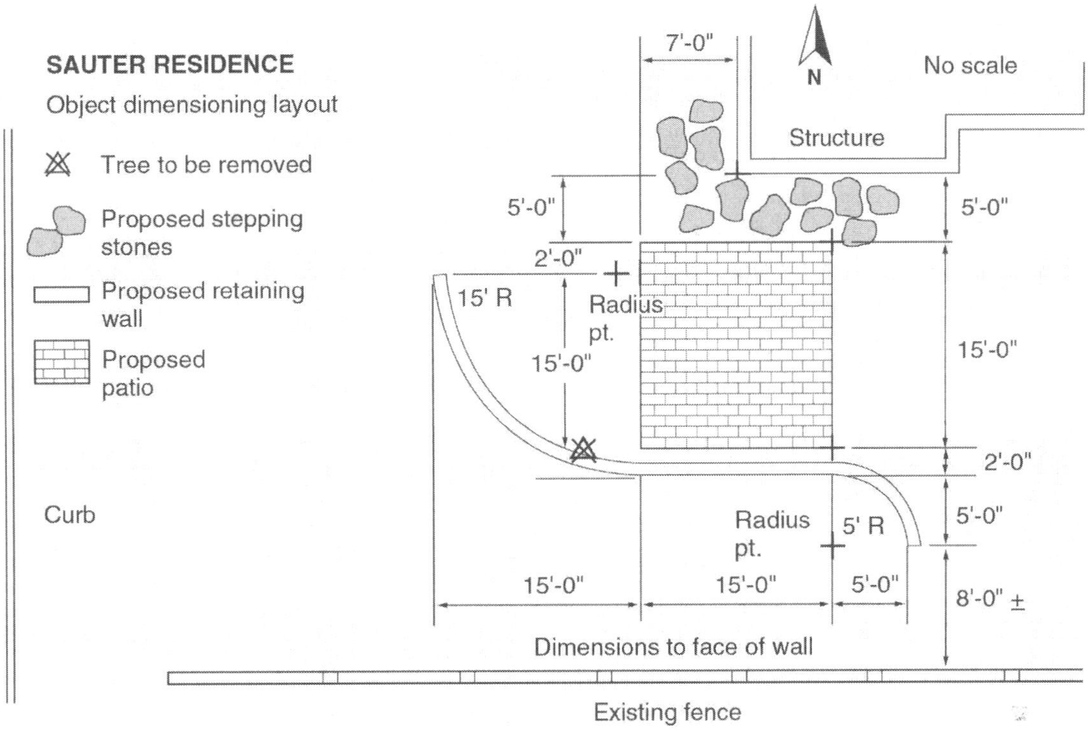

Figure 4-8 Layout plan using object dimensioning. Project elements are located by measuring off other nearby objects that have already been located. In this example, measurements would begin at the structure and continue outward toward the wall.

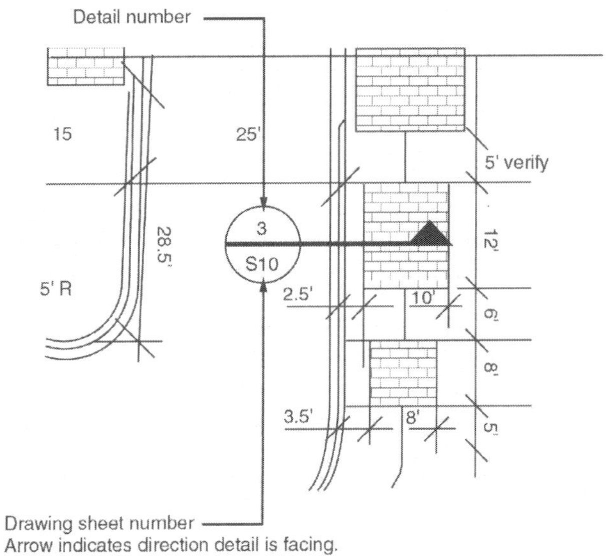

Figure 4-9 Keying details on a construction drawing. This detail key indicates a cross section of paving, with the arrow showing the direction the detail is facing. This detail can be found in Figure 4-14.

Grading Plans

Grading plans show the vertical location of all proposed improvements. Grading plans may also include information about water runoff, storm sewer construction, and storm water retention facilities. A key element of a grading plan is the **benchmark** for the site. The benchmark is a set elevation that serves as a reference for all existing and proposed grades for the site.

Benchmarks should be placed at a permanent location and should be easily accessible from the site. Using **contour lines** and **spot elevations**, the grading plan indicates the desired height of site elements and the direction of slope. All contours and spot elevations for a grading plan should be set in reference to the benchmark.

Contours are lines that connect points of similar elevation. Although useful for indicating general slope direction and steepness, contours are not sufficient to install improvements at specific grades. Contours are read by locating the elevation number printed in or directly on top of the contour line. Larger numbers indicate elevations that are higher than contours with lower numbers. Grading plans should include existing contours shown as dashed lines and proposed contours shown as solid lines. The closer contour lines are spaced, the steeper the slope. Contours spaced farther apart indicate a shallow, or more level, slope. Landforms used in landscaping, such as **berms** and drainage swales, have a distinct contour signature (Figure 4-10). When a site is graded, the finish grade must match the direction, slope, and elevation indicated by the contours. To supplement contour interpretation, arrows indicating the existing and/or proposed direction of surface runoff may be added.

Spot elevations indicate elevations of specific points in reference to the benchmark. Permanent improvements such as structures, footings, paving, and walls require specific elevations to build the improvement; and spot elevations provide that data (Figure 4-10). Spot elevations typically include a notation that indicates if the elevation is for the top, bottom, or some other part of the object being measured. Indications of direction and degree of slope can be obtained by calculating the difference between spot elevations.

To interpret the information on a grading plan, Figure 4-11, follow these steps:

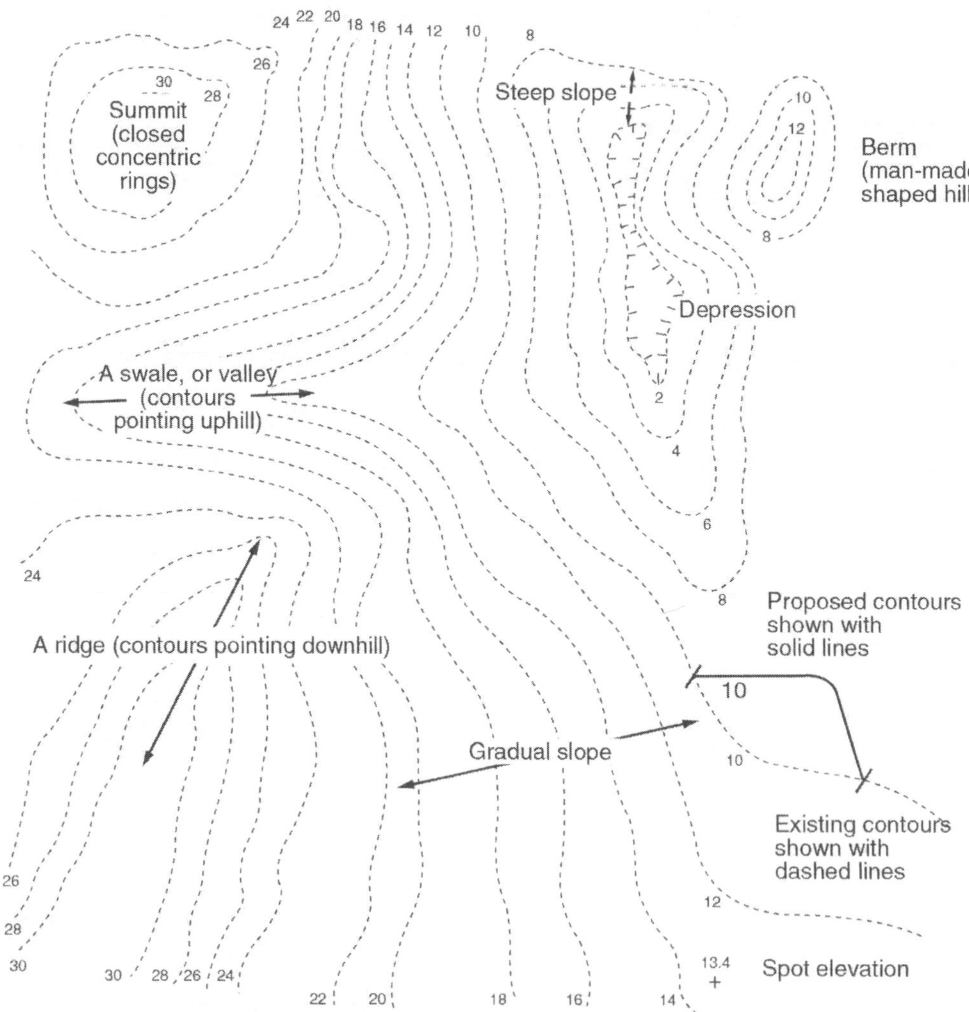

Figure 4-10 Typical topographic landforms and notations.

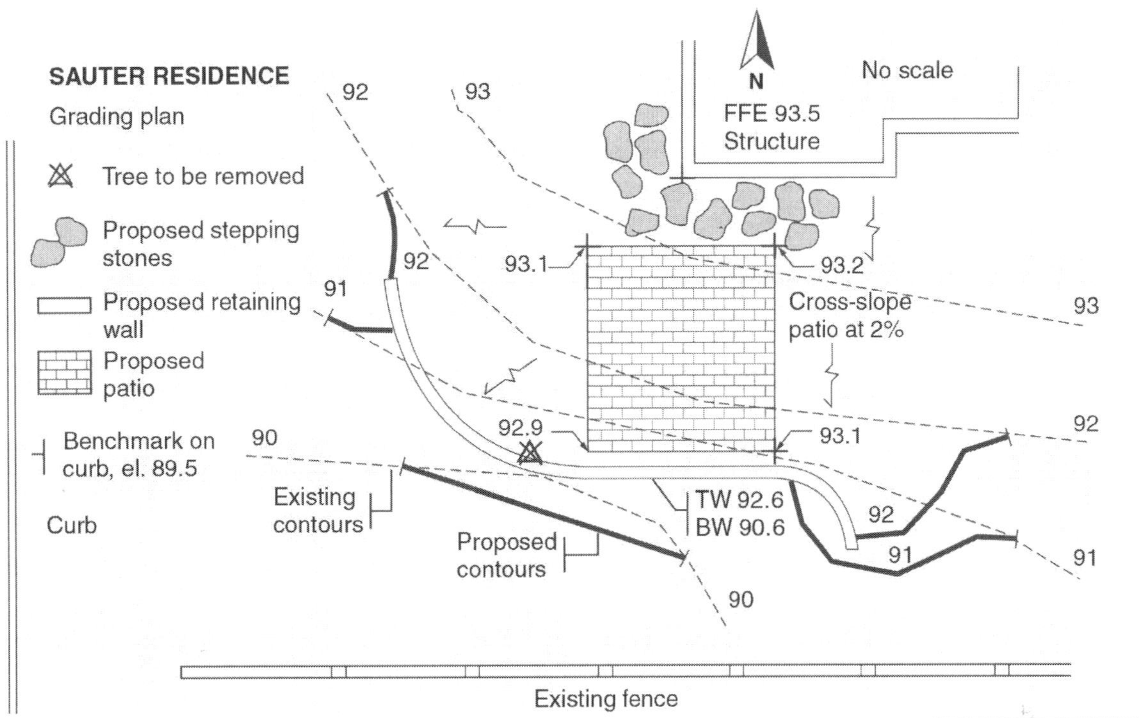

Figure 4-11 Grading plan showing spot elevations and existing and proposed contours.

- Obtain and read all plans and specifications related to the grading plan for the project.
- Review the symbols, textures, and abbreviations used on the site grading plan and locate and read any special notes placed on the plan.
- Become familiar with the drawing layout and locate major improvements such as buildings, roadways, parking lots, and natural features.
- Locate benchmarks and the range of elevations (high and low points) of the site.
- Identify existing contours and analyze the current "lay of the land."
- Identify proposed contours to determine the proposed changes and areas where significant amounts of cutting or removal of earth, and filling or adding of earth, will be required (color-coding cut and fill areas can be helpful).
- Identify major proposed landforms (berms and drainage swales) by their contour signature.
- Locate proposed spot elevations of major structures and compare them to existing grades to determine amounts of cut or fill required.
- Locate proposed spot elevations of other site improvements to determine if cut or fill is required.
- Look for drainage arrows and symbols indicating which direction walks, paved areas, and open areas are to be sloped.

Utility Plans

Utility plans show location, type, size, and depth of proposed utilities. Although other contractors may install many of these utilities,

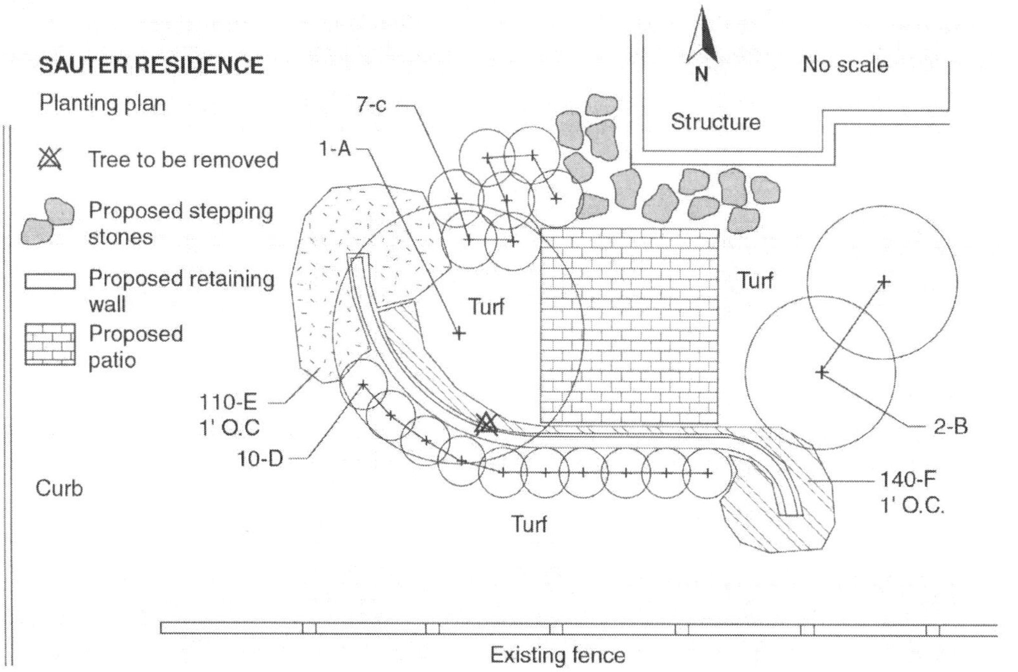

Figure 4-12 Planting plan. The key refers the reader to the plant schedule (Figure 4-13) for details about the plants.

landscape contractors may find irrigation work included in landscape contracts. A separate schedule on this sheet may contain relevant data regarding fixtures, such as pipe sizes and irrigation head model numbers. Irrigation installations are typically indicated by lines on the drawings with notations regarding the type, depth, and size of the utility.

To interpret the information on a utility plan, follow these steps:

- Obtain and read all plans and specifications related to a utility for the project.
- Review the symbols, textures, and abbreviations used on the utility plan and locate and read any special notes placed on the plan.
- Become familiar with the drawing layout and locate major improvements such as buildings, roadways, parking lots, and natural features.
- Find the type, location, and size of utility lines.
- Determine depth of utility lines.
- Locate irrigation components to be installed, including service, controllers, main lines, lateral lines, valves, and heads.
- Locate major utility structures, such as drainage inlets, manholes, utility poles, and light footings, and note their grade (cross-reference the grading plan, if necessary).

Planting Plans

Planting plans indicate the location and type of plant material to be installed. Individual trees and shrubs are shown with circles indicating the approximate spread of the plant, and the location of each plant's center plant is indicated by an *X* or similar type of mark. The centers of identical plant materials are connected by a line, or leader, that will include a label of the type and number of plants in that "string" (Figure 4-12). Labels may include a key that refers to the plant schedule. Some labels may use multiple naming schemes, such as the plant's common or botanical name.

Occasionally, the designer may include on the leader planting information that indicates spacing, planting elevation, or other pertinent data. A planting plan usually includes several of these leaders if several plants are labeled. Alternative methods used to label plants are placing a letter next to the planting location for each plant or using a different symbol for each different type of plant. Both the letter and the symbol should refer to a plant schedule for plant type, size, and details.

Masses of smaller plants, such as ground covers, may be shown using line or dot textures covering the area where plants are to be installed. Leaders for masses of such plants typically include the plant name, quantity of plants in the area labeled, and the spacing of individual plants.

Plant Schedule. Usually included with the planting plan is a **plant schedule**, which lists all proposed plants with their quantity, size, condition, and special instructions for planting (Figure 4-13). The detail from this schedule should be complete enough to allow ordering of all plant material to be used on the project. Notations may also be included on the planting plan that indicate the amount and type of mulch to be used, spacing of plants, staking or wrapping requirements, and other plant-related instructions. Written technical specifications typically provide other details regarding planting.

To interpret the information on a planting plan, follow these steps:

- Obtain and read all plans and specifications related to the planting plan for the project.
- Review the symbols, textures, and abbreviations used on the planting plan and locate and read any special notes placed on the plan.

SAUTER RESIDENCE					
PLANT SCHEDULE					
KEY	COMMON NAME	BOTANICAL NAME	QTY.	SIZE/COND.	REMARKS
A	Burr Oak	*Quercus macrocarpa*	1	2″ B&B	specimen quality
B	Shadblow Service berery	*Amalenchier canadensis*	2	8′ cont.	
C	Dwarf Compact Yews	*Taxus cuspidata "nana"*	7	7 gal.	
D	Cranberry Cotoneaster	*Cotoneaster apiculata*	10	5 gal.	
E	Purpleleaf Wintercreeper	*Euonymus fortuneii coloratus*	110	flats	space 1′ on center
F	Daylillies	*Hemerocallus sp.*	140	1 gal.	space 1′ on center
					species selected by owner

Figure 4-13 Plant schedule.

- Become familiar with the drawing layout and locate major improvements such as buildings, roadways, parking lots, and natural features.
- Review the plant schedule for special symbols and keys. Plants may use a variety of key types to coordinate the plan and plant schedule. Alpha characters, numbers, symbols, or partial genus and species names are typical keys. Some plants may even be labeled directly on the plan, eliminating the need for plant keys.
- Locate each type of plant material in the order indicated on the plant schedule.
- Identify all plant locations, review the species, quantity, and spacing (if plants are grouped together).
- Note for each plant location the elevation, nearby utilities, and other site improvements in thevicinity.

Construction Details

Construction details provide information about specialized elements that need to be built for the project. Items that are usually detailed include bridges, specialty paving, amenities, stairs, walls, lighting, and other construction items that benefit from being shown in greater detail. Details may show cross sections, elevations, or large-scale plans that illustrate more detail of specialty construction (Figure 4-14). Materials, dimensions, and notes are included to aid in proper construction. Scale for each individual detail is noted below the detail, and detail references, or keys, are typically placed on site construction staking plans.

To interpret the information on a site detail, follow these steps:

Obtain and read all plans and specifications related to the area of work for the detail.

- Locate the detail on the appropriate detail sheet.
- Identify the type of drawing used for the detail (section, elevation, plan).
- Identify the scale of the drawing.
- Analyze the detail to determine the dimension of the improvement and the materials used for construction.

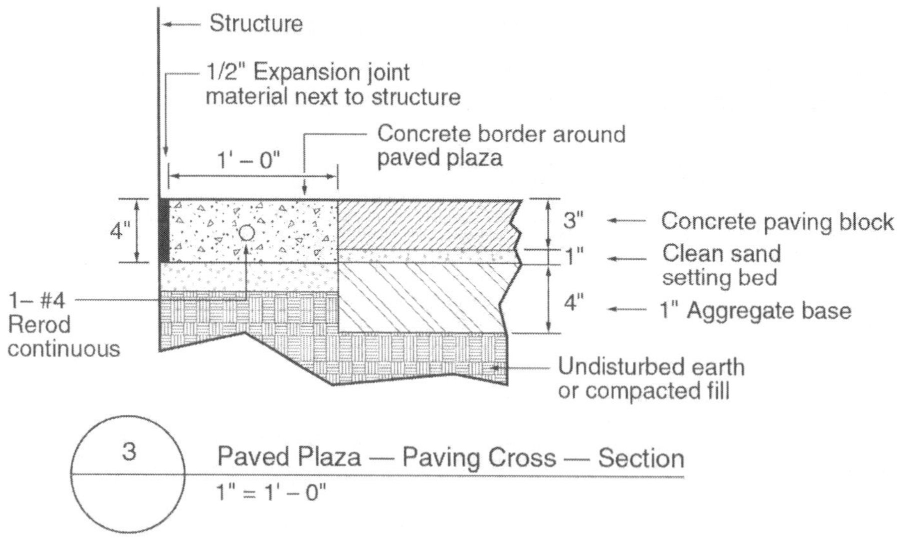

Figure 4-14 Construction detail.

CHAPTER 5

CONSTRUCTION MATH

OBJECTIVES

By reading and practicing the techniques described in this chapter, the reader should be able to successfully complete the following activities:

- Perform basic landscape construction math calculations.
- Calculate material quantities for a landscape construction project.

Whether ordering materials, establishing grades, laying out a walkway, or performing any one of the many activities of landscape construction, the contractor needs to perform basic math operations. In this chapter are the building blocks of math operations for landscape construction. Included as basic calculations are the concepts of item counts; linear, perimeter, area, and volume measurements; and weight conversions. Formulas that use these basic measurements to obtain specialty calculations are also included in this chapter.

Math and project measurements can be made easier if the decimal system is used, rather than measuring in inches and fractions. Most math functions benefit from converting numbers to feet and tenths. Conversions related to construction math can be found in Appendix C.

CONSTRUCTION CALCULATORS

One of the more valuable tools available to the contractor is the construction calculator. Operated much like a typical numerical calculator, the construction calculator uses preprogrammed instructions to perform typical construction-related calculations, saving time doing extensive math calculations in the field. Depending on the manufacturer and model, the construction calculator includes functions that perform dimensioning; conversions of feet/inches to decimals and decimals to feet/inches; calculating center points, area measurements, volume measurements, board feet and block calculations; and geometric calculations, including circles and arc, rise/run calculations, rafter calculations, slope; and trigonometric calculations.

CALCULATING AVERAGES

In construction, calculating the average of several numbers may be required. The formula for calculating an average is:

Sum of all numbers/*N*, where *N* equals the number of numbers added together (Figure 5-1).

ITEM COUNT

Items such as benches, lights, plant material, and other amenities are measured and ordered by quantity of each item used. An item count requires only a "head" count of each separate item being used.

LINEAR MEASUREMENTS

Linear measurements are used to calculate quantities for items that are purchased by length, such as edger and fence. Expressed as linear feet (LF), the linear measurement is also the building block for area and volume calculations. Linear measurements are performed by measuring directly from one point to a second point.

Three methods for performing linear measurements are common in the landscaping field. The level of accuracy needed determines the choice of method for making linear measurements. Direct measurement should be selected if an accuracy of 2% is required. **Pacing** can be used if the margin of error can range up to

Sum of all numbers/N, where N equals the quantity of numbers added together

$$\frac{A + B + C + D}{4} = \text{AVERAGE} \quad \frac{\text{(the numbers added together)}}{\text{(the quantity of numbers added together)}}$$

EXAMPLE:

$$\frac{4 + 2 + 5 + 5}{4} = \frac{16}{4} = 4$$

Figure 5-1 Calculating averages.

5%, and estimating is acceptable if the margin of error can be as high as 10%. Actual percentage of error for each measurement technique will vary, depending on how the user applies the technique. Techniques for each method are identified in the following paragraphs.

Direct Measurement

Direct measurement involves the use of a tape measure or measuring wheel to determine the distance between two points. Obstacles or slopes between the two points can affect the accuracy of this method. If obstacles prevent a direct measurement, take the measurement along a route parallel to the one that requires measuring. Use of a screwdriver to anchor the zero end of the tape allows one person, instead of two people, to take measurements. A measuring wheel is easy and convenient to use, but most wheels have an accuracy of 1 foot and provide no increments between feet (inches or tenths).

Slope also affects the accuracy of linear measurements. Horizontal distances are less when measured on a flat surface than when they are measured on a sloped surface. To accurately find a location on a sloped surface, begin by extending a tape measure from the point where the measurement begins. Hold the tape level and along the alignment for the measurement (Figure 5-2). At the correct measurement on the tape, lower a **plumb bob** to obtain the desired location on the ground. Measurements that are longer than one length of the tape can be made by repeating these steps, extending the level tape from each new location found with the plumb bob. Very steep slopes may require several short measurements to maintain accuracy. To accurately measure a point on a slope, hold the measuring tape level and hold the plumb bob directly over the point being measured. Move the tape adjacent to the plumb bob, and read the dimension where the plumb bob line intersects the tape.

Pacing

Pacing can be useful because it requires no special tools and can be adapted to nearly every site or terrain. More than walking, pacing uses the consistency of a person's normal pace to derive a linear measurement for a site. To determine average pace, set up a course that is 100 feet long and walk the course several times, counting the number of steps each time. Divide the distance by the average number of steps to calculate the average pace (Figure 5-3). It is important, both when calculating average pace and when performing measurements with this method, that you maintain a normal step. Attempting to step an even distance or altering the normal step will result in inconsistent results.

Learning. Estimation

When accuracy is not critical, estimating linear dimensions is a viable option. Estimating requires

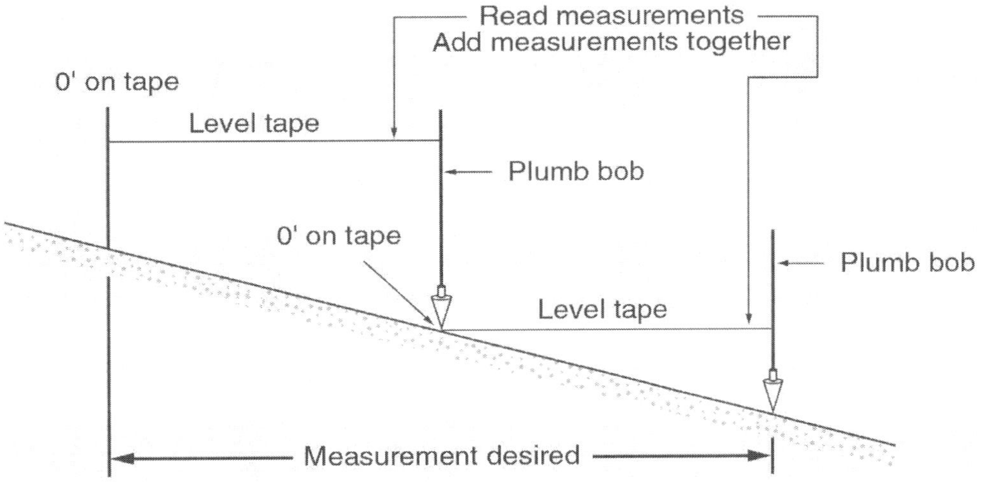

Figure 5-2 Making accurate measurements on a hillside.

1. Set up and pace course three times:

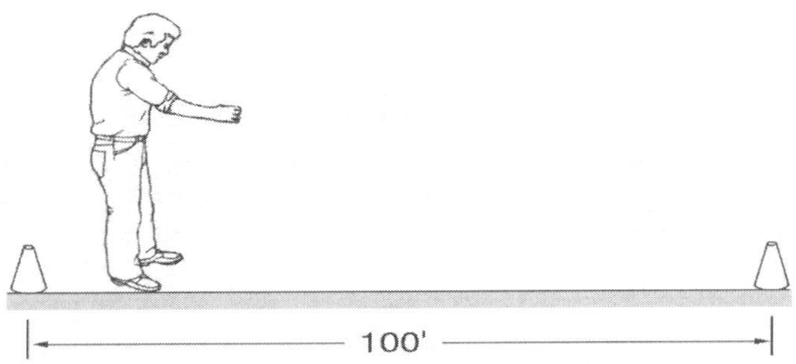

(note: course should be level and free of obstacles)

2. Average the number of paces:

   1st pass: ____________

   2nd pass: ____________

   3rd pass: ____________

   $$\text{Total paces} \div 3 = \frac{1 + 2 + 3}{3} = \text{average number of paces}$$

3. Divide average number of paces into 100' to obtain typical pace:

   $$\frac{100'}{\text{Average number of paces}} = \text{average pace}$$

Figure 5-3 Calculating your pace.

determining a distance based on visual observation or comparison with a known dimension. Visual determination is developed by experience in working with outdoor spaces, whereas comparison requires visually comparing the distance to be measured with an object of known measurements. Items such as structures, door openings (usually 7 feet high), and sidewalk squares can be used to make comparative measurements.

Perimeter Calculations

Installation of edging or materials placed around a shape requires calculation of the perimeter of an object. To perform perimeter calculations, identify the shape being measured, and then make linear measurements of portions of that shape. If working with an irregular shape, you may find that the fastest method for measuring a perimeter is to pace or to take a direct measurement. If measuring standard geometric shapes, use the formulas identified in Figure 5-4 to obtain perimeter measurements. Figure 5-5 provides sample calculations. Common shapes include:

- Square/Rectangle/Parallelogram: Shapes with two sets of parallel sides. Squares and rectangles have right-angled corners, and parallelograms have no right-angled corners.
- Trapezoid: Shape with one set of parallel sides and two right-angled corners, one adjacent to each parallel side.
- Circle: Round shape with edges equally distant from the center.
- Ellipse: Rounded egg shape with edges at variable distances from center.
- Circle Sectors: Partial segments of a circle. Defined by length of the outside arc or the enclosed angle of circle measured in degrees.
- Triangle (right or equilateral): Shape with three sides. Right triangle has one right angle; equilateral triangle has three sides of equal lengths.
- Irregular Round: Kidney or irregular shaped circles for which a center radius can be located.

AREA CALCULATIONS

- Materials such as brick, seed, and sod are purchased based on the area of the space they cover. Quantities of materials necessary to cover flat surfaces require area calculations. Expressed as square feet (SF) or square yards (SY), measurement of area requires recognizing the shape (or collection of shapes) of the space to be covered and calculating key dimensions for that shape using linear measurements. Formulas for calculating the area of standard shapes are shown in Figure 5-4. Figure 5-5 provides sample calculations.

Many methods are available for obtaining area calculations. New computer design programs automatically calculate the area of shapes. A **planimeter** is an engineering tool used to measure the area of random shapes. Even with no computer or planimeter, you can break down any shape into a collection of measurable geometric spaces. Once you determine the dimensions of these shapes, you can then calculate the areas and add them to obtain the area of irregular shapes.

To calculate square footages by using the sum of shapes, begin by analyzing the space for which an area measurement is required. Observe if the space is an easily measurable single shape or if one or more of the geometric shapes previously mentioned is recognizable (square/rectangle, parallelogram, circle, or triangle) within the boundaries of the shape. These shapes should closely cover the majority of the area being measured (Figure 5-6). Using the formulas in Figure 5-4, make the measurements and perform the calculations required for each shape; then total the answers to obtain the area for the shape. Be certain all calculations are correct; and if only a portion of the shape is used (such as one-quarter of a circle), reduce the total appropriately.

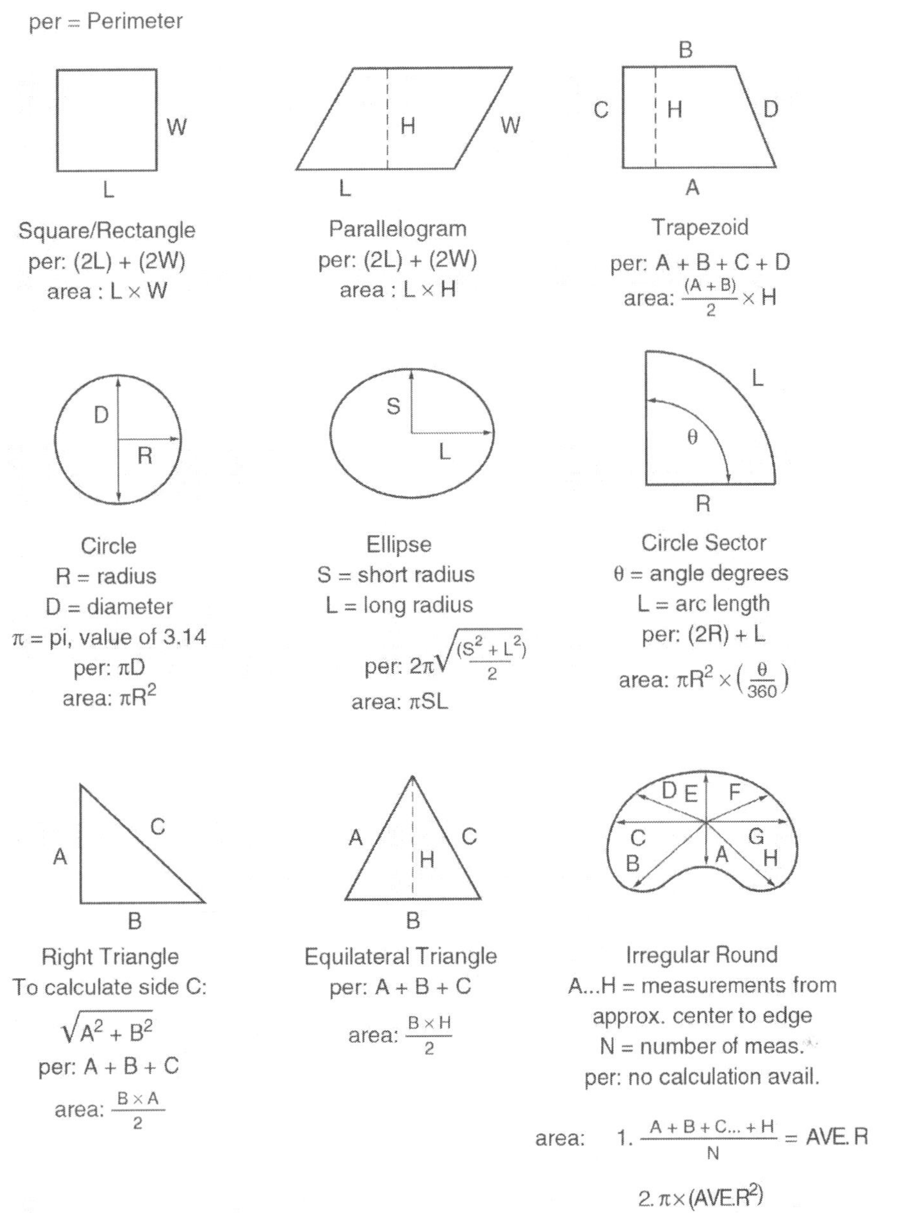

Figure 5-4 Perimeter and area formulas for common shapes.

Be forewarned that this method will have a substantial margin of error, so if material orders are critical, a more precise method of measurement should be selected.

Area × Height = CF (both area and height must be expressed as feet or decimal portions of feet)

Some conversions applicable to area measurements follow. Appendix B includes additional conversions.

- If the measurement required must be expressed as square yards, divide the square foot total by 9 to obtain square yards.
- To obtain the number of acres, divide the square foot total by 43,560.
- To obtain squares for sod, divide the square footage by 100.
- To obtain rolls of sod (each sod roll being 1 SY), divide square footage by 9.

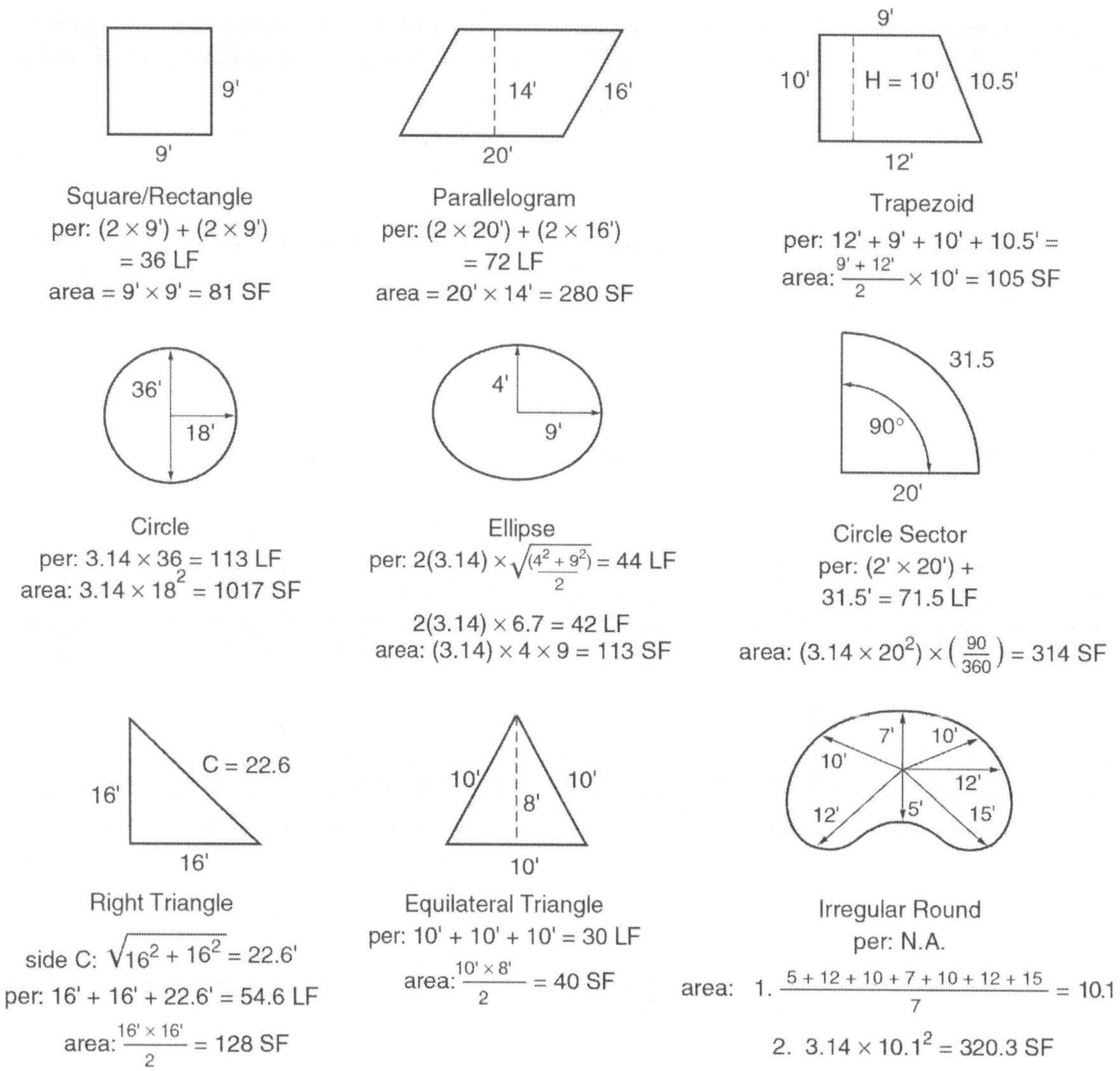

Figure 5-5 Examples of calculating perimeter and area for common shapes.

VOLUME CALCULATIONS

For materials that are purchased in bulk, a volume measurement is typically required. Bulk measurements are expressed as cubic feet (CF) or cubic yards (CY) and, to be calculated, require an area measurement and knowledge of the depth of the material.

To calculate volumes for landscaping, begin with the square footage of the area that is to be filled. Determine the depth of the layer to be filled and place the numbers in the following formula (Figure 5-7):

$$\text{Area}\ (\text{in SF}) \times \text{Depth}\ (\text{in inches})\ /\ 12 = \text{CF}$$

Note that the depth is not converted to feet but is left in inches.

Determining the volume of plant root balls requires a formula used to calculate the volume of a sphere. Once you have calculated the volume, use a weight conversion to convert to pounds. The formula for calculating the volume of a sphere is as follows (Figure 5-8):

1. Identify shapes and measure dimensions of each.

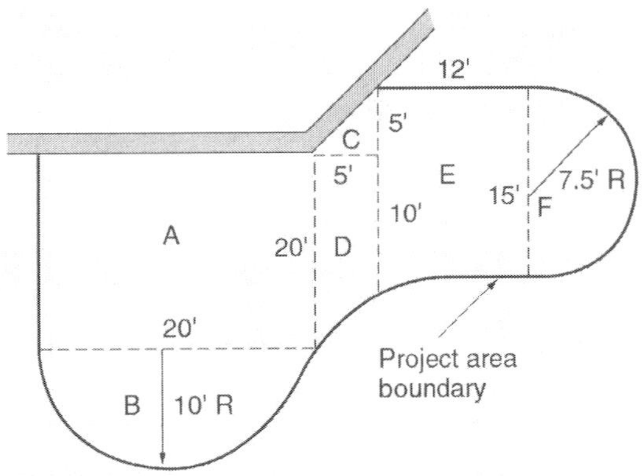

2. Add together areas for each of the shapes identified within the project area boundary (refer to Figure 4–4 for formulas for each shape).

A Square		= 400	SF
B (Half) Circle	314/2	= 157	
C Triangle		= 12.5	
D Trapezoid		= 75	
E Rectangle		= 180	
F (Half) Circle	176/2	= 88	
		± 912.5	SF

Figure 5-6 Calculating the area and volume of an irregular shape.

Volume formula:

$$\frac{\text{area (in SF)} \times \text{depth (in inches)}}{12} = \text{CF (cubic feet)}$$

Examples from Figure 4–5:

1. 6" layer of topsoil over square shape of 81 SF

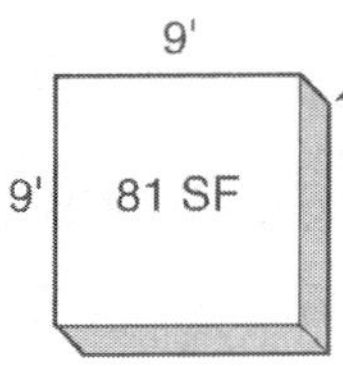

6" depth

$$\frac{81 \times 6}{12} = 40.5 \text{ CF}$$

$$\frac{40.5}{27} = 1.5 \text{ CY (cubic yards)}$$

2. 4" layer of mulch over ellipse shape of 113 SF

$$\frac{113 \times 4}{12} = 37.6 \text{ CF}$$

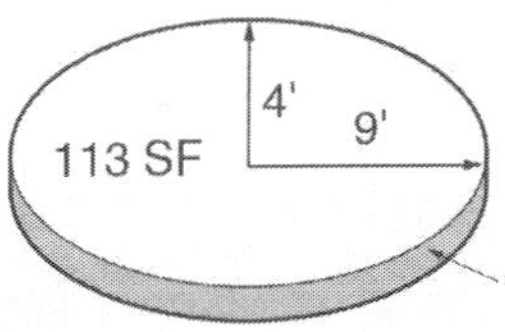

$$\frac{37.6}{27} = 1.4 \text{ CY}$$

4" depth

Figure 5-7 Formula and examples of calculating volumes for materials placed in layers.

Volume of Sphere:

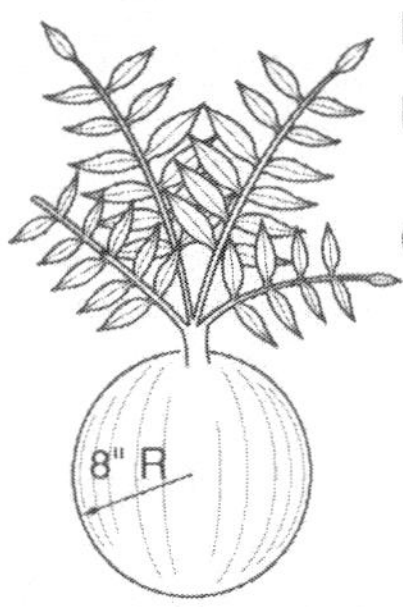

Formula: $4.18 \times R \times R \times R = \text{CI}$

Example: $4.18 \times 8 \times 8 \times 8 = 2140$ CI

Conversion to CF: $\frac{\text{CI}}{1728} = \text{CF}$

$$\frac{2140}{1728} = 1.24 \text{ CF}$$

Volume of Cylinder:

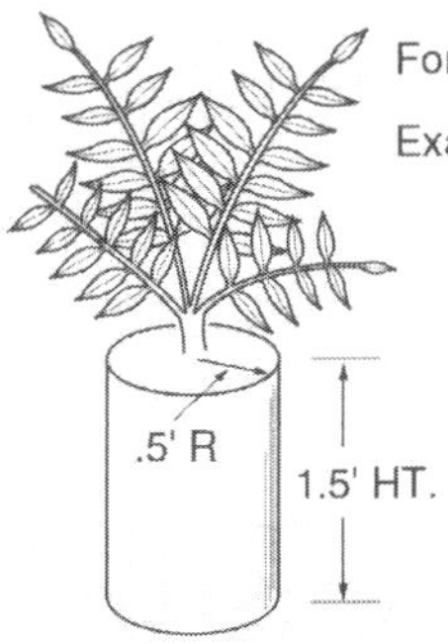

Formula: area of circle × HT. = CF

Example: $(.5 \times .5 \times 3.14) \times 1.5 = 1.18$ CF

Figure 5-8 Formulas and examples of calculating volumes for spheres and cylinders.

Expressing *R* as feet (or decimal portions of feet) will provide an answer in CF (cubic feet).
To calculate the volume of a cylinder, use the following formula (Figure 5-8):

$4.18 \times R \times R \times R = CI$ (cubic inches) when R is expressed as inches.

Some conversions applicable to volume measurements include:

- If the measurement required is in cubic inches and must be converted to cubic feet, divide the cubic inches total by 1,728 to obtain cubic feet.
- If the measurement required is in cubic feet and must be expressed as cubic yards, divide the cubic foot total by 27 to obtain cubic yards.

See Figure 5-6 for an example of volume calculations.

WEIGHT CONVERSIONS

Materials purchased in bulk may require a weight, rather than a volume, measurement. In this case, use the following chart to convert volume to weight for each of the following types of materials by multiplying the CY or CF by the conversions:

- 1 CF soil, dry and loose = 90 pounds
- 1 CF soil, moist = 75 to 100 pounds
- 1 CF sand, dry = 100 pounds
- 1 CF limestone, uncrushed = 160 pounds
- 1 CF concrete = 140 pounds
- 1 CY fill dirt, dry and loose = 1.2 tons (2,400 pounds)
- 1 CY concrete sand, dry = 1.5 tons (3,000 pounds)
- 1 CY aggregate (class 5 aggregate, 1 inch roadstone, or equal) = 1.25 tons

SPECIALTY CALCULATIONS

Certain work areas within landscape construction require adaptations of the basic math operations to perform required calculations. These calculations are presented in the sections that follow.

Included are calculations required to determine slope, calculate wall material requirements, determine riser/tread dimensions for stairs, order paving and base materials, and similar specialty calculations. Additional calculations for landscape construction activities can be found in Appendix D.

SLOPE CALCULATIONS

When establishing grades or installing storm water drainage systems, it is critical to maintain downward **slope**. Although many contractors accomplish this task using visual estimation or a level, the ability to calculate slope is a valuable math skill. Slope calculations are presented for two applications: calculating the existing slope between two points and determining the amount of vertical change required to obtain a certain slope over a given distance.

Calculating the Slope Between Two Points

- To determine the slope of a uniform grade between two points, use the following steps. Measurements must be in the same units; feet and tenths are recommended (Figure 5-9).
- Measure the vertical difference between the two points (*V*). Use a carpenter's level resting on a straight 2 × 4 or a survey instrument to accomplish this.
- Measure the horizontal distance between the two points (*H*).
- Insert the measurements into the following formula:

$(V / H) \times 100 = \%$ of slope.

- The answer is the slope percentage.

Calculating the Vertical Change Required to Obtain a Given Slope Between Points

When staking improvements, you may need to construct a slope at a certain percentage from a first point to a second point. To calculate the amount of elevation change, use the following formula. Measurements must be in the same units; feet and tenths are recommended (Figure 5-9).

- Measure or set the elevation of the first point (use 100.0 if the actual elevation is not known) (*X*).
- Measure the horizontal distance between the first point and the second point (*H*).
- To determine the change in elevation (Change), multiply the horizontal distance times the slope required between points:

H×.PS = Change

(*PS* is the percent slope expressed as a decimal, such as a 2% slope shown as .02).

- If the slope is to go down toward the second point, *subtract* the Change from *A*.

A – Change = Elevation of second point.

- If the slope is to go up toward the second point, *add* the Change to *A*.

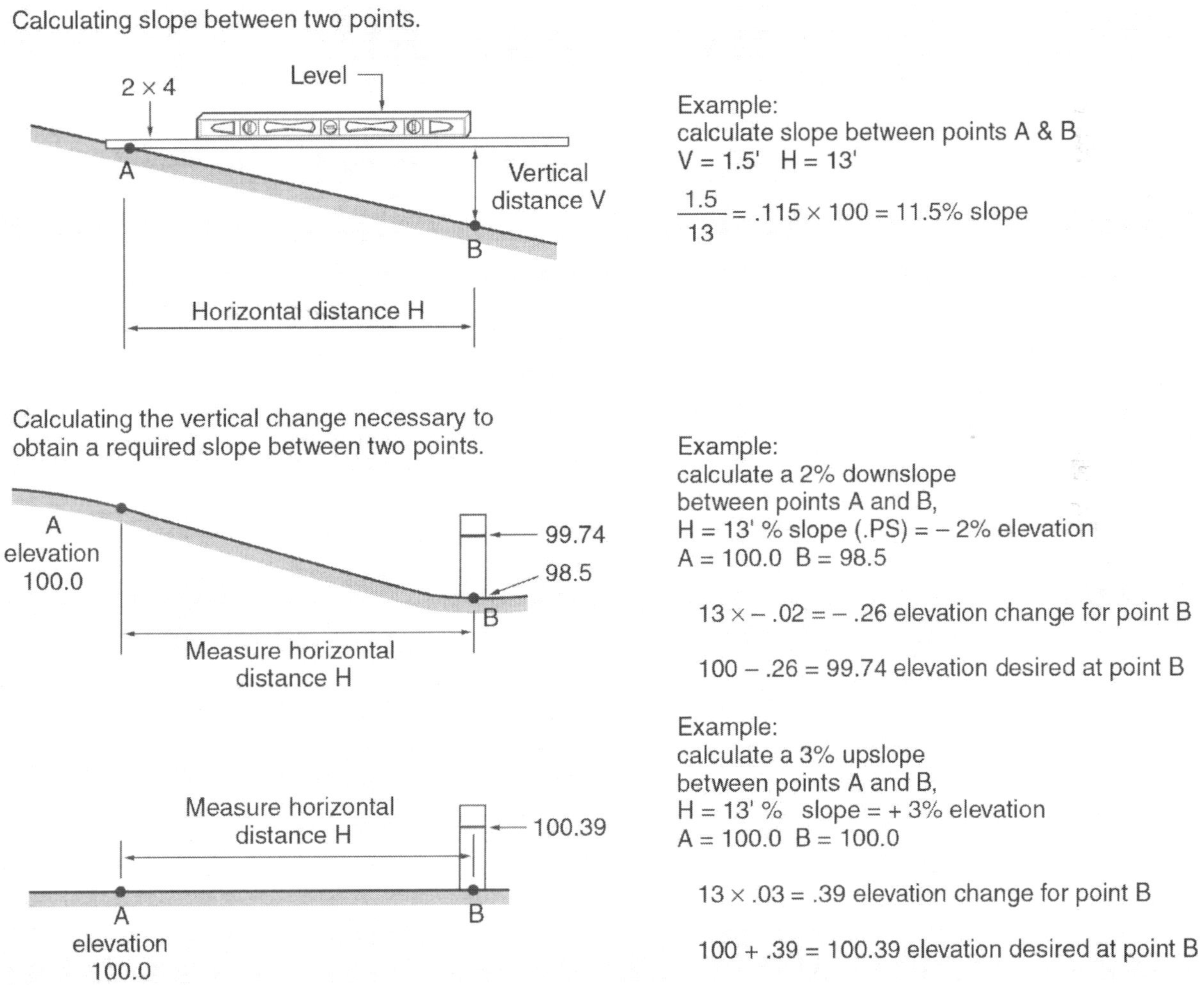

Figure 5-9 Calculating slopes.

WALL MATERIAL CALCULATIONS

Determining how much wall material is needed requires calculating the surface area of the wall to be built. To perform this calculation, you will also need information from the manufacturer regarding how much surface area a single unit of wall material covers (Figure 5-10).

To determine the surface area of a wall that has a consistent height (Figure 5-10):

- Perform an area calculation by measuring the height and the length of the wall.
- Add 1 foot to the height measurement to accommodate a buried base, and multiply by the length to obtain square footage of the wall.

If the wall varies in height over its entire length (Figure 5-10):

- Obtain the average height by making multiple measurements at points where the wall is tallest and shortest, adding them, and dividing by the number of measurements taken.
- Add 1 foot to the height measurement to accommodate a buried base, and multiply by the length to obtain square footage of the wall.

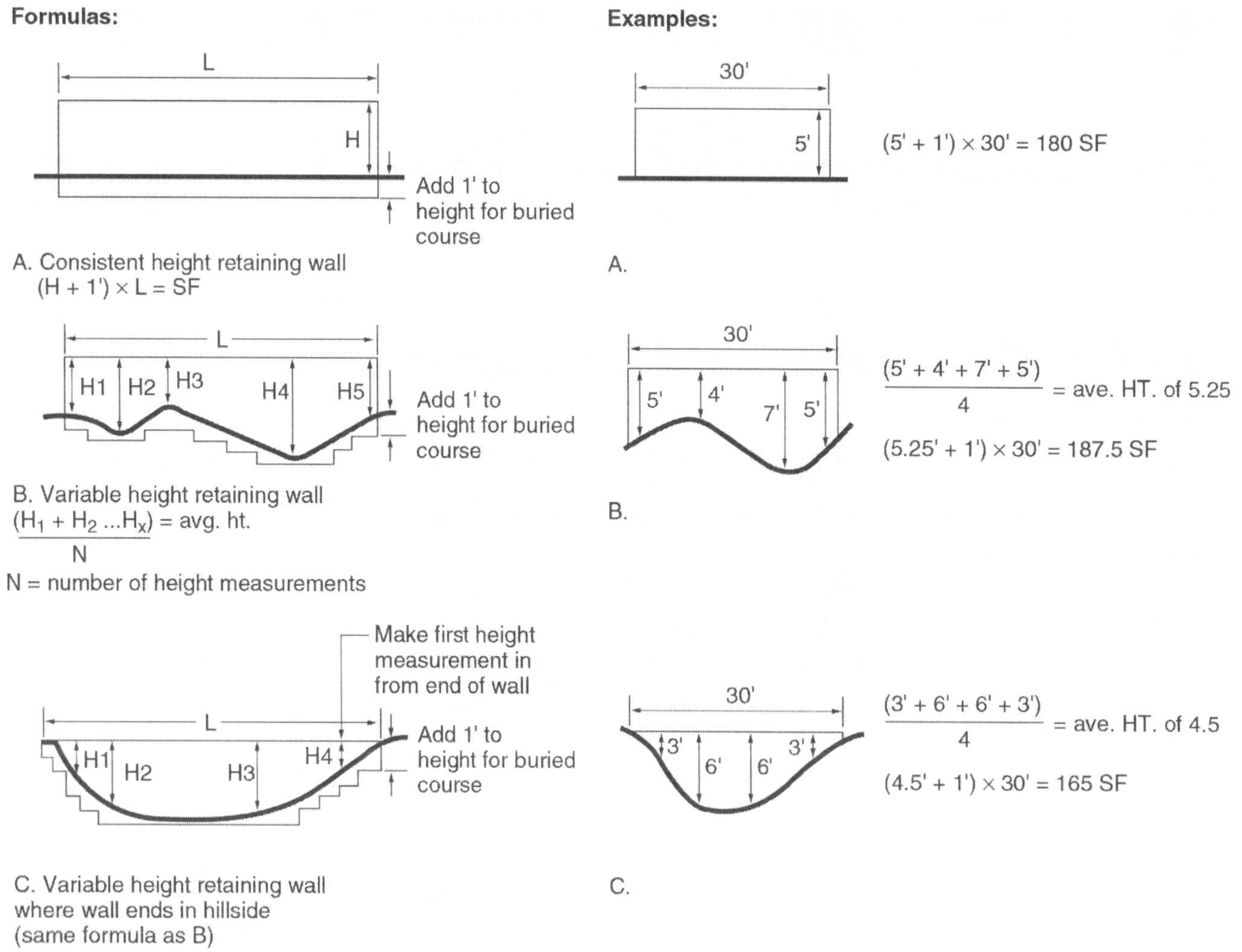

Figure 5-10 Wall material calculations.

If the wall is consistent in height except for a few small sections, such as return or cheek walls (Figure 5-10):

- Measure the small sections 5 feet from the ends and several times along the consistent height portion; then calculate as a variable height wall.
- Add 1 foot to the average height measurement.
- Multiply by the length to obtain the square footage of the wall.

If the project contains multiple walls, the square footage of each wall must be measured and added to obtain a total.

Segmental Unit (Precast) Calculations

Add the area of all wall sections when square footage calculations are complete. To determine how many segmental units are required, obtain the square footage of a single unit. Suppliers typically can provide this information, or you can calculate it by performing an area measurement on the surface of one unit (typical areas range from .5 SF to 1.25 SF). Divide the wall square footage by the surface area of one unit to obtain the number of total units required for the wall.

Segmental Unit Capstone Calculations

Capstones are usually ordered by the number of linear feet they will cover. Use a direct measurement of the total linear feet of the wall, and multiply by the conversion number (number of capstones per linear foot) supplied by the manufacturer.

Stone Calculations

To calculate the tonnage of stone required for a wall, divide the square footage of the wall by the number of SF that 1 ton of stone will build. The quarry or supplier can provide this conversion number, typically around 16–25 SF of wall per ton of stone.

Tie/Timber Calculations

Calculations for ties and timbers require the same area calculations just performed. However, the area is divided by conversion numbers to determine the number of ties and timbers to order. Find the material being used in the following list, and then divide the wall SF by the conversion number (Note: Height is the vertical dimension when looking at the side of the material.):

- Railroad tie, 8 feet long by 8 inches in height: divide by 5.0
- Railroad tie, 8 feet long by 7 inches in height: divide by 4.0
- Railroad tie, 8 feet long by 6 inches in height: divide by 3.5
- Timber, 8 feet long by 6 inches in height: divide by 3.7
- Timber 6 feet long by 6 inches height: divide by 2.8

To calculate the number of ties/timbers required for deadmen or verticals, divide the total wall length by 5. Add the wall ties/timbers numbers to the deadmen or vertical numbers to determine the number of ties/timbers to order.

STAIR CALCULATIONS

Calculation of stair dimensions requires an understanding of both slope and stair components. There is a relationship between the dimension of the vertical portion of the stair, or the **riser**, and the horizontal portion of the stair, or the **tread** (Table 5-1). The combination of these two dimensions will determine if the stairs are comfortable to use and fit the space reserved for stair construction. The math presented here applies to exterior stairs constructed of wall materials, concrete, and wood.

Riser/Tread Relationship

The riser/tread relationship, which can be expressed in a formula, maintains dimensions that produce stairs matching a human's normal stride. If one of these two dimensions is beyond the normal standards, the user may have difficulty navigating the stairs. If the sum of these two dimensions is beyond the normal standards, the user may have a difficult time maintaining a normal pace up the stairs. Considering the limitations of many of the materials from which steps are constructed, stairs in landscaping should follow this relationship as closely as possible. A formula for riser/tread relationships and a chart illustrating standard riser heights and tread depths derived from the formula are shown in Table 5-1.

Having no set standard for the maximum depth of a tread provides flexibility, and problems, for stairs constructed in the landscape. It should be noted that using a tread depth greater than those determined by the formulas shown in Table 5-1 will create an uneven, perhaps even dangerous, stepping pattern. Stair dimensions in the landscape are complicated further by the fact that many materials used to construct stairs are materials with dimensions that cannot be adjusted. Riser heights may be limited to wall material thickness, and the corresponding tread depth may be set by the riser dimension.

Table 5–1 Relationship Between Riser Height and Tread Depth in Stairs $2r + t = 26''$ where: r = riser; t = tread

if r is …	then t is …
4 inches	18 inches
5 inches	16 inches
6 inches	14 inches
7 inches	12 inches
8 inches	10 inches

r should not be greater than 8 inches or less than 4 inches

t should not be less than 10 inches

Note: Some formulas use values of 27″ or 28″ to replace the 26″ shown in this formula. Building codes may dictate the dimensions used.

In addition to these considerations, stairs that serve the public must follow local, state, and national regulations. Specific requirements for access by persons with differing physical abilities may determine the actual stair dimensions. Stairs accessed by the public should be designed by a design professional.

Process for Calculating Risers/Treads

Calculating the number of risers and treads required for a project requires measurements for the thickness of materials from which the stairs will be constructed (timbers, wall units, wall units plus caps, stone, etc.), the horizontal length of the slope that must be traversed (measured from **top of slope** to **toe of slope**), and the vertical distance that must be covered. To obtain the horizontal and vertical distances, consider using the measuring techniques described in Chapter 9, Construction Layout. These measurements can be used to calculate stair requirements.

Using the following steps and the riser/tread formula, determine how many risers and treads will be required for the project (Figure 5-11):

1. Convert the vertical and horizontal distances into inches.
2. Divide the vertical distance by a selected riser height. This answer will indicate how many risers are required to traverse the slope. Numbers over .5 can be rounded up; numbers under .5 can be rounded down. As mentioned earlier, the thickness of the construction material may dictate the riser height of the stair. If material thickness is not an issue, speed the process by selecting a high riser value if the slope is steep or a low riser value if the slope is shallow.
3. Subtract 1 from the number of risers.
4. Multiply the answer from the previous step by the tread depth required for the selected riser height. Use Table 5-1 to find the corresponding tread depth for the selected riser height. This answer will provide the horizontal distance covered by the stairs.

5. Compare the horizontal distance required for the stairs and the measured distance.
    - If the distances are equal or very close, use that riser/tread combination.
    - If the difference between the measured and required distances is less than the depth of one tread, add the distance to either the top or bottom to create a landing.
    - If the difference exceeds the dimension of one tread depth, choose another riser height and recalculate. If riser height is fixed by materials, add a landing at the top or bottom or consider adding a landing in the center of the stairs.
6. If horizontal dimensions cannot be matched with adjustments, the stairs will require excavation farther back from the top of the slope to accommodate the longer horizontal distance required.

SETTING BED AND BASE COURSE CALCULATIONS

One or more layers of supporting materials are often placed under paved areas to assure pavement stability. To calculate this quantity, the contractor will need accurate measurements taken from the construction plans and the details, as well as a description of the material from the specifications or plans.

Setting Bed

Setting bed material should be placed in a layer over a compacted base. This material should be ordered by either the cubic yard or ton. To determine the quantity needed, calculate the area to be paved and insert that number in the following equation:

- Area paved (SF) × depth in inches/12 = CF of material required
- CF/27 = CY of material required
- CY × 1.5 = tons of material required

Base Course

Base course material should be placed in a layer over the compacted subgrade at a depth the designer has specified. This material should be ordered by either the cubic yard or ton. To determine the quantity required, calculate the area to be paved and insert that number in the following equation:

- Area paved (SF) × depth in inches (X)/12 = CF of material required
- CF/27 = CY of material required
- CY × 1.25 = tons of material required

PAVING MATERIAL CALCULATIONS

Determining the quantity of paving material required for a project will use the area formulas for a unit paving material, such as brick or limestone, or the volume formulas for concrete or granular paving materials. Extra unit pavers should be ordered to allow for cutting and variation in pallet quantities. Orders increased by 10%–15% typically provide an adequate surplus.

Unit Paving

To calculate unit paver quantities, determine the area of the space to be paved. Obtain from the manufacturer the number of unit pavers per square foot for the style of paving to be used.

Most pavers range from 3.5 to 5.0 units per square foot. Standard 4-inch × 8-inch brick requires 4.5 pavers per square foot. Use the following formula to determine material requirements:

- SF of paved area × units per square foot = number of pavers to order

Stone

To calculate stone quantities, calculate the area of the space to be paved in square feet. From the supplier, determine the amount of square footage covered by 1 ton of stone material (standards for stone are typically 40–80 square feet of coverage per ton). Use the following formula to determine material requirements:

- SF of paved area/SF coverage per ton = tons of flagstone to order

Concrete

Concrete orders require measurements in cubic yards for the area paved. Concrete is ordered by the CY; so once a volume calculation is complete, no further calculations are needed. The following formula can be used for this calculation:

- Area paved (SF) × depth in inches (X)/12 = CF of material required
- CF/27 = CY of material required

Granular

Although granular paving projects do not require a leveling course, they do require calculations for volume of wearing course material and linear feet of edge stabilization if it is used. To perform volume calculations, use the following formula:

- Area paved (SF) × depth in inches (X)/12 = CF of material required
- CF /27 = CY of material required
- CY × 1.25 = tons of material required

CHAPTER 6

PROJECT PRICING

OBJECTIVES

By reading and practicing the techniques described in this chapter, the reader should be able to successfully complete the following activities:

- Identify if a client needs an estimate or a bid.
- Calculate an estimate or a bid for a landscape project.
- Submit a bid to a client.

Determining the price of a project requires a combination of calculating the costs of the various aspects and formatting the costs in one of several ways for presentation to a client. Preparation of costs requires application of many of the formulas and concepts presented in Chapter 5, Construction Math. However, the formulas are not the only variables important to project pricing. Effective preparation of estimates and bids requires input from historical records of a firm's activities, data obtained from textbooks that cover the process of estimating, and judgments from the contractor regarding profit and contingency. Without this external input, the methods presented here create only a framework for calculating project pricing.

RELATED INFORMATION

Information in this chapter is supplemented by instruction provided elsewhere in this text and in other sources. Before undertaking the activities described in this chapter, read the related information in these sources:

- Interpreting Construction Documents, Chapter 4
- Construction Math, Chapter 5
- North Carolina Landscape Contrators' Guide to Business, Law and Project Management

ESTIMATES AND BIDDING

Prior to engaging in the preparation of cost estimating, the landscape contractor should determine if the client desires an estimate or a bid. The way the numbers are used affects the level of accuracy in calculating project costs. There is little need to spend hours calculating detailed project costs if the only question a client has is whether the project is within his or her general price range. On the other hand, a rough estimate is risky if a client expects to receive a bid to compare with bids from other contractors. Knowing what stage the project is in and preparing the proper type of cost estimate or bid are essential to an efficient operation.

Estimates

Estimates are exactly what the term implies. When a potential customer wants to know how much a project will cost so that he or she can decide whether to proceed with more detailed work, an estimate may be in order. Preparation of an estimate may be as simple as quoting a range of prices based on similar types of projects. Estimates may also be prepared based on unit costs for general types of materials the customer inquires about, such as deck (SF), plantings (cost per tree), or fill dirt (CY).

Be cautious when asked to prepare an estimate for a client. Misunderstandings can develop when the client is not informed that the estimate is not a firm price. If an estimate is to be converted into a contract, it is important to qualify the proposal, stating that additional costs may be incurred if the project is changed or if unknown conditions are discovered.

Bidding

Formal proposals to clients in the form of bids serve as a prelude to binding contracts. Prices prepared for bids should be carefully calculated, and the contractor should be prepared to up- hold the price if the owner accepts it. Bids are common for all types of projects, public and private. Calculation of a bid requires a design that provides all potential bidders a common document(s) from which to prepare the bid.

The bidding process typically begins with the advertisement, or invitation, to submit a bid. Invitations to bid often come in the form of a written RFQ (Request for Qualifications) or an RFP (Request for Proposal). This notice provides instructions that describe the project, client, method of bidding, form of bid, bonding requirements, and the time and place when and where the bid must be submitted. The advertisement typically informs contractors where they may obtain or review contract documents and when bids will be opened and reviewed. After bids are opened, the design professional will canvass the bids to assure there are no irregularities or mistakes in the proposals. If all is in order, a contract is awarded, bonding and insurance documents are submitted to the client's representative, and a notice to proceed is issued.

CALCULATING PROJECT COSTS

Accurately calculating the cost of a project, whether for an estimate or for a bid, is a combination of the science of calculating and the art of estimating. The wide variety of ways that a contractor can arrive at the price of a project requires that numerous skills be developed. These skills include:

- Skill at reading and interpreting specifications and drawing for projects
- Ability to research cost-estimating sources
- Ability to compile, from one's own past projects, what resources were required to complete similar jobs
- An understanding of the abilities of the contractor's workforce to perform the required tasks
- Knowledge of conditions and special requirements for working in a particular geographic region
- Knowledge of the client for whom the work is to be performed. If you do not know prospective clients, check with friends in the business and through normal channels to verify that they are honest and trustworthy.

Even with this skill set, contractors will find that interpersonal relationships with clients, politics, labor disputes, material shortages, and other factors beyond their control may affect their success in obtaining work. Regardless of factors that contractors believe will influence their ability to bid successfully, one element they can control is the calculation of the project prices.

Sources for Preparing Project Costs

Various sources are available to obtain the prices for materials, labor, and overhead needed to prepare an estimate or a bid. The most effective sources are the contractor's own historical records. As contractors gain experience in various aspects of construction, they should maintain records of the time spent on each aspect of the project and costs associated with that aspect. Data that should be compiled include the specific tasks completed (e.g., preparing base for concrete, forming for concrete, pouring concrete, finishing concrete, performing cleanup), the number of worker hours associated with the tasks (include time for all laborers working directly on the task), and the costs for materials used to complete the task. Data should also be collected regarding equipment rented for a specific activity and the amount of time the equipment was used. Special situations, such as delays, site problems, and extenuating circumstances that changed the time and materials originally planned for the project, should also be noted.

Armed with this data, contractors can assemble unit costs. By calculating the labor costs for specific tasks and adding the materials, then dividing by the total units completed (e.g., square feet of concrete walk), contractors can obtain a number that provides detail from which they can generate a bid can. This information also allows contractors to review worker productivity, determine benefits of various construction techniques, and assess differences based on project conditions such as location or client type.

If contractors have limited historical cost records, they can refer to sources that provide cost data. Several landscape construction cost reference guides, including Means©, Sweets©, Kerry© and Dodge©, provide detailed breakdowns of the material, labor, and related costs for a wide variety of landscape construction types. Most are available as textbooks, and newer versions include software applications for estimating. Such sources typically provide this data as unit costs similar to what contractors can calculate based on historical records. Most cost references break the costs down into materials and labor and provide a composite cost. Some provide markups and overhead estimates as well. Keep in mind that any cost data may need to be adjusted based on local conditions. Items such as distance from suppliers, availability of supplies in your area, higher costs for labor or insurance, and availability of utilities all have the potential to influence project costs.

Regulatory Influences on Pricing

Several potential governmental regulations may affect project costs. Visit with local government officials to determine if special conditions apply before preparing your estimate or bid. Factors such as governmental requirements for use of local products, special regulations regarding work hours, and limitations on plant removal and pruning all may increase project costs. If the project involves state or federal funds, a plethora of regulations ranging from anti-kickback rules to prevailing wage laws will certainly adjust your costs. Such regulations should be noted in project specifications; but before preparing a bid or an estimate, contractors will need to verify with the owner and local government officials whether restrictions or regulations apply to the project.

Several components play key roles in calculating project costs. Accurate take-offs, or calculations, of materials required to build the project must be determined. Labor, or the time spent by employees installing projects, must be estimated. Although materials can be calculated accurately, labor can vary greatly, based on the type of operation and project situation. **Overhead**, or nonlabor or material costs of operating a business, can also range widely among firms of different size and management styles. Overhead can be separated into assignable overhead and unassignable overhead. Providing a percentage of project costs to cover contingency issues is another related project cost. Determining profit is also an essential piece of the pricing scheme. The totals from this list can be combined in many formats to arrive at a project price for presentation to the client.

Materials

Material costs are calculated using the design prepared for the site. Begin by performing a material **take-off**, or a calculation of the quantity of all materials to be used for the project. Organization of a material take-off can take whatever form provides the results required. To develop a method that reduces the potential for missing aspects of the proposed work, thoroughness and consistency from project to project are important when performing take-offs. Using a method that interfaces easily with the system used by the accounting department to track work activities will provide information that is valuable for both current and future projects.

An early step in determining material costs is to review the project plans and specifications to determine what landscape contractors are to provide. A detailed review of the entire set of plans and specifications may reveal that work must be done at certain times, under certain conditions, or in a manner in which contractors have no experience. Because many landscape contractors participate in projects as subcontractors, determining exactly what is included in the scope of each subcontractor's work is critical.

Interpretation of project specifications also requires careful reading to determine the quality and brands of materials that must be provided and whether or where substitutes may be proposed. Typically requiring written approval of the owner's representative, substitution for specified material and products could save contractors money if lower priced brands of identical quality can be substituted for more expensive proprietary brands. Examine the specifications to see if a specific product is listed, if the specifications state "or equal," or if no brand name is listed. These last two clauses open the door to proposing an alternative brand to the owner. Specific examples of where substitutes are common include hardscape materials, irrigation supplies, amenities, and even plant material.

Also important is a review of the plans and specifications for errors and omissions. These mistakes are not opportunities to take advantage of the situation by omitting work or changing materials. Most specifications include a clause that requires contractors to notify the owner's representative of any errors found in the construction documents. This clause does not relieve contractors of their responsibility.

When performing a material take-off, consider increasing the actual quantity required for certain materials. Landscaping projects typically use many materials that could settle during shipping, be blown away, eroded, or otherwise lose "bulk" from the time they are first loaded to the time they are placed on the site. To accommodate this loss, it is not uncommon to add 10%–15% to bulk material orders to ensure that adequate supplies exist to complete the job. Materials that are typically treated in this manner include soil, sand, base material, and other bulk granular materials.

Bulk materials are not the only material that should be overordered to accommodate construction conditions. Unit pavers and wall materials typically experience waste as high as 5% when the design requires cutting. Concrete is another material that should be overordered by 2%–3% to avoid short load charges (additional fees added to concrete prices when customers order less than a full load). To accommodate plant mortality and waste, ground cover plants and sod are typically overordered by as much as 5%.

Overordering may require hauling excess material from the site, but this expense compares favorably to the cost of additional materials delivered to the site. Excess hauling and material storage adds to the cost of operating a business, so careful review of the project is required to determine which materials should be considered for overordering. Maintaining stockpiles of materials that can be loaded and taken to the site with a work crew can reduce the quantity of overorders required. Items calculated using an item count should not be overordered.

Contractors who stockpile common materials used in construction can also realize some cost savings. Contractors who regularly install similar elements of the design find it more profitable to purchase and store large quantities of base, pavement, wall material, lumber, or other materials rather than to purchase small quantities each time they begin a job. If they stockpile, contractors must have space for storing materials and a means for loading and transporting them to and from a site.

Labor

Calculating the time required to install a project is one of the most difficult tasks. Experienced contractors can calculate with a reasonable degree of accuracy the amount of time employees will require to complete most tasks. However, unusual site conditions and unforeseen problems can challenge even the most experienced contractors.

For purposes of calculating project costs, time is typically presented in an hours-per-unit format. This format presents the number of hours it will take a laborer to complete one unit of a task. Units are typically the measurable elements of a work task, such as square feet of retaining wall or a square of sod, and hours are typically based on one hour of a worker's time. A theoretical example might be a wall construction hour-per-unit rate of 1 hour per square foot of wall. If a project requires 100 square feet of wall, the take-off would calculate 100 hours for construction of the wall. Rates can be calculated for work teams as well as for individual workers.

Hours-per-unit rates are typically determined based on reviews of project designs, the site, and skills and quantity of labor available. Maintaining records that track past projects provides a historical basis for calculating project time and material requirements. When calculating hours, it is important to distinguish among the different types of tasks being tracked. Granular paving and unit paving are both surfacing tasks, but they have significantly different hours-per-unit rates. Businesses can divide the total hours required to complete a particular task for a project by the size of the task to obtain hourly rates-per-unit of work for various types of construction activities. Tracking several projects under different conditions improves the system's accuracy.

Assistance in determining hourly rates is also available in time standards that estimating firms have developed. Time standards provide typical hourly rates-per-unit of construction for most types of landscape work. When using such standards, contractors should compare them to actual costs and make adjustments based on the region and construction methods used.

Overhead

Another cost that can be directly or indirectly associated with the work being done is overhead. For purposes of calculating project costs, overhead should be split into two categories—assignable overhead and unassignable overhead.

Assignable Overhead. Assignable overhead includes nonlabor and nonmaterial costs that can be directly attributed to a project. Included in this category are special permits, equipment rental, special insurance or bonding requirements, temporary utility costs, and related project activities that do not directly benefit any project but the one currently being bid. These costs should appear as a line item on the take-off for identification purposes. For presentation purposes, assignable overhead may be presented as such or folded into other project costs as required by the proposal format.

Careful review of the specification sections related to temporary facilities, warranties, and care of a project until accepted by the owner may reveal costs that the landscape contractor bears alone or shares with another contractor on the project. Of particular concern are the utility costs for construction. Rental of generators or the cost for watering plants that have been installed before the end of the project are examples of how utilities can significantly increase overhead. Even the rental of portable toilets can upset the delicate balance of bidding. Negotiating with the owner or general contractor regarding who provides such temporary utilities may reduce the landscape contractor's costs, and sharing costs with other contractors may limit the landscape contractor's obligations.

Unassignable Overhead. Unassignable overhead includes the costs of operating a business that cannot be attributed directly to a specific project. Included in this category are the cost of equipment and vehicles, gas, tools, insurance, payroll expenses, debt service, mortgages, office expenses, maintenance, fees, vacation, sick days, benefits, and many other additional expenses. Approaches to recovering these expenses include calculating costs and adding them on a per project basis or establishing an hourly cost for overhead and adding this to hourly labor costs.

This addition to the hourly cost, often called a **multiplier**, is determined by calculating total overhead expenses for the year (or reporting period) and dividing by the number of hours billed to clients for work performed during the year (or reporting period). Because not all worker hours are spent working on projects, using billed hours, rather than total hours worked by employees, is essential to obtain an accurate markup. The multiplier may be adjusted up or down based on anticipated changes in upcoming work.

Reducing Overhead. To reduce the high cost of overhead, successful contractors have discovered methods for improving the efficiency of their operations. By crafting procedures, approaches, and relationships, contractors may be able to improve their bidding and/or profit situation in many jobs. Following is a sampling of ideas that may reduce overhead and improve the efficiency of a construction business.

- The timing of the installation of improvements may help improve pricing. Being able to access a site and begin work when crews are in a slow period may even out a busy schedule and reduce overtime costs. Verifying that any work installed before the project is finished will not be damaged or disturbed will save repair time. Overhead costs can increase significantly when the contractor installs plant material as requested but the owner delays accepting the project. During this delay, the landscape contractor is often required to water, prune, mow, and perform other maintenance that should by now be the owner's responsibility. If requested to install perishable improvements, ask the owner to sign a release or maintenance contract for care of these elements should the project's acceptance date be delayed because of another contractor's failure to meet obligations or deadlines.
- Warranties and guarantees can also increase overhead. Most contracted work states the time period for which the contractor will ensure proper performance of project elements, but in some cases that time period will exceed the manufacturer's warranty. Negotiating with the manufacturer to extend the warranties, or alerting the owner to problems with materials that, in past experiences, are unlikely to perform through the warranty period may save both the contractor and the owner headaches with product replacement.
- Insurance costs comprise a large part of unassignable overhead for many companies. Some insurance underwriters offer premium reductions to companies that institute safety programs, employ drivers with safe records, promote safety on the job, insure multiple vehicles, or have multiple policies with the same carrier. Contractors may also be able to negotiate better rates for engaging in specific sizes and types of jobs or working with specific clients. Higher deductibles are also an option for reducing insurance premiums.
- Contractors are always tempted to buy specialty tools and equipment to complete work tasks, even if they will use the equipment for only a few days per year. Consider sharing such high-cost equipment with other contractors or leasing the equipment for the time needed rather than buying it. When contractors purchase equipment, they should search for quality equipment that will reduce breakdowns and repair time.
- Discussion within the contracting world often focuses on the techniques of construction and dealing with regulatory issues, but little is said about sound business operation. Adherence to acknowledged business practices can often mean the difference between success and failure in any business, and contracting is no exception. Begin by securing the services of a reliable accountant who can structure the business to take advantage of tax regulations.
- Consider adopting regular training programs that improve employees' technical and performance skills. Many schools offer coursework developed specifically for retraining the workforce.

Taxes and Fees

Landscape contractors must remain current in all applicable federal, state, and local taxes and fees.

Contingencies

No contractor can accurately determine the extent of weather and material delays, labor shortages, equipment breakdowns, and unknown underground obstructions. Because such conditions are unpredictable, reserve a portion of the project cost as a contingency fund. Typical contingency funds range from 5%–10% of the total project costs to material and to labor costs. When presenting costs, contractors typically include this number in the overhead multiplier to avoid disputes regarding refunds of unused contingencies.

Another method for developing contingency funds is requesting that clients establish one. This method minimizes the issue of unused balances. A dollar amount equal to a fixed percentage of construction costs is then available to contractors when specifically defined conditions arise. The owners retain unused contingencies, and contractors have a method for recovering unforeseen expenses arising from circumstances beyond their control. Definition of this arrangement should be included in the contract.

Profit

Determining what amount of profit is appropriate and knowing how to calculate that amount require insight regarding the market and competition, judgments about income requirements, anticipation of business conditions during the upcoming season(s), and advice from trusted financial advisors. Profit margins are far from standardized in the green industry, and the choice for determining profit remains both a personal and a business decision.

The methods for calculating profit are even wider than the margins expected. Profit is sometimes generalized as a percentage of the cost of materials and labor used in a business. Large projects may operate on a smaller margin, whereas services that are in demand may have a significant markup. Businesses working in the field have materials marked up as much as two to three times their cost to cover overhead and profit. Labor costs are sometimes doubled to provide adequate income for overhead and profit. These markups must be based on the company's actual costs of doing business. Profit expressed as a percentage of total project costs ranges from lows of 3%–4% to highs of 25%.

Profit can be included with overhead when presented to the client as part of the hourly charge for employees or, as in some presentation formats, presented as a separate, negotiable line item in a bid.

Material and Labor Take-Off Form

One format for calculating project costs that includes many of the aspects previously identified is illustrated in Figure 6-1. With the aid of a computer spreadsheet program, this form can be created and modified to suit individual business needs. In this illustration, the work tasks are listed as headings down the left-hand side of the chart, with specific materials used in the task listed below the headings. Quantities of materials required and overages (overorders) from the next two columns are added and multiplied by the current unit cost from the column titled "Unit Cost." The total for materials is then placed in the column titled "Mtl Total." Hours for completing a specific task are calculated and placed on the same row as the task heading. Hours are multiplied by the current hourly rate to obtain the total labor cost. Related construction items, costs, and notes are placed in the far-right column. Rows at the bottom of the form provide space for adding additional billable costs described in previous paragraphs.

Performing the take-off should follow a consistent pattern for each project. Use a standard form formatted to the type of work performed. Check the plans to make sure the scale is accurate and has not been reduced or enlarged when printed. When a plan has been estimated, mark it with a large *X* to avoid duplication. Fewer mistakes will result if only one side of the take-off form is used, avoiding missed back pages. Use printed measurements over scaling whenever possible, and look for written notes and notations such as *N.I.C.* (not in contract, so no price is needed), *typ.* (meaning all subsequent elements are similar), and *N.T.S.* (not to scale, so written dimensions must be obtained). Converting to decimals makes take-off calculations easier, but be consistent with your measurements, always using the same unit and measuring in the same manner. When measurements are complete, check your placement of decimal points and

		MATERIAL AND LABOR TAKE-OFF FORM									
Job: Sauter residence		Job no: 9969			Address: 2854 H. Avenue			Date: July 20, 2015			
MATERIALS							**LABOR**			**NOTES/RELATED EXPENSES**	
Description	Unit	Qty	Over.	Total	Unit Cost	Mtl. Total	Hrs.	Rate	Labor Total	Description	Total
SITE PREPARATION											
sod removal	SF	700		700		$ -	4	$ 35.00	$ 140.00		
excavation	CY	10		10		$ -	2	$ 85.00	$ 170.00	skidsteer operator rate	
small tree removal	EA	1		1		$ -	4	$ 25.00	$ 100.00		
				0		$ -			$ -		
WALL INSTALLATION				0		$ -			$ -		
segmental wall material	SF	150	10	160	$ 8.00	$ 1,280.00	20	$ 35.00	$ 700.00		
4" dia. Perforated tile	LF	50		50	$ 2.00	$ 100.00	1	$ 35.00	$ 35.00		
aggregate backfill	TON	2		2	$ 25.00	$ 50.00	4	$ 35.00	$ 140.00		
clean topsoil backfill	TON	24	5	29	$ 20.00	$ 580.00	4	$ 85.00	$ 340.00	skidsteer operator rate	
				0							
PAVING INSTALLATION				0		$ -			$ -		
4" deep class 2 base	TON	3.5	0.5	4	$ 30.00	$ 120.00	6	$ 35.00	$ 210.00		
1" deep sand setting bed	TON	1.5	0.5	2	$ 25.00	$ 50.00	4	$ 35.00	$ 140.00		
interlocking concrete pavers	SF	225	20	245	$ 4.50	$ 1,102.50	24	$ 40.00	$ 960.00		
metal paver edging	LF	60	5	65	$ 9.00	$ 585.00	3	$ 35.00	$ 105.00		
flagstone stepping stones	SF	75		75	$ 4.00	$ 300.00	6	$ 35.00	$ 210.00		
				0							
PLANTING MATERIAL				0		$ -			$ -		
trees	EA	3		3	$ 175.00	$ 525.00	4	$ 35.00	$ 140.00		
shrubs	EA	17		17	$ 35.00	$ 595.00	5	$ 35.00	$ 175.00		
ground cover	SF	200	20	220	$ 3.00	$ 660.00	5	$ 35.00	$ 175.00		
mulch	CY	5		5	$ 30.00	$ 150.00	2	$ 35.00	$ 70.00		
sod	SQ	8		8	$ 10.00	$ 80.00	5	$ 35.00	$ 175.00		
post planting care	-			0		$ -	2	$ 35.00	$ 70.00		
				0							
BILLABLE OVERHEAD	HR	4		4		$ -			$ -	sod cutter rental	$ 6[illegible]
				0		$ -			$ -		
ITEM TOTALS						**$ 6,177.50**	105		**$ 4,055.00**		**$ 6[illegible]**
PROJECT TOTAL										**$ 10,292.50**	

Figure 6-1 Sample form used for material and labor take-offs for landscape projects.

math. Round only when calculating the final figure. Consider taking two or three dollars off the price to avoid the angst of matching or being slightly over the bid of someone using similar bidding methods.

PRESENTATION FORMAT FOR PROJECT PRICES

Totals obtained from calculating project costs can be combined in a number of different ways for presentation to clients. The following sections identify methods to arrange the various cost aspects into bid or estimate formats. Selection of an appropriate method will be based on project requirements. Examples of how the material and labor take-off from Figure 6-1 can be presented in the following formats are provided in Figure 6-2. Examples of project bid forms can be found in Appendices.

Lump Sum

Lump sum is a bid format in which all projects costs are provided to the client in a single number. All components of the project are added together to obtain a lump-sum bid. Although this bid is easy to compare from one contractor to another, it is difficult to change because there are no itemized materials or labor costs. Bids may sometimes include an add or deduct request in which a specific amount is added or deducted from the lump-sum total for the addition or deletion of a project component.

LUMP SUM		
Total project cost	**$ 10,292.50**	

ITEMIZED		
appearance and prices same as shown in Figure 6-1		

TIME AND MATERIALS		
Material costs:	$ 6,177.50	
-walls		
-paving		
-plant material		
Assignable overhead	$ 60.00	
-equipment rental		
Time	$ 4,055.00	
-- hrs @ $85.00 Hour		operator rate
--hrs@ $35.00 Hour		skilled laborer rate
--hrs@ $40.00 Hour		specialist laborer rate
Total estimated project cost	**$ 10,292.50**	
Note: Actual costs will be based on hours worked multiplied		
by above rates		

COST PLUS FIXED FEE		
Materials	$ 5,559.75	
-walls		
-paving		
-plant material		
Equipment rental	$ 54.00	
Labor (105 hours)	$ 3,649.50	
Fixed Fee (10% of estimate)	$ 1,029.25	
Total estimated project cost	**$ 10,292.50**	
Note: Hourly rates for work beyond estimate are $85/hour for		
equipment operator, $40/hours for specialist laborer,		
$35/hour for skilled laborer		

UNIT COSTS	$ 410.00	
Site preparation	$ 3,225.00	
Wall construction	$ 3,782.50	
Paving	$ 2,815.00	
Planting	$ 60.00	
Equipment rental	**$ 10,292.50**	
Total project cost		

Figure 6-2 Typical presentation formats for landscape pricing. Values are taken from take- offs shown in Figure 6-1.

Itemized

An **itemized bid** or estimate not only provides a total project price, but it also has a detailed listing of project materials or work tasks. This form of bid is easy to compare and adjust if work is changed. Prices can be itemized by unit of work (see following paragraphs) or with lines for each item used in calculating costs. A detailed itemized cost presentation is similar to the format presented in Figure 6-1.

Time and Materials

When either the customer or contractor is wary about the amount of time required to complete a project, a time and materials bid may be the best presentation. This is a form of bid that provides for a set price for materials and assignable overhead, plus an hourly cost for labor. Labor costs on a time and material bid may be represented by an estimated number of hours multiplied by the hourly rate to obtain a general idea of labor costs. Materials and assignable overhead costs do not change significantly during the project, and compensation for labor is based on the rate times the actual hours worked. Unassignable overhead, contingency, and profit are assigned to hourly rates for employees.

Cost Plus Fixed Fee

When uncertainty exists about the amount of time required to complete a project, the cost plus fixed fee form of bid may be useful. The **cost plus fixed fee** bid is a time and materials bid with the profit listed as a fixed line item, rather than being assigned to the employee hourly rate. The contractor is compensated for actual time and materials, but the owner is not responsible for additional profit as a result of delayed completion. Unassignable overhead and contingency costs remain assigned to employees' hourly rate.

Unit Costs

Unit costing is an estimating tool used to provide general project costs. Rather than being itemized by traditional divisions such as materials, labor, etc., costs are presented according to units of work areas, such as square foot of paving.

Development of unit costs requires tracking previous jobs over a variety of installation situations. Calculate unit costs by dividing the total costs associated with a particular aspect of the job by the size of that portion of the job. For example, the total costs for all items associated with the decking for a project totaled $10,000, and the total area of the deck was 500 SF. The unit cost for that project would be decking for $20 per SF. These types of costs can be tracked over several projects to obtain a more accurate picture of actual costs.

Pricing to a General Contractor

Contractors my function as subcontractors for landscape portions of jobs. In this situation, the general contractor will require the subcontractor to provide a price. The process used for this pricing should be formal, with a written proposal or letter of agreement submitted. Typical formats used for pricing to a general contractor include lump-sum and itemized bids.

CHAPTER 7

SAFETY IN THE WORKPLACE

OBJECTIVES

By reading and practicing the techniques described in this chapter, the reader should be able to successfully complete the following activities:

- Identify hazards in the workplace.
- Avoid unnecessary accident and injury.
- Institute practices that minimize workplace hazards.

RELATED INFORMATION

Information in this chapter is supplemented by instruction provided elsewhere in this text and in other sources. Before undertaking the activities described in this chapter, read the related information in these sources:

- The Landscape Construction Process, Chapter 2
- Legal Requirements, Chapter 3
- North Carolina Landscape Contrators' Guide to Business, Law and Project Management

CAUTION

Practice of the profession of landscape construction is filled with safety and health hazards, and use of this book without proper experience or supervision will place the reader at risk.
The reader assumes all risk when engaging in unsupervised activities.

Like most construction occupations, landscape contracting carries with it the risk of disabling or serious injury or death if workers are unaware of the hazards and proper techniques for preventing potential accidents. The many benefits and rewards of landscaping can be quickly erased by a serious or debilitating injury. Fortunately, most of the hazards of the landscape workplace are identifiable. In this chapter, many common on-the-job hazards and strategies for reducing risk are identified.

PREVENTING ACCIDENTS

Prevention of accidents begins by providing required information to workers regarding hazards in the workplace. Implementation of a safety training program for new and existing employees will assist in improving their awareness of work hazards. Employees should be properly trained before operating equipment or engaging in new construction activities. Signage and postings that warn of health hazards should be present in all areas, including vehicles and structures, that workers frequent. Be certain that warnings and instructions on safety are placed in highly visible spaces and are presented in language(s) that all employees understand. Material Safety and Data Sheet (MSDS) sheets should be read when first received and periodically reviewed and updated.

Material Safety and Data Sheets (MSDS)

Businesses are required to keep on file in the workplace a **Material Safety and Data Sheet** for every material that poses a potential risk to employees and to others who may come in contact with such materials. These sheets should be kept in a file in a vehicle at each job site and in each shop and structure used for the business.

Site Inspections

Each contracting company should train all employees and contractors on procedures for maintaining a safe work site. In addition, each company or work crew should designate an employee as a safety "officer," who is responsible for verifying that safety rules are observed and practiced. Conducted before and after each work day, regular inspections of a work site will help ensure that conditions are safe for workers and safe when the site is not occupied.

Maintaining a record of work site inspections is a valuable tool in documenting problems that could lead to serious consequences.

Actions and Behaviors on a Work Site

Many accidents can be prevented by developing good work habits. Maintaining awareness of safety and keeping focused on the work being performed are initial steps in keeping a workplace safe. Additional preventative actions include not working when overly tired, not running at a work site, and keeping the work site clean. In all cases, using or being under the influence of illegal drugs and alcohol while on the job is prohibited. Also, both employers and employees need to understand and acknowledge how prescribed medications may affect a worker's ability to operate equipment and machinery.

First Aid

Employees who are required to work in a potentially hazardous environment benefit from basic first aid and CPR (cardiopulmonary resuscitation) training. Placing first aid kits in vehicles and structures used in the business and providing means to communicate problems with appropriate officials will aid in addressing emergencies. In addition to first aid kits, **personal protective equipment (PPE)** should be provided. When used properly, this equipment protects workers from blood borne pathogens. PPE should include at a minimum latex gloves and CPR mouthpieces. In addition, all employees should know the location of the nearest hospital or medical center in relation to their current job site. Directions to these facilities should be placed in each vehicle and on each structure.

Medical Conditions

Employers and employees should be familiar with chronic health problems that work conditions may inflame. Dust or pollen from work sites may trigger allergies and asthma attacks, and emergency treatment for such medical conditions should be reviewed prior to beginning work. Employees should also obtain current boosters for tetanus prior to performing landscape construction activities.

REDUCING PERSONAL INJURY

The most important tool in the contractor's repertoire is the human body. Protecting the body from injury is necessary to ensure workers can remain productive throughout their careers.

Several potential challenges that landscape contractors face when completing their work tasks are next discussed, along with recommended methods to counter these threats to their safety.

Clothing and Protective Equipment

Protection of the body is a logical starting place when attempting to reduce personal injury. Essential equipment includes proper work boots with steel toe protection, heavy-duty work gloves, and eye protection when using equipment or engaged in activities that create hazardous conditions. In addition, contractors should consider using hard hats for overhead work, appropriate back support for lifting activities, and skin protection for long-term exposure to the sun. Dust masks and ear protection should also be considered when performing landscape construction tasks that involve constant noise and/or dust. When performing tasks that require long periods of kneeling, workers will find that using kneepads provide protection and make doing those tasks more comfortable. Hats or nets that keep hair from becoming entangled in equipment are also recommended.

Heat and Cold Injuries

Because most people think of landscaping as fair-weather work, they give little consideration to protecting themselves from heat and cold injuries. Although the likelihood of suffering a cold injury is quite low, workers need to wear proper clothing and to protect themselves to prevent hypothermia and frostbite when working in extreme temperatures. Threats from heat injuries are more obvious to the landscape contractor. In addition to protecting their skin from sunburn and excessive exposure, workers need to use caution and protect them-selves from heat exhaustion and heat stroke when they plan activities on very hot days. Performing tasks during the cooler hours of the day, taking ample breaks, and drinking water are ways workers can protect themselves when temperatures climb.

Threats from Wildlife

Working outdoors places the worker at potential risk from wildlife. Threats include exposure to insects and smaller animals, such as bees, wasps, snakes, and scorpions, and possible confrontations with hostile, larger animals. Use caution when performing site preparation tasks that require the removal of potential animal habitat. Old structures, brush piles, dead trees, shrubs, wells, ravines, and other secluded areas are generally harbors for potentially dangerous animals. Review the site carefully before beginning work to locate animal habitats. Carry insect spray to repel insects. Examine equipment, tools, and clothing left unattended at the site to determine that wildlife has not adopted these items for shelter.

If wildlife, threatening or not, is discovered, consider contacting animal control, local animal shelters, or wildlife protection centers. Some organizations will relocate animals to new habitats before problems arise.

Hazardous Plants

Workers should be aware of any plants that may trigger dermatitis when contacted. Remove or avoid poisonous plants, or wear proper protective clothing to avoid direct contact with the skin. Some plants should be avoided altogether. Other plants, such as poison ivy, are caustic when burned. Obtain positive identification of all suspected plants and take appropriate precautions.

Back Injuries

If not properly executed, the actions and motions required to complete every task of land-scaping have risks of physical injuries, especially to the back. Improper lifting of heavy objects and repetitive improper lifting of light objects produce strain on muscle groups in the back. Too often, workers are tempted to bend over and pick up materials and tools that they need for work. After performing such a motion numerous times without injury, workers give little thought about the potential risk. However, placing undue strain on back muscles over time can accumulate into an injury. Learning how to lift and following simple rules will help reduce back injury from performing the various landscape construction activities. Performing simple stretching exercises before beginning work and following long periods of repetitive motion is also beneficial (Figure 7-1).

Proper lifting technique is designed to direct the strain of lifting to the proper muscle groups:

- Lift by bending at the knees, rather than bending at the waist. This transfers the stress to the thigh muscles, which are better adapted to lifting such weight (Figure 7-2).
- Avoid twisting motions while lifting. Move the feet, rather than twist.
- Hold the load close to the body when lifting. Holding the load at arm's length greatly increases the stress on the back.

Other techniques that will help reduce back strain are:

- Get help when lifting heavy objects.
- Wear back support braces approved by the Occupational Safety and Health Administration (OSHA) and appropriate health organizations.

Figure 7-1 Warm-up stretching exercises.

- Warm up properly and rest at intervals when engaging in **repetitive motions** such as laying brick or planting ground cover.
- Use labor-saving devices, when available, to lift.

Extended sitting and kneeling can also cause muscle injury. Interrupt periods of sitting that are longer than 20 minutes with a stretching period. Use proper seating and cushioning for back and knees when performing tasks that require long-term sitting and kneeling. Additional suggestions on preventing back injuries are available from injury prevention and rehabilitation organizations.

Figure 7-2 Proper lifting by bending at the knees.

Confined Spaces

Although not common in landscape work, confined spaces such as manholes, vaults, or cisterns pose risks for contractors. Do not enter confined spaces that are restricted, and avoid entry when conditions of the space are unknown. Also avoid entry into spaces where a person could be trapped or engulfed in hazardous materials or if the spaces have no obvious secondary exit points. Never enter such spaces without a co-worker present in the immediate vicinity.

WORKING AROUND UTILITIES

Cutting through or running into utility lines that serve a site introduces several potential risks to landscape contractors. Personal injury or death can occur from electrocution, explosion, or fire if utility lines are disrupted. Contractors also incur financial risk in the cost of repairing damaged utilities. In addition, the project may suffer immediately or in the future from utility damage and activities required to repair that damage. Particular care should be taken when working with electrical, gas, and communications utilities, which, if damaged during construction, pose the greatest risk to contractors.

> **CAUTION**
>
> *Always* call NC811 for location of utilities lines or cables at least 72 hours before performing *any* work at a site.

Public Utilities

Risk can be substantially reduced by calling for location of utility lines or cables prior to beginning your work . In North Carolina it is illegal, in most cases, to perform demolition or excavation prior to having the existing utilities located. North Carolina has instituted the NC811 program. 811 is a phone number that provides a centralized locate service for a portion of the utilities located on a site. NC811 will *not* contact all utilities that are potentially located on a site. You will still be responsible for verifying which utilities are not contacted by NC811.

Suggestions for using this service include:

- Call at least 72 hours prior to beginning construction.
- Have the address and specific location of the project ready when you call the service.
- Identify the type and extent of work.
- Indicate who is calling and provide an address and email address.
- Provide construction starting dates and times.
- Provide a phone number the directory service can call with responses and questions.

In certain situations, the utility company may choose to have a representative present while work around its lines is in progress.

Landscape contractors involved in large planting projects or projects that have footings or new utility installation can also mark out their work prior to a utility locate. As long as markings are complete and accurate, this action will aid the utility company in safely identifying its lines. To aid in identification, use white flags or paint to locate landscape improvements to avoid confusion with utility markings. Utility companies have adopted standard colors to identify various types of utilities. This color coding systems is as follows:

- Red: electrical
- Yellow: gas
- Orange: phone, communication, possibly **fiber optics**
- Blue: potable water
- Green: sewer
- White: proposed excavation
- Pink: temporary survey markings
- Purple: reclaimed water (irrigation)

Once utilities have been located, carefully hand-dig for 2 feet on either side of the utility marking. Should the utility be slightly mismarked, hand-digging reduces the chance of disrupting the line. Certain utilities place a locator tape or cable with or slightly above the actual utility line to aid in its location and to warn that the utility is close. Trenching perpendicular to the marking and gradually working deeper aids in locating lines that are not directly below the mark. Work the soil gently with a shovel and in small amounts. Avoid chopping into compacted soil or using the shovel as a lever to remove large sections of soil.

Private Utilities

Before beginning a project, review the site for utilities that may not have been marked. Lines privately installed do not show up on utility company records and *are not marked* by locators. Look for outbuildings with power, yard lights, wells, gas tanks, septic tanks, or other site facilities that would obviously have some sort of connection to a utility line. Inspect inside buildings, particularly in the basement, for utility lines leaving a structure. Check the buildings on site for electrical breaker panels. Shutting off service at any unknown or unmarked breaker will stop service to areas served by those controls, but this precaution may also reduce the chance of accidental shock. Utility-locating equipment can be rented to help find private lines. Instructions for operating this equipment are critical because connections are often made to the utility line to trace its location. If utilities cannot be located, then contractors may have no choice but to unearth the entire utility line from source to end to find the location.

Locking Out Electrical Circuits

When performing work on electrical circuitry, contractors face the risk of accidental electrocution if they do not use standard electrical lockout procedures. When using a circuit or power cord leading to a task that involves the use of electricity, the contractor performing the task should lock out and tag the circuit or cord; and that same contractor should be the only one to reactivate the circuit or cord.

WORKING BELOW GRADE

If the soil about them is unstable or if they are deep, trenches can collapse. Workers should be aware that any trench poses a hazard when they need to bend down to perform work tasks near the bottom. Special precautions should be taken any time the trench is more than waist deep.

Shoring reduces risk to workers when the trench exceeds a safe working depth. Sheets of plywood separated by 2 × 4s can provide sidewall protection for shallow trenches in unstable soils. Larger trenches will require the use of metal trench shoring. To reduce the possibility of collapse, equipment should not be operated near the edges of open trenches. Always work in pairs when performing trench work. People caught in a trench collapse are often helpless to free themselves; nor are they able to call for help.

OPERATING POWER EQUIPMENT

Personal injury, disability, and death can result from the improper operation and use of power equipment. See Chapter 8 for instructions on performing basic construction activities, including operation of many pieces of equipment. Tractors, **skid-steers**, **chainsaws**, and power tools all pose a risk of serious injury if workers do not follow the rules of operation. Never modify equipment or remove safety guards. Read all manufacturer's safety instructions and heed the safety risk labels found on nearly every tool or piece of equipment used. These labels are the foundation of workplace accident avoidance.

Care should be exercised when using electrical equipment in landscape applications. When strung around a construction site, cords can be easily, if accidentally, severed, creating a potential for shock. Water also poses another potential hazard when using electrical equipment outdoors. Verify that electrical circuits being used have ground fault protection against shock and electrocution.

Operation of tractors, loaders, and skid-steers creates additional hazards for the work site. Use care when backing such equipment because the operator often has no clear vision behind the vehicle. Warning bells or beepers when equipment or vehicles are geared to reverse should be kept in working order, and all workers in the immediate area should be alert when the operator backs the equipment. Potential for tip-over increases when equipment is operated on a slope or when loads become top-heavy. The center of gravity keeps most equipment operating on all four wheels (or on two tracks). When this center of gravity approaches the outside edge of the equipment's operating base (wheels or tracks), instability results. If the center of gravity moves outside the operating base, a tip-over occurs. Most equipment is designed with a low mass, but when equipment is used to carry a load in a bucket or when it is operated on a slope, that center will change (Figure 7-3). Two good rules

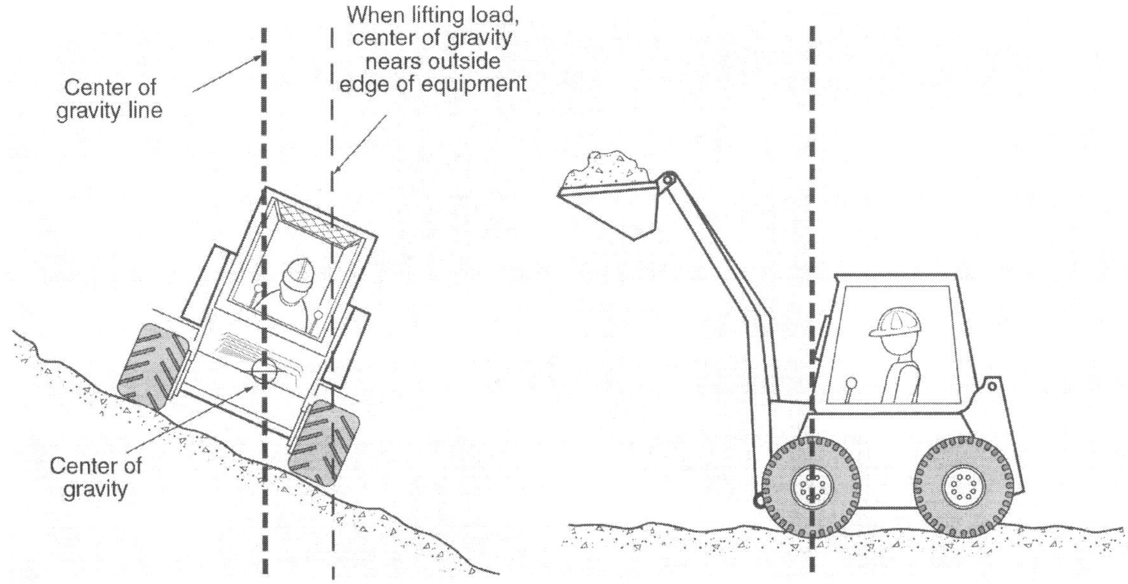

Figure 7-3 When the center of gravity for equipment passes beyond the outside edge, a tipover may occur. Tip-over may also occur when a load is lifted too high. Use caution when operating equipment on slopes or when lifting a load.

to follow: Work slopes steeper than 3.5:1 (3½ feet of horizontal distance for each foot of vertical fall) from bottom to top, rather than from side to side, and always carry loads low.

Caution should also be exercised when using power washers, both compressed air and sprayers. Never aim the spray at exposed skin or body parts. Serious damage to the eyes and skin can result from a direct spray at high pressure, including contusion and cutting of skin or the penetration of materials into skin.

WORKING WITH CHEMICALS

Serious injury, particularly burns, can result from misuse of chemicals associated with landscape construction. Painting, staining, and cleaning masonry work necessitate the practice of safety techniques to reduce chemical injury.

Acids and Volatiles

Acids and volatile chemicals found in exterior finishes can present a risk to landscape contractors. Following a few simple rules when working with muriatic acid, TSP (tri-sodium phosphate), wood preservatives, stains or paints, and other volatiles can reduce the potential risk. Safety rules include:

- To reduce the chance of injury, wear proper protective clothing when mixing and applying volatile chemicals. Eye and face protection, rubber gloves, and complete coverage of body and limbs will afford protection when working with chemicals.

- Mix and use chemicals in open areas with ample ventilation to avoid asphyxiation by high concentrations of fumes.

- When mixing acid and water, always add the acid to the water. Never add water to acid. Adding water to acid will cause the mixture to spray and splatter, creating the potential for burns. Always wear protective clothing, gloves, and eyewear when mixing chemicals.

Follow the manufacturer's recommended procedures when applying any chemical.

CHAPTER 8

BASIC CONSTRUCTION TECHNIQUES AND SMALL EQUIPMENT OPERATION

OBJECTIVES

By reading and practicing the techniques described in this chapter, the reader should be able to successfully complete the following activities:

- Operate basic construction tools in a safe and efficient manner.
- Perform basic landscape construction activities.
- Included in this chapter are basic construction techniques and equipment operation instructions that will be referred to in subsequent chapters. Construction techniques that are specific to a particular aspect of landscaping are described in the appropriate chapter.

CAUTION

It is assumed that the reader of this text possesses basic skills necessary to safely perform construction activities and to operate construction equipment. Readers who lack these skills must obtain instruction in these essential areas before attempting to undertake the activities described in this text. Always read and follow manufacturer's instructions when using any piece of equipment.

The process of selecting appropriate construction equipment and techniques starts with understanding the task to be completed and the operator's capabilities. First and foremost among these considerations is safety. The appropriate tool for the work must be selected, and the operator must be familiar with the safe and effective use of the tool. Failure to make the correct selection increases the risk of injury, disability, or even death.

Another important issue is the size and capacity of the tool selected to complete the task. Moving hundreds of cubic yards of soil with a shovel is inefficient, as is installing only two nails with a power nailer. Choosing a tool that is too large wastes energy and is seldom costeffective. Likewise, choosing equipment that is too small to efficiently complete the task increases the effort and extends the time necessary to finish the work. Carefully evaluate the task and then consider the best tools and equipment available, including hand tools, small power equipment, and large power equipment, to appropriately complete the work.

RELATED INFORMATION

Information in this chapter is supplemented by instruction provided elsewhere in this text and in other sources. Before undertaking the activities described in this chapter, read the related information in these sources:

- Safety in the Workplace, Chapter 7

EXCAVATION

Use of hand tools cannot be avoided in the field of landscape construction. Although working with them is labor-intensive, hand tools can make work easier and more productive when used properly (Figure 8-1). When the work with a particular hand tool is extensive, consider the economy of renting or purchasing the powered alternative. Several powered tools can be substituted for much of the hand labor that is common on landscape jobs. Some common tools include power augers, sod cutters, edging machines, jackhammers (see "Digging" below), trenchers, backhoes, skid-steers, tractors, and dump trucks, including the variety of attachments for these pieces of equipment. Operation of most power equipment is embedded with the specific task or is addressed in general in this chapter. Ideally, operation of power equipment should be learned under the supervision of an experienced practitioner.

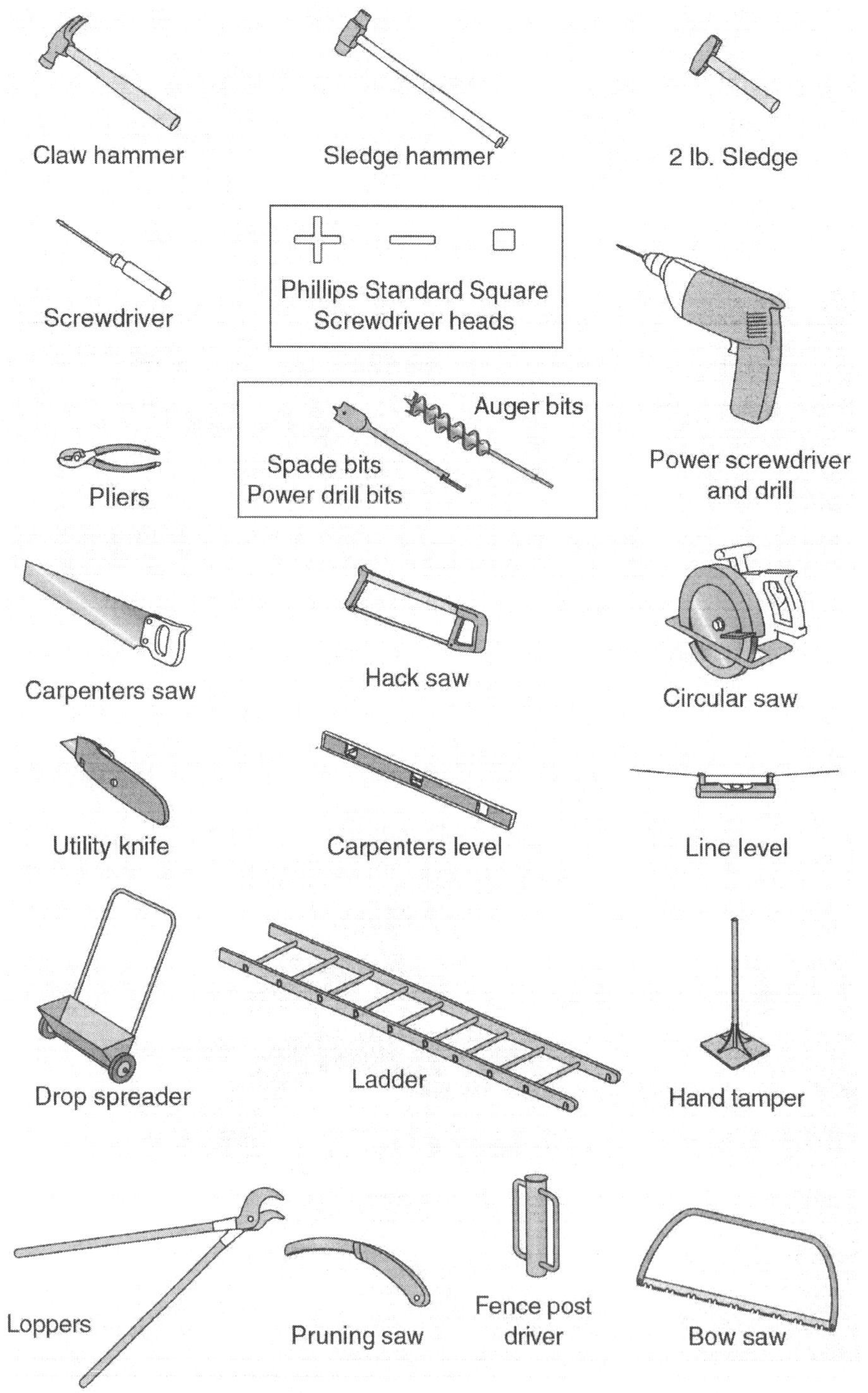

Figure 8-1 Common tools used in landscape construction.

Digging

Nearly every task in the landscape construction field requires digging in some form. Consider using a skid-steer for excavations of more than 5 CY, but smaller excavations and portions of larger jobs will require hand excavation. Proper selection, use, and care of shovels greatly eases the burden of hand-digging.

Selection begins with determining whether a spade or shovel is required (Figure 8-2). A round-nosed shovel has a curved surface with raised edges and is designed for excavating and scooping material. Scoop shovels have very wide blades (12–18 inches wide) designed for large-scale moving of mulch, rock, and other landscape materials. Square-nosed shovels have a medium width blade with squared corners designed for cleaning out wide base or utility trenches and skimming soil and scooping material. Trenching spades have long, narrow blades (6 inches wide) that are designed for excavating narrow utility trenches. Shovels and spades also come with long handles, which provide more leverage, and short handles, which work better in tight situations. Additional tools that are helpful in moving and removing materials are picks, mattocks, breaker bars, and pitchforks. Identify the type of digging tasks required and select the proper tool to accomplish the task. The experienced contractor carries a variety of tools to accommodate almost any digging chore.

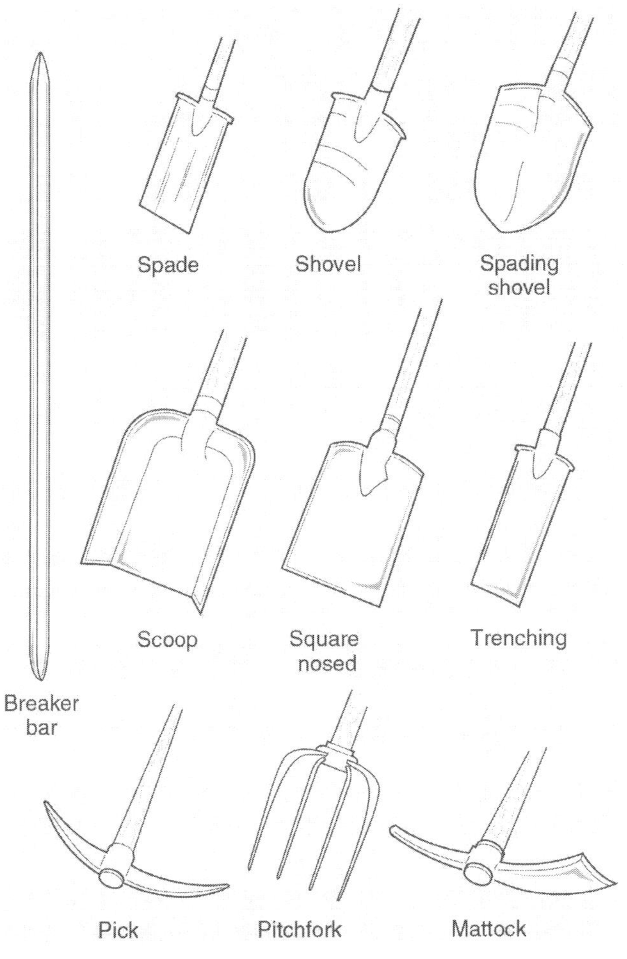

Figure 8-2 Typical landscape construction excavation tools.

To obtain the proper excavation technique, position the digging tool so that the blade is perpendicular with the ground. Place the instep of your foot on the shovel to push the blade completely into the ground and pull back on the handle to leverage material out. Alternate sides and digging positions to avoid overexertion of one muscle group. Use your arms as much as possible in lifting the load of soil. Drop your load using a motion that swings the shovel forward and down, letting the material slide from the shovel blade. If the location for dropping the load is not directly in front of you, pivot on one foot to the correct direction, rather than twisting your back and body (Figure 8-3). Excavate in reasonable amounts that fit onto the spade or shovel without spilling. Proper digging involves many repeated steps, rather than two or three giant shovelfuls. When faced with hard compacted soil that is difficult to excavate, first loosen the soil using a **breaker bar** (also called a *pry bar*), pick, landscape axe, or mattock. The breaker bar is a long, narrow, heavy bar that can be lifted and thrust downward onto hard soil (Figure 8-4). Picks, landscape axes, and mattocks use a chopping motion to loosen compacted earth. Break apart small sections; then excavate using a shovel or posthole excavator.

As an alternative to a breaker bar, use a jackhammer with a spade bit. Make an initial excavation using the jackhammer; then move the equipment back a few inches and work toward the loosened soil (Figure 8-5). Jackhammers are

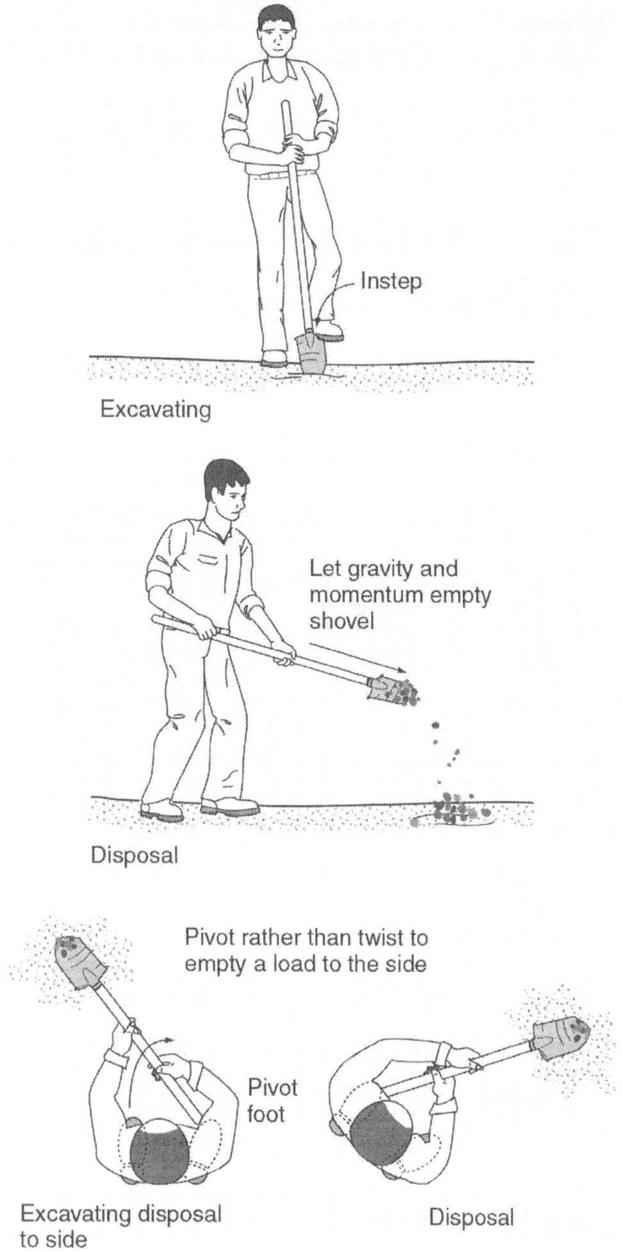

Figure 8-3 Proper spading techniques.

available in electricand gas-powered models and can often be rented from equipment stores. When operating the jackhammer, the operator should stand squarely on two feet and maintain proper balance. The equipment is heavy, and operators can fall if they lose balance. In addition to the spade bit, point and chisel bits are also available to aid in removing pavement.

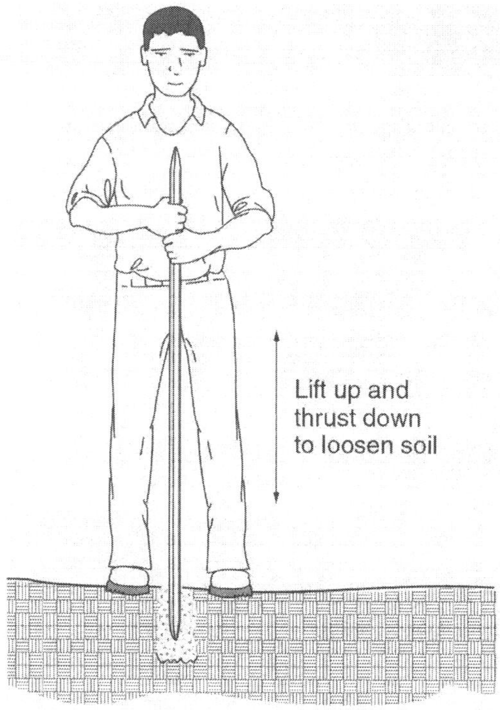

Figure 8-4 Loosen hard soil using a breaker bar.

If the desired excavation is shallow, use a rototiller to loosen the soil and any existing cover crop (Figure 8-6). Work the rototiller across the site, and then repeat at a right angle to the initial passes. The surface can then be scraped off using square-nosed shovels.

Keep all excavation equipment clean and sharp. Use a file to maintain an edge on the blade of the shovel or spade to ease cutting through tough soils and roots. When not in use, digging tools should be cleaned completely, their surfaces oiled, and then stored in dry locations.

Excavating Postholes

Postholes can be excavated using **clamshell diggers, augers**, and powered augers. Augers work by positioning the tool over the hole location and twisting until the auger is full (Figure 8-7). Lift from the hole and tap on the ground away from the hole to remove the excavated material (Figure 8-8). Continue auguring until you reach the proper depth, checking the hole periodically for depth and plumb. Operate clamshell diggers by holding the handles

Figure 8-5 Loosening soil with a jackhammer.

Figure 8-6 Loosening the surface layer of soil using a rototiller.

together and driving the blades into the ground at the hole location by dropping or thrusting the tool downward with the arms (Figure 8-9). Avoid pinching fingers between the handles. Spread the handles to capture a load of material and lift it out of the hole. When working in dry soil, add a small amount of water to the excavation. This will create a soft mud that is easier to remove from the hole than is a loose dry powder. Continue this process until the hole is excavated. Excavating is faster with either tool if depths are marked on the handle (Figure 8-10). If soil in the hole is dry and spills out of the digging tools while you extract it from the hole, add a small amount of water into the hole to create a light mud that you can excavate more easily. Clamshells are difficult to use on deep excavations, whereas augers have difficulty maintaining plumb excavations. Starting an excavation with a clamshell and finishing with an auger will more effectively excavate a hole. Keep a sharpened, long-handled trenching spade or pair of lopping shears handy to cut any roots that disrupt hole excavation.

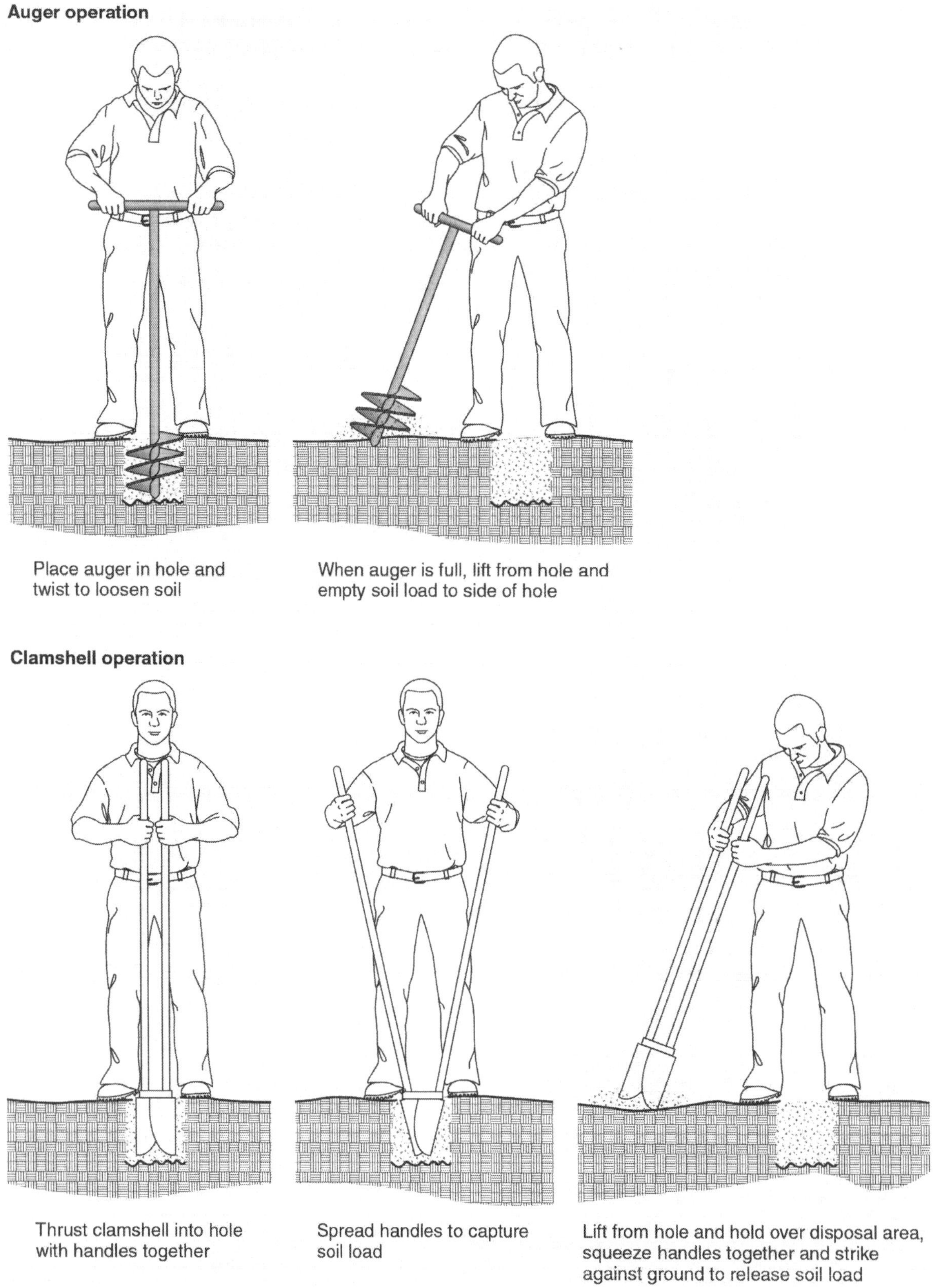

Figure 8-7 Steps for using posthole excavators.

Figure 8-8 Operating an auger-type posthole excavator.

Excavating a hole can be laborious; so if several holes are planned, consider renting a power auger to perform the work. Power augers have a gas engine that turns a spiral auger to excavate the hole. Two people are required to operate the power auger. The area around the hole must be clear of objects that could block the operators' activities. Begin by marking the location of the center of the hole. Using a round-nosed shovel, excavate a 6-inch deep, coneshaped centering hole. This small hole will help keep the auger centered on the hole as it starts the excavation. Start the engine and, with each operator firmly grasping the handles, position the auger over the hole. Accelerate the engine and push down on the auger. The auger will bite into the soil and pull the material out of the hole. Maintain the auger in a plumb alignment for the entire depth of the hole (Figure 8-11). Work the auger in an up-and-down motion to periodically clear the blade, but avoid pulling the auger completely out of the hole. Keep a firm grip on the auger. Any solid object

Figure 8-9 Operating a clamshell-type posthole excavator.

encountered while digging will jerk the auger to the side.

Trenching

By using the proper hand trenching method, you can dig larger quantities of trenches that are more stable in shorter amounts of time. Begin with selecting the proper tool. A trenching shovel should be used to dig narrow slit trenches. Using the full length of the shovel blade allows trenches to reach maximum depth. When trenching, turn the spade at a 45-degree angle to the side of the trench, rather than digging perpendicular to the edge. This will limit trench collapse when the soil is levered out.

Figure 8-10 Excavation depths marked on the handle of an excavation tool.

Leveling

Hand leveling an area typically involves the use of garden or landscape rakes. Using a pulling and pushing motion, you can redistribute soil and other materials into a smooth surface. If a digging action is required to dislodge material, use the tine side of the rake while pushing down with force. When materials are loosened, they can be shifted to the desired location using the tines. For smooth leveling, turn the garden rake upside down and use the bar portion rather than the tines.

Compacting Fill Materials

Compaction of fill materials can be accomplished by hand or mechanical means. All filling activities are more effective if fill material

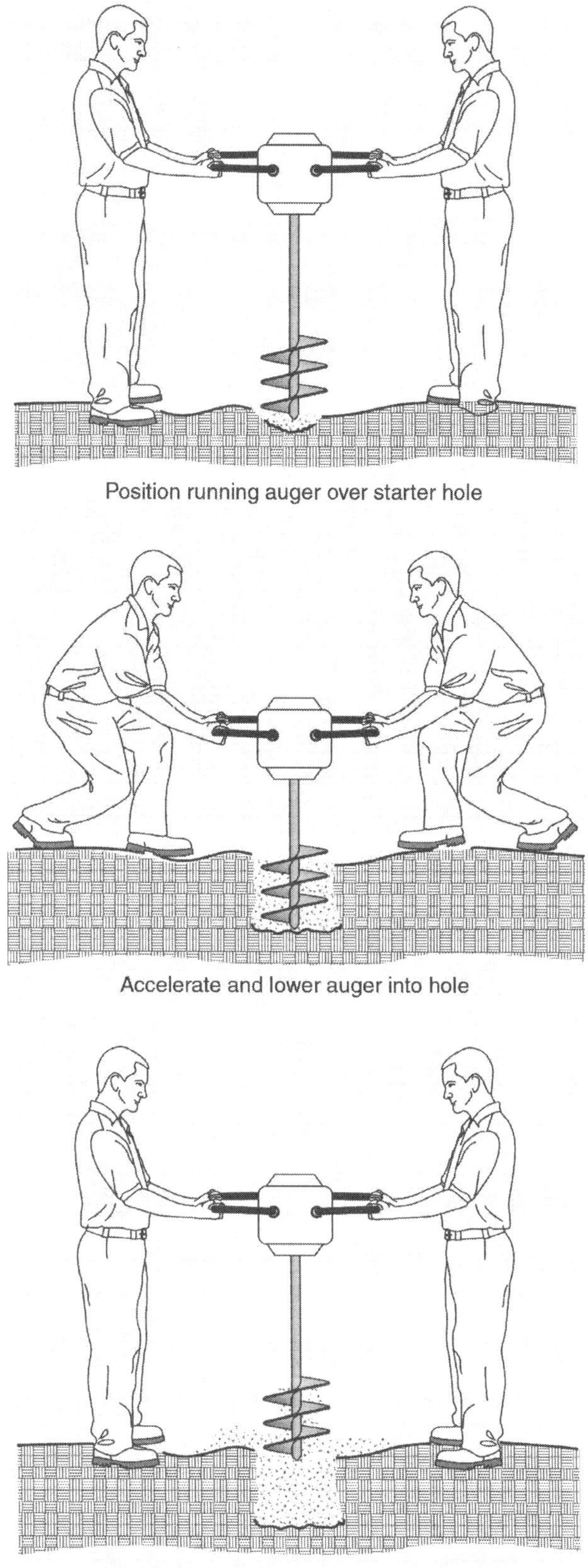

Figure 8-11 Operating a power posthole auger.

is placed and compacted in layers, also called lifts, 6 inches thick or less. Hand-tamping requires pounding the fill area repeatedly using a handtamping plate or the end of a 4 × 4. Mechanical pounding can be accomplished with the use of a **vibratory plate compactor.** The plate compactor operates similarly to a self-propelled lawn mower. Start the compactor and adjust the throttle and settings. With no need for you to push it, the compactor moves forward; and you can steer it using the handle. To turn sharp corners, lift the handle vertically and spin the compactor.

Larger compaction jobs can be accomplished using other mechanical equipment (Figure 8-12). **Rammers,** or **jumping jacks,** are handheld, gas-powered, compaction devices used for compacting trenches, particularly in areas where settling may be a problem. To use a rammer, start the equipment and position it in an upright position. Accelerate the rammer and guide it slowly through the area to be compacted.

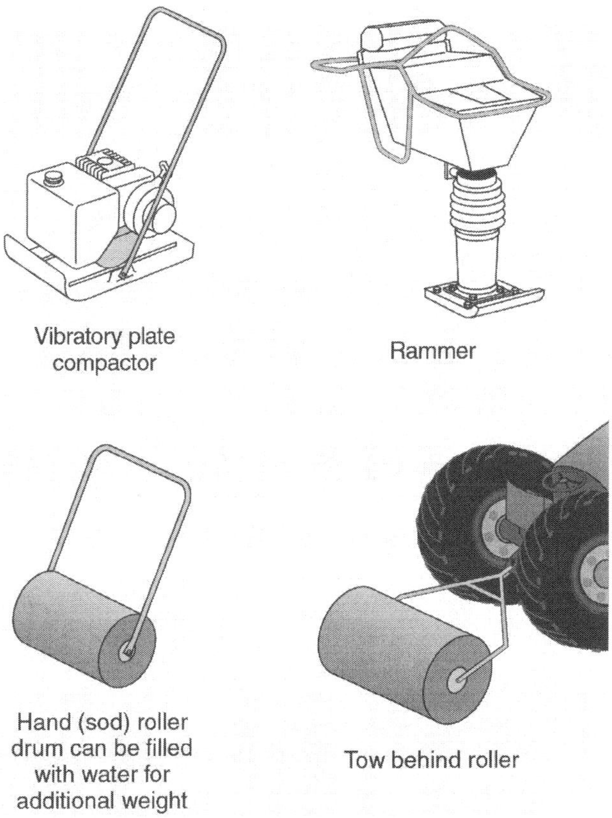

Figure 8-12 Common compaction equipment.

The rammer will "bounce" up and down to compact. Repeat the process at least twice over the entire area. **Static** and **vibrating rollers** are available as hand-operated or towed equipment for large open areas such as lawns and roadways. Both rollers can typically be weighted down by adding water to the rounded drum, and both should be guided through the area to be compacted at least twice. If possible, make the initial pass over the site with the rollers in one direction and then make a second pass at right angles to the initial compaction.

STAKING AND CONSTRUCTION FENCING

In performing their jobs, landscape contractors often stake perimeters and erect or install fencing. Although fencing the perimeter of a project may not create a physical barrier, it does alert those in the area that construction activity is taking place on a site. For projects where it is imperative that nonauthorized entry be restricted, contractors must rely on chain-link or security fencing to protect the project boundary.

Driving Stakes

Driving, or forcing stakes into the ground, typically requires the use of a small (1–2 pound) or large (4–5 pound) sledgehammer. Position the stake in the proper location and lightly strike the top of the stake to start it into the ground. Stakes may shift location when driven, depending on the size of the stake or its taper, the end being driven into the ground. If the stake shifts when being struck, use your foot to hold it in position. When the stake is standing on its own, remove your foot and continue striking, increasing the force of the blows until the stake is driven to the required depth. Maintain eye contact with the top of the stake while striking with the sledgehammer.

Driving Metal Fenceposts

When installing chain-link fence or other fence with metal posts, you will need to drive the posts into the ground. To drive metal posts, place the base of the post at the location where the post is to be set. Lean the post down until the **post**

Figure 8-13 Prepare to drive a fencepost by leaning the post at an angle and inserting the post into the driver. Return the post and driver to plumb and begin driving.

driver can be slipped over the top of the post (Figure 8-13). Check the post to make sure it is in the proper location and oriented properly (notches to the fabric side for fabric fences). Straighten the post and driver to a plumb position, lift the driver, and let it drop on the top of the post. If soil conditions are dry or if driving the post is difficult, apply downward force on the driver to sink the post to the desired depth.

Installing Temporary Fencing

Construction fence may also require that posts be driven and surfacing attached to control traffic at the project boundary. Lean the fence surfacing against the fence, and connect it by passing plastic or wire ties through an opening in the fence, around the post, and back through another opening in the fence. Then fasten the two ends together by twisting or tying.

CUTTING AND JOINING PIPE

Landscape contractors will often have to measure, cut, and join pipe. Whether repairing irrigation, plumbing a fountain, or placing drainage pipe, the proper techniques for cutting and joining pipe will be necessary. This section addresses the best practices for working with pipe.

Measuring Pipe Before Cutting

Two methods work best for measuring pipe before cutting. The first is to measure the distance between fittings at either end of a length of pipe and add the length of pipe that will be placed inside the fittings. The second method is to hold the pipe section up to the opening where the pipe will fit and directly mark the location of each end in the fitting at either end of the pipe.

CAUTION

Cutting pipe may create sharp edges. Wear gloves and use care when handling.

Cutting and Joining Corrugated Plastic Drainage Pipe

Corrugated plastic drainage pipes are manufactured in a variety of types and diameters and include a wide range of drainage fittings and accessories. Drainage pipe is typically manufactured in diameters of 3, 4, 6, 9, and 12 inches and in varying gauges. Lightweight tubing gauges are very flexible and are available in perforated, nonperforated, and socked versions for use in various drainage situations. Heavier piping gauges are very rigid and can be used for subdrains and culverts. Fittings include connectors to downspouts, inlets, sump pump basins, and a variety of Ts, Ys, and elbows.

You can cut corrugated pipe with a utility knife or hacksaw. Place the pipe on a stable surface, mark the cut locations, and make a

Figure 8-14 Cutting corrugated plastic drain pipe with a utility knife.

Figure 8-15 Joining corrugated plastic drain pipe to a premanufactured elbow fitting. Pipe "snaps" into fitting.

perpendicular cut (Figure 8-14). Most fittings for drainage pipe are available with snap fittings. These fittings allow the pipe to be slipped into the fitting and held in place with flanges on the fitting (Figure 8-15). Wrap the joint with duct tape (Figure 8-16) to obtain a longer-lasting fit.

Cutting and Joining Poly Pipe

Note: Irrigation contracting is a licensed trade in North Carolina. Irrigation information provided here is for reference only. Refer to the North Carolina Irrigation Contractors' Licensing Board for additional information on licensing and exemptions. A flexible plastic pipe, **poly pipe** or swing pipe is primarily used for swing joints for sprinkler heads. Poly pipe can be cut with a sharp utility knife. Connections are made using barbed fittings that are inserted into the ends of the pipe.

To cut and join poly pipe, use cutters or a sharp utility knife to make a square cut at the proper location (Figure 8-17). Join by lining up the barbed fitting with the end of pipe and inserting with a rocking/twisting motion (Figure 8-18). Insert the fitting until all the barbs are secured inside the pipe. Pipe that has been set in the sun for a short time to soften the poly will make inserting fittings easier. Verify the fitting is securely seated before moving to the next connection (Figure 8-19).

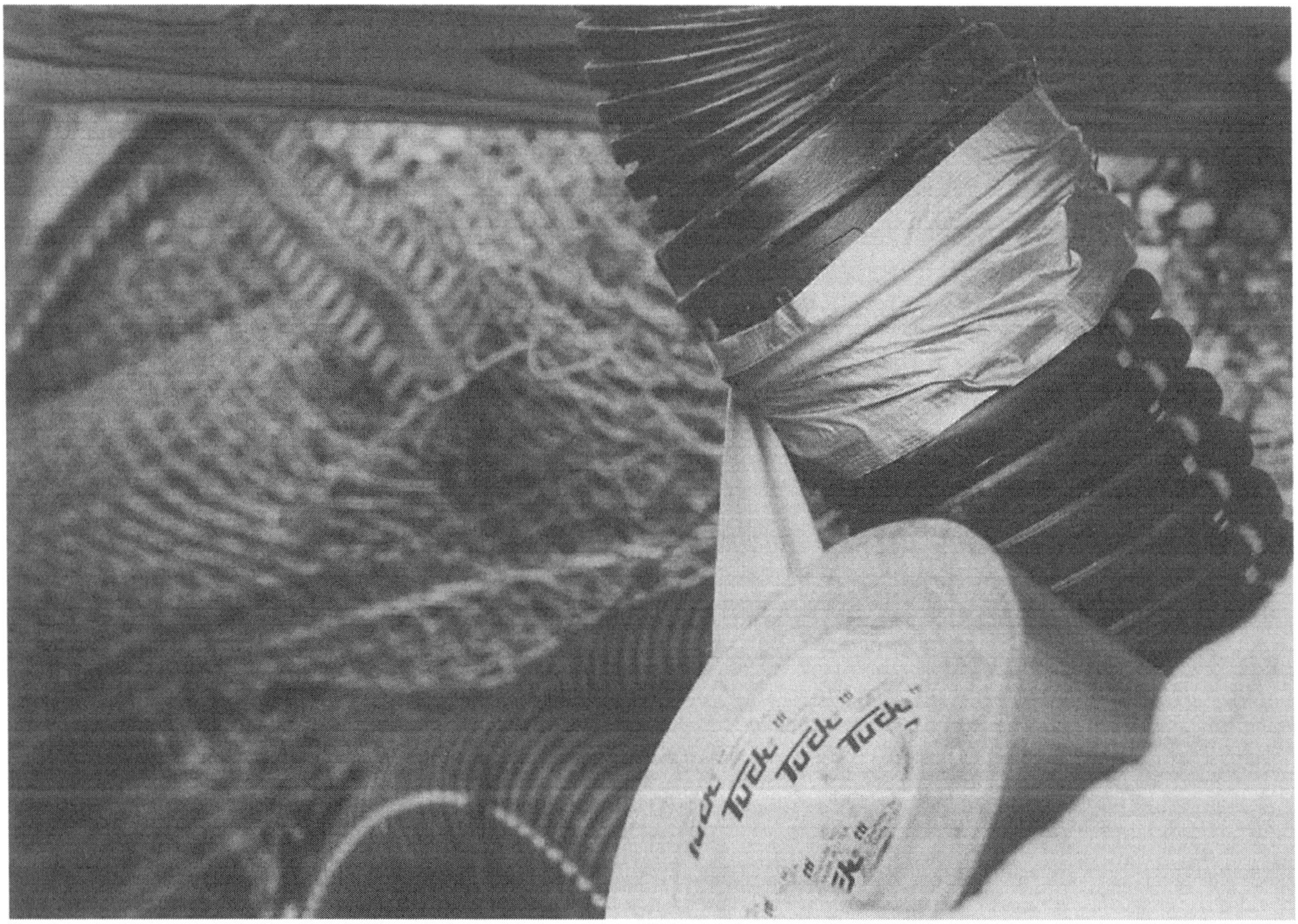

Figure 8-16 Securing corrugated plastic joints with duct tape.

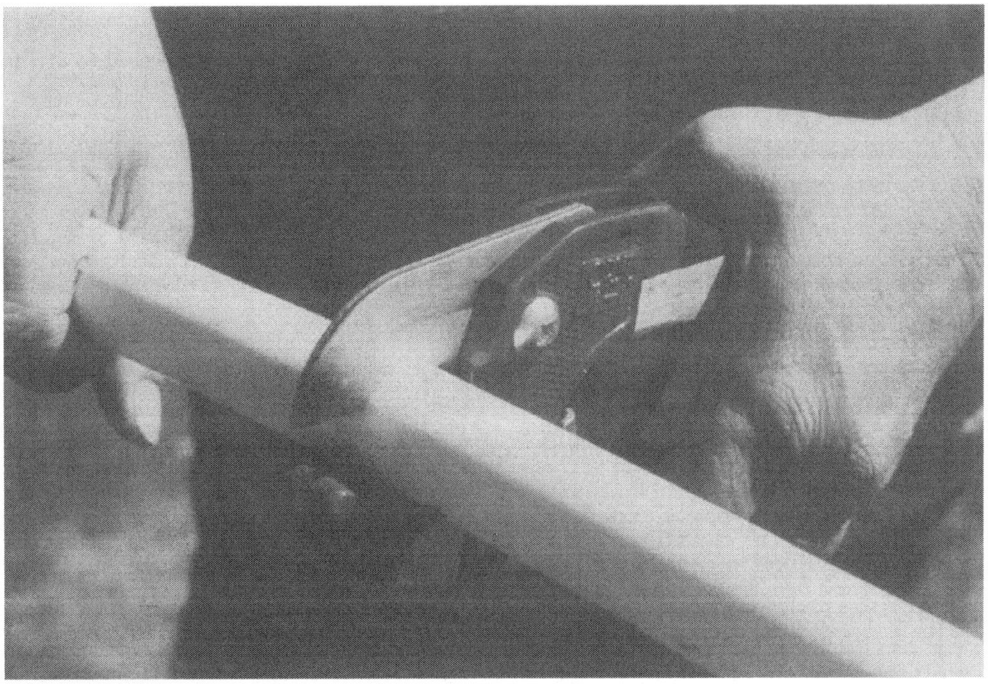

Figure 8-17 Making a square cut on a PVC pipe.

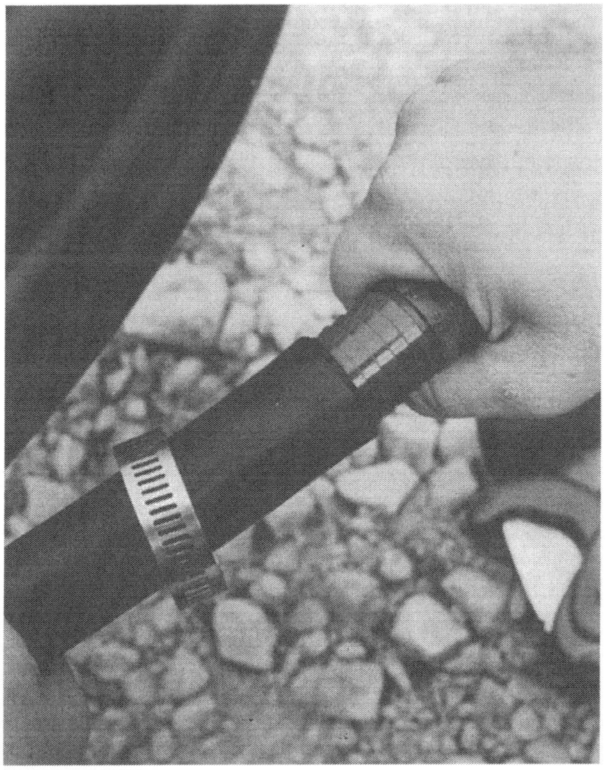

Figure 8-18 Joining poly pipe with a plastic fitting.

Figure 8-19 A secure barbed fitting for an in-line drip irrigation system.

Cutting and Joining Poly Drip Irrigation Pipe

Drip irrigation line connecting laterals to drip heads is typically a flexible poly tubing in ¼-inch, ½-inch, and ⅝-inch diameters. Drip irrigation line can be cut using the cutting tool, a sharp utility knife or sharp heavy duty scissors. Smaller diameter poly tubing is joined using barbed fittings that are forced into the end of the tubing (Figure 8-23), whereas larger diameter tubing is connected using compression fittings especially designed for drip irrigation applications (Figure 8-24). The diaphragm inside the fittings prevent leakage when properly joined. To connect compression fittings, push the tubing into the fitting until snug.

Cutting and Joining PVC Pipe

Polyvinyl chloride, or **PVC,** pipe is a rigid pipe that comes in a variety of diameters. PVC can be

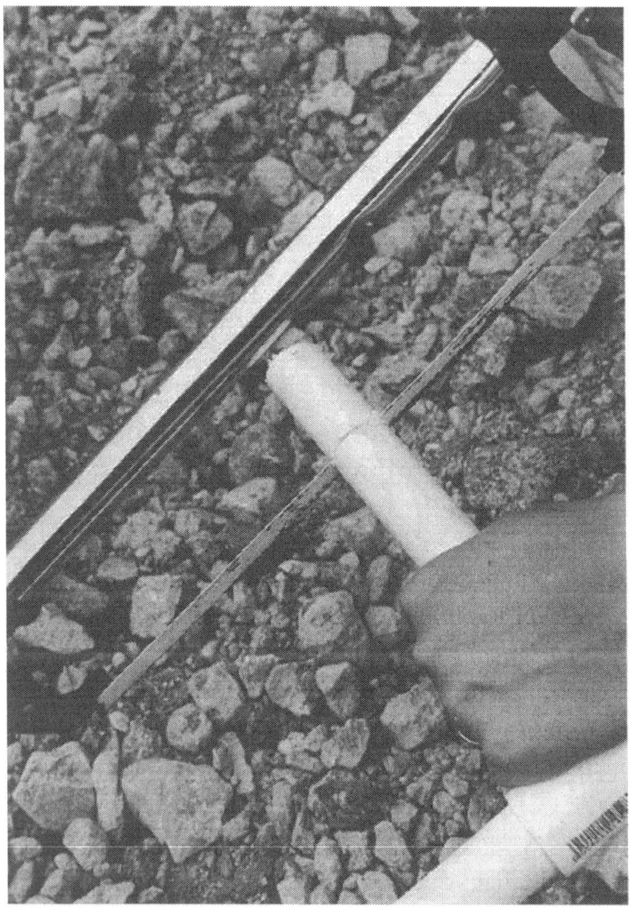

Figure 8-20 Cutting PVC pipe with a hacksaw.

Figure 8-21 Cleaning PVC pipe with pipe cleaning solution. Clean both the outside of the pipe and the inside of the fitting. When dry, liberally apply glue in the same manner. Most cleaning and joining solutions provide a swab applicator in the can.

thin-walled or thick-walled (Schedule 40). In addition to the many sizes of piping, PVC offers a full range of fittings, valves, and accessories for exterior applications. PVC is suitable for use as irrigation, water lines, and sewer lines. As part of the installation planning, verify the type of pipe required for the application with local plumbing codes.

PVC pipe can be cut with a pipe cutter or a hacksaw (Figure 8-20). Mark the cut location and make a square cut through the pipe. To use the pipe cutters, slip them over the pipe and squeeze the handle several times, or until the pipe cuts.

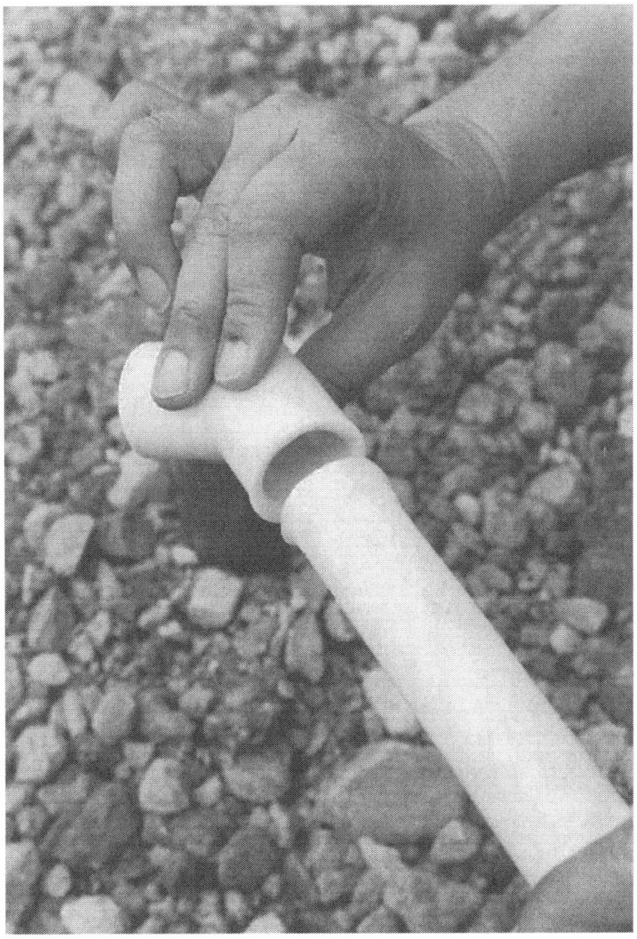

Figure 8-22 Joining PVC pipe after applying glue. Use a twisting motion to push pipe completely into fitting.

Use a reaming tool, wire brush, or sandpaper to clean burrs from the inside of the cut pipe.

The outside of the PVC pipe and the inside of all PVC connectors must be cleaned before the pipe can be joined. Wipe dirt and dust from the end of the pipe and liberally brush the primer over the parts to be joined (Figure 8-21). While the primer is still wet, apply PVC joint compound to both the pipe end and the connector, push them firmly together, and twist oneeighth to one-quarter turn (Figure 8-22). Verify that the alignment of the fitting is correct. The compound will set in approximately 10 seconds, and you cannot correct errors without cutting new sections of pipe. Always follow manufacturer's recommendations and specifications.

Cutting and Joining Copper Pipe

Copper pipe is typically used for supplying water to service points within a site. Copper is available as rigid lengths of pipe or as flexible tubing. Each type has a special method for joining. A variety of pipe sizes, fittings, valves, and accessories are available for exterior uses.

Both rigid copper pipe and copper tubing are cut using a pipe cutter. Clamp the pipe cutter onto the pipe at the cut location and rotate the cutter around the pipe. With each successive turn, the clamp tightens until the pipe is cut. Use a reamer to remove burrs from the inside of the pipe after cutting.

> **CAUTION**
>
> Use caution when lighting and operating a torch. The heat zone for a torch extends well beyond the visible flame. Always direct flames away from people and flammable objects. Let all heated items cool before handling.

Rigid copper pipe is joined using sweat fittings, or heated joints into which solder is drawn to seal the joint. To sweat a fitting, begin by cleaning both the end of the pipe and the fitting with sandpaper or wire pipe reamer. Apply a substance called *flux,* which aids in the bonding between pipe and solder, to both the cleaned pipe and connector. Slide the fitting over the end of the pipe and position at the proper angle. Set the joint on a wood block or hold the pipe with locking pliers; then heat the fitting using a propane torch. When the joint starts to turn a darker color, remove the heat, touch a piece of solder to the joints, and hold the solder there while it melts and is drawn into the joint. When the solder starts to drip, the joint is filled. Let the joint cool before handling.

Copper tubing is joined using solderless compression fittings. The compression fitting has two parts that sandwich around the end of the tubing and are twisted together using a wrench to complete the joint. Slip the end of the fitting with the open center over the tubing. Insert any washers provided with the fitting. Ream the end of the tubing and insert the part of the fitting with the rounded end. Apply joint compound or joint

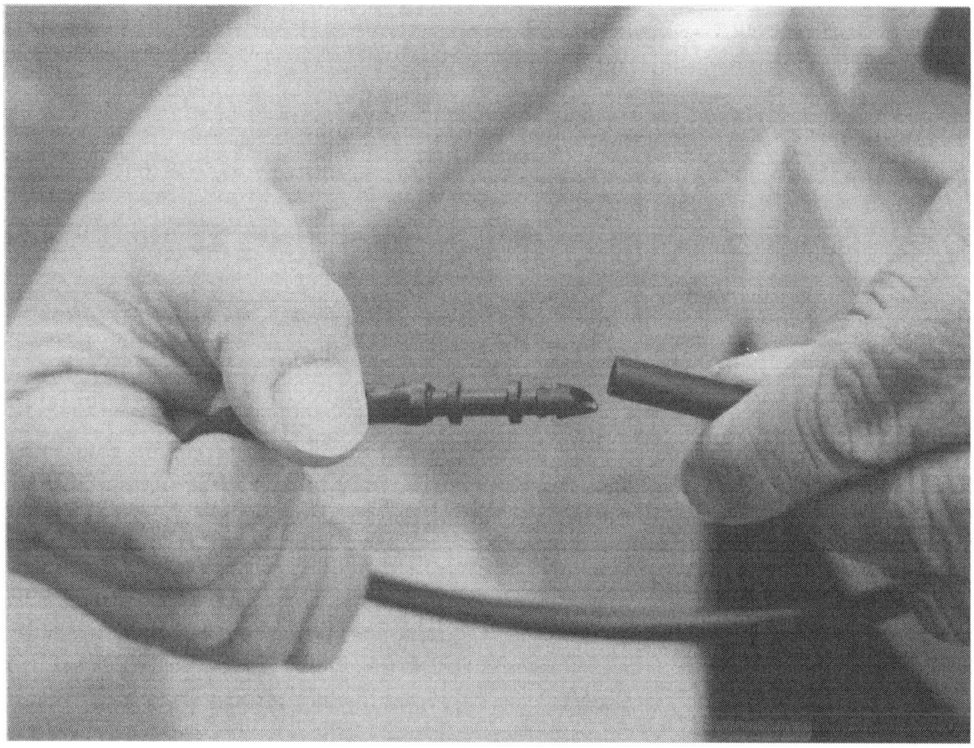

Figure 8-23 Using a barbed fitting to join small diameter drip irrigation tubing. Push the tubing firmly onto the fitting over the ridges of the fitting.

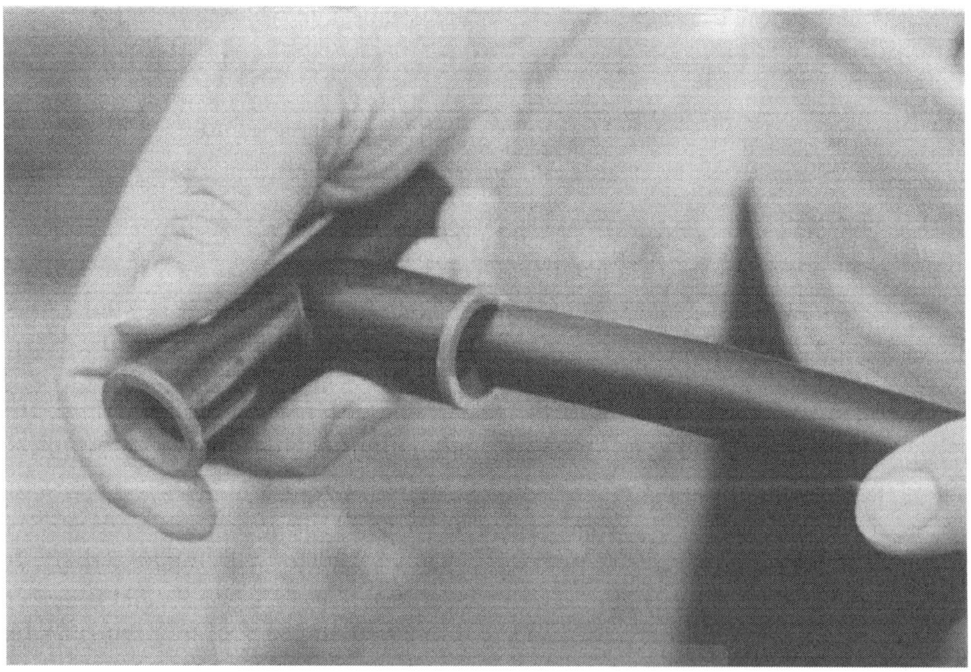

Figure 8-24 A compression fitting to join larger diameter drip irrigation tubing. Push the tubing firmly into the fitting.

compound tape over the threads of the second piece. Slide the first part up the tubing to the second part and twist together tightly.

Copper installations should be laid out beginning at the supply point, cutting and joining pipe as the installation moves toward the service point. If placing copper piping in a trench, carefully lay the piping and pressurize the system, checking for leaks. Carefully backfill the trench.

CUTTING PAVING AND WALL MATERIALS

Few landscape materials arrive at a job site ready to install without modification. To complete many of their projects, landscape contractors will need to measure and mark and then cut paving and wall materials.

> **CAUTION**
>
> When cutting any wall material, wear proper clothing and safety equipment. Use cutting equipment according to manufacturer's instructions.

Marking Materials

The simplest way to mark for cutting is to hold the material in position and use a pencil to transcribe the cut location directly onto the material. Measuring can be done if a high degree of accuracy is maintained. Marking with a magic marker or lumber pencil provides better visibility of the mark when you use a wet masonry saw. Make the mark on the scrap side of the cut location so the mark will not be visible when you place the material. Most paving and wall material must be cut to within ⅛-inch of required dimensions to avoid problems with fit. Irregular and angle cuts may take two pieces to get the correct shape. Cutting methods make curved cuts difficult, and notching is difficult to obtain with all cutting tools except a wet masonry saw.

Brick or Stone Set

Clay brick can be cut, or cleaved, with a wide chisel-like tool called a set (also called brick set

Figure 8-25 Cutting paving materials with a brick set. Set the paving material on a flat surface or on sand. Place the blade of the set along the line where you want the stone to cleave; then strike firmly with a hammer.

or **stone set**) (Figure 8-25). Place the brick on sand and align the brick set along the mark for the cut. Lightly tap the set with the hammer to create a weakened joint. Strike the end of the set with a hammer. The brick should cleave along that angle (Figure 8-26). Concrete paving block can be cut in this method with reasonable success, but precast concrete does not cleave well with a set. Stone is cut in a manner similar to that used for clay brick, although there may be some irregularity in the edge of stone after being cleaved. Stone can also be scored along the cut line with a cutoff saw and then struck on the opposite side with a stone set to cleave.

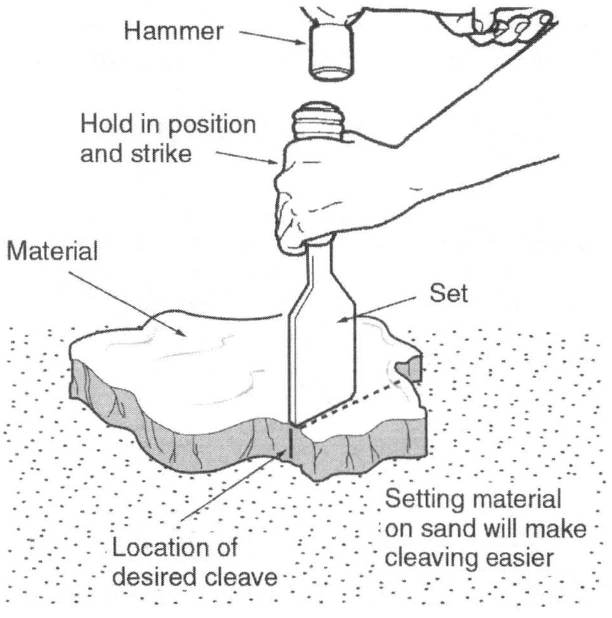

Figure 8-26 Cutting paving material with a set.

Brick/Stone Hammer

Striking stone with the pointed end of a brick hammer can chip or cleave certain types of stone (Figure 8-27). You can use the blunt end of the hammer to knock off bumps or edges that prevent a tight fit. To reduce splitting of the stone, strike the offending piece from the side rather than from the top.

Hydraulic Block Splitter

The double blade **hydraulic splitter** is a piece of equipment that will accurately cleave stone, brick, or precast units. Wear gloves and safety glasses when operating a splitter. The material is set on a table with the cleave location directly below a striking bar. The bar is lowered to the stone manually and is tightened. An operator then repeatedly presses a foot pedal that applies pressure to the striking bar through a hydraulic cylinder. When the cylinder reaches the right pressure, the material is cleaved. Although this is a fast way to cleave materials, waste can be excessive when using a hydraulic cutter (Figure 8-28).

If the splitter is so equipped, the tilting base plate will help improve the cleaving of

Figure 8-27 Shaping stone edge with brick hammer.

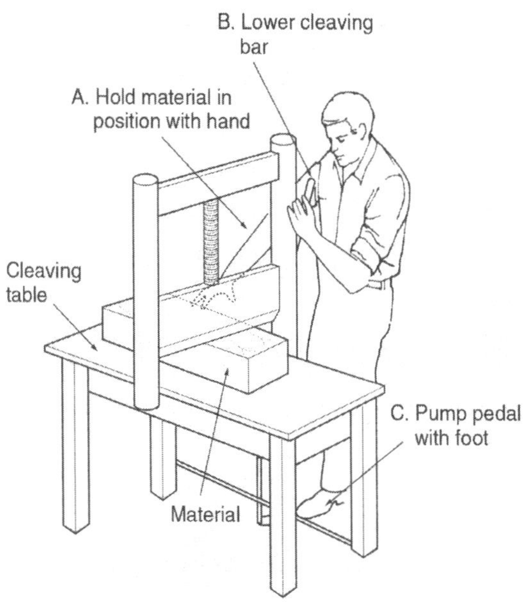

Figure 8-28 Cutting materials using a hydraulic splitter.

interlocking concrete pavers. When the bar is lowered, angle paving material downward away from the cut location. This will provide a slightly undercut angled end that will improve the pavers' placement.

Cutoff Saw

A **cutoff saw,** a handheld cutting tool, is powered with a gas motor and has a circular diamond or carborundum blade for cutting. Operated similarly to a chainsaw, the cutoff saw creates a large amount of dust. However, the saw is portable and useful for remote sites without electricity. To cut with a cutoff saw, mark the cut location and anchor the material to avoid movement while cutting. If necessary, place a block underneath the material to avoid cutting into the surface below. In applications where the cut edge cannot show, mark the underside and score, or cut, the material almost halfway through and along the entire length of the mark. Then place a 2 x 4 under the score and apply a heavy downward pressure to one side of the cut to finish the splitting. Wear gloves, safety glasses, dust mask, and ear protection. Start the saw and position it over the material to be cut. Run the saw to full speed and slowly lower it onto the paving material. Let the saw pass completely through the material before removing the blade from the cut (Figure 8-29).

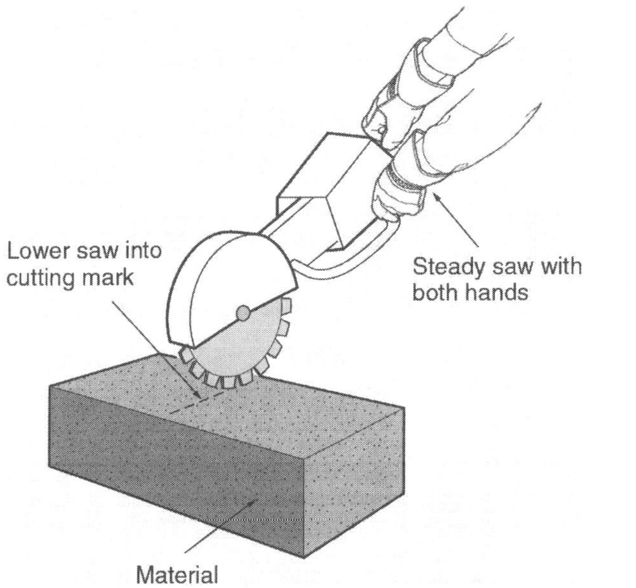

Figure 8-29 Cutting materials using a cutoff saw.

Wet Masonry Saw

A wet masonry saw uses a moving table to pass materials through a fixed diamond blade.
A fine spray of water helps remove debris and reduce dust. To cut with a wet masonry saw, mark the cut location and adjust the saw blade to the proper depth. Wear gloves, safety glasses, and ear protection. Start the saw and make sure the water is flowing. Set the paver on the moving cutting table, and align the cut mark on the paver with the saw blade. Slowly pass the paver through the blade (Figure 8-30). If the motor begins to slow (the pitch of the motor will be noticeably lower), back the material up and restart the pass through the blade at a slower pace.

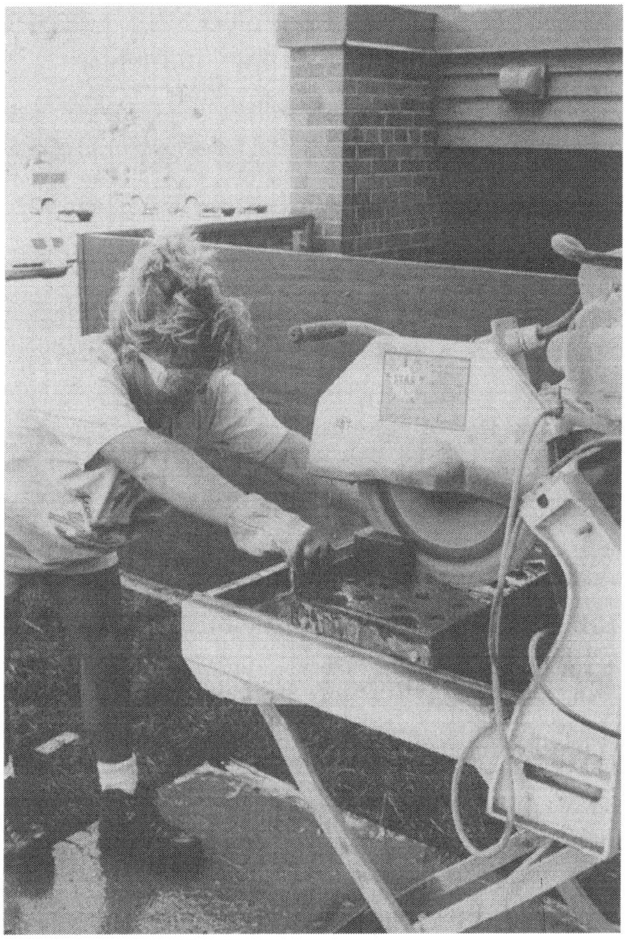

Figure 8-30 Cutting paving materials with a wet masonry saw. Cutting with a masonry saw is slow but accurate.

Notching with a Wet Masonry Saw. When cutting unit pavers to fit around objects in the paved surface, notching may be required. This difficult task can be accomplished with varying degrees of success using a wet masonry saw to make the cuts (Figure 8-31). Mark the cuts. Turn the paver over and cut along the long dimension 1 inch beyond the mark. This extra cut length will be on the back side of the paver and hidden when installed. Turn the paver on its side and adjust the saw blade to match the depth of the second cut. Leaving the block on its side, position the block and pass it through the blade. The two cuts should meet and complete the notch.

You can also notch pavers by using repeated passes with the wet masonry saw. Position the material and make a first pass that removes a portion of the material. If the notch is on an edge, begin at the outside of that edge. Adjust the material to the side and repeat with another pass of the saw. Continue adjusting and cutting until the entire portion to be notched has been removed (Figure 8-32). Rounded notches can be accomplished in a similar manner if an experienced operator carefully holds or supports the material being notched.

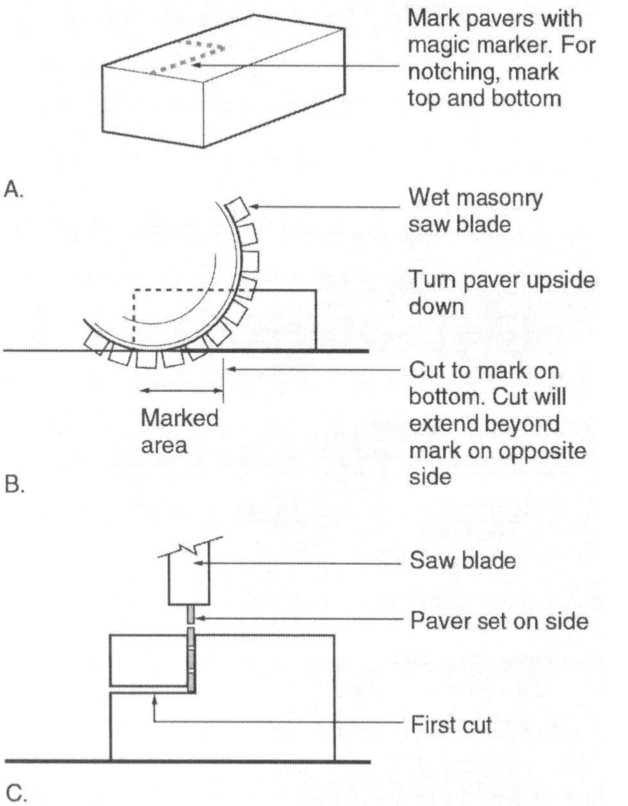

Figure 8-31 Notching pavers. (A) Marking paver. (B) First cut for a notch. (C) Second cut for a notch.

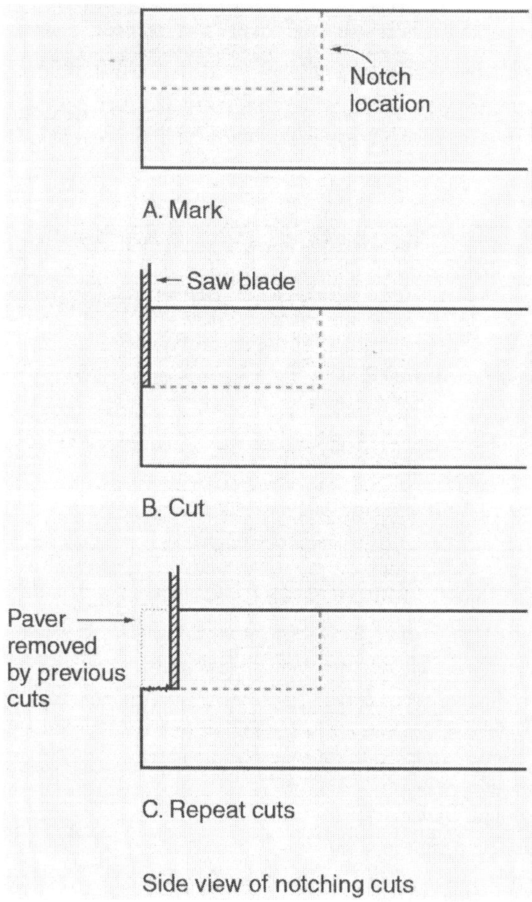

Figure 8-32 Side view of notching cuts.

Chainsaw

Wood wall products are best cut with a chainsaw. If the material requires several cuts and if you plan to use a chain saw, bring extra blades, oil, and the maintenance kit for the saw. Mark the tie/timber and place it so that the longer portion will have adequate support. Wear gloves, safety glasses, and ear protection. Use your foot to safely anchor the tie/timber or have a coworker, standing at a safe distance, hold the piece. Set the saw on the ground to start it. Rev the saw to full speed and then slowly lower it into the material.

Cut with the material close to the saw body. Avoid contacting the blade tip with any material. Move the saw with a slight rocking motion as it passes through the material. Make a square cut beginning on the top side, letting the shorter piece fall freely when cut (Figure 8-33).

Cutting Resilient Pavers

Rubber-like resilient pavers are difficult to cut using common cutting methods. Thin-bladed saws and knives work best. A pruning bow saw, hacksaw, or bread knife works best. Mount the paver in a vise to secure it while making cuts.

Alternatives to Cutting Paving Materials

In any unit paving project, the cutting of pavers is inevitable. Few projects are laid out to match the dimensions of unit pavers perfectly. Cutting can be reduced, however, if factory produced halves and edging pavers are available.

CUTTING, DRILLING, FASTENING, AND CONNECTING WOOD MATERIALS

When building decks, arbors, trellises, and other landscape elements from wood, the landscape contractor will be required to prepare and assemble a variety of wood components. This section addresses some best practices and procedures to cut, drill, fasten, and connect wood materials.

Figure 8-33 Using a chainsaw.

Cutting Wood Materials

Cutting is one of the basic carpentry techniques that is required to install wood improvements. Proper cutting begins with learning the basic cutting techniques. Four basic cuts are predominantly used in exterior carpentry—the crosscut (or square cut), miter cut, rip cut, and the bevel cut. (Figure 8-34). The square cut, the most common cut for exterior work, can be used for executing most types of joints. This cut requires the contractor to mark and remove a portion of the board at a right angle to the board's edge and face. Used in joining railing, at corners, in rafters, and in other non-square portions, and in cuts where the end grain of the lumber is not exposed, the miter cut runs at a right angle to the board's

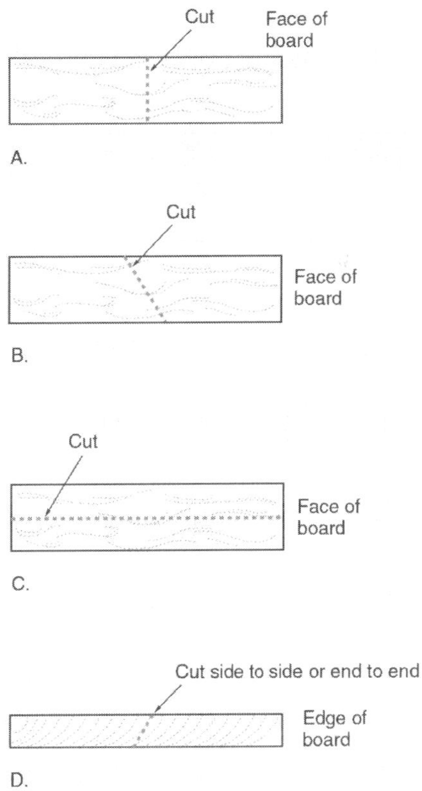

Figure 8-34 Basic lumber cuts. (A) Square crosscut. (B) Miter cut. (C) Rip cut. (D) Bevel cut.

edge but at a predetermined angle across the board's face. The rip cut runs the length of a board parallel to its edge and at a right angle to the board's edge. Any of the three previous cuts can be angled to the board's edge to create a beveled cut. The bevel cut is used when overlapping materials to prevent warping and when placing lumber on edge. Occasionally, usually in rafters, a complicated beveled miter cut may be required. This type of cut makes calculated angles to both the board's face and edge.

When marking lumber for cutting, develop the habit of using a *V* mark where the point of the *V* indicates the desired measurement. This avoids confusion as to which end of a single mark is correct. To mark cut lines with a carpenter's square, position the square with one leg resting on the cut mark and the other leg resting flush against the side of the material to be marked. If necessary, adjust the square along the board's side so that the first edge is directly on the cut mark. Hold the square firmly and draw a line

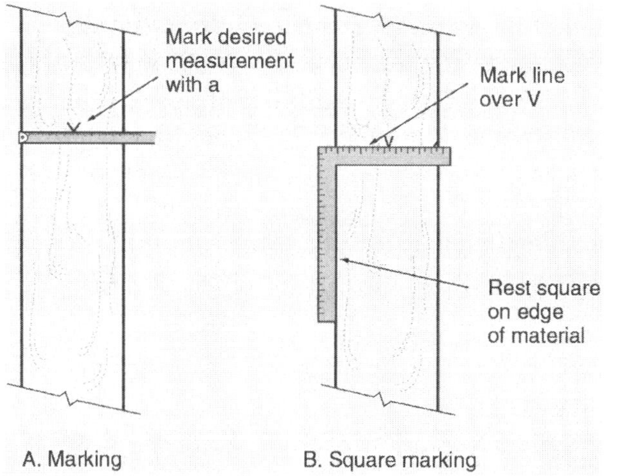

Figure 8-35 Marking dimensions and marking for square cuts.

along the edge of the square that passes through the mark (Figure 8-35).

Cutting with saws requires support for the piece of lumber. Rest the lumber on a flat, solid surface with the portion to be trimmed extending

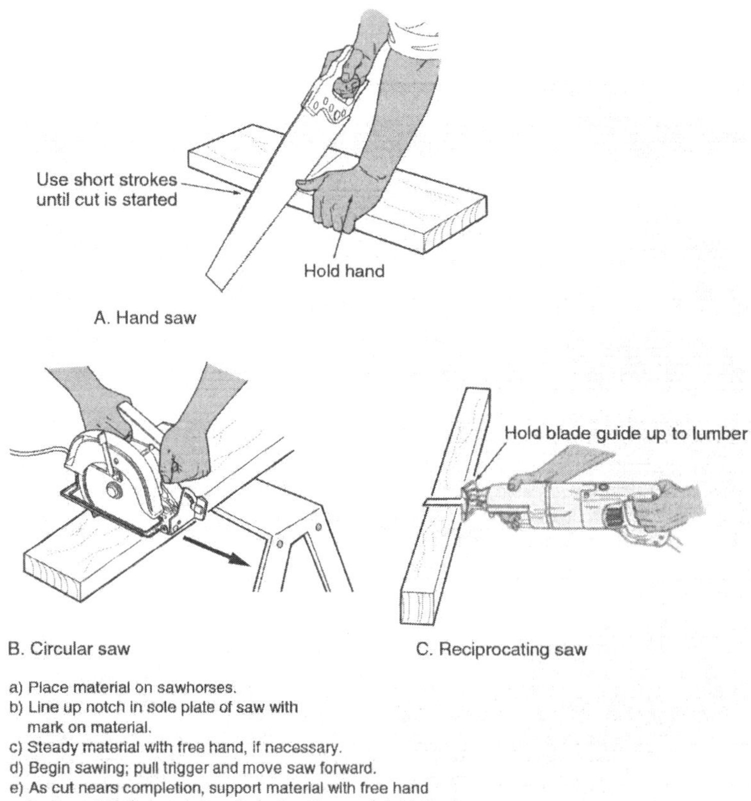

Figure 8-36 Sawing and cutting techniques.

beyond the edge of the surface. If the trimmed portion is so long that it needs to be supported by hand while cutting, be sure the support does not bind the saw blade. The holder should not grasp the piece of lumber but, instead, should place a hand below the piece and allow the wood to rest lightly. Most short pieces being trimmed can be cut without support and allowed to fall after being cut (Figure 8-36).

CAUTION

Read the manufacturer's instructions before operating power equipment.

Cutting with a Circular Saw. The direction of cut when using a circular saw should place the weight of the saw motor on the supported portion of the lumber. While sawing, position the body so that both the mark and the blade at the point of the cut can be observed. Verify that the power cord is not near the saw blade. The bottom plate of the saw should rest flat on the lumber being cut. Align the blade or directional mark on the guide with the mark on the lumber, start the saw, and run the motor to full speed; then run the saw slowly forward along the mark and through the material (Figure 8-37). When cutting thick materials such as 4 × 4s, you may need to mark both the top and bottom of the lumber. Cut the top, turn the lumber over, and make a second cut aligned with the first cut (Figure 8-38).

Notching wood materials requires using a handsaw or sabre saw to avoid overcutting the material. Notch by marking and cutting with a circular saw until the tip of the blade reaches the intersecting mark. When the blade stops, remove the circular saw and complete the cut using a sabre saw or a handsaw. Hold handsaws so that the blade is cutting straight up and down when notching.

Combination cuts require additional planning and setup. Combination cuts use two of the basic cuts described earlier, such as a beveled miter cut. Although not common in the landscaping field, the specialty technique is sometimes used when joists, rafters, and trim are placed at angles

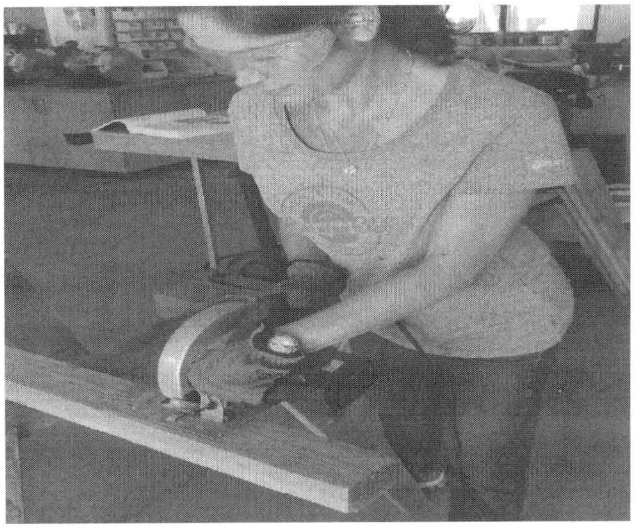

Figure 8-37 Proper cutting technique with a circular saw.

(Figure 8-39). Before executing the cut, double-check all measurements and angles to verify they are correct.

Cutting with a Sabre or Reciprocating Saw. If the cut involves the use of a **sabre,** or **reciprocating saw,** use the same procedures and

Figure 8-38 Cutting large dimensioned lumber with two cuts.

Figure 8-39 Bevel/rip cut along length of dimensioned lumber.

© Delmar/Cengage Learning.

precautions as previously described for a circular saw. The reciprocating saw, which works similarly to a large version of a sabre saw, is often used to trim pieces of lumber that have already been installed. Long blades for this saw allow access into tight corners and even allow the blade to bend slightly to saw around corners. To reduce the heavy vibration that the reciprocating saw causes, hold the blade guide firmly against the piece being cut (Figure 8-40). Trimming of posts and unanchored wood members is best accomplished with a circular saw to reduce the chance of vibrating the member out of place.

Figure 8-40 Cutting using a reciprocating saw.

© Delmar/Cengage Learning.

Cutting with a Handsaw. When using a handsaw, position the saw at the mark and hold it in position with your thumb against the saw blade. Begin with short strokes until you cut a groove along the mark that holds the saw blade in position; then pull back your thumb and extend the stroke to the full length of the blade (Figure 8-41). Downward pressure on the saw

Figure 8-41 Proper handsawing technique.

is not required to cut—let the saw blade do the work. Any piece of lumber less than 1-inch thick, including trim and lattice, should be cut using a hand miter saw or other blade type with very fine teeth.

Drilling Wood Materials

Drills are used for boring holes and driving fasteners. When drilling pilot holes, select a wood bit for small holes or a spade bit for larger diameter holes. Insert the bit into the drill and tighten securely using the chuck key. If the bit penetrates through the wood, place a block of wood under the piece being drilled. Position the bit over the hole location and hold the drill at the same angle as the desired hole. Start the drill, run motor to full speed, and apply downward pressure (Figure 8-42). If drilling deep or wide holes, you may need to pull the bit out of the hole every 2–3 seconds to clear the wood shavings out of the bit.

When using the drill to drive fasteners, install the appropriate bit for the drill. Tighten and secure the bit using the chuck key. Place the fastener on the drill bit and, while holding the fastener, position the tip at the location where the fastener is to be installed. Hold the drill and fastener at the angle desired for driving the fastener. Lightly hold the top portion of the fastener shank while slowly starting the drill. When the fastener "bites," or begins to enter into the wood, release the shank. Increase the drill speed, apply increasing downward pressure, and continue driving until the fastener is completely installed. It is important to maintain downward pressure on the drill to assure that the bit remains in contact with the fastener head; otherwise, the bit will slip out and strip the head. Maintain a straight alignment between the drill and fastener to assure solid contact between bit and fastener head (Figure 8-43).

When removing fasteners, reverse the drill direction and place the bit on the fastener head. Maintain downward pressure while removing the fastener. The friction may make fasteners hot for a few seconds after removal.

JOINING, SPLICING, AND FASTENING MATERIALS

For work that is stable and long-lasting, the landscape contractor must learn the standard techniques for joining, splicing, and fastening exterior materials. The following section addresses the best practices and procedures for accomplishing these tasks.

Joining Materials

Landscape contractors have several methods for joining materials, with two primary ways for

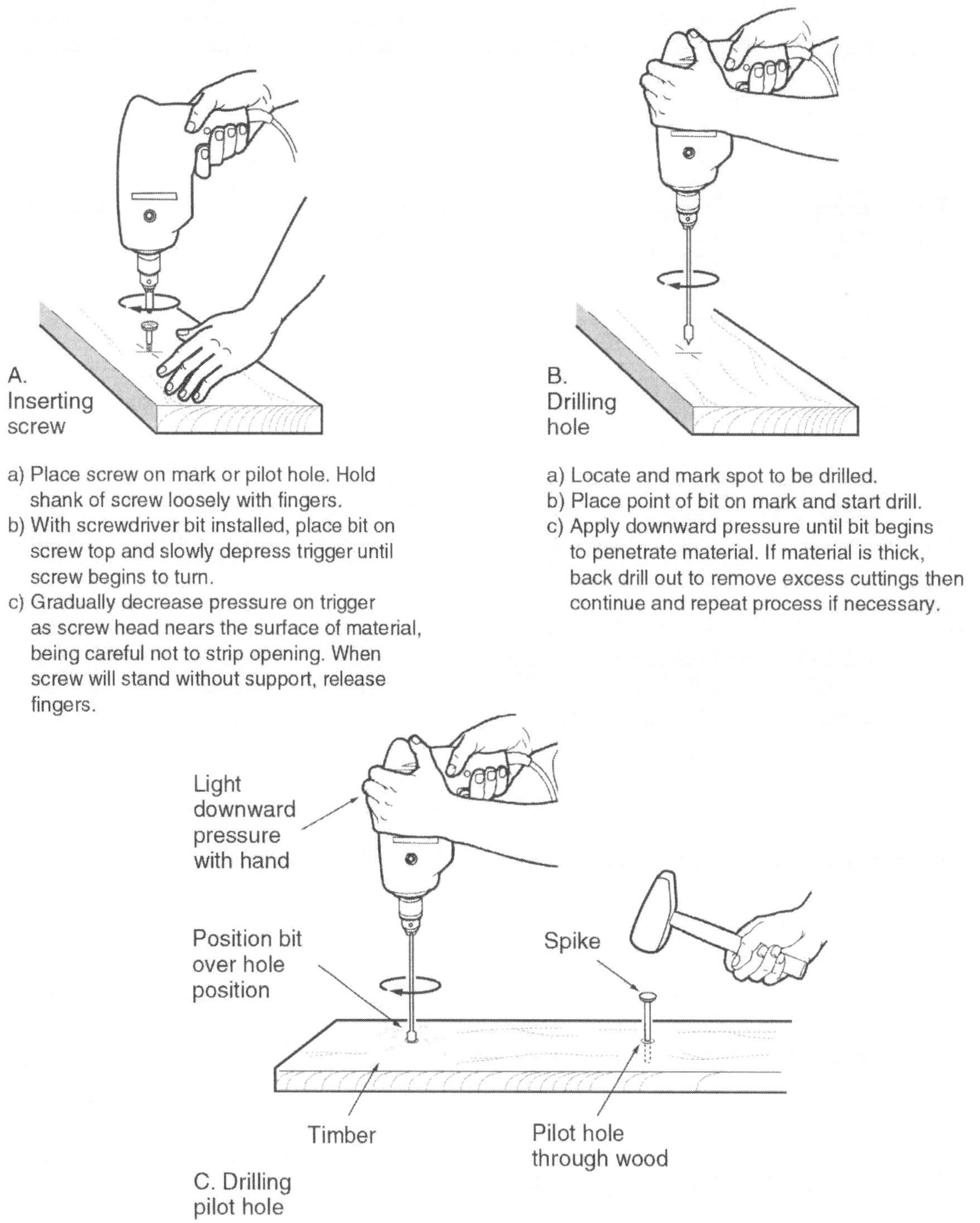

Figure 8-42 Drilling and fastening with a power drill.

exterior applications (Figure 8-44). Selection of the proper method is based on the appearance and durability required of the joint. Connecting two lumber pieces often involves placing the square ends of pieces of lumber end to end in what is called a **butt joint.** Requiring square cuts on the ends of each piece of lumber being joined, butt joints are acceptable for structural applications and work in situations where the lumber is setting

Figure 8-43 Drilling holes using a cordless drill.

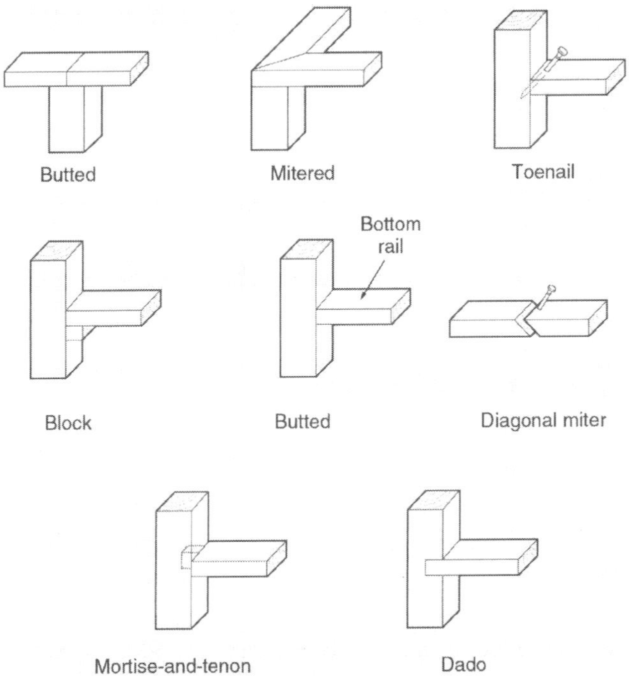

Figure 8-44 Typical lumber joining techniques.

on edge or laying flat and can be executed using direct nailing, **toenailing,** or many of the other connection techniques described in the following sections. The joint formed when cutting pieces of lumber with a miter cut and placing the angled edges together is termed a **mitered joint.** Mitered joints are typically used for appearance and practicality when pieces of lumber meet at a corner or to prevent warping along straight runs. Mitered joints can be executed with the lumber setting on edge or laying flat.

The mortise-and-tenon joint and the dado joint are among other available, but seldom used, lumber joints for exterior carpentry. These joints are seldom used because they tend to hold moisture and work counter to good drainage recommendations in exterior structures.

Splicing

Strengthening joints in structural situations may require a special technique called splicing. When one piece of lumber will not cover the length

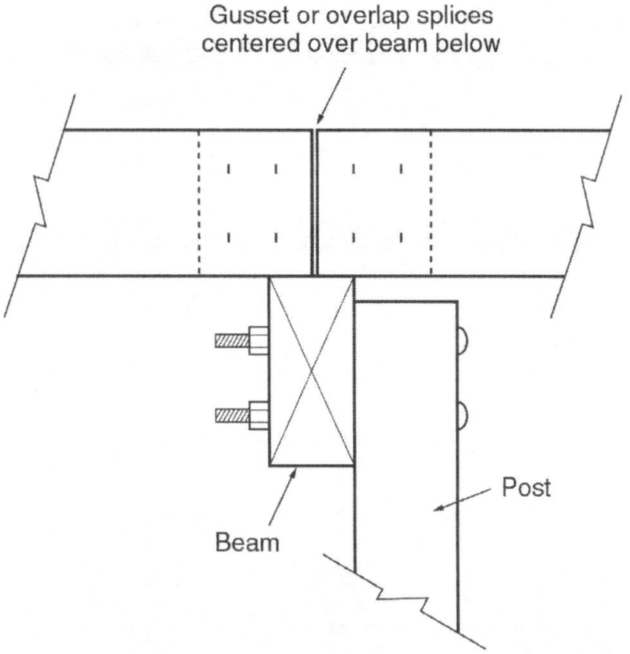

Figure 8-45 Splicing lumber begins over beams.

© Delmar/Cengage Learning.

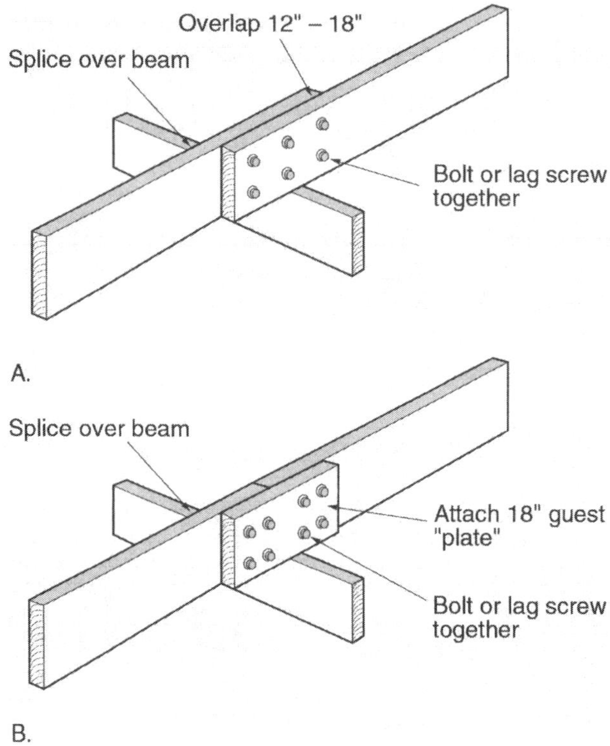

Figure 8-46 Splicing lumber. (A) Overlap splice. (B) Gusset splice.

© Delmar/Cengage Learning.

required and you must connect two pieces to make a structural support, use either the overlap or gusset method of splicing. Good planning of a project will minimize the number of splices required. However, if splicing is required, place the splice over a structural support (Figure 8-45). Unsupported splices can sag over time.

To overlap-splice two pieces of lumber, extend each piece past the end of the other by 1 foot and bolt them together. If the structural member is composed of more than two pieces, the ends of the pieces can be staggered and overlapped. A minimum of four bolts are required to make a connection, and six to eight may be required for longer spans or larger members (Figure 8-46).

If the pieces being spliced must maintain a straight alignment, you may need to install a gusset. A **gusset** is a piece of dimensioned lumber that is bolted alongside the pieces being spliced. To install a gusset, cut a 2-foot length of 2 × treated lumber the same width as the pieces being spliced. Place the gusset flush with the spliced pieces, drill pilot holes, and install a minimum of six bolts—three in each spliced piece (Figure 8-46). Placing eight bolts in a rectangular pattern will provide additional strength.

Fastening Materials

Methods for fastening wood materials continue to evolve. The basic premise for fastening remains one of providing maximum strength with appropriate efficiency. As the use of power equipment increases in the landscape contracting field, quality of workmanship has also entered into the picture. Pneumatic nail guns and screw guns have appeared, adding speed at the expense of (according to many) quality. A contractor's selection of the appropriate fastening method remains a choice based not only on strength, but also on value and workmanship.

Nailing. The most common fastening method for lumber is nailing. Except for special situations, nails should be driven at a right angle to the face of the lumber. Holding the nail lightly between

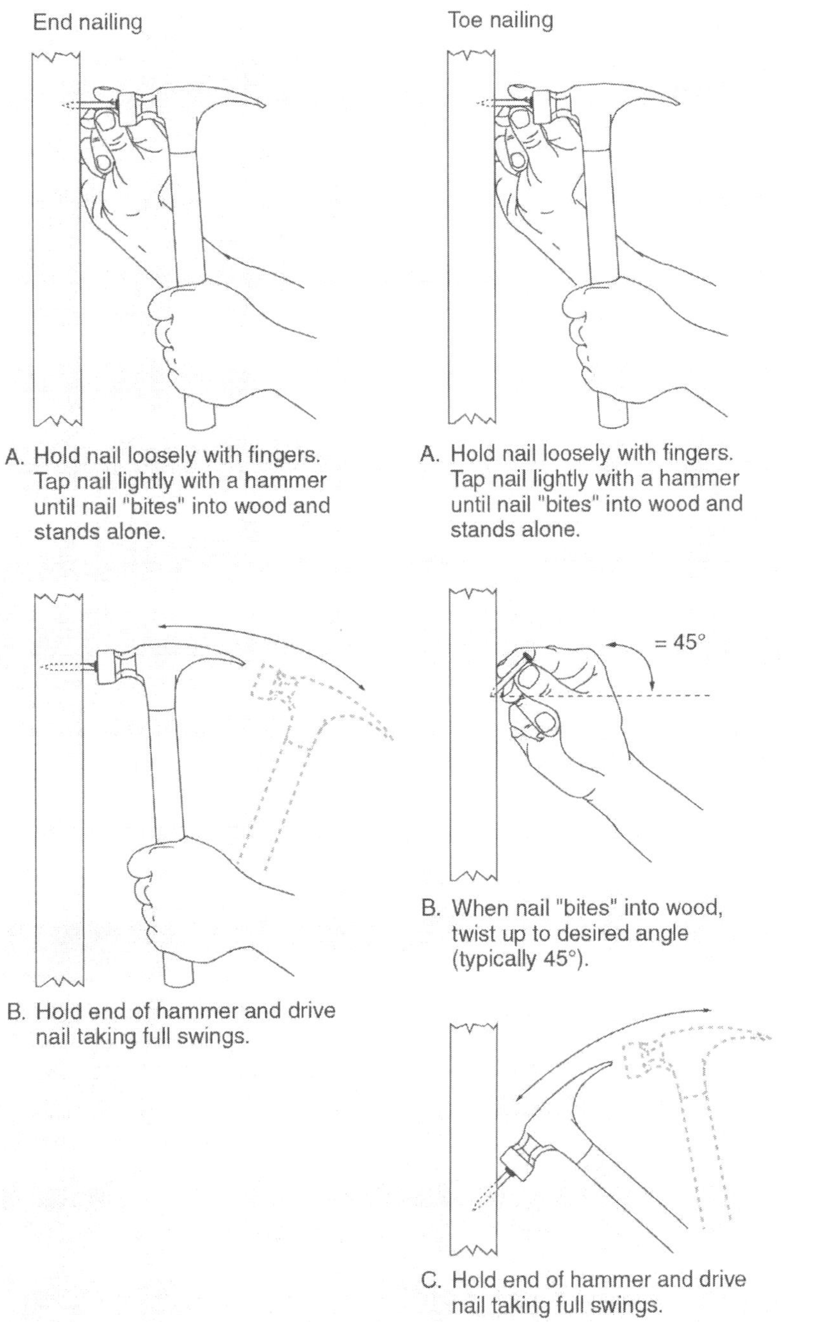

Figure 8-47 Proper hand nailing technique.

your thumb and index finger, position it at the location where the nail is to be installed. Grasp the end of the hammer handle and tap the nail until it is driven into the wood far enough that it stands on its own. Continue driving the nail, lightly at first, until the nail begins to enter the wood, and then with full force, until the head is flush with the piece of lumber. Effective use of the hammer's leverage requires that it be grasped at the end of the handle, not near the head (Figure 8-47). To avoid missing or misdriving the nail, focus your eyes on the head of the nail during the entire driving process.

When fastening wood members that butt against each other, use either end nailing or toenailing (Figures 8-47 and 8-48). A warning

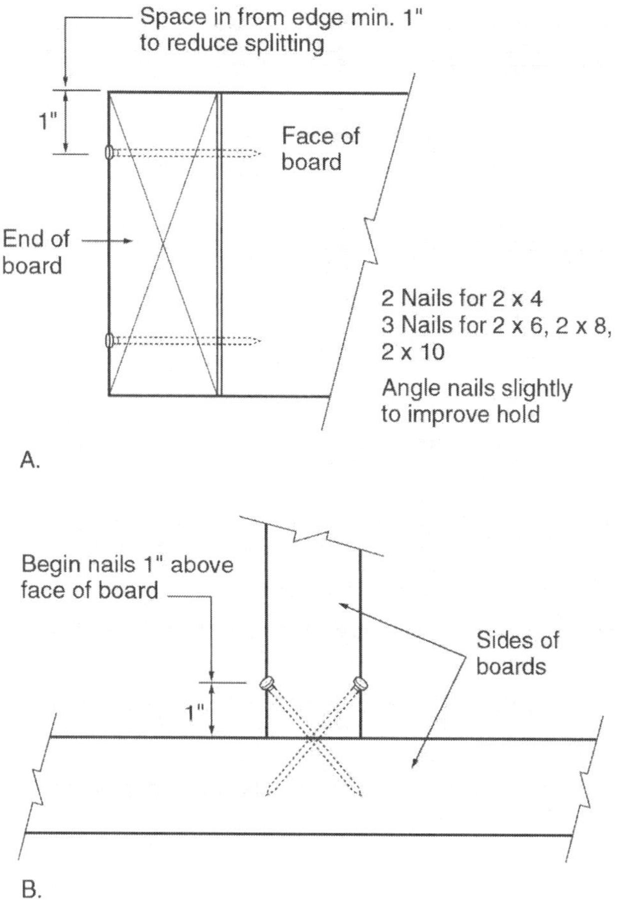

Figure 8-48 Nailing lumber. (A) End nailing. (B) Toenailing.

about connections of this type: End nailing is not a strong connection because the nail enters the lumber parallel to the grain. Review all alternatives for fastening wood members before making your selection. End nailing is accomplished by driving nails through the face of one piece of lumber into the end of the other.

Slightly angling the nail will strengthen the connection. When one piece of lumber butts against another piece that is thicker than the length of the nails, toenail the pieces together. Toenailing requires driving the nail at a 45-degree angle through the face of one piece of lumber into the face of the second piece. To toenail properly, position the nail back from the second piece about one-third the length of the nail. Drive the nail lightly into the first piece at a right angle. When the nail bites into the surface of the first piece, tilt the nail to the 45-degree angle and complete driving the nail. Toenailing will require holding the first piece of lumber in proper position so that it does not shift when driving the nail. When improperly done, toenailing can also create a weak connection.

When you are nailing into pieces of unsupported lumber, the wood tends to bounce, which makes driving the nail difficult. If you position another hammer or baby sledgehammer against the wood on the opposite side from which you are hammering, the second hammer's weight will absorb some of the bounce. Start the nail and then drive the nail with one hammer while holding the second hammer with your free hand.

Nailing can easily split thin lumber such as lath and lattice. Examine the end of the nail and observe that the point is diamond shaped. Orient the long dimension of the diamond perpendicular to the wood's grain to reduce splitting (Figure 8-49).

Screwing. Fastening materials with screws provides an extra measure of strength that nails do not offer. As weather and extremes in temperatures move the wood around, nails tend to pull out from the wood pieces they are

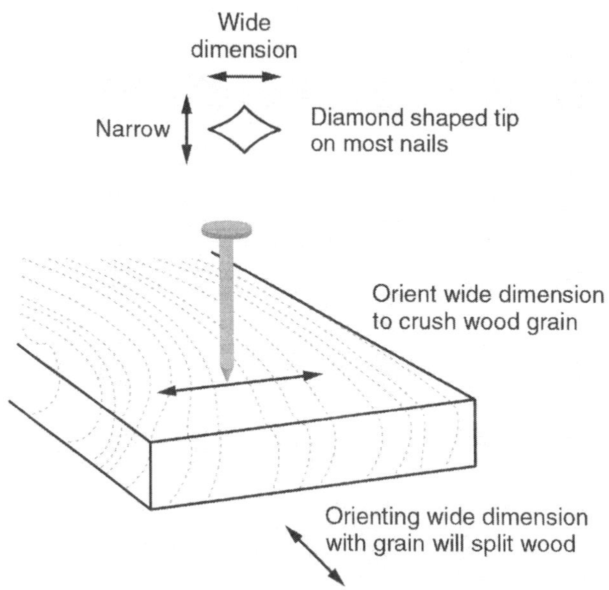

Figure 8-49 Orienting nails to reduce lumber splitting.

connecting. Screws remain in position despite minor structure movements. The variety of shapes, materials, and sizes makes screws a practical choice for aesthetic, as well as structural, connections.

Installation of screws is best executed by positioning the piece of lumber, temporarily nailing it if necessary, and drilling a pilot hole.

The pilot hole should be slightly smaller than the diameter of the screw shank. The pilot hole and screw installation should be at right angles to the board's face and edge. Some woods are soft enough to be fastened without the pilot hole. Regardless of wood type, drill pilot holes if working within 2 inches of the end of the board or within 1 inch of the board's edge, if using screws with a shank diameter of 1/4 inch or more, or when using any carriage bolt. Holding the screw by the end, hand twist the screw into the pilot hole to start the connection. Continue twisting the screw into position using hand or power tools, lightly holding the smooth portion of the shank until the screw can stand in the pilot hole without assistance (Figure 8-50). Screw holders that eliminate the need to handhold the fastener are available. Attach the screw holder in the same manner you would attach a drill bit; then insert screws into the holder.

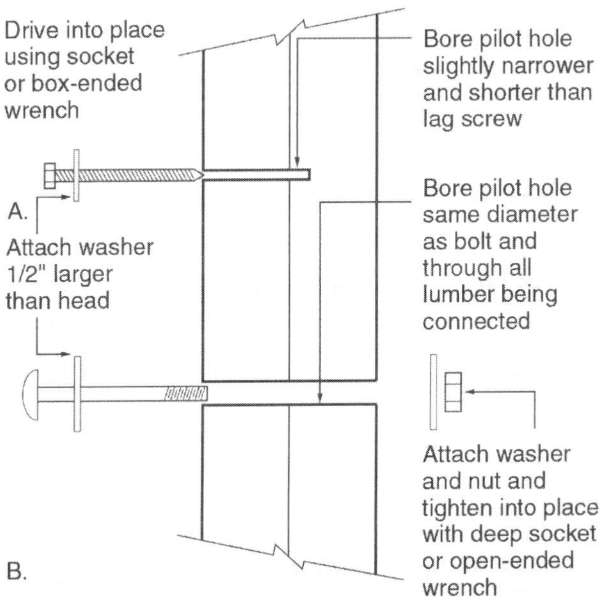

Figure 8-50 Installing lag screws and carriage bolts. (A) Lag screw. (B) Carriage bolt.

Bolting. Although they make strong structural connections, bolts are seldom used for surfacing or aesthetic situations. To install bolts, position the piece of lumber, temporarily nailing it in place if necessary. At the location where the bolt is to be located, drill a pilot hole that is slightly larger than the diameter of the bolt though all lumber pieces being connected. Select galvanized carriage bolts that are 1 inch longer than the combined thickness of all lumber pieces being connected. Drive the bolt through the hole (Figure 8-50). Whenever possible, the head of the bolt should be located on the side where the public will view the connection. Install a washer and nut on the opposite side and tighten. Check alignment and elevations before completely tightening the bolt.

Gluing. Gluing exterior connections is limited to locations that will not be exposed to moisture. Use exterior glues, which are resistant to exposure, for fastening caps and surface trim when other fasteners will not work.

> **CAUTION**
>
> Unsafe operation of equipment can cause injury or death. Read the instructions and obtain safety and operation training before operating any equipment. The instructions listed below provide a general overview of each category of equipment. Verify the specific requirements for the specific piece of equipment you plan to operate. Before working on any gas-powered equipment, disconnect the spark plug wire. Always keep all safety guards on equipment, and never place any body part near moving equipment parts. Wear appropriate personal protection equipment.

Avoiding Problems with Connections

When making connections, consider alternatives that will reduce damage to the wood or structural failure. When connectors are installed near the ends or edges of boards, the lumber could split.

The best solution is to predrill pilot holes slightly smaller than the connector's diameter. Dulling the end of the nail, or turning the nail so that the wide point of the diamond tip is perpendicular to the board's edge, may also help (Figure 8-49).

Structural failure can result from using too few connectors or spacing them improperly in a piece of lumber. Having too few connectors may result in structural failure or instability, whereas improper spacing may weaken the lumber. Figure 8-51 identifies typical nailing and bolting patterns that should provide improved strength.

RELATED POWER EQUIPMENT

To implement their projects, landscape contractors use a variety of equipment, some handoperated and others powered by other means. Although many pieces of power equipment were described earlier in this section, there are additional tools, including gasand pneumatic-powered equipment, used to prepare a site and to fasten materials.

General Notes Regarding Gas-Powered Equipment

Many pieces of equipment listed in this section have gas-powered, two-stroke engines. Unlike larger pieces of equipment that have automatic starters and take regular fuel, two-stroke engines often have special requirements for operation. Before operating, verify whether the piece of equipment uses an oil/gas mixture (common in most small engines such as those found on mowers and string trimmers) or whether the equipment has separate tanks for oil and gas. Placing the wrong fuel mixture into the tank can ruin the equipment when operated.

When starting a two-stroke engine that is cold (has not been run for a period of time), the operator will typically have to apply the choke lever to enrich the fuel mixture reaching the engine. Apply the choke and attempt to start the equipment; and when it starts or sounds like it is about to start, disengage the choke. For equipment that utilizes pull-cord starting, make sure the equipment is securely anchored before pulling the cord. When pulling the cord, pull the cord lightly out until you feel resistance from the engine; then complete the pull with a sharp snapping motion.

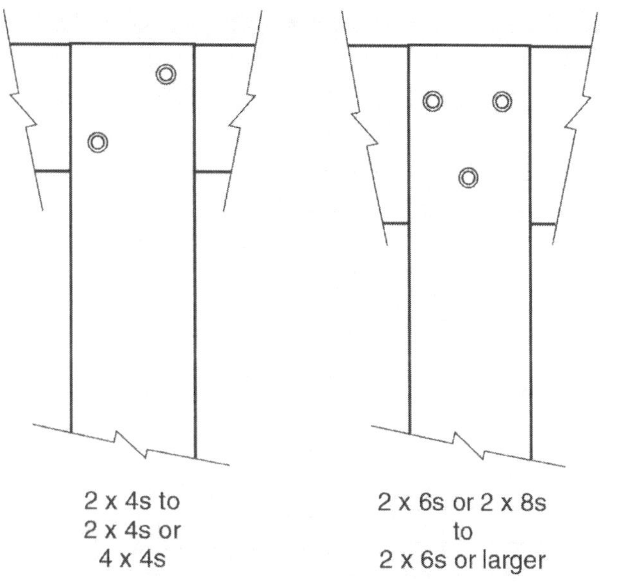

Figure 8-51 Fastening patterns that provide maximum stability.

Portable Generator

When working on new construction or remodeling sites, landscape contractors are often without power for all or part of the project duration. To provide power for the job site, many contractors use a portable generator. Portable generators are typically gas-powered motors that turn a generator to provide electrical power through outlets mounted on the equipment (Figure 8-52). Before operating a portable generator, check the piece of equipment to verify that it is in good working condition and that all fluid levels are correct. Turn the engine switch on, choking if necessary. Pull the start cord until the engine engages; then set the throttle to the full setting. You may now plug electrical cords into the outlets on the generator.

Air Compressor

Air compressors are necessary to power pneumatic tools. Most air compressors have an electric motor that places air in a storage tank under high pressure. The pressure from this air

Figure 8-52 Portable generator showing outlets for power cords.

tank then passes through pneumatic hoses to the equipment. To operate the typical air compressor, make sure all valves to the compressor tank are closed. Set the pressure release valve for the desired pressure (dictated by the type of equipment). Plug the compressor into a power source and turn on the motor. Compressors typically shut off when the desired range of pressures is reached. Hoses are typically attached using quick-connect fittings that require the user to pull the socket sleeve back, slide the fitting over the plug, then release the socket sleeve to securely connect the hose (Figure 8-53). Perform all regular maintenance required by the compressor manufacturer to maintain proper working order. This may include draining moisture from the pressure tank on a regular basis. Disconnect the equipment from the compressor, and unplug the compressor when not in use. Some pneumatic equipment requires that lubricant be added to the pressure tank.

Pneumatic- and Battery-Powered Nailing and Screwing Tools

For large carpentry projects; using powered nailing and screwing tools is more efficient than using hand tools. Large projects include framing projects, decks of over 500 SF, and installation of deck screws on large decks. Powered nailing and screwing equipment can use air from compressors or from portable cylinders, or they can operate on battery power. Regardless of the power source, most operate in a similar manner. For both types of equipment, load and service the equipment with the power source detached. Nailers deliver nails from a nail cartridge stored in a housing sleeve. Place the delivery tip of the nailer where desired and push down on the tool to depress a trigger in the tip (Figure 8-54). Then squeeze the trigger and the nail is driven into the materials being fastened. A screw gun works in a similar manner. Placing the delivery tip where desired and push down to depress a trigger in the

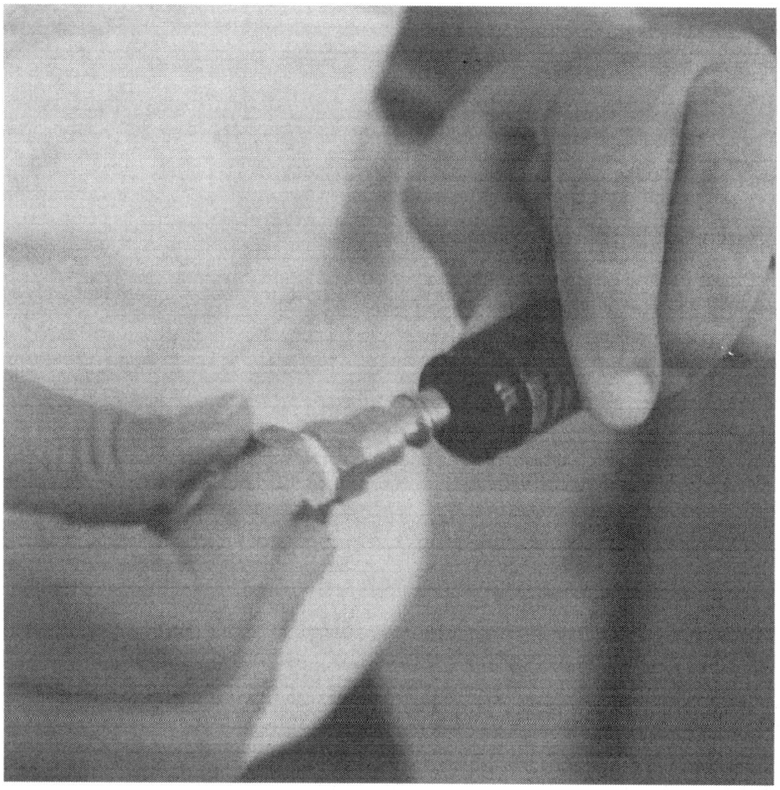

Figure 8-53 Air compressor fitting. Pull the socket sleeve (on the right) back and slide it over the plug (on the left); then release the sleeve to secure the fitting.

Figure 8-54 Pneumatic nailer showing the tip where the fastener is discharged.

tip. Then depress and hold the trigger until the screw is installed. Use caution when operating any powered nailing and screwing equipment. NEVER aim the tool in a direction where it is not intended to deliver a nail or screw.

Sod Cutter

The sod cutter is invaluable in removing and salvaging large areas of turf from a construction site. A self-propelled, gas-powered motor with an oscillating blade, the sod cutter works by running the equipment over a lawn in a pattern similar to a lawn mower. The blade severs the sod from its roots just below the rhizome level. Before operating the cutter, set the blade to the desired depth of cut and carefully plan the route for removing the sod. When operating the sod cutter on mild slopes, always work perpendicular to the slope. Avoid operating on steep slopes (over 3 feet run to 1 foot rise).

To operate the equipment, place the transmission in neutral and turn off the blade. Start the engine and engage the transmission at low speed. Maneuver the sod cutter to the desired starting point and place the transmission in neutral. Engage the cutting blade and increase the throttle; then place the transmission in gear. Guide the cutter as it moves along the planned route. You may need to exert downward pressure on the handles to force the blade under the sod at the beginning of a pass. Alternately, remove a swath of sod along the ends of each run to make it easier to get the blade under the turf. When reaching the end of a row or finished cutting, place the transmission in neutral and disengage the blade. Place the equipment in gear and move it off the site when finished. The sod may now be rolled or stacked for reuse or composting.

Rototiller

A valuable tool, the rototiller can loosen soil for a gardening project. Most rototillers are self-propelled engines mounted on top of a series of rotating blades. Some rototillers have transmissions with both forward and reverse; others offer only a forward gear. Before operating the equipment, plan the excavation so that you know the boundaries of the tilled area. Operate the equipment perpendicular to slopes and avoid steep slopes (over 3 feet run to 1 foot rise) with tillers.

To operate a rototiller, position the equipment at the location where tilling is to begin. Make sure the transmission is in neutral and the blades are disengaged. Start the engine and engage the blades. Increase the throttle, place the transmission in gear, and guide the tiller along the desired path. Maintain a firm grip on the handles of the tiller to maintain control of the machine. In many cases, you must hold the tiller back to achieve the desired depth of excavation, letting the machine "eat" slowly forward. When finished tilling, put the transmission in neutral and disengage the blades. Place the transmission in gear and move it off site.

Trencher

Installation of irrigation lines often requires extensive trenching. A gas-powered trencher may be appropriate when several linear feet of main and laterals must be installed. Trenchers use a gas engine to power cutting teeth around a blade, with a screw attachment that throws soil to the side of the trench. Many trenchers have a transmission with forward and reverse gears.

Unlike many pieces of equipment, trenchers work by pulling the cutting blades, rather than having the cutting tool on the front. You must work with your back to your work in many situations. Prior to using a trencher, plan the location of all trenches. Verify location of all utilities prior to trenching.

To operate the trencher, position the trencher at the beginning of the excavation. Make sure the transmission is in neutral and start the engine. Increase the throttle, engage the blade, and engage the transmission. Maintain a careful grip on the handles as the equipment slowly cuts along the planned route. When reaching the end of a trench, place the equipment in neutral and disengage the blade. Place the equipment in gear and move to the next trench or off site. Use extreme care when moving and turning the trencher because the blade extends well beyond the piece of equipment. If the blade hits them, improvements or plant material can be severely damaged.

Rotary Concrete Mixer

On the occasions that you need a small amount of concrete for a job, a portable mixer may be more efficient than hand mixing or paying short load charges for ready mix. A portable mixer has an electrical motor turning a rotating drum that has a large opening for adding and removing materials (Figure 8-55). The drum rotates and tilts, usually by hand, using a geared wheel that allows the operator to adjust the speed of the mixing and dumping. Before operating the mixer, verify that it is located on a stable level area and that there is access to the mixer for wheelbarrows or skid-steer. Also make sure that there is a place to clean the mixer without harming existing elements and new improvements to a site.

To operate the mixer, place the angle of the drum at approximately 45 degrees. Add ingredients to be mixed, plug in the mixer, and start the rotation. Add water to the drum as the ingredients mix. If ingredients are not mixing, lower the angle of the drum. When the batch is completely mixed, place a wheelbarrow under the open drum and lower the angle until the mix flows out. When the wheelbarrow is filled, raise the drum and remove the wheelbarrow. Leave the drum rotating until the entire batch has been emptied. Never place any body part or piece of equipment inside the drum while it is rotating. To avoid dumping the load, have a worker positioned to stabilize the wheelbarrow when the batch is emptied. Watch for spatter from the drum while it is mixing and while it empties.

CAUTION

When using a power washer, never aim the equipment at a person, object, or property that is not the target of the washing operation. Mask off all surfaces that may be damaged by the high-powered water stream. Always wear proper personal safety equipment, including eye protection, when operating a power sprayer.

Figure 8-55 Emptying the drum of a rotary concrete mixer.

Power Washer

Cleaning decks, concrete surfaces, and paved areas is easier using a portable power washer. Powered with a gas motor, the power washer is a pump that increases the normal water pressure available from a garden hose spigot. Most power washers are portable and come with a range of nozzles that produce concentrated steams to wide fans of spray. The nozzles are attached to a trigger-operated wand. To operate the power washer, verify that you have a hose that will reach the sprayer. Install the nozzle you wish to spray with, and connect the sprayer hose and wand to the outlet side of the pump. Connect a garden hose to the inlet side of the pump, but do not turn the water on until the pump is started. Start the pump and turn on the water from the garden hose. Aim the wand and pull the trigger to begin washing.

CHAPTER 9

CONSTRUCTION LAYOUT

OBJECTIVES

By reading and practicing the techniques described in this chapter, the reader should be able to successfully complete the following activities:

- Locate proposed improvements on a construction site.
- Determine the grade of proposed improvements on a site.

Regardless of a project's size, contractors will need to identify the location and elevation of the landscape elements to be constructed. Determining how to perform construction staking work will require a judgment regarding the complexity of the project and the level of accuracy required. If the project involves only a short walkway, hiring a land surveyor would be inefficient. On the other hand, it would be challenging to measure a large project with only a tape measure. Construction staking addresses techniques used in locating improvements on the site, establishing the elevation of improvements, and locating plant material. Each of these three construction staking requirements uses different approaches and should be performed in a logical order.

Locating improvements in the horizontal plane is typically performed first, followed by establishing the vertical elevation. These first two steps need to be completed before construction begins and may require that improvements be measured and restaked several times during the project. Location of landscape plantings is typically completed later in the construction process, often after finish grading has been completed.

Projects that may require restaking several times benefit from establishing permanent reference points, or control points. Horizontal plane reference points depend on the type of location method used. Typical references are corners of structures, edges of roadways, fence lines, baselines, or other permanent improvements that can be accessed and will not be disturbed by the construction. If existing permanent improvements do not exist on a site, establish reference points by driving fenceposts into the ground and painting them for visibility.

Although at least three such reference points are required for most construction staking systems, more locations will be beneficial. Vertical measurements should be controlled by a benchmark, or permanent marker, where the elevation is known. Benchmarks for projects can be set on existing foundations, fire hydrants, manhole covers, or other objects that will remain throughout construction, will not move, and can be seen from locations where a level will be established.

LAYOUT EQUIPMENT

Layout of work requires the use of specialized equipment designed to make the work easier and more accurate. The amount of layout you perform, the accuracy required by the projects, and the cost of the equipment determine the choice of equipment. Typical layout equipment includes the following (Figure 9-1):

- Tapes. A tape measure is an essential piece of equipment for all contractors. Useful in measuring horizontal and vertical distances, handy to carry, and marked for levels of accuracy acceptable to almost every building trade, the tape measure remains the one indispensable piece of equipment for layout. Landscape contractors may need tapes that measure in both feet/inches and feet/tenths. Having at least one tape that measures distances of

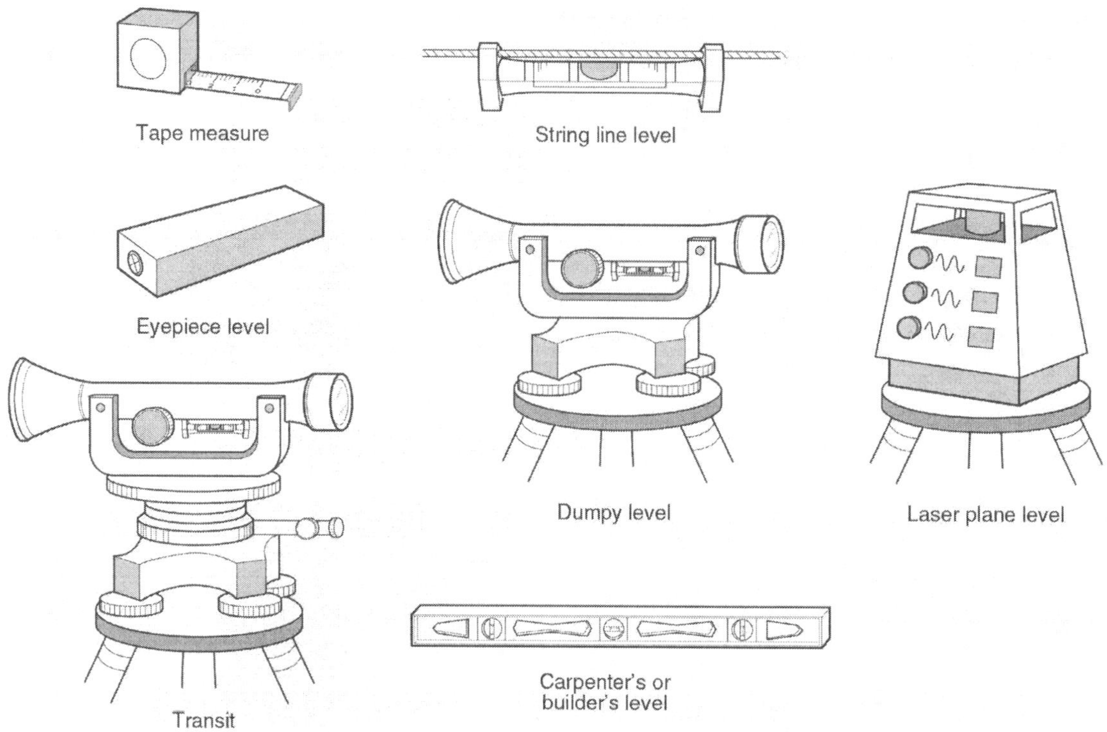

Figure 9-1 Layout equipment and tools.

100 feet or more is also advisable. If only one person measures or marks, having a large screwdriver to anchor the zero end of the tape will be handy.

- Builder's Levels. Builder's levels allow contractors to determine slope, plumb, and, in advanced models, angles with a high degree of accuracy. The effectiveness of a level can be increased by selecting a piece of dimensioned lumber that is straight and resting the level on top of the board. This technique is common for determining grade for walks and paved areas.
- String or Line Levels. A string level is a simple bubble level that hangs from a line stretched between two points. String levels are handy for determining slope or level for paved areas, walks, decks, and other landscape elements that require a consistent grade between two points.
- Electronic Measurement Tools. A single operator can use electronic measurement tools in many exterior applications. Laser measurement devices project a light beam toward the object being measured to obtain a dimension. Depending on the model, exterior laser measurement tools are capable of measuring distances up to 500 feet and will, in addition, measure slopes up to 45 degrees. The battery-operated tools often provide a magnified rangefinder and project a clear light point, making operation by a single operator possible. Many models include calculator functions programmed into the device and come with tripods for more stable operation.
- Clinometer. The **clinometer** (also called inclinometer or tilt sensor) is a visual device used to measure the degree of slope. Looking through a lens, the surveyor can sight along the slope and see

the degree of slope reflected in a mirror from a vernier mounted on the instrument.

- Dumpy Level. **Dumpy levels** also known as auto levels, are tripod-mounted focal instruments that provide a magnified eyepiece for the contractor to look through. The dumpy level has crosshairs that allow accurate measurement at long distances without serious distortion. The level and tripod are also adjustable, allowing contractors to set up on a variety of terrains. A surveyor's rod, a vertical stick with measurements, or a tape measure is required to complete measurements with this level.
- Eyepiece Level. The eyepiece level is a small, handheld version of the dumpy level. Because of its limited accuracy, this tool is used only to establish rough grades for planting or turf areas and rough grading. A rod or tape measure is required to complete measurements with this instrument.
- Laser Plane Level. The **laser plane level** is a technological advancement from the optical level. When properly set up, a laser plane level sends out a rotating beam of high-intensity light in a plane that matches the instrument's height. A receptor mounted on a survey rod then picks up the light beam. The laser plane level allows the measuring and marking of elevations without requiring an operator to focus through the telescope eyepiece, hence improving the speed and accuracy of measurement.
- Robotic Surveying Stations. Robotic surveying stations use laser and servomotor technology to implement site surveying and layout. The surveyor carries a survey pole with a prism that is "tracked," or followed by an unmanned survey instrument. Using a laser or infrared beam, the instrument can calculate the location and elevation of points that the surveyor requests. The information is transferred between survey rod and instrument via radio waves. Robotic stations can be used for layout if adequate control points are established.
- Transit. **Transits** are dumpy levels that provide a means for measuring horizontal and vertical angles. Used by surveyors, such instruments are useful if working on a steep site or when making measurements from a single point. A process called **stadia** uses the eyepiece crosshairs to measure both level and distance in one step.

CAUTION

Do not look directly at the light beam emitted by the laser plane level, robotic survey instrument, electronic measurement tool, or any tool using laser or infrared for measurement.

LAYOUT AND MEASUREMENT TECHNIQUES

Following in this section are suggestions that will make layout work easier and more accurate.

Measuring Distances

Measuring distances in open spaces requires the location of a beginning point, then stretching a measuring tape straight in the desired direction to locate the required dimension. Mark the beginning and ending points to preserve the location until no longer needed.

Using Electronic Measurement Tools. Although extremely accurate, laser measuring devices have limitations. The device selected must be engineered to work in exterior applications, and the maximum measureable distance must be adequate to cover dimensions of your project. Many objects can be measured by aiming the device directly at the object being measured. However, if the measurement is long (typically over 300 feet), the activity may require a second person to hold or position a target plate to reflect the beam. Nontarget items, such as brush or trees, may also affect measurement with a laser device.

To use the laser distance measuring devices, power up the instrument and verify that all settings are correct according to the manufacturer's instructions. Stand at the point where the measurement is to start and aim the instrument at the point where the measurement is to end. Activate the laser and read the measurement on the instrument's digital readout.

Using Global Positioning Systems (GPS). When measuring sites with extreme overgrowth or severe grade changes, contractors may use a **global positioning system (GPS)** to locate horizontal and vertical dimensions. GPS uses signals from satellites to triangulate the sender's position. Using a hand instrument or backpack-mounted instrument with design data already loaded into it, the person who is staking is guided about the site to key locations. Although GPS has limited accuracy for detailed layout, it can locate general improvements with an acceptable degree of accuracy. One advantage of GPS is that it reduces the need for brashing, or the clearing of brush along a survey line.

Measuring Short Slopes

Select a long, straight 2 × 4 and lay one end at the top of the slope. Place a builder's level on the 2 × 4 and adjust the board up or down until it is level. Using a tape measure, measure the distance from the bottom of the 2 × 4 to the toe of the slope. This distance is the fall of the slope (also referred to as the *V* in some formulas) (Figure 9-2). The run, or horizontal distance, can also be calculated by hooking your tape over the end of the 2 × 4. Holding the 2 × 4 level, measure along the board until directly above the toe of the slope.

Measuring Long Slopes

When slopes exceed lengths of 10 feet, elevation measurements using a straight 2 × 4 and level are difficult. To measure long slopes, use mason's twine anchored at the top of the slope with a screwdriver. Stretch the mason's twine to the bottom of the slope and hang a string level on the twine. Holding the twine level, extend a measuring tape from the twine to the ground to obtain the slope's vertical measurement.

If the slope is steep, you may have to repeat this process several times. For subsequent measurements, always move the screwdriver holding the twine to the location where the measuring tape contacted the ground in the previous measurement. Add all measurements to obtain the slope's vertical dimension.

Measuring Slopes with a Clinometer

The clinometer (discussed above under "Layout Equipment") is a device for measuring angles above and below an artificial horizon. Contractors use the clinometer to measure the angle of slopes for wall and stair construction, as well as for grading, and to calculate the angle/height of vertical objects in the landscape.

Compass Clinometer. Holding the compass clinometer in the vertical position, sight along the instrument with both eyes. One eye reads the scale inside the hole on the clinometer, and the other eye sights along the slope to be measured (or slightly above it to accommodate your height). The horizontal band aligns with the slope, and the slope measurement is read on the scale.

Abney Spirit Level Clinometer. An Abney clinometer is an eyepiece mounted on an adjustable tubular spirit level, which is also connected to a vertical scale (Figure 9-3). To use the Abney, you look through the eyepiece and align the crosshairs (horizontal index line) with the slope being measured. Next to the crosshairs is a reflected image of the spirit level. Adjust the level until the bubble is centered and aligned with the crosshairs. The angle is then read on the vernier scale.

Electronic Clinometers. Available to the industrial, navigation, and aircraft industries, electronic versions of clinometers perform precise measurements of inclination and slope. Although these instruments are highly accurate, they are not directly applicable to landscape operations.

Figure 9-2 Determining slope by holding a level board from the high point and measuring from the bottom of the board to the low point.

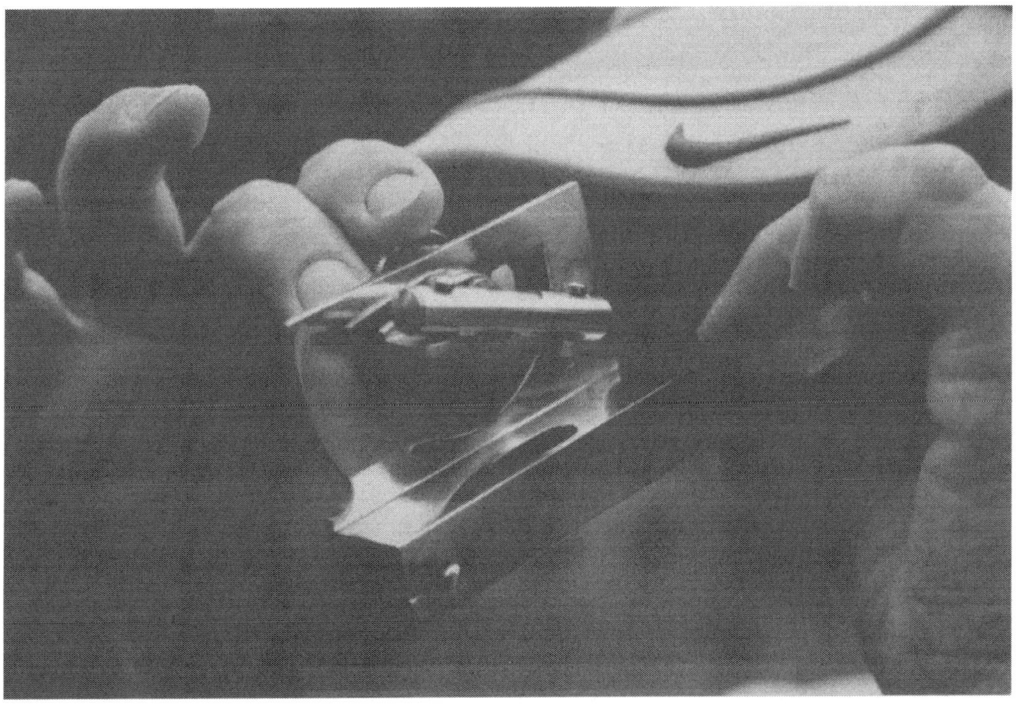

Figure 9-3 Using a clinometer to measure the angle of a slope.

Using Offsets

Another component of project layout is establishing accurate layout markings that do not interfere with the construction. To accomplish this, the construction markings made on a project may use the concept of offset. **Offset** places the stake or identification for the improvement at a consistent, predetermined distance and direction from where the improvement is to be actually installed. Typical offsets may place the construction stakes 5 feet outside of where the improvement should be placed (Figure 9-4). Dictated by project conditions, actual distance and direction should be consistent throughout the project. A common form of offsetting horizontal and vertical markings is the use of **batterboards,** which are ideal for many aspects of landscape construction, especially the building of decks, structures, and paved areas. Construction of batterboards is covered under "Location of Improvements" in this chapter.

Floating Dimensions

Dimensions labeled with a plus or minus sign in front of them are considered floating dimensions. Floating dimensions provide flexibility in locating the actual object being measured; that is, they accommodate the lack of accurate existing measurements. An object labeled with floating dimensions may also be located in another manner, such as being aligned with other objects or adjacent to a fixed object.

Locating Points with Triangulation

To locate a single point on a site, you can use the triangulation method. To perform this measurement, locate two known points within a short distance of the object to be located. Measure from each known point to the object to be located. On a plan that shows the two known points, draw an arc from each the distance measured. Where the arcs cross is the location of the unknown point (Figure 9-5). You can reverse this process to locate an object in the field. Measure from two known points on a plan to the object to be located. Find those known points in the field and swing the arc from each the distance measured. Where the arcs cross is the unknown point.

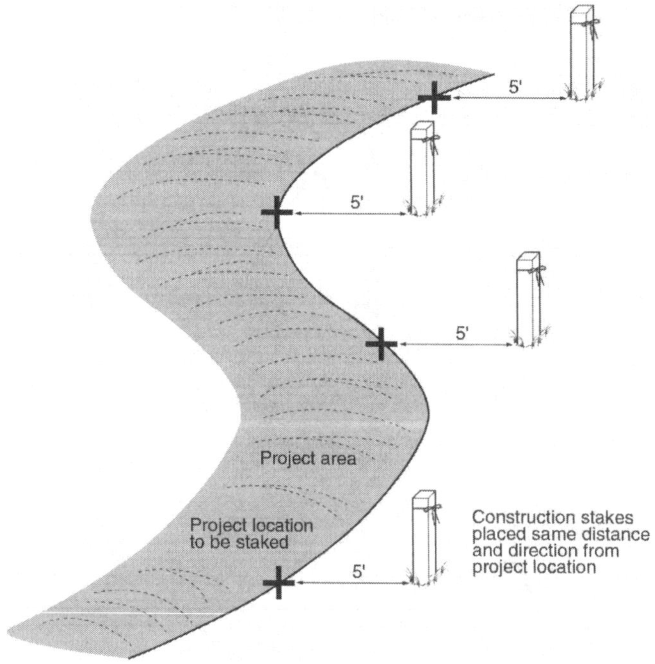

Figure 9-4 Staking with offsets to reduce restaking time.

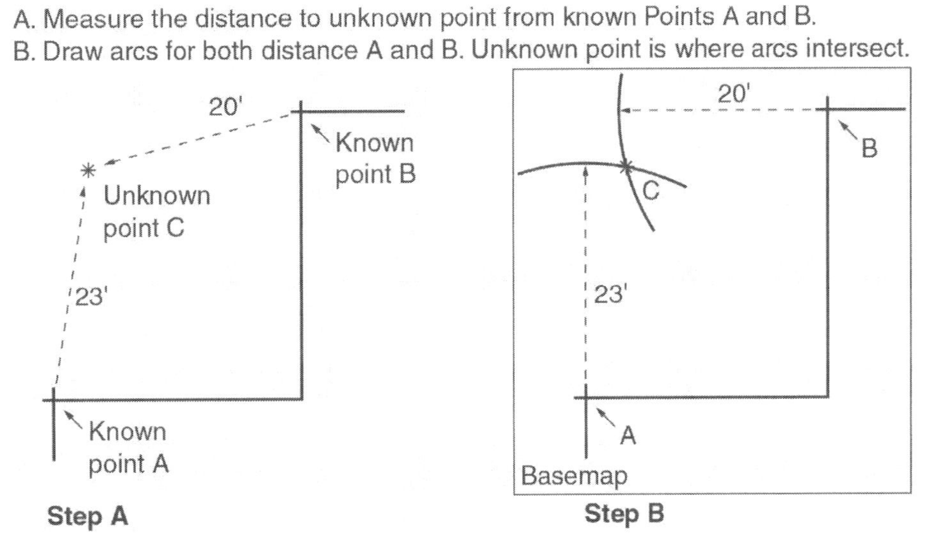

Figure 9-5 Locating objects using triangulation.

Laying Out Right Angles with the 3,4,5 Triangle

Determining if an angle is exactly 90 degrees can be difficult in field construction. Using a carpenter's square will help for small elements; but when laying out a large paved area, the square may not provide the level of accuracy required. To perform this layout task, use a method known as the 3,4,5 triangle (Figure 9-6). (Math majors will recognize this as an application of the Pythagorean theorem.)

Along the project edge from which you are turning the angle, mark the point from the point where you need the perpendicular, or right-angled, line to begin. (This may also be the corner of the project.) From that point, measure 3 feet along the edge you are turning the angle from and make a second mark. From the beginning mark (or corner), stretch a tape in the direction you want the perpendicular line to run. Hold the tape at the 4-foot mark. Place another tape at the second mark and stretch the tape to 5 feet. Adjust both tapes until the 4-foot mark on the first tape and the 5-foot mark on the second tape intersect. Mark directly below that point. A line traveling from the first point marked (or corner) and passing through that third point where the tapes intersect will be at a right angle to the first edge. When **squaring** decks or paving, you

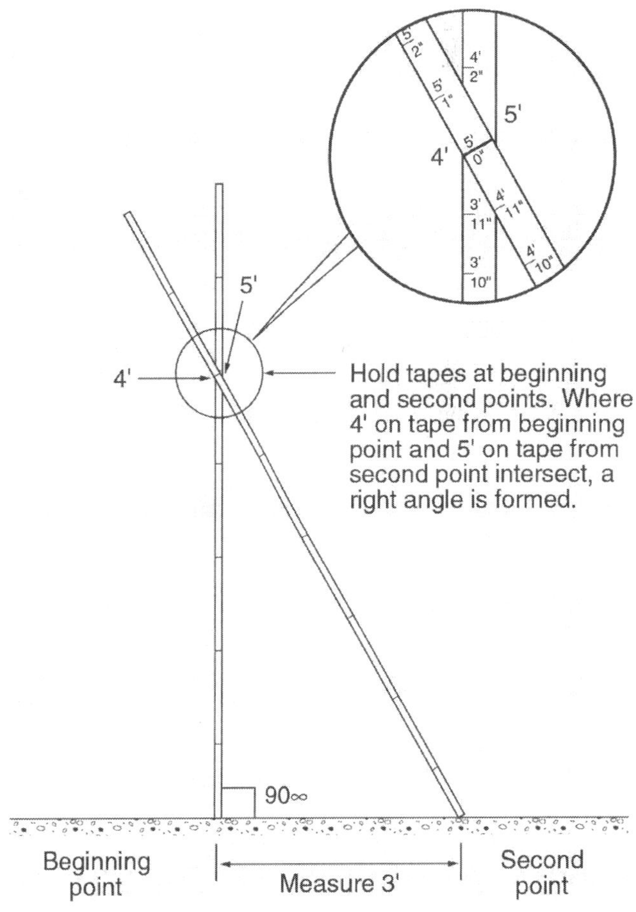

Figure 9-6 Using a 3,4,5 triangle to turn right angles.

may use the 3,4,5 triangle method by marking the 3-foot and 4-foot marks on the joists, then using a single tape to measure the 5-foot mark.

Laying Out a Right Angle Using the Isosceles Triangle Method

Obtaining a perpendicular, or right-angled, line to a baseline or any other straight line can be done using the triangle method (Figure 9-7). Measure two points an equal distance on either side of the point on the baseline from where the perpendicular line is to be located. The distance is not critical as long as it is the same on both sides, but minimum measurements of 3–5 feet are recommended. From each of these two points, stretch the tape measures in the direction of the perpendicular. Select a measurement on one of the tapes and match it with the same measurement on the second tape. Mark the point where these similar measurements intersect. A line laid out from the original starting point through this intersection will be at a right angle to the baseline.

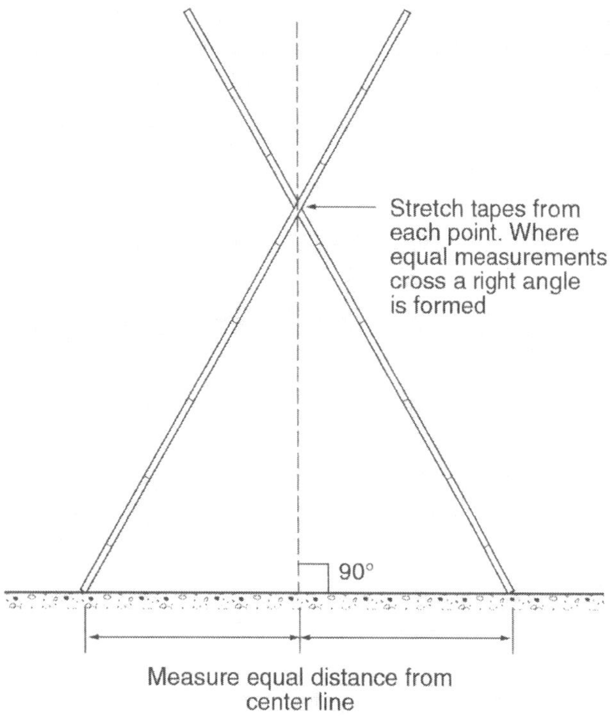

Figure 9-7 Layout of a perpendicular line using the triangler method.

Checking for Square

When laying out a landscape element that must maintain a square (or rectangular) form, check your work using diagonal measurements (Figure 9-8). Using a tape, measure from diagonal corners and compare measurements. If the measurements are equal, the shape is square. If one measurement is longer than the other, the long corner must be pushed in slightly and the short corner pulled out slightly until the measurements match.

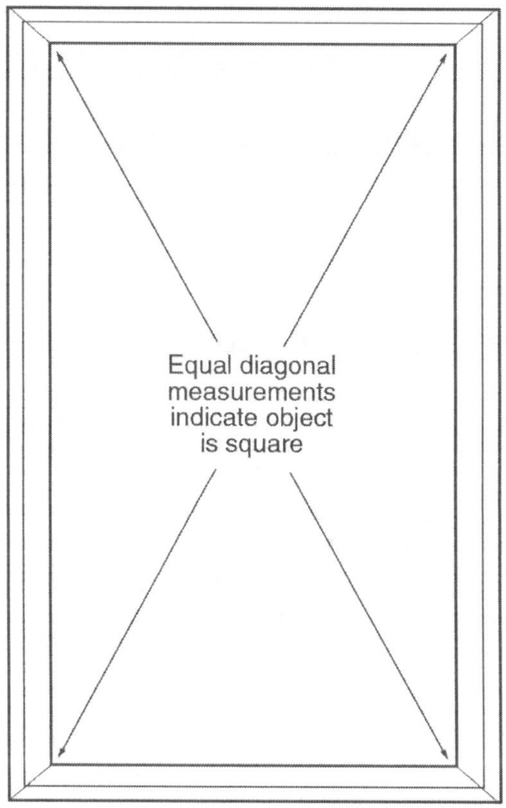

Figure 9-8 Checking for square using diagonal measurements.

Using Stringlines

When street trees or other improvements are to be laid out in a straight line, using a **stringline** will save time over locating each individual plant. To obtain a straight line, place a stake at each end of the line and stretch a mason's line between the two stakes. Measurements can be made down the line to required improvements. If the line interferes with construction operations, offset it 1–2 feet.

Locating Curves

Curves can be measured by locating three points—the beginning of the curve, the end of the curve, and the radius point. Use baselines or coordinates to locate the beginning and ending points. If the radius of the curve is identified but the radius point is not, locate the radius point by turning a right angle (see the 3,4,5 triangle) from the curve beginning point. Marking as you go, swing a tape anchored at the radius point along the alignment where the curve is to be located (Figure 9-9).

Using a deflection angle and chord length, if that information is provided, you can mark ending points for curves. To use this method for locating curves, you must locate the beginning point of the curve and extend the tangent adjacent to the beginning point beyond the beginning point of the curve for 2 feet. The deflection angle indicates the degrees to the left or right of this extended line where the end of the curve is located. Extend a second line from the beginning point of the curve that is at the noted deflection angle to the first line. Measure the chord distance along this second line to locate the end point of the curve. This method does not locate the radius point for the curve.

Laying Out Arcs and Tangents

Designs that have a series of straight lines (**tangents**) and curves (**arcs**) can be successfully laid out by first locating the tangent sections and then connecting the arcs. If available, use coordinates to find each end of the tangents on the site. To locate the radius point of the curve, turn a right angle at the end of the tangent and measure down the right angle the radius distance as noted previously. This is the radius point from which the curve can be "swung" (Figure 9-10). If your curve does not intersect the end of the next tangent, recheck your measurements for accuracy.

If the layout provided does not give coordinates for the tangent end points, begin the layout using a tangent at the beginning point. Measure this tangent; then measure and turn the radius at the end of the tangent. This method will require measuring the angle of the curve to obtain an accurate layout.

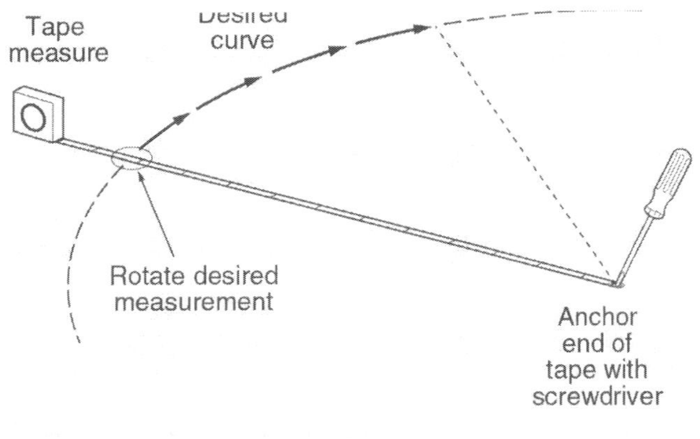

Figure 9-9 Layout of curves using a large screwdriver anchored at the center point and swinging a tape measure to mark the correct radius. Mark the radius as the tape is moved.

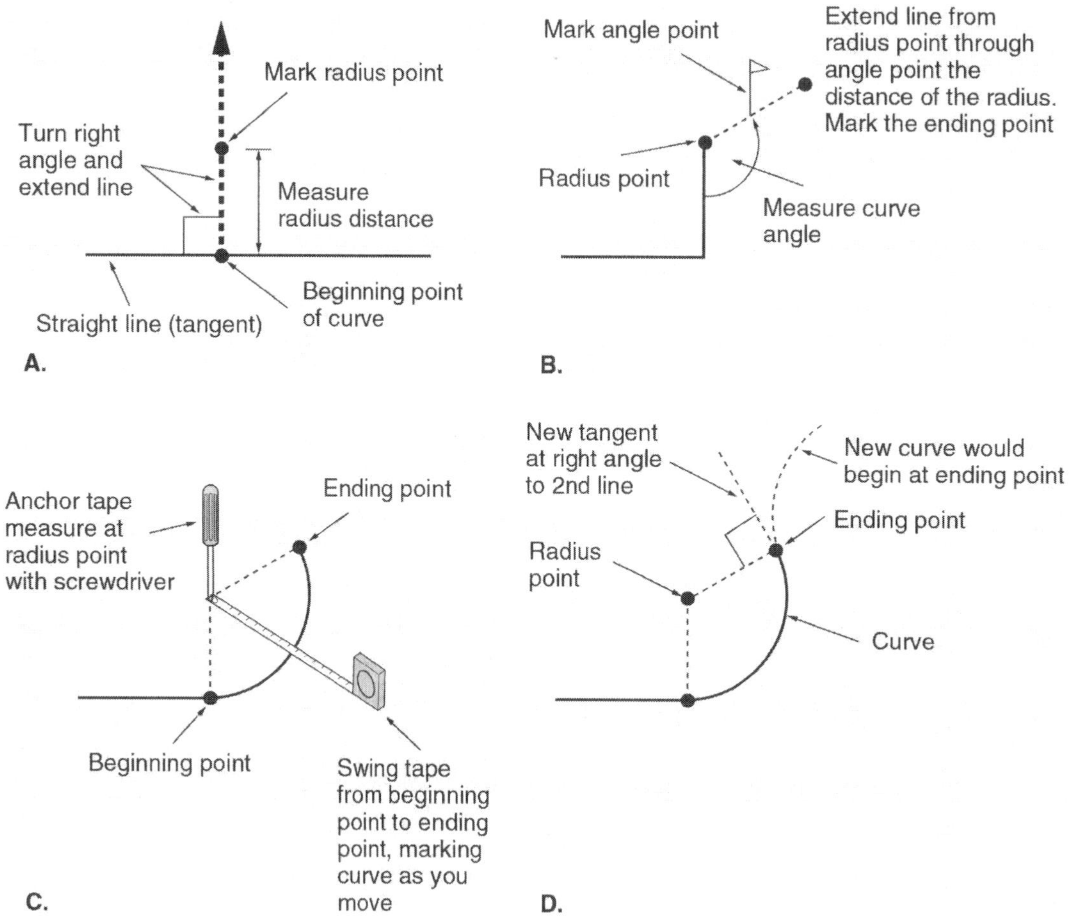

Figure 9-10 Locating radius points and marking a radius for curves.

Laying Out Circles Using Radii and Chords

For designs with complex curvilinear layout, you can easily locate the curved element if the design professional has provided the radius and the chord for each segment of the curve. To locate curves using this method, begin at the first curve by locating the beginning of the curve. From this point, turn a right angle and use the radius measurement to locate the radius point. Set up a measuring tape anchored to the radius point (as shown in "Locating Curves"). Set up a second measuring tape anchored to the beginning point of the curve and extend this tape to the length of the chord (Figure 9-11). Adjust the first and second measuring tapes to the point where the radius and the chord intersect. This is the ending point of the curve, and you can now mark the curve from this point back to the beginning point using the radius measuring tape. If the curve continues without a tangent, you can locate the next radius point by aligning the radius point and ending point for the previous curve and extending a line to the new radius point.

Marking

Cutting and joining elements such as lumber, wall stone, and pavers can be simplified by marking the cutting or joining point. This frees one hand to perform the work, rather than having to hold the tape. Using a *V* to mark points eliminates the confusion of determining which end of a mark is the correct measurement. When temporarily locating elements in the field, use white spray paint or base-path chalk to locate

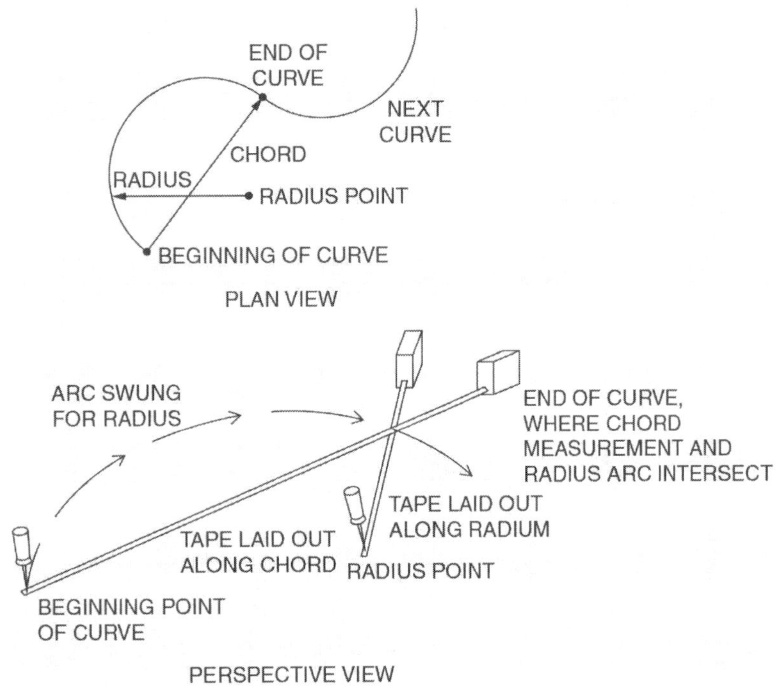

Figure 9-11 Using radii and chords to lay out circles.

edges. You can also use a hose or rope to temporarily locate edges of a curve. Experiment until you are satisfied with the alignment; then replace the hose with permanent markings.

Marking Center Line Locations for Digging

To aid in excavating holes, use paint to mark a large *X*, with the center of the *X* aligned with the center of the hole and the legs of the *X* extended beyond the excavation. If the legs of the mark are extended far enough, reference marks will remain after digging begins. You can use these reference marks to relocate the center of the hole at any time during the excavation.

LOCATING UTILITIES

Chapter 7 addressed the need to locate utilities on a site before construction. The best time to locate utilities, both public and private, is during the layout phase of the project. Contractors may choose to use white flags or stakes to mark the locations of improvement so that their markings do not conflict with those of the color-coded utility markings. Any conflicts between proposed improvements and utilities must be addressed prior to beginning construction.

LOCATING IMPROVEMENTS

Establishing the work area for a project should begin with locating all elements on a horizontal plane. Among the typical items located during this process are corners of structures, edges of paved and planted areas, center lines for walkways and drives, and locations of points, edges, or center lines for all permanent improvements for a site. Site layout plans typically locate major objects on a plan, leaving specific dimensions to details. On sites that require substantial grading and until major earthmoving has been completed, only key improvements, such as structures and roadways, are located. Waiting until the rough grade has been generally established saves time restaking items that were in areas disturbed by the grading process. Locating elevations of improvements (described below), should be completed after major improvements have been located. Contractors can reuse the stakes for locating improvements to mark any grade change required.

Location of landscape improvements requires a method that provides accuracy and efficiency. Contract projects will typically have a site layout plan, which dictates the location method to use. One of the methods described in the following sections, or a hybrid of these methods, is common on projects that landscape architects or site design professionals design. Projects that have no site layout plan require a method for locating improvements. Four methods—object dimensioning, baseline layout, grid layout, and bearings or survey lines—are typical for locating project improvements. The first three of these methods are the most common.

Complex layout problems should be contracted to a registered land surveyor. By combining the methods described below with the techniques addressed earlier, landscape contractors can accomplish simple layouts. Remember, however, that contractors must correct errors in staking at their expense.

Grid Layout

If a project has buildings and roadways, the grid layout method may be the best choice for accuracy. Grid layout uses a series of **Cartesian coordinates** (*X* and *Y* measurements) to locate improvements on a site. These coordinates can be located with a pair of baselines set at right angles to each other. The beginning points and orientation of these baselines should be located on the layout plan (see Figure 3-6).

For a grid layout, each point to be located will have an *X* and *Y* measurement that corresponds to the distance the point is from the *X* and *Y* baselines. To locate an object, select the point to be located and locate the measurement along the *X* baseline. From that measurement, extend a line perpendicular to the *X* baseline slightly beyond where you estimate the point is located. Locate the measurement along the *Y* baseline and, from that measurement, extend a line perpendicular to the *Y* baseline, which intersects the line extended from the *X* baseline.

The intersection of the two lines is the correct location for the point in question. This process is repeated for all points that require location.

Baseline Layout

Baseline layout uses a straight line that runs through the entire site and is measured from a beginning point. Landscape elements are located by making a measurement down the baseline from the beginning point and using a second measurement perpendicular to the left or right off the baseline (Figure 9-12). Baseline layout is common for small-to-medium sized projects that have a great deal of open space on the site. Baselines also work well if a straight curb line, roadway, fence line, or other existing baseline can be used.

Object Dimensioning

Object dimensioning is used when the location of improvements can be measured off existing landmarks such as structures. For most small landscape projects, object dimensioning provides adequate accuracy (Figure 3-8).

Bearings and Survey Lines

The bearings and survey lines method uses lines measured a determined direction (bearing) and distance from a reference point to locate objects on the site. Using an established beginning point such as a property corner, objects are located by providing the bearing and distance from that point. Additional points along a boundary can be located by measuring a second bearing and distance from the previous point. Curves are typically located by interpreting curve data, such as chord and curve length or radius point. Layout of objects described in this manner requires a registered land surveyor to perform the staking.

Batterboards

As related under "Using Offsets," batterboards are an excellent tool for maintaining locations and grades for project corners. When properly constructed, batterboards are the only markings needed throughout the construction of a paved area, a deck, or a structure. Following are instructions for installing a batterboard for one corner of a project with an offset beyond that

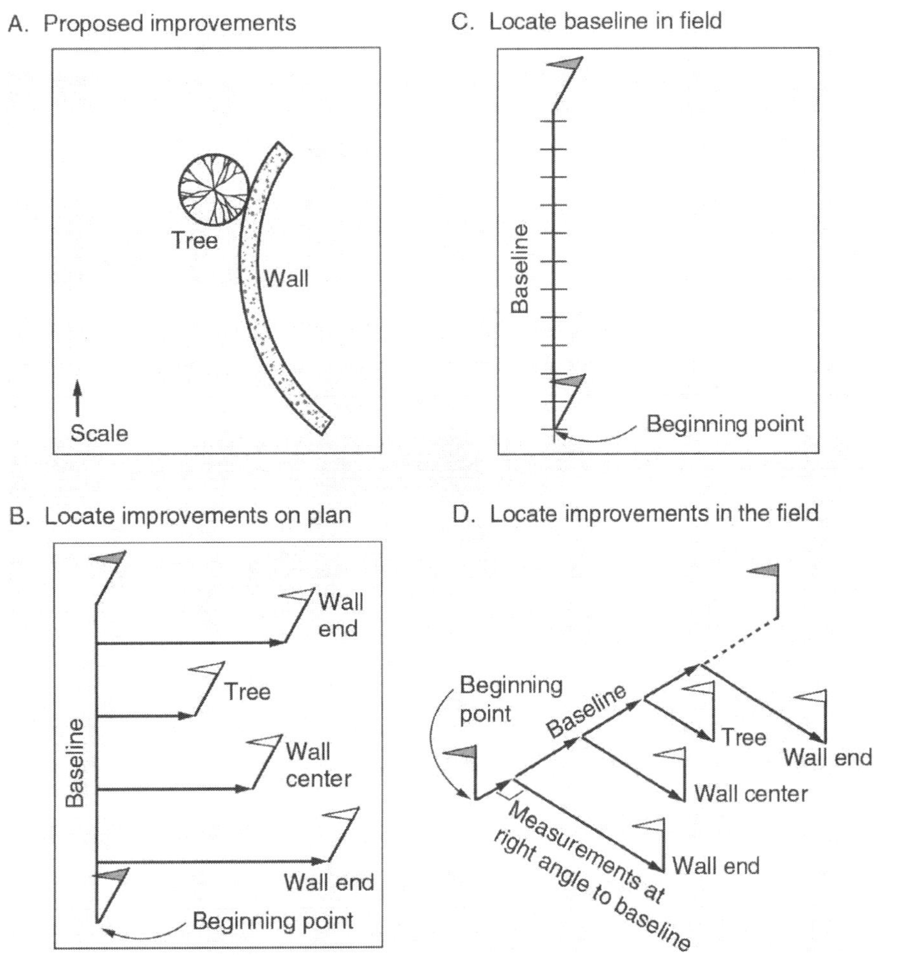

Figure 9-12 Using a baseline to locate improvements in the field.

corner being staked (Figure 9-13). The actual offset is determined by how much of the area outside the project will be disturbed by construction. Construct a batterboard using the following steps:

- Select three, pointed 2 × 2 stakes that are 4-feet long and two 1 × 6s that are 4-feet long.
- Stretch a stringline along the alignment of each side of the project being staked. Extend the stringlines 4 feet beyond the corners of the project in each direction.
- Drive the three stakes into the ground. The stakes should be in an *L* pattern, with each leg of the *L* paralleling one side of the project. The *L* should be located 2 feet beyond and straddle the stringlines.
- Halfway up each stake along one side of the *L*, connect a 1 × 6 between the two stakes. Using deck screws allows connections to be made with minimal disturbance to the stakes.
- Connect the other 1 × 6 between the two remaining stakes.
- Place a second set of stringlines directly above the first set. Using a small nail, connect the stringlines to the 1 × 6.
- Measure to verify the stringlines are set at the project dimensions. Adjust lines left or right and reset if necessary.

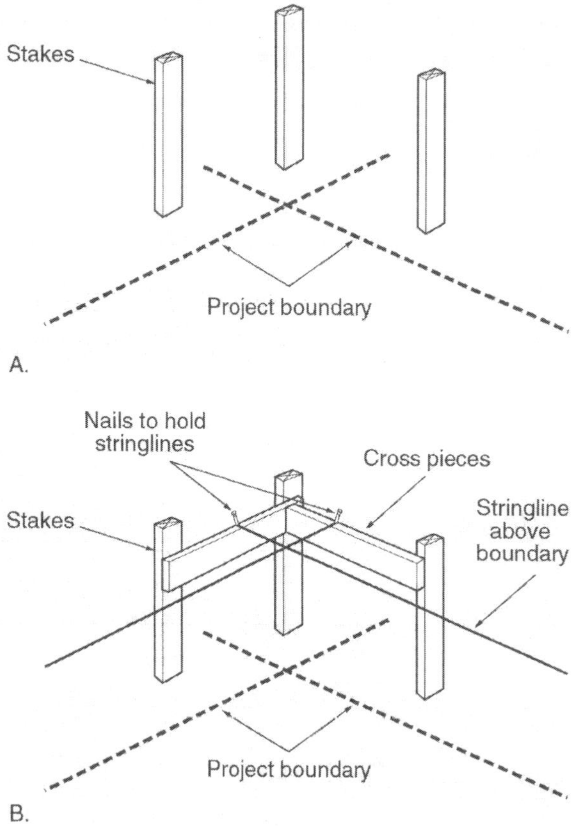

Figure 9-13 Constructing batterboards. (A) Install posts outside the project edges and straddling the boundaries. (B) Attach cross pieces and lines marking project boundaries. Height of the cross pieces can be set to project elevations if you want to locate boundaries and elevations with the same batterboards.

ESTABLISHING ELEVATIONS

Once locations of improvements have been identified, the proposed elevations can be marked. Selection of a method for identifying elevations depends on the accuracy demanded by the project. Projects with no grading plan or with a single layout drawing may state elevations by indicating the direction and percentage of slopes. Another form of identifying elevations is to mark proposed heights of objects by labeling the object with a spot elevation. It is important that drainage from structures and important improvements be maintained when establishing elevations. If grades are critical, consider hiring a registered land surveyor to perform the staking. As with layout staking, contractors must correct errors at their expense.

Similar to the site's horizontal layout, elevation measurements may require restaking as the project progresses. Often the site is first staked to allow the grading contractor to perform rough grading activities and then restaked or remeasured when areas within the site are built. Individual portions of the project, such as grades for tile inlets, paved areas, and slabs for structures, may be remeasured as they are built. Accuracy for rough grading should be within 2–3 inches. Finish grades should be accurate within 1 inch for lawn and planting areas and under .1 inch (one-tenth inch) for paved surfaces.

Offsets for construction staking of grades are sometimes unnecessary. Rough grading layout typically places a grade stake at the correct location, and the grading contractor adds or removes soil around the stake until the new surface is at the correct level. Cut areas leave the stake on a mound of soil that is removed when the surrounding area is at the correct level. In fill areas, soil is piled around the stake until a mark on the stake is reached.

Batterboards and Stringlines

If the proposed finish elevation of the corner being staked is known, vertical layout functions can be obtained from the batterboards described above. Adjust the height of the 1 × 6 so that the stringline passes over the corner at the proposed elevation. The batterboard can now hold the stringline for the project's edges in the correct location, as well as at the correct elevation.

Slope Direction and Percentage

When a plan indicates no specific spot elevations, contractors must rely on indications of slope direction. Most likely used when defining drainage patterns for lawns, this method may also be used for paved surfaces. Using the slope arrows as a guide, grade the project with a consistent slope in the direction indicated. Set the elevations for structures, paved areas, and utilities first, followed by grades for lawn and planting.

Cross Grades

When plans indicate a slope direction but not a specific percentage, a straight 2 × 4 and carpenter's level can be used to stake the grade. Set the desired grade on one side of the construction area; then lay the 2 × 4 from across the project. Set the level on top and adjust the second side up or down until the level reads the general slope direction required (see Figure 9-2).

Dumpy Level or Laser Plane Level

When specific elevations are indicated for points of a project, contractors must accurately measure and mark each of the points. Staking in this manner requires the use of a level to calculate the precise elevation. The surveyor's rod that is used must match any grading plan measurement increment. If feet and inches are used on the plan, use a rod calibrated in feet and inches; if decimals (feet and tenths) are used, use a rod calibrated in decimals. Math is easier to calculate using decimal measurements, and most grading plans use decimal markings. A registered land surveyor should stake calculations that require angles and elevations.

Setting Up the Level. Setup for a survey instrument that is leveled manually will be the same for a dumpy level or a laser plane level. A self-leveling instrument requires only the steps through mounting the instrument. For placement of the level, select a location that has good visibility of the benchmark and all locations that will require construction staking. This site should be in an area as level as possible where construction traffic and activity will not disturb the instrument. Set the tripod by first spreading the legs and positioning them with the mounting plate at a comfortable height and as close to level as possible. When mounted, the instrument should be at eye level for ease of operation. Push the legs of the tripod securely into the ground to avoid accidental movement.

Remove the instrument from its case and secure it to the mounting plate. Some levels have a threaded connector that is attached through the mounting plate; others screw directly onto the plate. The telescope is leveled using the four thumbscrews that support the instrument on the mounting plate. A small bubble level below the telescope indicates if the instrument is properly leveled. Begin leveling by turning the screws gently until all four are in contact with the mounting plate. Turn the telescope so it is aligned with one pair of thumbscrews (Figure 9-14). Turn the thumbscrews in opposite directions to center the bubble. If the level bubble needs to move to the left, turn both screws toward the center of the mounting plate. If the level bubble needs to move to the right, turn both screws toward the edge of the mounting plate. With these motions, the screws are actually turning in opposite directions and cause the telescope to tip in one direction or the other. Continue adjusting until the level bubble is centered.

Figure 9-14 Leveling a survey instrument. Always turn the leveling screws in opposite directions.

Turn the telescope 90 degrees to the right and repeat the leveling operation with the second pair of screws. When level in that direction, turn the telescope back to the original direction and repeat the leveling process. The telescope should now be level. Test by turning the telescope in all directions and verifying that the bubble stays centered. If the bubble is not centered, repeat the leveling process. The base of the thumbscrews should always remain in contact with the mounting plate. If any screw lifts from the plate, the entire process needs to be redone.

If the survey instrument being used is self-leveling, position the tripod with the level attached and set the instrument for level. Small motors within the instrument will level the telescope.

Using the Level. When operating the level, use extreme caution not to bump the instrument out of place. Any movement will require resetting the level. Gently aim the telescope in the direction where you will be taking measurements. Look through the telescope using one eye and use the knob on the side to focus (Figure 9-15). When the telescope is properly aimed and focused, you should see the leveling rod (or tape) clearly.

A laser level will send out a level beam in an arc around the construction site. Operators holding rods with laser receptors will position themselves wherever a sighting is required. Do not look directly at the light beam. The operator will raise or lower the receptor until the beam is captured, usually indicated by a beeping noise from the receptor. The reading is taken from the receptor rod, completing the backsite or foresite.

Taking a Backsite. The first step in calculating elevations is to take a **backsite.** Have a second worker set the surveyor's rod on the benchmark. Look through the telescope, focus, and read the elevation on the rod. If you are unable to read a foot number, the rod operator may need to lift the rod until a foot reading is visible. Add the reading to the elevation of the benchmark to obtain the **height of instrument** (Figure 9-16).

Taking a Foresite. The rod operator may now move to a location where an elevation measurement is needed. Drive a construction stake into the ground at that point (one may already exist from locating the improvements). Look through the telescope, focus, and read the number on the rod. Subtract the reading from the height of the instrument to obtain the elevation of the spot where the surveyor's rod is setting.

Marking and Reading Grade Stakes. Read the grading plan from the construction documents to determine the proposed elevation for the spot where the rod is setting. If the proposed and existing elevations are the same, the stake will be marked *0* (no cut or fill).

If the proposed finish elevation is higher than the existing elevation, subtract the existing elevation from the proposed elevation and mark

Figure 9-15 Focusing a survey instrument. Use caution not to bump the instrument out of level.

the stake as a fill, using the difference as the fill amount. Fill stakes are marked *F+ X.X* or *F X.X*, where *X.X* is the amount of fill necessary (1 foot of fill would be marked as *F+ 1.0* or *F 1.0*). To aide the contractor performing the grading work, a dark line can be drawn on the stake that indicates the proper fill level. If the proposed finish elevation is lower than the existing elevation, subtract the proposed elevation from the existing elevation and mark the stake as a cut, using the difference as the cut amount. Cut stakes are marked as *−X.X* or *C X.X*, where *X.X* is the amount of cut necessary (2 feet of cut would be marked as *−2.0* or *C 2.0*). This process is repeated for each spot elevation that must be marked (Figure 9-17).

Moving the Instrument. If the instrument must be moved, take a foresite at a location that is visible from both the existing and new instrument locations. Have the rod operator stay in the same location while the instrument is moved to the new location and leveled. Take a backsite to the same rod location. Calculate the difference between the foresite and backsite. If the backsite is less than the fore site, subtract that difference from the old height of the instrument to obtain the new height of the instrument. If the backsite is greater than the foresite, add that difference to the old height of the instrument to obtain the new height of the instrument. Continue taking foresites and calculating elevations using the new height of the instrument.

LOCATING PLANT MATERIAL

Locating plant material for a site usually involves marking the boundaries of planting beds and identifying tree and shrub locations. Locating

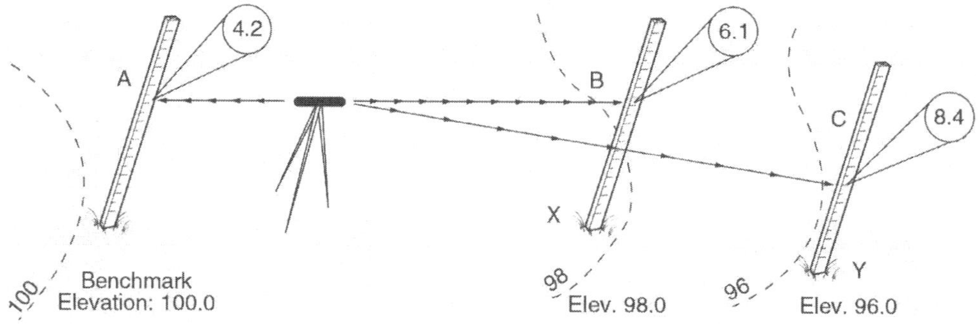

Surveyors Notes:

Point	Backsite	H.I.	Foresite	Elevation
BM	4.2 (A)	104.2		100.0
			6.1 (B)	98.1
			8.4 (C)	95.8

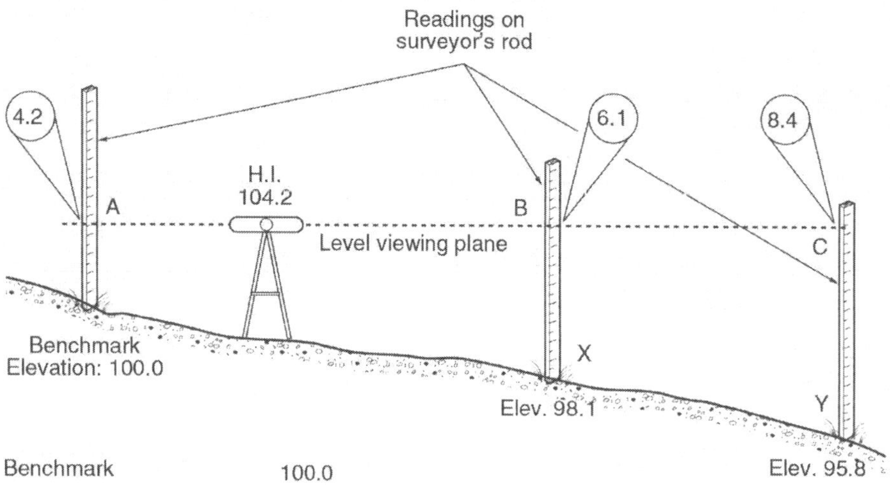

Benchmark	100.0	
Backsite A	+ 4.2	
Height of instrument	104.2	
Foresite B	− 6.1	
Elevation of point X	98.1	(H.I. – Foresite B) (104.2 – 6.1 = 98.1)
Foresite C	− 8.4	
Elevation of point Y	95.8	(H.I. – Foresite C) (104.2 – 8.4 = 95.8)

Figure 9-16 Performing elevation calculations. The surveyor's notes and calculations are shown above the figure.

trees and shrubs can be done with construction flags placed at the center point of the proposed planting location (Figure 9-18). Because they are less likely to be confused with standard utility markings, white or green flags are recommended. In projects with many varieties of plants, printing the name of the plant on the flag is beneficial. Planting bed edges can be marked with white paint, indicating the edge between the bed and lawn or other types of plantings. Plantings within a bed may be marked by stringlines or paint lines placed on the ground, or reference markers may be placed along the edges of the planting bed. As with all markings, these indicators may need to be replaced several times during the course of a construction project. Use existing improvements, when available, as references for plant material location.

Figure 9-17 Cut markings on a grade stake. This stake shows a cut of 1.6 feet below existing grade (existing grade is indicated by the markings at the bottom of the stake).

Figure 9-18 Flagging of proposed plantings to review placement.

SECTION 1

SUMMARY

How well contractors prepare for the work often determines the success of a landscape project. Before contractors turn a single shovel of soil, all preconstruction activities should be completed. Section 1 describes the construction process, legal requirements, interpretation of construction documents, construction math, project pricing, safety in the workplace, basic construction techniques and small equipment operation, and construction staking activities typically required before undertaking a landscape project.

Landscape construction should be approached as a process with several interlocking steps. To maintain work efficiency, contractors should complete these steps in an orderly and logical fashion that allows current work to build on, rather than disturb, work previously completed. Although contractors may make adjustments to address particular project requirements, the typical steps to complete a landscape project include preconstruction activities, protection and removal of existing elements, rough grading (including drainage and temporary erosion control measures) utility installation, retaining wall installation, paving, decorative landscape features, finish grading and freestanding wall construction, amenity installation, planting and project closeout.

Landscape contractors must address legal and contractual concerns similar to those that building contractors address. Building codes, ordinances, and legal controls guide the installation of the portions of the project that may put the public at risk. In many jurisdictions, permits or review of plans may be required before construction can be approved. Work that is bid typically has a set of plans and specifications that bind contractors to the details of the project. Protection for contractors, their clients, and the public is obtained in the form of insurance, bonding, and licensing. In addition to providing quality services, contractors are also required to work within legal boundaries. Before beginning a construction business, contractors should be aware of common torts and activities that may lead to legal action against them.

Occasionally, landscape projects are designed as a general concept or an open-ended project, providing contractors a great deal of flexibility in layout, detailing, and material selection. In many cases, particularly projects that design professionals prepare, contractors must work from a specific set of instructions. Construction plans and specifications (specs) are prepared to guide the location, materials, and installation procedures used in completing landscape improvements. Plans and specs are part of the contract for construction and must be followed to satisfy legal terms of the contract. Various plans may be included, depending on the design professional, but they typically address the preparation (or demolition) of the site, site layout of the improvements, grading and elevations of the improvements, utility installations, plant material installation, and details of critical entities of construction. Specifications provide detailed information regarding the materials and installation methods required for the project, along with general information such as warranties, storage, and other topics related to the work. Interpretation of plans and specs requires that contractors obtain and review a complete set of construction documents. Landscape Contractors must also understand the concept of drawing scale and be able to comprehend the variety of graphic standards, symbols, abbreviations, and textures that design professionals use to convey design ideas.

Mathematics is applied to landscape construction in virtually every phase of work. Whether calculating a bid or ordering materials, contractors must master basic measurement and calculation techniques to succeed. Typical math applications that are found in landscaping work include calculating averages, item counts, linear measurements, perimeter measurements, area calculations, volume calculations, and weight conversions. Landscape Contractors must understand the formulas involved in these calculations and know when they are appropriate to use.

Landscape construction also requires an understanding of the estimating and bidding process and of calculating business operating costs such as labor, overhead, fees and taxes and profit. Understanding the techniques that various types of firms use to calculate and present project costs to potential clients can be equally as important to the success of a business as the work performed.

Safety is an overriding concern in any industry, and landscape construction is no exception. Although the risks of the landscaping industry may not be as obvious as those found in other professions, the potential for serious injury or death is just as real. Safety in the workplace should begin with prevention and with education of workers in safety precautions. Wearing proper safety clothing or equipment and being aware of risks on the job will reduce the risk of injury.w Proper lifting of the materials used in landscaping is important in reducing muscle injury. Because of the amount of excavation in landscape work, utilities pose a significant risk. Calling for locates before digging is essential and required by law. Landscape contractors should also be aware of the potential hazards from working below grade, operating power equipment, and working with the variety of chemicals used in construction.

Basic construction techniques should be practiced and mastered before construction begins. Basic techniques range from digging to mastering essential carpentry skills. Operation of specialized equipment is also required to successfully complete landscape projects.

Proper construction layout of the project begins the project on the right track. Staking the location and elevation of improvements is necessary to install landscape elements in the correct position. Contractors must be prepared to locate improvements for a project or to interpret a site layout plan, which uses object dimensions, baseline layout, grid layout, or batterboards. Establishing proper project grades requires understanding of batter boards, stringlines, contours and spot elevations, and slope calculations. Landscape contractors must also be prepared to locate, or interpret the locations of plant material and planting beds for a project.

SECTION 2

EXISTING SITE ELEMENTS

INTRODUCTION

The path to improving a site begins with properly preparing for construction operations. Generally, this step can be considered in two steps—preserving existing site elements and removing unwanted elements. Site preparation, or site demolition as this phase is termed in some contract documents, requires the same level of precision in workmanship as does any other phase of work. Failure to properly perform the steps of preparation may lead to reconstruction, hazards and penalties, damage to the environment, or expensive replacement of landscape elements.

The chapters of this section address preservation of existing site elements and removal of unwanted elements. Preservation begins with the identification of site access and storage areas, definition of construction limits, and securing of benchmarks and layout baselines. Preservation of existing site elements continues with the fencing or sheltering of plant material, structures, pavement, and utilities. The chapter on removal of unwanted site elements identifies techniques for removing plant material, pavement, minor utilities, and landscape waste.

Landscape contractors should carefully read specifications and discuss the project with their general contractor to determine if any or all of the site preparation work is prescribed in their contract. On large-scale projects, the general contractor or the grading contractor typically undertakes this aspect of the work. Smaller projects may require landscape contractors to protect and remove existing site elements prior to the start of grading and utility work.

PRODUCTIVITY SUGGESTIONS

Activities listed as preconstruction work should be completed at the beginning of site preparation. Some specific suggestions that may be of benefit during this stage are:

- Have any questionable boundaries surveyed before beginning work.
- Early in the project, locate a secure material storage area.
- Before beginning work, review the site for elements scheduled for demolition that may be recycled.

SUSTAINABILITY SUGGESTIONS

To create a more sustainable worksite and work environment, follow these suggestions:

- Minimize the disturbance of the site. Work only in areas necessary and keep to a minimum the footprint of disruption to the natural condition.
- Preserve the existing plant material on site.
- Take efforts to reduce erosion of soil from the site.
- Recycle and reuse any elements that can economically be salvaged, including old piping, paving, lumber, granular materials, soil, and plant material.
- Compost plant material and sod that must be removed.

CHAPTER 10

PRESERVATION OF EXISTING SITE ELEMENTS

OBJECTIVES

By reading and practicing the techniques described in this chapter, the reader should be able to successfully complete the following activities:

- Identify elements of a construction site that need protection.
- Effectively protect site elements from damage as a result of construction activities.

Few landscape bids include the price for replacing a 50-year-old oak damaged during construction or replacing a bay window that a skid loader struck. The cost of one construction mishap often exceeds the profit built into a project; hence, proper techniques for preserving existing site elements should be practiced throughout construction.

The concepts of environmental protection and sustainability should be integrated throughout the activities covered in this chapter. Protection begins with a design that considers the impacts of construction and plans mitigation of activities that are detrimental to the site and its environment. Ideally, the design professional provides leadership in protecting valuable resources. The initial physical step to protect a site is to minimize the disturbances when starting construction and to protect portions of the site that are to be preserved throughout the project. During the site preparation phase, establish construction limits and physically protect elements of the site that cannot be disturbed. Beyond avoiding protected areas, search the project for activities that have the potential to damage the site without apparent intrusion, including inappropriate material storage areas, drainage that will foul existing waterways, and temporary access or utility installations that damage plants or disturb soil. Astute contractors will also minimize activities that may introduce unwanted noise, light, dust, or other nuisances into a neighborhood. Consideration must be given to all activities related to construction to appropriately preserve the plants, soil, waterways, and other elements of the site's environment.

RELATED INFORMATION

Information in this chapter is supplemented by instruction provided elsewhere in this text and in other sources. Before undertaking the activities described in this chapter, read the related information in these sources:

- Safety in the Workplace, Chapter 7
- Basic Construction Techniques and Small Equipment Operation, Chapter 8
- Erosion Control, Chapter 16

SITE ACCESS AND STORAGE AREAS

Defining the location of a site access may fall under the design professional's responsibility, but this is sometimes left to the contractor's discretion. Selection of a site access could be as simple as finding a level spot to drive off an adjacent roadway, or selection could be more difficult by a remote, heavily wooded site with steep topography. Considerations for selecting a route to your work should include the following factors:

- Legal Access. Access should not cross another property without the landowner's permission. In certain communities, permanent and temporary access off-public roads must be approved.

- Visibility. Visibility for vehicles entering and exiting the site should not be restricted.
- Traffic. Because unloading may have to take place from streets, traffic should be light during construction hours.
- Level Grades. Level grades make the transitions from street to access easier.
- Size and Type of Vehicles. Verify that openings are large enough for vehicles that will require access to construction areas.
- Utility Locations. Overhead wires and fragile underground utilities should be avoided.
- Construction. Select a route that will not be in the way of present or future construction.
- Minimal Disturbance. Site disturbance should be kept to a minimum.

For sites that require a new permanent access (either walkway or drive), roughing out that new access may provide the best route to the construction site. If a construction site is to be completely disturbed, access may take place at any point until the late stages of construction.

Projects that involve only landscaping may require a route across a lawn, which must be restored after construction is complete. Access for pedestrians and small equipment may be accommodated by placing sheets of plywood on the ground to reduce soil compaction and to protect turf. Regardless of the situation, expect your access to create a disturbance that will require some level of restoration, ranging from aerating compacted soil to removing temporary driveways.

Selecting the simplest route that will serve all construction is usually the best choice, even if it involves some work to prepare. Once in place, barricades or a temporary gate should be installed to reduce liability and security problems. The greater the risk, the more secure the perimeter should be. Parking for workers should be located off-site if possible. Finding a street or leasing a parking area near the site reduces the damage that a large number of employees can do with daily trips to and from the site.

Storage areas for work materials require many of the same considerations as site access, along with the following additional concerns:

- Delivery may take place from semitrailers, requiring the storage area to be accessible from both a public street and the construction access.
- Security of stored materials may be a problem in some environments. Fencing may be necessary to protect valuable supplies from theft.
- Temporary utilities may be required if plant material is watered or if materials are prepared (cutting, planing, trimming, etc.) in a storage area.
- Storage for plant material should provide the proper environment for plant health, including access to water and shade, if required.

Similar to construction access, the simplest storage site usually works best for most construction projects (Figure 10-1).

Figure 10-1 Selecting a simple and accessible storage site.

EQUIPMENT CHOICES

Limiting damage to site elements, such as trees and soil, begins with selecting the equipment for performing work on the site. Choosing equipment that is oversized for the job will result in unnecessary site destruction. Equipment that is light and small can pass more easily through wooded areas and causes less compaction than does large, heavy equipment. Choosing appropriate tools and equipment will save both money and time, as well as be less destructive to the environment.

CONSTRUCTION LIMITS

Where you will be performing work is usually not in question. However, areas where you are *not* to work can be confusing. Projects may have limitations on the areas that your construction activities can disturb, and the construction limit line defines these boundaries. Identified in construction documents as a line around the project, limits should be located early in the project and fenced or marked to prevent violations of boundary restrictions. If the project does not have construction limits, verify that the limits are the owner's property. Hire a land surveyor to locate property lines that are in question. If no limits are defined for your project, care should still be taken to avoid and protect sensitive areas. Another concern is how your work may affect areas outside your construction area. Chapter 3, Legal Requirements, identifies some of the off-site problems that could arise from your construction activities.

The effort made to lay out the horizontal and vertical controls for your site should be protected by clearly marking benchmarks, grade and layout stakes, and other reference marks that will be referred to often (Figure 10-2). Protection could be as simple as spray painting with a bright fluorescent color to aid in identification. In some cases, however, protection may require setting a fencepost or metal stake. Providing several options for reestablishing destroyed references, multiple reference points ease the pain of an accidental disruption.

Figure 10-2 Baseline reference markings for project layout.

PLANT MATERIAL PROTECTION

For landscape contractors, the need for providing plant material protection should be obvious. Unfortunately, many tradespeople are not familiar with plant culture and fail to practice proper protection techniques when working around plant material. Construction poses several perils to mature plant species at a site; and, in most cases, the damage does not become apparent until several years after the construction project has been completed. For this reason, members of the landscape contracting industry must become stewards of the site by practicing sound plant protection techniques. Familiarizing yourself with the identification and cultural requirements of plants helps you recognize which plants are most sensitive to construction and which construction practices pose the greatest risk to plants. Using the philosophy of trying to keep protected plants in their same preconstruction environment throughout construction will help reduce overt and latent construction damage.

Begin the preservation process by judging which plants require the application of preservation techniques. An unfortunate, but necessary, aspect of the process is evaluating plants to determine if they should be afforded the effort of preservation. Although many plants deserve protection, some plants should be removed rather than protected. To make such a judgment, consider the following factors:

- Is the plant in good health? A plant in serious state of decline will probably not survive attempts to preserve it through a construction project. Evaluate the plant to see if it has serious structural flaws, disease, or insect infestations, or is in generally poor health. Do not assume that size is the best determinant of a plant's health. In some cases, the larger plants may be in worse condition than are the smaller, healthier plants. The best philosophy is to protect plants that are currently in good health.
- Is the plant suffering from prior damage? Evaluate the plant's crown, branches, trunk, and roots to see if it is currently suffering from old injury. Significant damage in each of these areas, particularly the root zone, may be reason enough to remove the plant, rather than protecting it.
- Will the plant survive the new environment after construction? Each plant has a set of cultural requirements to ensure its survival. A plant may be able to survive the construction phase only to decline as a result of significant changes in its immediate environment. Although these issues may have been addressed in the planning phase, designers sometimes

miss the obvious. A plant that is shade-loving but will now be in full sun, a floodplain plant now in dry conditions, or a plant that has grown in a forest now placed in an unprotected position are examples of a significant environment change. Conditions such as these are likely to lead to the plant's premature decline. In many situations, it is more effective to remove the plant during construction, rather than after project completion.

If you cannot determine whether these conditions exist, consider asking the advice of an arborist certified by the International Society of Arborists, or a certified urban forester. These professionals should be able to judge whether preserving a plant is a cost effective and environmentally sound option.

Protection techniques vary, depending on the species and maturity of plants and the construction activity taking place. Overstory (shade) and understory (ornamental) trees are at the greatest risk of damage from site construction activities. This risk stems from the errant belief that if the contractor does not damage the trunk or canopy, the tree will not suffer damage.

This belief fails in not recognizing that a plant's **root zone** is as equally important as its trunk and canopy. A trees critical root zone extends well beyond the tree's **dripline** and is often considered to extend 1.5 feet out from the base of the trunk for every caliper inch of the tree. For example, a 20" caliper shade tree would have a critical root zone that extends 30 feet from the base of the tree. Some municipalities may actually dictate the dimension of the critical root zone. Compaction, trenching, mixing of chemicals, excavation, storage of materials, and related construction activities within a plant's critical root zone may damage its root system and eventually damage the remainder of the plant. Protection from damage must extend at least to the plant's drip line; and, in some cases, consideration must be given to restricting activities outside the drip line (Figure 10-3).

Figure 10-3 Fencing placed at a tree's drip line to protect the root zone.

Because of their size and vigor, many shrubs are more durable when exposed to construction activities. However, shrubs should be afforded the same protection given to trees to increase the chances of their survival.

Compaction

Compaction from traffic and material storage within the critical root zone must be avoided. The best method of preventing compaction is not allowing any activity in the area. This includes vehicle and product storage as well as vehicular, equipment and foot traffic. Fencing a plant at the critical root zone and leaving the fence in place throughout construction will divert traffic and activities from the plant. If traffic within a critical root zone is absolutely necessary, create a pathway by applying 12 inches of shredded bark mulch over the area and overlaying the mulch with logging mats. Avoid piling mulch against any plant's trunk. Water the mulch daily. These techniques will only reduce the compaction of root-zone soil.

Root-Zone and Canopy Damage

Because it entirely severs the root structure from the plant, trenching within the drip line should be avoided. Reroute utility lines from the area under the plant's canopy when possible. If utility lines must pass within the drip line, bore the lines 3 feet deep to pass under the plant's root zone. Excavation within the root zone creates the same type of disturbance as trenching, whereas filling within the drip line will suffocate many plants by blocking the path of gases and nutrients to their root zones.

In many cases, aerating the root zone may assist in partially mitigating construction damage from compaction. One method to improve aeration and to reduce compaction is to place 2–4 inches of loose organic mulch over the plant's root zone. When adding mulch, do not place it next to the plant's trunk. The second method of aerating a plant's root zone is to vertical mulch. To perform this activity, drill 12-inch deep by 3-inch diameter holes 3 feet on center throughout the root zone. Fill the holes with pea gravel, peat moss, or mulch to allow air and water to infiltrate the root zone (Figure 10-4). A third technique is to use radial trenching. Select five to seven locations radiating from the tree's trunk, avoiding major roots if possible. Beginning approximately 4 feet from the trunk, excavate a 12-inch deep by 2-inch wide trench to the plant's drip line. Excavate by hand or use a compressed air excavation tool (Airspade®) to reduce damage to roots and utilities in the excavation area. Backfill the trench with loose soil or compost with mycorrhizal fungi added (Figure 10-5). This technique may encourage new root growth to replace those damaged by construction. Contractors have used both vertical mulching and radial trenching with mixed results in a variety of applications, including root zone soil compacted by construction activities.

Tree wells (Figures 10-6 and 10-7) are recommended where possible to reduce the damage from excavation and filling. Tree wells should be constructed outside the plant's critical root zone and should be designed to maintain the original grade and drainage patterns. Long term survival of a tree being saved is not guaranteed. Always compare the cost of extraordinary tree saving measures to the cost of tree replacement. Often times the cost of the construction could pay for a healthy new tree of considerable size that includes a warranty.

In locations where fill must be placed over large portions of a tree's root zone, contractors' attempts to construct tree wells and associated aeration systems have had mixed success in preserving plant material. Aeration systems involve placing a large, porous fill and aeration tiles over the original grade to facilitate the exchange of gases in the root zone. Research on the impact of such systems has shown that, in some situations, the systems help plant survival. However, variables such as tree species, type of fill, and percentage of root zone covered all play a part in preserving the plant.

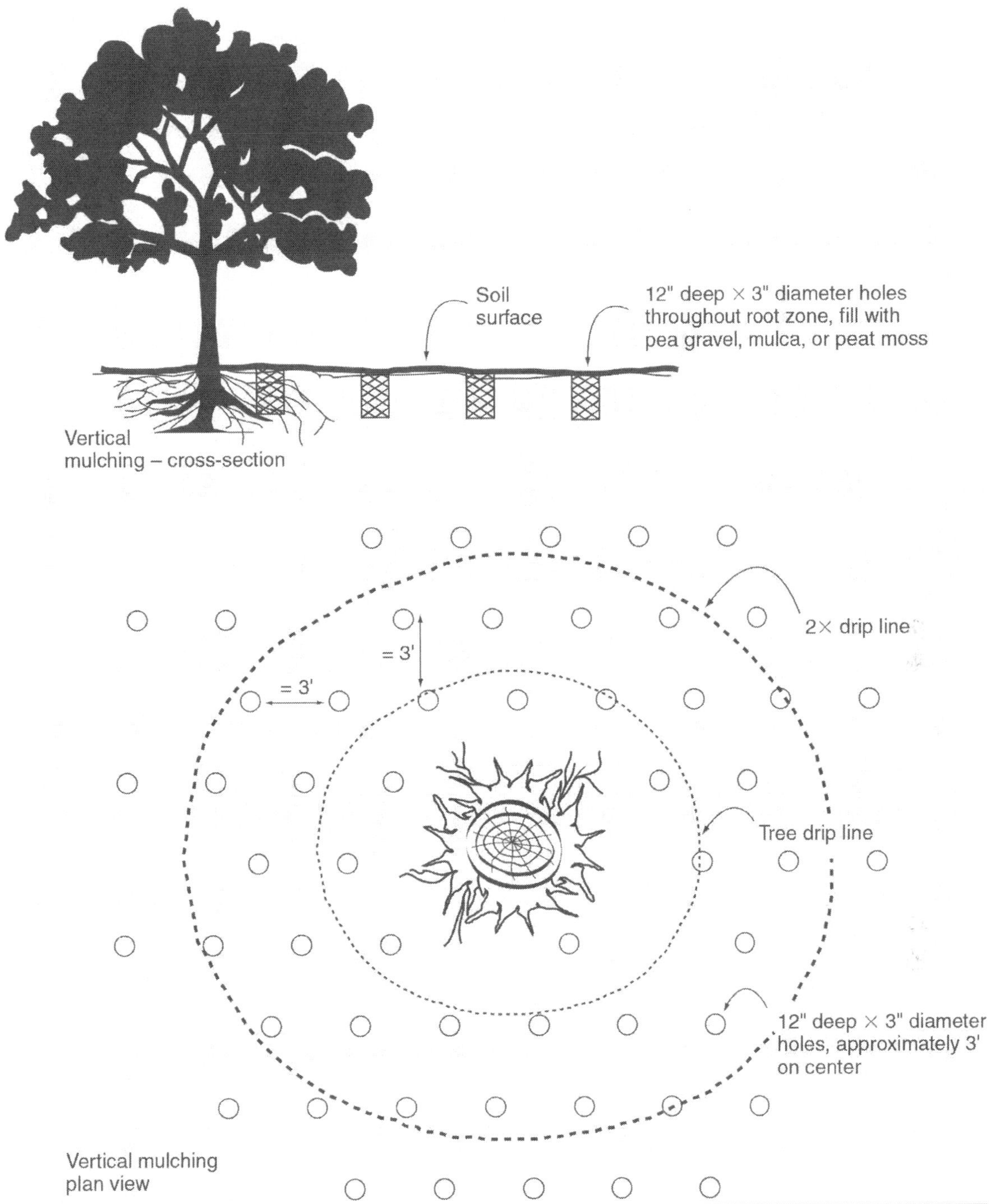

Figure 10-4 Vertical mulching.

To construct an aeration system, begin by building a retaining wall the height of the fill and at least 2 feet from the tree's trunk. Lay out a tile system of socked perforated 4-inch tile following the tree's drip line in the area that will be filled (Figures 10-8 and 10-9). On the lowest portion of this tile, install a T and a drain tile that outlets beyond the area where the fill is to occur. Every 10 feet along this tile, install a T facing upward. In each T, insert a 4-inch nonperforated drain tile riser that will extend above the fill. Install a stake, and tie the upright tile to the stake for support while filling.

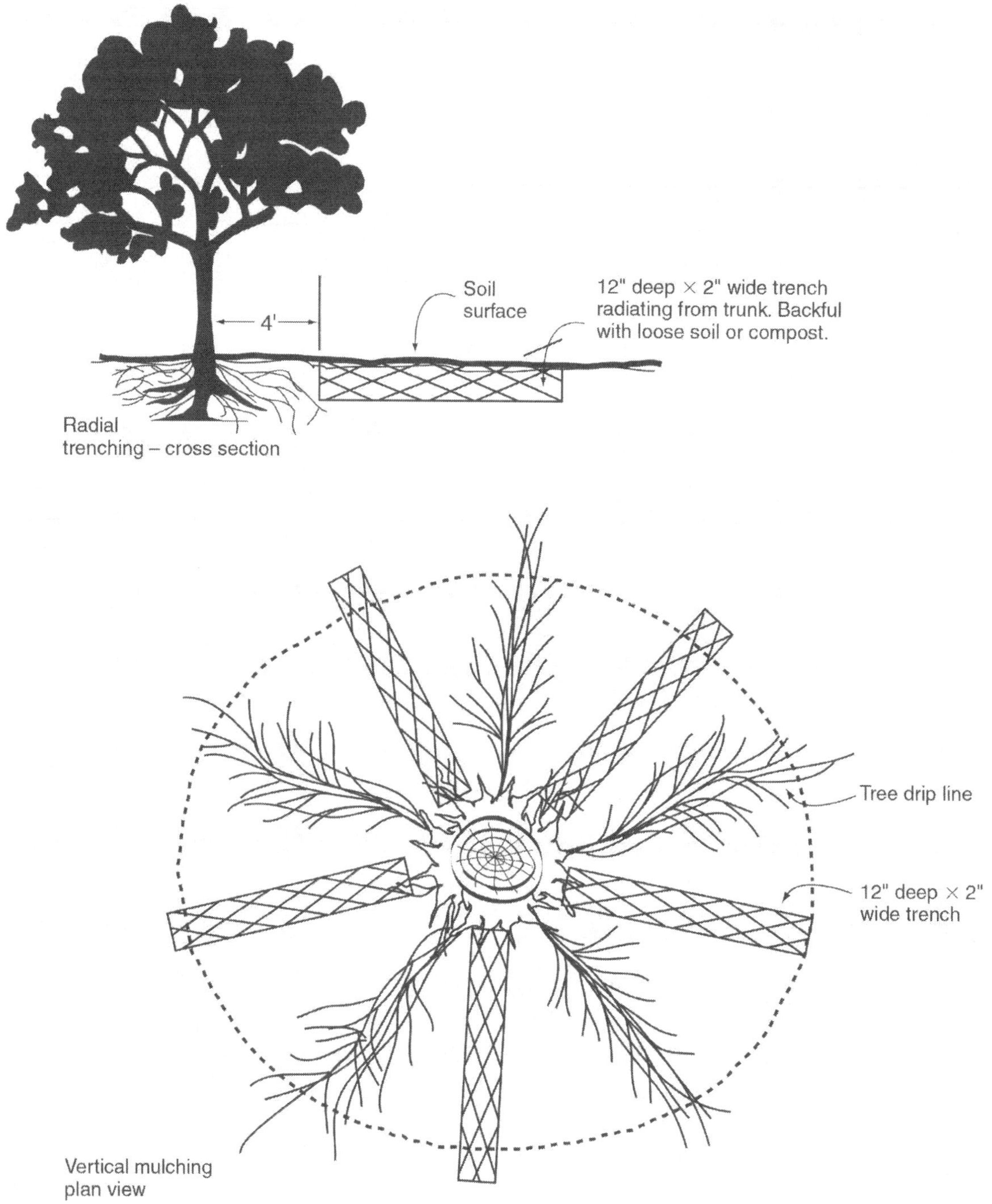

Figure 10-5 Radial trenching.

After the tile system is complete, carefully place 4–8 inches of rounded stone in a layer at least 2-feet deep (or to within 6 inches of the surface) over the entire area to be filled. The stone should be free of fine material and create significant amounts of pore space below the fill. Place a geotextile fabric over the stone and complete the fill.

Design for walls and footings around mature plant material should take into consideration protection of the root zone. Avoiding long

Figure 10-6 Tree wells installed to protect existing tree root zone from fill.

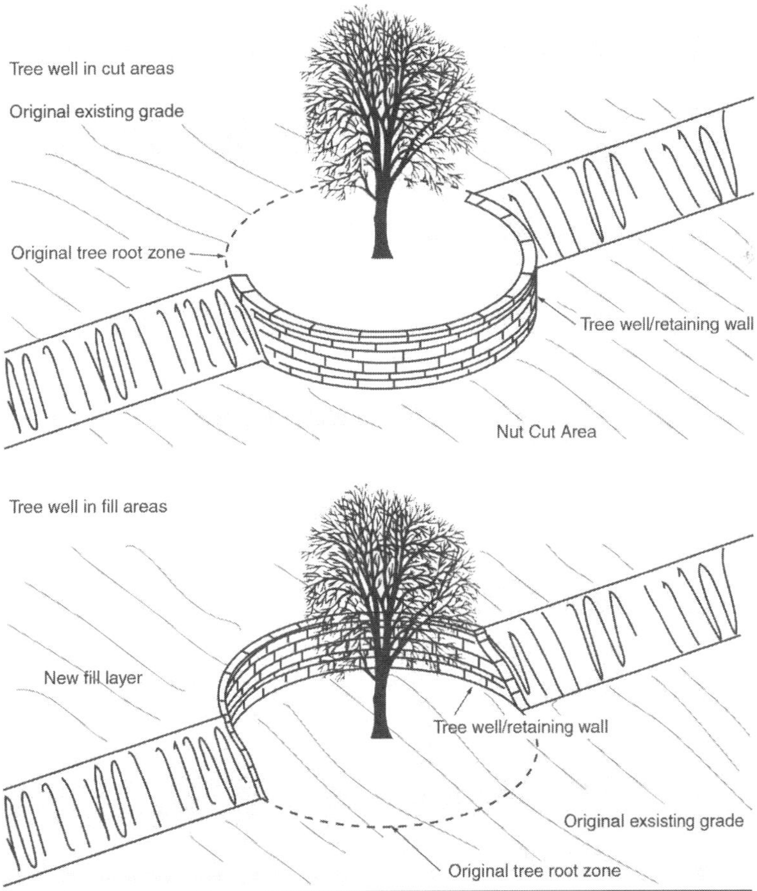

Figure 10-7 Tree well in fill areas.

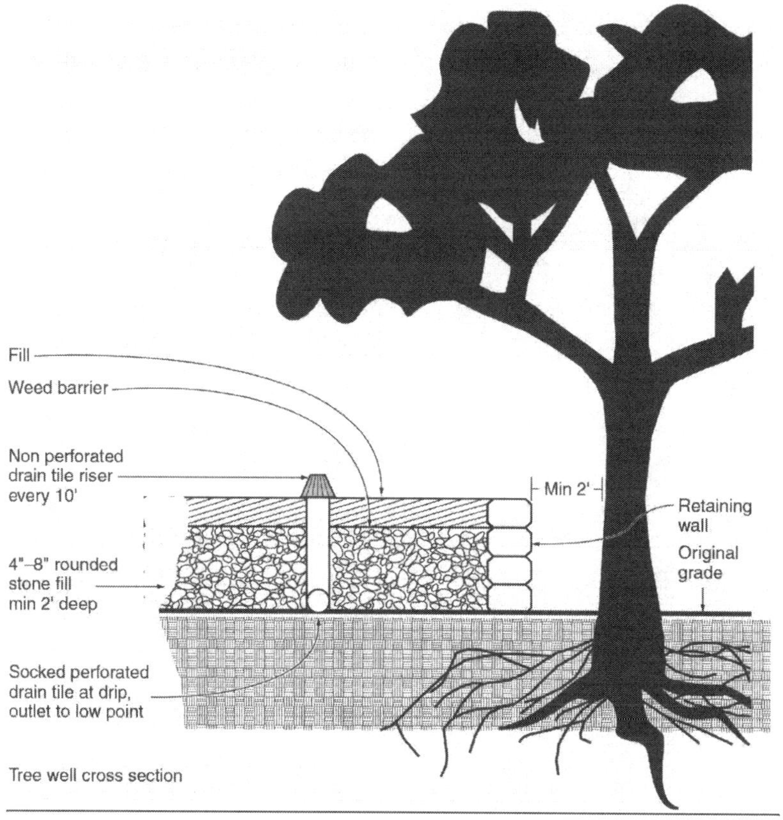

Figure 10-8 Cross section view of a typical tree well.

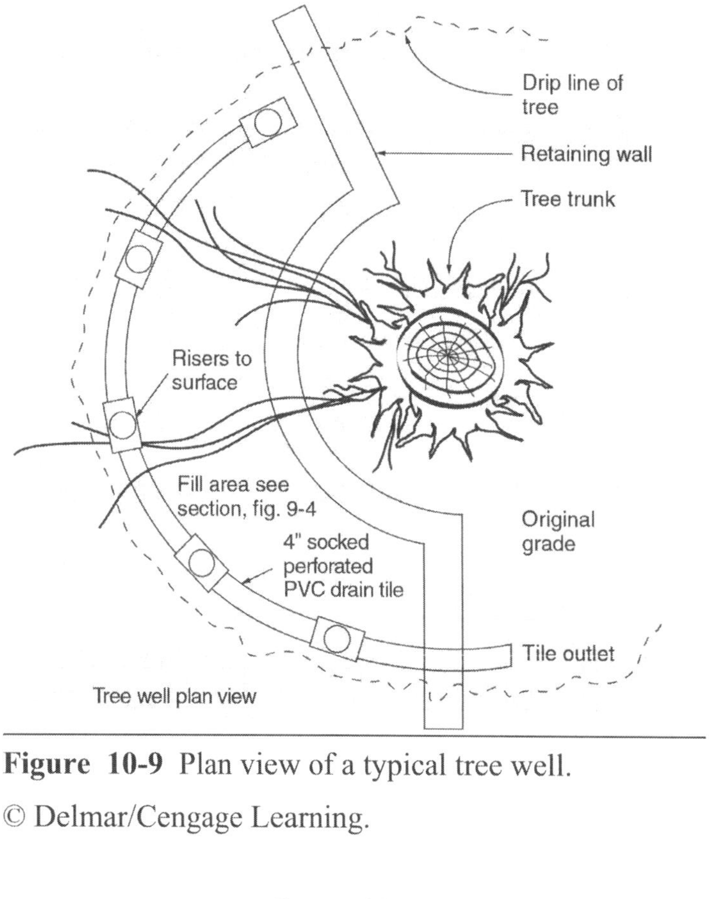

Figure 10-9 Plan view of a typical tree well.

continuous footings, or installing footings using the grade beam described in the retaining wall unit, will begin the preservation process.

Hand-dig in the root zone to the greatest extent possible. When it is unavoidable to remove roots, cut them with a pruning saw, rather than ripping them apart with equipment.

On some construction sites, the source of damage to plant material is well beyond the drip line. Contractors who take advantage of a shade tree to mix caustic chemicals run the risk of damaging plants from spills and leaks. Even changes in drainage patterns from grading activities can lead to plant material damage.

Protection of plant canopies from construction damage can include covering the plant or temporarily tying the branches up/back to keep them out of harm's way. Secure the plants loosely, and do not leave them tied for more than 2–3 days to avoid permanent damage. Placing sheets of plywood over turf will provide temporary protection in an area that may be subject to heavy traffic for a few days. Again, only leave such protection in place for 2–3 days to avoid permanent damage to turf areas.

For locations where occasional traffic will be routed under existing trees, prune the lower branches to a height that is above the equipment's height. When trees must be cut down, direct the tree's fall from plant material to be saved. Limit pruning in stands of trees that are to be protected so that the impact of a sudden change in microclimate is mitigated. Lastly, to make all contractors aware of the concerns regarding protecting the plant zone, post signage that indicates the area to be protected and the prohibited activities within protection zones.

STRUCTURE PROTECTION

Structures are provided a level of protection by their size and their dominance of the land- scape. Even with this inherent protection, structures are vulnerable to damage from landscaping operations when care is not taken. Windows can be covered with plywood to protect from shovels, gravel, and other flying objects. Staple or tape sheets of plastic over finished side walls of structures to prevent damage when painting, pouring concrete, cleaning surfaces, or performing any activities likely to splatter materials. Corners of structures can be protected by placing wood fenceposts on either side of the corner, particularly in locations where traffic is routed near a corner. Routing traffic from a structure and placing storage areas apart from buildings also reduce the potential damage from equipment and activities.

PAVEMENT PROTECTION

When a construction project requires that foot or light traffic be routed across existing paved areas, care should be taken not to damage such surfaces. Rubber track equipment will minimize damage to concrete and asphalt surfaces unless the pavement base is already in poor condition. Rubber deposits may be left on concrete after construction and can be removed with water and scrubbing. Unit paved surfaces, such as brick and limestone, may be damaged by any equipment and should be protected using the methods outlined for heavy traffic.

Heavy traffic requires protection that will prevent cracking and settling. Simplest among the protection techniques is to route traffic around the paved area. If rerouting is impossible, mound 12 inches of soil over the pavement in the area where the traffic will be crossing (Figure 10-10). This will redistribute the weight and reduce the stress on the pavement. An alternative is to build a temporary bridge out of 4 × 4s and large-dimensioned (4 × 12, and up) wood planks (Figure 10-11). This method will transfer the weight to the ground surrounding the pavement.

UTILITY PROTECTION

Damage can occur from heavy traffic passing over utility lines buried at a shallow depth. Particular concern should be given to shallow irrigation lines, shallow gas lines in copper or PVC pipe, and PVC or clay drainage tile. Protection can be provided in these instances by increasing the soil depth over the line or by placing 2 × 12 lumber in the tracks of the path over the utilities. Low overhead utilities should be avoided or temporarily relocated to reduce the risk of contact with vehicles and workers.

Figure 10-10 Building a temporary bridge during construction.

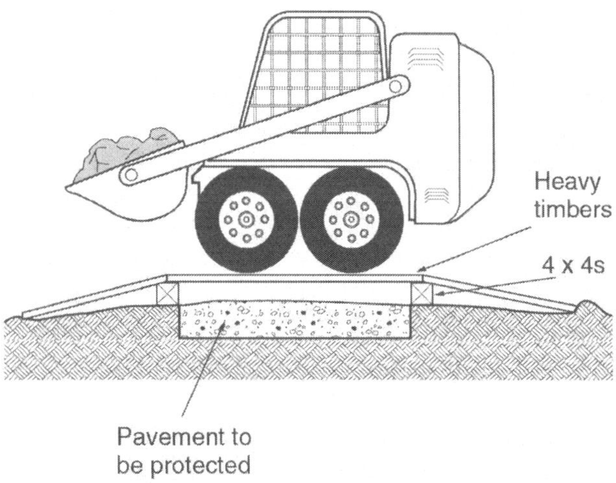

Figure 10-11 Temporary bridging to protect paving from construction traffic.

PERIMETER PROTECTION OF CONSTRUCTION SITE

Temporary fencing should be erected at all construction sites to protect the public from the hazards of an in-progress work area. Broken or removed pavement, open excavations, and unfinished surfaces are just a few of the potential danger areas from which an unsuspecting public could sustain injuries. Temporary fencing can be brightly colored utility fencing stretched tightly between posts (Figure 10-12) or chain-link fencing temporarily installed or anchored in concrete blocks (Figure 10-13).

PRESERVATION OF SOIL

Soil, like plant material root zones, is often overlooked when providing protection to a construction site. Assumptions are made that soil

Figure 10-12 Installing temporary fencing at a construction site to protect the public from hazards.

is a benign element of the site and, if damaged, can be easily replaced. Many contractors do not know that healthy soil is a living organism that, through its many components, provides life for the plant material on which landscape contractors base their livelihoods. Soil is a blend of minerals, organic matter, air, water, and soil organisms that produce the nourishment that plants rely on for growth. Damage to the soil, whether by grading, compaction, or trenching, disrupts this complex organism to the point that it can no longer provide that nourishment. Whenever possible, completely avoid construction activity on healthy soil. If construction is necessary, consider adding a 4–6 inch layer of mulch over the soil to limit compaction. When soil is disturbed, consult a landscape architect or horticulturalist to determine the best way of mitigating the damage. Damage can be compounded when soil repair with inappropriate amendments is implemented.

PROTECTION OF ENVIRONMENTALLY SENSITIVE AREAS

Construction activities that deal with exterior environments are likely to have issues regarding protection of sensitive areas. Recognizing the importance of preserving delicate natural environments has led to approaches that mitigate the negative impact of construction on areas such as woodlands, wetlands, prairies, dunes, and wildlife habitats of all types. Probably the most important ingredient in the approach to sensitive areas is the contractor's awareness. As workers who are engaged in the development of the environment, we must be the first to recognize the need to value these areas and to actively engage in preservation activities.

The most effective step in protecting sensitive areas is to avoid direct and indirect construction activities in them. Compaction of soil in a

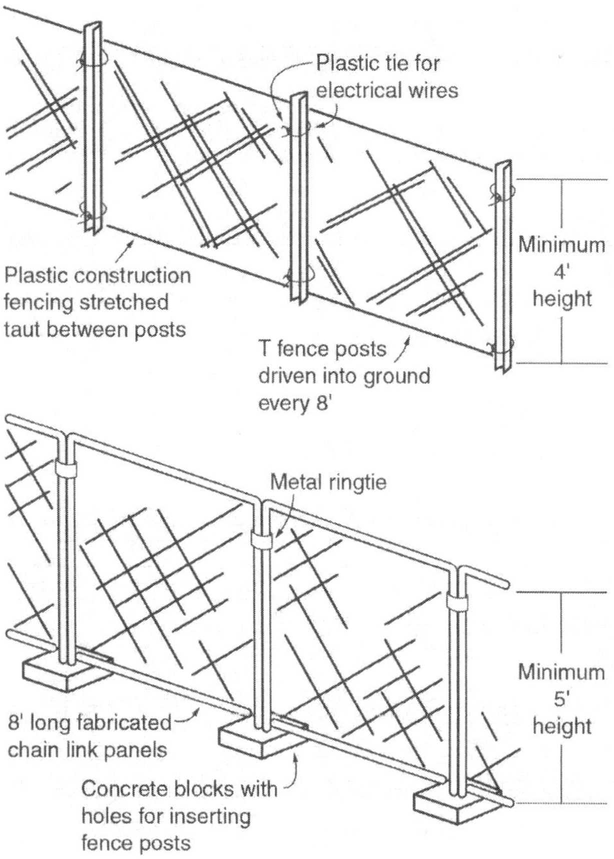

Figure 10-13 Temporary fencing methods used to protect public from construction hazards. Top figure shows plastic fencing on posts, and the bottom figure shows temporary chain-link fencing.

wooded area or even temporary draining of a wetland can do irreparable damage. Even minor changes in the environment around the area can change the characteristics of a wetland or a forest. If construction can avoid the sensitive area, the chances of preservation are improved. Contractors from nonlandscape trades may lack the knowledge to identify and preserve sensitive landscapes; hence, identification is an initial step to preservation. Fencing the area beyond the perimeter will assist in identification. Notifying all workers and inspectors will also aid in protection. Indirect construction can also play a significant role in damaging sensitive areas. Runoff from projects should be redirected if possible. Silt fence (see Figures 13-2 and 13-3) should be installed to prevent eroded soil from passing into a protected area.

In the event that construction must take place within the boundaries of a sensitive area, certain precautions can be taken to minimize the potential damage. Limit disturbing activities such as grading, utility work, and deliveries to a single corridor through sensitive areas. Provide temporary cover such as mulch or planking for the circulation routes through such areas. Suggest boring utilities under protected areas, rather than trenching through them.

CHAPTER 11

REMOVING UNWANTED SITE ELEMENTS

OBJECTIVES

By reading and practicing the techniques described in this chapter, the reader should be able to successfully complete the following activities:

- Identify elements of a construction site that need to be removed.
- Effectively remove site elements.
- Removing existing landscape elements seems foreign to the concept of landscape construction, but most projects require some level of demolition to make way for new elements.

RELATED INFORMATION

Information in this chapter is supplemented by instruction provided elsewhere in this text and in other sources. Before undertaking the activities described in this chapter, read the related information in these sources:

- Safety in the Workplace, Chapter 7
- Preservation of Existing Site Elements, Chapter 10
- Erosion Control, Chapter 16

PLANT MATERIAL REMOVAL

Techniques for removal of plant material differ, depending on the type and size of plants being removed. When removing plants, you must remove the majority of their vegetative parts. Uneven settlement will occur in paving or finish grades if, for example, you leave large portions of stumps in place to decay. Excavating all roots is impractical, but you should remove root crowns and large feeder roots. Also, do not bury plant material waste in areas where finish grade is critical.

Stripping sod and ground cover requires scraping a thin layer of plant growth off a large area. Cut and remove the material by hand or use a sod cutter, and pick up debris with a skid-steer. A technique for larger areas is using a skid-steer with a toothed bucket to peel the sod away from topsoil. This technique requires an experienced operator and more fill because the bucket removes more topsoil with the sod. For very large projects, contractors may use huge earthmoving equipment such as a paddle scraper to successfully peel the ground cover away from the topsoil over large areas.

Removing Shrubs

Shrub removal requires two steps to successfully remove plant debris. Canes or branches of shrubs are cut and removed; then the crowns or roots are dug out and removed. To facilitate the removal of shrub canes, tie twine around the canes and pull them into a bundle; then cut at the base using a chainsaw. This technique works for all but a few spreading and prostrate shrubs and speeds the removal and disposal process. Remove the crowns by hand-digging around and under the crown or by excavating a trench around the roots, hooking a chain around the crown, and pulling the crown out with a tractor. A backhoe will speed the process by excavating the entire crown in one operation. Prostrate shrubs can be removed in a single step by undercutting and lifting them out with a skid-steer.

Removing Trees

Tree removal requires a systematic removal of plant parts, from crown to roots. Begin with the removal of as much of the plant's crown portion as can be removed safely from the ground. Using the steps outlined in the following list, fell the remaining portion of the tree. Remove and dispose of the remaining crown and trunk portions; then remove the stump. To safely cut down trees that do not meet the restrictions outlined in the Caution, follow the steps listed.

CAUTION

Safe felling of a tree requires the operator to be aware that even a small tree carries a great deal of weight and force when falling. These operations require specialized training, equipment and insurance and should be performed only by those professionals with the proper training and experience.

CAUTION

Removal of trees requires use of power equipment. Follow manufacturer's safety instructions for equipment operation.

- Determine the direction for the tree to fall. The direction of fall can be controlled to a certain degree, but gravity will tend to pull the plant in any direction it is leaning.
- Verify that an area twice as long as the tree's height and twice as wide as the tree's spread is clear of any improvements and other large plants.
- Clear an escape path from the tree and from the direction planned for the tree to fall (Figure 11-1).
- At approximately 4 feet above the ground and on the side of the tree facing the direction the tree is planned to fall, cut a *V*-shaped notch one-third of the way through the trunk.
- On the side opposite and slightly above the *V* cut, begin cutting down at an angle toward the point of the *V*. Do not cut all the way to the *V*, and do not stop cutting until the tree begins to fall (Figure 11-1).
- When the tree begins to fall, remove and stop the saw and walk away along the planned escape route. For even a small tree, move 10–15 feet away from the tree to avoid the possibility of the tree "kicking back" toward the operator.

When the tree has been **felled**, cut the side branches off the main trunk. Use caution when completing this operation because the trunk may shift when a supporting branch is removed. Branches may be bent under the tree and snap back when cut. After removing side branches, cut the trunk into manageable pieces that can be hauled away. Grub small stumps using a skid-steer with forks or a backhoe. In some circumstances, you may want to rent a stump grinder to remove the aboveground portion. Large stumps require a great deal of excavating to remove the majority of the roots.

PAVEMENT REMOVAL

Removal of pavement and other permanent improvements is a labor-intensive operation. Rental of specialized demolition equipment for this phase of work is highly recommended if large areas of pavement need removal.

Preparation for removal of pavement varies, depending on the type of pavement being removed. If portions of the pavement are to be saved, cutting with a concrete saw is required before removal can occur. Unit paver surfaces require the removal of edge-restraint material to allow access to the surface. Slab pavement usually requires that the slab be broken into pieces for removal and hauling. For small areas, you can perform this operation by hand with a sledgehammer or jackhammer; but for larger areas, you will need equipment such as a backhoe or excavator.

Portable jackhammers are either air-or pneumatic-powered. To effectively remove pavement using a jackhammer, use a breaker bar to score the concrete into pieces small enough to be hand removed. Start the jackhammer removal by driving shallow indentations every 4 inches along the score line. Have an assistant place a

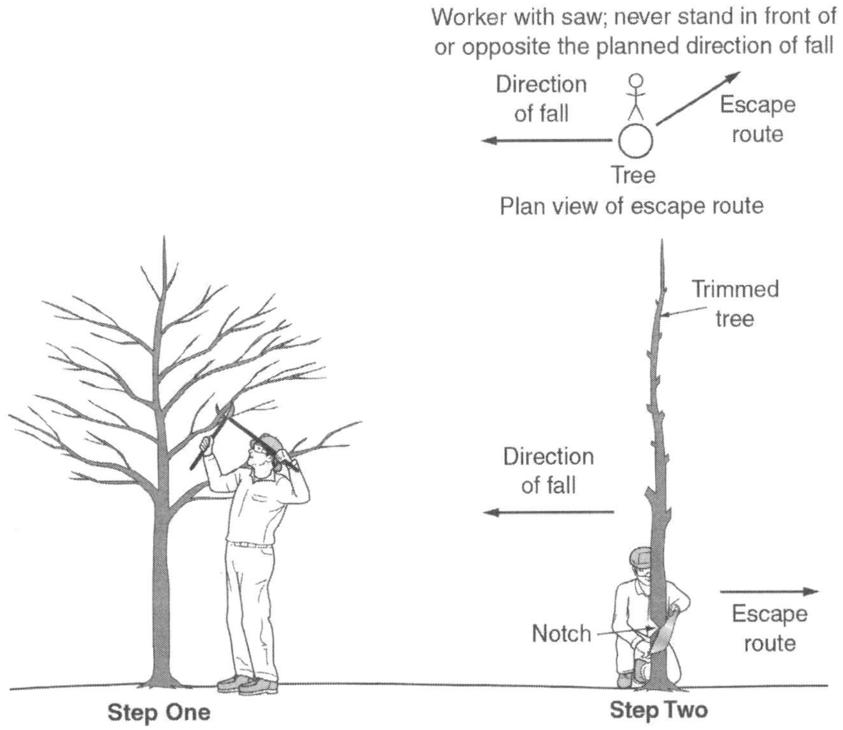

Figure 11-1 Removal of a small tree.

levered bar under the portion you are attempting to remove and lift up on that piece. As you continue working down the score line, the pavement should break (Figure 11-2). You know concrete is fracturing when the tone of the hammering becomes deeper. If the pavement does not fracture after the entire piece has been hammered, repeat the process; but this time drive the point of the hammer completely through the pavement. If the driving point becomes stuck in the pavement, disconnect the jackhammer. Install another point in the jackhammer and drill around the stuck point until the concrete is loosened.

When larger areas of pavement need to be removed, contractors often use a skid-steer or other large equipment. A skid-steer bucket can lift and drop the pavement, breaking it into more manageable pieces, or contractors can pre-saw the slab into pieces and then lift them out with the skid-steer bucket. Some contractors rent larger equipment that can remove slab pavement without breaking it into smaller pieces.

After the slab is broken into manageable pieces, locate a spot along the edge where equipment can work under the pavement to begin lifting it out. Excavate soil away from that portion of the slab to allow access under the slab. Work carefully in removing the old surfacing. Caution is advised here; pieces of the pavement should not be forced against structures, footings, or other improvements that need to remain intact. Working at right angles to, rather than toward, structures can reduce damage to existing footings or foundations. Backhoes are used to excavate working areas around footings and foundations that are buried to frost depth. Using the backhoe bucket, the operator can then break and remove these structures.

CAUTION

When removing concrete, always wear protective clothing and gear. Eye wear, gloves, long pants, and ear protection are essential.

Figure 11-2 Using a portable jackhammer to break up pavement to be removed from a site.

UTILITY ABANDONMENT AND REMOVAL

Unearthing and removing old cables and pipes for utilities will reduce confusion for future excavation projects. These processes are often regulated by local codes, ordinances and easement restrictions and are usually performed by specialty contractors. Abandoned utilities for a site are usually disconnected, capped, and left in place. A certified technician should perform these operations, particularly for gas, electric, fiber optic, potable water, and sanitary sewer lines. If possible, abandoned utilities should be physically removed.

Landscape construction crews sometimes encounter storm water drain lines and tiles. If the lines are active, they should be reconnected or rerouted to avoid new construction. Inactive lines should be capped or plugged to prevent subsurface drainage problems. Such lines can be capped with a PVC cap placed over the end of the pipe, or they can be plugged by placing mortar or **bentonite** into and over the end of the abandoned line. Abandoned utility lines, particularly drainage and sewer lines, may appear inactive during part of the year but then run at capacity during other times. For this reason, removing drainage and sewer lines to their source, rather than capping or plugging them, is often the better option.

BURIAL AND ABANDONMENT OF UNWANTED SITE ELEMENTS

Contractors may be tempted to cover over existing site elements, rather than removing them. This practice is not recommended for the following reasons:

- Local codes and ordinance may regulate this practice.
- There is always uncertainty and confusion when utility lines are later uncovered.
- Buried site elements can restrict plant growth. Roots for trees and shrubs may not

be able to reach groundwater levels, and sod may dry out faster over an old improvement left in place.

- Future excavation is made more difficult and expensive when old footings or slabs are uncovered.
- Settlement of topsoil will take place at different rates over old site elements left in place.

If on-site burial of waste is planned, be certain that the operation is legal and the waste pit is in an area free of any existing or planned structures, pavement, or utilities. Burial pits should be covered with a minimum of 5 feet of soil to provide adequate base for plantings.

RECYCLING AND WASTE DISPOSAL

Methods for waste disposal in landscape construction run the range from using landfills to creative recycling and reusing by-products. Whether environmentally sensitive or insensitive, disposing of landscape waste is an issue for which landscape contractors must prepare. Restrictions on placement of organic waste in landfills and markets for recycled material now counterbalance the temptation to place all waste in a landfill. Because quantities of recyclable materials are generally small for a single project, contractors may find that stockpiling of materials or taking several small loads to the recycling plant is more cost-effective. If contractors make the effort to reuse and recycle, they can use many by-products of site preparation in other aspects of landscaping.

Use caution when removing, transporting, recycling, and disposing of hazardous materials. The following paragraphs discuss ways to dispose of materials that are removed from the landscape.

Reusing Landscape Materials

Piecemeal adaptive reuse of old landscape materials has been taking place for decades. Following are a few creative suggestions for reusing hardscape material:

- Stone can be reused. This material is timeless and has several applications as walls, paving, steppers, edging, or lining swales.
- Bricks or pavers can be reused as paving, edgings or steppers.
- Concrete pieces can be used for paving and wall material or can be ground and spread as a loose aggregate surfacing. Verify that all reinforcing materials have been removed before reusing concrete pieces as a surfacing material.

Recycling Landscape Materials

Landscape contractors can recycle healthy, woody plant material by using a chipper to create shredded and chipped mulch. The parent material determines the quality and reuse value of this mulch. Material composed primarily of woody plant parts can be used for landscape beds, whereas material with small branches and foliage may be acceptable only for field mulch or **composting** purposes. Diseased or insect-infested plant material should be burned or buried, the choice depending on the disposal technique recommended for the ailing plant. Sod that is stripped from the site can be composted, along with miscellaneous plant waste.

Most landscape materials can be recycled. Many recycling centers accept metals from fences, wood from decks, plastic and metal from edging, concrete and asphalt paving, crushed bricks, wiring and piping, and many other undesired landscape materials. The quantities of waste generated and the time required to separate and deliver the materials often limit the extent to which contractors can engage in recycling.

Using Landscape Waste as Fill Material

When properly placed and compacted, certain waste soils can be used as fill. This filling procedure can be done on-site or transported to an off-site facility. Clean soil of the proper type and without debris is satisfactory for this procedure. Soil contaminated with wood, paving, or other nonsoil material is not suitable for trenching and future underground and should not be used. Soil surfaces become unstable when large quantities of organic material decompose; hence, sod strippings are not suitable as fill material.

Disposing of Material in a Landfill

Placing waste in the local landfill requires a minimum of effort, but this option can be expensive to contractors and the environment. Many localities enact strict regulations on what materials can be placed in landfills, including limitations on plant material. Paying fees based on the tonnage of material disposed, contractors typically haul and place the waste material. Organic materials, including green plant matter, are sometimes composted if the solid waste facility has the processing equipment.

Transporting Waste

When hauling waste over public roadways, contractors must ensure that proper enclosure is provided to prevent spillage. Using vehicles with tailgates or enclosed cargo areas or covering or tying down loose plant waste may be required. Review with municipalities and state transportation departments for regulations regarding proper hauling of waste.

SECTION 2

SUMMARY

Initial work for a landscape site includes preparing for the planned construction. Any site elements to remain should be identified and protected, and those elements not incorporated into the design may need to be removed. Section 2 identified construction techniques basic to these steps, along with standard site protection and demolition activities.

For large projects, preservation of existing site elements can cover many activities; for small projects, a simple marking of plant material may be the only activity needed. Typical considerations when preparing a site for construction include identification of a safe, legal access to the site and secure storage of materials. Most projects will also require identification and, in some cases, fencing the limits of the construction. If layout was performed using benchmarks or baselines, those reference points should be clearly marked to avoid future disruption.

Throughout the project, landscape contractors should consider how construction impacts existing plant material. Plants to be preserved should be protected from compaction, trenching, and other construction activities within, at least, the critical root zone. Permanent improvements such as structures, pavement, and utilities also require protection from construction damage. These preservation techniques may range from marking to fencing the improvement. Environmentally sensitive areas also require special attention when construction activities are in proximity of wetlands, prairies, woodlands, and similarly protected plant and wildlife areas. Avoiding the sensitive area provides the best measure of preservation. However, in cases where avoidance is impossible, contractors may have to provide protected corridors and perimeter protection. Installing tree wells to protect mature plant material is one example.

Removal of unwanted site elements may require cutting out plant material or demolishing old site elements. Attention to safety should be a priority when removing old site features, particularly large plants, structures, and utilities. Because the action impacts future work, burial or abandonment of unused site elements is not recommended. Proper disposal, including reusing and recycling of landscape waste, is required for any demolition project.

SECTION 3

GRADING, SITE DRAINAGE, AND EROSION

INTRODUCTION

Water and soil play leading roles when considering the many elements of the typical landscape. A contractor's ability to properly manipulate these two elements often determines a project's long-term success or failure. Soils vary significantly in terms of composition, texture, stability, and fertility. If the soil is not the right type or not placed in the proper amount using appropriate procedures, improvements may settle prematurely and plants may perform poorly.

Water's role in the landscape is probably more extensive than that of any other element. Controlling water can reduce the impact of such landscape problems as drought, frost heaving, **erosion,** settling, and ponding. The interaction of water and soil can cause erosion, one of the most devastating landscape problems. Improper manipulation and inadequate protection of a site's surface are common problems in landscaping projects of all sizes.

The chapters of this section explore the steps of the grading process, methods for effectively draining water from a site, and protecting a site from common forms of erosion. Included is a review of the grading process, which is often split into rough grading steps that occur during the initial steps of the construction process, and finish grading, which typically occurs near the end of the process. Performed in concert with grading, development of drainage systems must effectively remove unwanted water from a site without flooding, eroding, or otherwise disturbing the site's surface improvements. This challenge is addressed in the development of surface drainage patterns and, if necessary, the addition of subsurface drainage structures.

Techniques are presented for grading surface slopes and swales to provide positive drainage throughout a construction site. Subsurface systems such as tiles, french drains, and storm sewers are also introduced as more comprehensive methods for dealing with large quantities of storm runoff and water problem areas. Erosion protection concentrates on protecting a site's perimeter from runoff, providing surface protection from sheet erosion, and reducing channel problems from gully erosion.

WORKING WITH SOIL

Essential to successful grading and erosion protection is understanding the types of soils on the site and the suitability of those soils to perform the functions required by the landscape plan. Soil is an amalgam of minerals, organic matter, and living organisms interspersed with voids of varying sizes that are filled with air and/or water. The mineral and organic components determine the physical and chemical properties that allow us to predict if we can build structures or grow plants on a given soil. The parent material that formed the soil and the environment in which the soil was formed determine these properties, which in many cases can be altered with soil amendments or, in the case of structural uses, removed and replaced with a more suitable soil.

A wide variety of living organisms enhance the mineral and organic components of soil. These organisms, which include bacteria, fungi, algae, arthropods, and many species of insects and micro-organisms, are responsible for the decomposition of the mineral and organic component into nutrients that plants use for growth. This living component of the soil also provides the "glue" that holds soil together, makes it resistance to diseases, and enhances the overall performance of plant material. Where soils have been undisturbed, even in poor environments, this rhizosphere (or root zone) is a fragile environment that cannot be recreated by adding amendments or soil replacements. Although some disruption to a site cannot be avoided during construction, making sound judgments about the soil environment and the extent of the disruption will ultimately lead to the best landscape possible.

Soil types have an impact on whether a soil can be reused on the site, whether it must be disposed of off-site, whether structures can be built on it, or how susceptible it is to erosion. It would be impossible to define the characteristics of all soil types in this text, but one basic trait of soil that provides clues to its workability is its composition. Soil is composed of three basic particle types—silt, sand, and clay. Each soil type is a combination of these particle types, and the percentage of each determines the soil's stability and suitability for landscape tasks.

Specific information regarding the suitability of site soils can be obtained from soil testing, a soil survey book, soil conservation service, or, for critical areas, from a soils engineer. The following Chapter on Soils includes detailed descriptions of the physical, chemical and organic characteristics of the soil that Landscape Contractors are likely to encounter. Reviewing and understanding this information will improve the success of any landscape project.

SUSTAINABILITY SUGGESTIONS

- Take whatever measures are available to preserve soil on your site. Soil is not just a site commodity to be manipulated solely for the purpose of supporting structures and sculpting the site. Rather, soil should be treated as the complex organism it truly is. Leaving soil undisturbed during construction would be the highest level of protection that can be afforded. Within soil is a complex network of minerals, organic matter, and organisms that, once disturbed by grading equipment, can seldom be recreated. Once soil has been dug, moved, compacted, or altered in other ways, it will take much time to return to its level of original productivity.
- Minimize erosion of soil from a construction site.
- Manage water on your site with conservation in mind. Use technologies that store water for reuse or allow water to be returned to the soil, rather than allowing rain and irrigation excess to run off the site.
- Carefully consider your equipment needs, rather than automatically choosing power equipment over hand labor. In fact, performing tasks with hand tools may be more cost-effective and more environmentally sound than hauling large pieces of gas-powered equipment to the site to perform those tasks.
- Consider alternatives to copper gutter and downspouts. Copper is harmful to certain fish in areas where runoff drains into natural waterways.

PRODUCTIVITY SUGGESTIONS

Grading a site is one of many weather-sensitive landscape activities. Effective completion of construction requires practice of techniques that counter the problems associated with weather. Following are some suggestions for reducing the impact of inclement weather:

- Avoid working soils high in clay or organic matter content when they are wet.
- When working in dry conditions, lightly wet the soil before compacting. Dry soil shifts rather than compacts.
- If rain is anticipated, do not strip sod and surface vegetation. The drying process takes longer if a site has been exposed to the elements.
- Consider how water will drain from the site at all stages of the grading operation. Avoid creating low areas where water will pond and drying will be slow.
- Provide temporary erosion protection throughout the grading process.
- Maintain a covered stockpile of dry topsoil that can be accessed when an exposed site is still we.

CHAPTER 12

BASIC SOILS FOR LANDSCAPE CONTRACTORS

OBJECTIVES

By reading and practicing the techniques described in this chapter, the reader should be able to successfully complete the following activities:

- Define soil
- Describe the importance of soil to the landscape
- Identify soil textures
- Identify soil structures
- Amend a soil to improve plant growth
- Identify a soil that will cause structural problems for hardscape
- Describe how water, gases and nutrients react in the soil
- Identify the pH of a soil
- Select a fertilizer for a soil

When walking through any landscape project it is easy to spot the impacts of soil. Whether supporting the paving you are walking on or anchoring the plant material, soil is a foundational element of the landscape. Yet despite this important role in the landscape soil is often overlooked, mistreated, or misunderstood. Builders seldom concern themselves with protecting soil as a resource and move the ground only to create the shapes that they desire. Landscape professionals shape and dig in the soil only to achieve the forms and grades needed for the garden. In almost every situation those who work on a site must consider that soil is not only a medium for building, but a living organism capable of supporting growth that can lead to success or failure of a project. Because of this ignorance of soil, this chapter is intended to share some of the basics of soil, from what makes it stable for building to what makes it a long-term medium for growing healthy and attractive plant material.

RELATED INFORMATION

Information in this chapter is supplemented by instruction provided elsewhere in this text and in other sources. Before undertaking the activities described in this chapter, read the related information in these sources:

- Preservation of Existing Site Elements, Chapter 10
- Site Grading, Chapter 13
- Erosion Control, Chapter 16
- Plant Material Installation, Chapter 34
- North Carolina Manual of Professional Horticultural Practice

SOIL DEFINITION

Soil can be described using many definitions. It has been defined as "a natural medium for the growth of land plants"[1], "a natural body comprised of solids, liquid, and gases that occurs on the land surface"[2] and "the highly dynamic epidermis of the earth"[3]. For the purposes of the

[1]SOIL SCIENCE SIMPLIFIED, PAGE 4:

[2]SOILS IN OUR ENVIRONMENT (2): 2006 KEYS TO SOIL TAXONOMY, SOIL SURVEY STAFF

[3]SOILS IN OUR ENVIRONMENT (3): Duane T. Gardiner, Raymond W. Miller

landscape industry the most useful definition would probably state that soil is a mixture of weathered rock, water, gases and organic material typically capable of supporting plant life and human activities. While this definition lacks the flowery descriptions found in many texts, it does characterize soil in the practical light that is unique to our industry.

IMPORTANCE OF SOIL

The landscape industry relies on soil to support almost every aspect of the industries work. Similar to the importance of water, the projects that are installed by the landscape construction professional would have no basis for support or growth were it not for the soil we build on and plant in. Soil provides the stability for a site, the medium of growth and the foundation for most of the hardscape elements that we place in our designs.

Plant Growth

Of the many functions of soil, supporting plant growth is probably the most important. Plants require a growing medium for stability and to thrive. Several key aspects of plant growth are provided by soil:

Anchorage. For plants to remain upright they need some form of structural medium in which the roots can grow. This medium is soil. Plant roots extend out from the base of the plant and into the surrounding soil, intertwining with soil particles and developing an extensive network of small roots that anchor the plant against movement.

Water. Almost the entire supply of water that plant material obtains is absorbed from the soil. The root system grows through the soil and intercepts or draws in moisture that is sequestered in voids in the soil structure. Without this soil moisture most plants would be doomed to a short life.

Oxygen. While plants are notorious for production of oxygen, they also require oxygen as one of the key nutritional elements for growth. Oxygen can be taken in through the atmosphere but plants also uptake oxygen through the root system. In addition, the microbial life that exists in the soil and breaks down nutrients for the plant require oxygen that is moving through the open channels and spaces in the soil.

Nutrients. Plants require a minimum of 16 different nutritional elements for normal growth, and those elements are provided through the weathered minerals and organic components of soil. In direct contact with the root system, these nutrients are released by the soil and taken in by the roots of the plant to support the many growth functions of the plant.

Structural Support For Building Projects

In the construction field, soil is literally the foundational element. Soil is needed in construction to "support a load or withstand stress without deforming excessively"[4]. This role for soil in the landscape is much different than the role of supporting plant material. When patios, walks, walls, structures and other hardscape elements are built the long-term stability of that element is dependent of the structural stability of the soil below it. Typically this requires soil with particular composition, as well as structural and textural qualities that resist movement when forces are applied. Sites may have soil with adequate structural characteristics to support what is built upon it, but if a site is lacking in stable soil it will impact the budget to have soil or base material brought in to provide that stability.

Affects On Erosion

The type of soil and any treatments applied to the soil can play a role in reducing the loss of soil to water or wind erosion. Conversely, soil vulnerable

[4]SOILS IN OUR ENVIRONMENT(13): Duane T. Gardiner, Raymond W. Miller

to erosion left unprotected can create an area where soil loss is possible. Clayey soils and soils that have been treated with soil binding agents (soil stabilizers) and soils that are planted are less likely to be taken away by wind or water. Soils that are sandy, loamy or that have no plant cover are likely candidates to be blown or washed away. Slope of the soil surface will be another factor that might protect soil from erosion or increase the possibility of soil loss.

UNDERSTANDING YOUR SOIL

Before beginning construction activities it is important to understand the type of soil that is present on your site and what characteristics of that soil will impact your work. The North Carolina Department of Agriculture offers soil testing service, and samples submitted can be analyzed for these characteristics (http://www.ncagr.gov/agronomi/sthome.htm). Testing required time to complete, so submit samples well in advance of beginning work.

SOIL MATRIX

To consider soil simply a mixture of degraded minerals would be understating its complexity. Soil includes materials that are in the solid, liquid and gaseous states, or phases, including a wide range of minerals, microorganisms, and decomposed plant and animal matter. While soils will differ based on their condition, location and composition, the ideal soil is considered to be 50% solid, 25% liquid (in the form of water) and 25% gas.

Solid. The portion of the soil that is in solid form would include minerals in various states of decomposition, living plant roots, decomposed plant and animal matter, and living microorganisms. The mineral component, typically making up approximately 45% of the soil, includes parent material from weathered rock. The rock has been broken down by physical or chemical means into progressively smaller particles to the point where the component elements of the parent material can be taken in by the plant as nutrients. The decomposed material, living plant roots and living microorganisms make up approximately 5% of soil. Each of these components play a role ranging from holding moisture, supplying nutrients, breaking down the mineral and organic soil particles to converting elements from one form to another.

Liquid. The liquid portion of the soil is water. For the ideal soil water is 25% of the soil volume, but this number can range considerably depending on soil conditions. When at the ideal state, water will fill a portion of the voids and channels in the soil performing a variety of functions.

Water is taken in by the plant for vital functions, but also aids in dissolving elements in the soil and transporting elements from one location to another. In soils with small or limited pore space the water percentage may be lower than soils with larger pores. In periods after rainfall or irrigation, water will displace the gaseous portion of the soil until it percolates or moves through the soil. These situations are acceptable if they occur on a periodic and temporary basis, but if the water fills and remains in the pores it will cause plant, and possibly, soil failure. In periods of drought, water can be reduced to only that microscopic layer of moisture that is bonded to the exterior of soil particles. In this case the lack of water can lead to failure of plants and almost complete drying of the soil.

Gas. The gaseous component of soil is the soil atmosphere and contains a similar range of gasses that would be found in earth's atmosphere. Again, in ideal conditions, the gas portion of a soil would compose 25% of its volume. Important in the soil atmosphere is the presence of oxygen. Oxygen is necessary for the microorganism component of the soil to perform their role of decomposition. When rainfall or irrigation occur the water displaces the gas portion of the soil. If this condition exists for an extended period the microorganisms and the plant material can be lost or severely damaged.

SOIL HORIZONS

Soil begins as rock, plant and animal material, and over time the forces of topography and climate

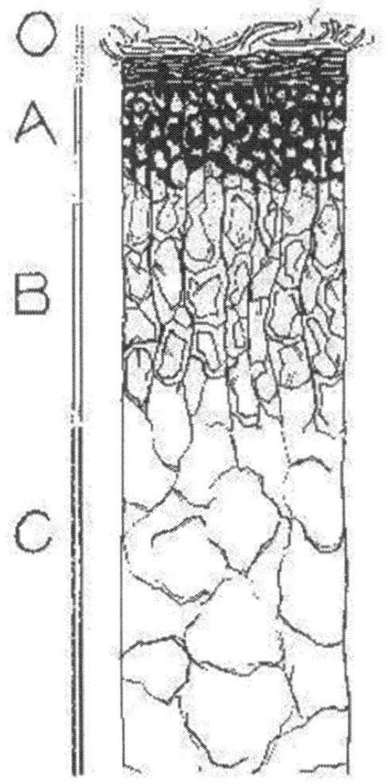

Figure 12-1. Soil horizons

break these elements down and recombine them into what we recognize. The soil forming factors of parent material, cover material and organisms, time, topography and climate work to compose a large number of unique soil types. In every region of the planet the differences in these factors have the potential to create a different soil. To study and classify soils science observes the layering, or horizons, of the soil to help determine formation and potential uses and limitations of a soil (Figure 12-1). Horizons are the horizontal layers of soil formed by the decomposition and deposition of parent material (rock and cover material and organisms) and, over time, leached to various depths. This text addresses only the major horizons found in a soil profile, but recognize that agronomists have classified numerous additional sublayers.

O – Organic Layer. Under the leaves and plant debris lies the organic layer. This horizon is comprised of decomposed (humus) or partially decomposed plant and animal matter and is typically very shallow.

A – Topsoil. Below the organic of a typical soil is a horizon dominated by minerals blended with organic material. The topsoil horizon is composed of a blend of mineral and organic materials that have been leached, or washed, downward from the organic layer. Once the plant debris on the surface is completely decomposed, water will pick up particles and carry then downward to mix with minerals. This horizon is also mixed through microorganism and small animal activity.

Decomposition is ongoing in this horizon as microorganisms continue to break the soil down into smaller and smaller particles. A horizons can range in depth from several feet in rich farmland to nonexistent in areas where there is little plant cover.

B – Subsoil. Below the topsoil is the horizon known as the subsoil. This horizon is predominantly clay particles, decomposed in the upper layers and carried downward by water and animal activity. B horizons can also range in depth from a few inches to several feet depending on formation conditions.

C – Parent Material. At the bottom of the soil profile is the C horizoSLifn. This horizon is a blend of mineral parent material that is in various states of decomposition mixed with clay from the upper horizons. It is not uncommon to find stones of various sizes scattered throughout this horizon. The C horizon can be several feet think and typically rests directly on bedrock.

SOIL TEXTURE

As the materials that make up soil (parent material or rock and cover material or plant/animal matter) decompose they are broken down into smaller and smaller sized particles. The mixture of various particle sizes along with other parts of the soil will determine how well water will flow through the soil, the fertility of the soil and other factors that relate to plant growth and support for structures. This mixture of particle sizes, also called soil separates, can be measured to determine a soil classification description called soil texture. Texture is the relative percentages of the three soil separates, sand, silt and clay, that are present in a given volume of soil. Once the texture of a soil is calculated, judgments can be made about the suitability for growing plants, how erodible the soil will be and if the soil can support landscape structures.

Soil Separates

It is the difference in size, arrangement and aggregation of the soil separates that make texture a valuable measurement for the landscaping professional. Knowing this characteristic of soil allows the landscape construction professional to determine if extensive modification of the site will be necessary before it can be planted or built. Classified by size, sand, silt and clay are the results of continued weathering and decomposition of the original parent materials. It is important to note that the terms sand, silt and clay refer to particle size and not the source or elemental composition of the particles (Figure 12-2).

Physical Characteristics of Separates

The characteristics of the soil separates determine in large part their ability to move water through the soil and the provision of aeration, nutrients and support. Each characteristic works in concert with the others to provide essential support for plant growth.

Size. The particles that compose soil are classified by size, with particles sizes determined by the following chart:

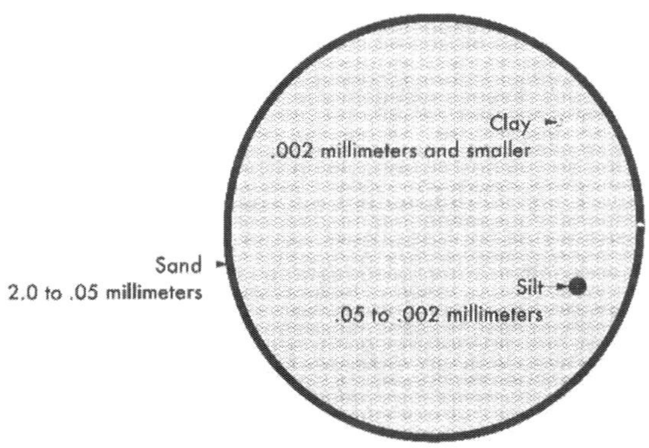

Figure 12-2. Soil separates.

- 2.0 to .05 millimeters Sand
- .05 to .002 millimeters Silt
- .002 millimeters and smaller Clay

Feel. Sand particles provide the grittiness that one feels in soil. When pressed between the fingers the sand will feel rough and grainy. Silt particles will feel smooth to the touch without stickiness. When dry silt feels much like flour when pressed between the fingers. Clay feels smooth and sticky to the touch. Pressing clay between the fingers will often leave a sticky residue.

Surface Area. Surface areas of soil particles can be deceptive. Clay, with its small size, has more surface area per unit volume than particles of silt and clay.

Pore Size. The shape of the separates dictates the amount and size of pore space within a soil. Clay particles are typically flat arrangements of molecules creating the resulting clay particles shaped like horizontal sheets. These sheets stack and arrange themselves in tightly packed layers of particles. This makes the pore spaces small, resulting in a strong molecular bonding with water and nutrients in the water. Sand particles are typically spherical in shape and stack with extensive open pores between particles that allow water to move easily through the soil. Silt particles are a variety of shapes that can both allow water to pass or gather.

Colloidal Impacts. Clay particles are composed of alternating layers of molecules of silicon and various elements. This unique structure exposes significant molecules with negative bonding sites on the surface of the particles. These bonding sites allow the clay particles to bond easily with particles with positive charges, such as water and many nutrients. Particles that exhibit this quality are termed colloids and the colloidal impact of clay particles is very high.

Soil Texture Triangle

Texture for a soil is described using terms that are descriptive of the proportional relationship of particle size within a sample. Example terms such as "sandy loam" and "loamy sand" describe two different soil textural classifications, each with a percentage of sand and clay but with the percentages of one particle size being larger than the other. Twelve classifications are used to describe soil textures based on the percentage of each particle size found in the sample. Several tests can be performed to determine texture including feeling the soil or squeezing a ribbon of soil between your fingers to get a general gauge, placing a sample in a jar and timing the settlement of particles and having a laboratory analysis performed.

In the more extensive tests that produce percentages of particle sizes, the chart below (Figure 12-3) is used to determine the classification. The chart, called the texture triangle, is read by locating the percentage of two of the particle sizes on the appropriate sides of the triangle.

From those locations follow the lines across the triangle in the directions the arrows are pointing. The location where the lines intersect will be in a sector of the triangle that is labeled with a texture classification. The entire triangle is divided into classifications that indicate the predominant physical properties of the soil being sampled. Located near the center of the triangle are seven sectors that use the term loam as part of the description. Loam is a textural classification for a "soil that does not exhibit the dominant physical properties of any of the (three particle sizes)"[5]. A loam does not necessarily contain equal parts sand, silt and clay, but loam shows properties of all three.

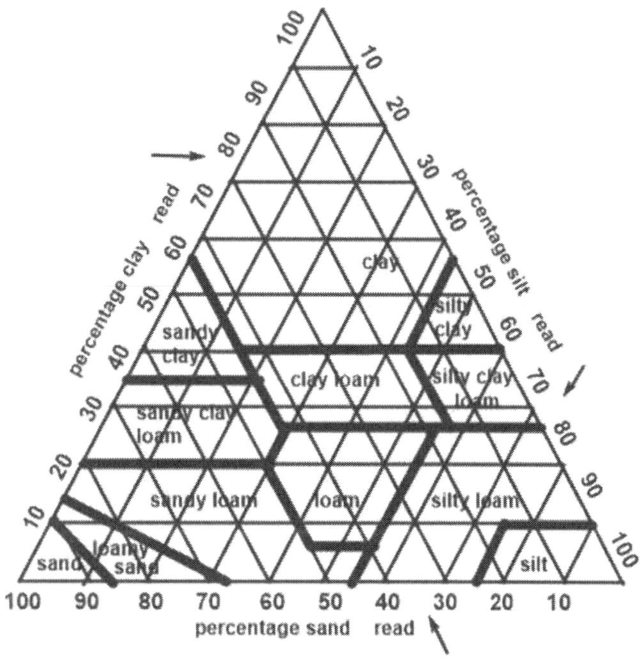

Figure 12-3. Soil Texture Triangle.

Affects Of Texture On Soil Behavior

Texture, as much as any physical property of soil, will impact the work done by the landscape construction professional. Soils that have a "fine" (clayey) texture will be less permeable yet be easier to compact, while soils that have a "coarse" (sandy) texture will be highly permeable but difficult to compact. Texture will also have an impact on erosion and other behaviors exhibited by soils.

Infiltration. Infiltration, or the rate at which water enters the soil, is very closely related to texture. When irrigating it is common that soils that are finely textured, clays and those soils in the upper half of the texture triangle, resist the infiltration of water. When dry, these soils may allow water to pass but when already wet the water will pool on the surface. Soils in the lower half of the texture triangle are more open at the surface and provide better infiltration when exposed to water.

Permeability. Permeability, or the movement of water through the soil, is also impacted by texture. Clayey soils and their tight pore spaces tend to draw water into their pore spaces and hold water more tightly than soils with open pore

[5]SOILS IN OUR ENVIRONMENT, pages 110-1), Duane T. Gardiner, Raymond W. Miller

spaces. Sandy and loamy soils typically have a looser structure for pore spaces and allow water to move in all directions freely.

Erosion. Erosion, or the loss of soil to the actions of wind and water, can be reduced or increased depending of the soil texture and related conditions. When dry, most soils can be eroded by wind, but coarse soils with high silt content are particularly vulnerable. When exposed to water all soils have the potential to erode, but silty and sandy soils can be washed away very quickly. This action is enhanced by increases in the slope and may make even clayey soils vulnerable.

Compaction – workability. Soils that are in the bottom third of the texture triangle will be challenging to compact without modification. Textures that include large amounts of sand tend to move when compacted, and soils with high silt amounts present the possibility of settling after being placed. For these reasons it is typically advisable to avoid soils high in sand or organic content as base for paving, walls and other structures that require stability. Clays and clayey sands, for the most part, provide good compaction for bases. It is important to know the type of clay that is present in the soil to avoid potential problems with the clay swelling when wet and shrinking when dry. This characteristic of clays such as smectite and vermiculite clays can be problems when used as base for paving and structures.

SOIL STRUCTURE

Soil structure refers to how the individual particles of soil clump, or aggregate together. Individual sand, silt and clay particles are bound together by organic substances, iron oxides, carbonates, silicas and other substances. The individual units of soil structure are termed peds. The result of this aggregation of peds is the creation of soil that has various behaviors based on the shape and size of the peds and the conditions under which the soil exists.

Peds Versus Clods

Someone who examines the soil may be able to easily identify the soil structure and view the individual peds. Peds are created by natural actions of climate, such as freezing and thawing, and the actions of water, decomposition and animal activity. Conversely, within the soil an observer may notice large aggregations of soil particles created by human activities such as tilling and excavation. These aggregates are considered clods, and will require the actions of nature or extensive hand work to break down into workable soil structures.

Types And Structural Traits Of Peds

The aggregates of soil structure can have distinct and varied shapes depending on their formation. While the shape is no guarantee of successful plant growth, peds that are granular are recognized as being the best soils in which to plant while the other shapes create limitations (Figure 12-4).

Crumb or granular. Granular soil structure is characterized by small, rounded peds that are glued together by organic materials and mixed by the actions of earthworms, rodents, frost and cultivation. Granular structures are found primarily near the surface of the soil and provide ample pores and spaces for soil water and gasses.

Platy. Platy structures are peds with a horizontal, flat orientation. Platy peds are typically found in areas where cultivation or compaction is common. These peds often bind tightly together and can difficult soils in which to grow plants.

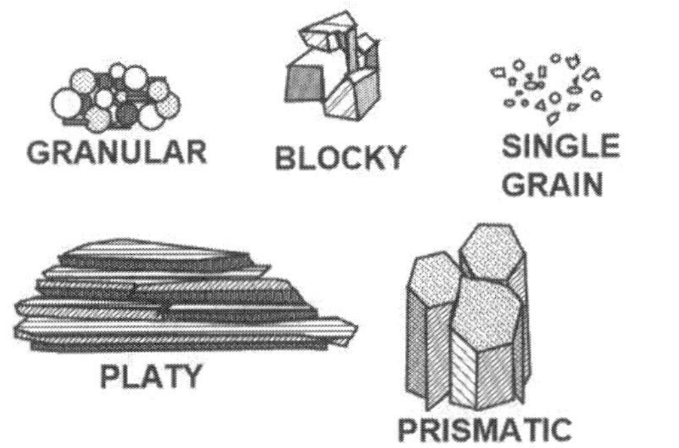

Figure 12-4. Soil structural peds.

Blocky. Block structures are composed of squarish or angular peds that are nearly equidistant on each side. Tiny blocks only a few millimeters across, block peds often are found in the subsoil and are characterized by high quantities of clay particles.

Prism Like. Prism structures are long aggregates with flat faces arranged in a prismatic shape. They are common to clayey subsoils. A closely related soil structure is columnar, which is similar to prism except for the rounded tops of the peds.

Structureless. Soils that lack any type of identifiable peds are classified as structureless. This would include soils that are non-consolidated sand (also called single grain structure), soils that have been heavily compacted or overworked and saturated clay (also called massive structure). In the latter two soils it is more likely to find clods rather than peds.

Soil Consistence

Soils exhibit an additional physical characteristic called consistence. Consistence is the soils ability to resist deforming or pulling apart when pressure is applied. Consistency will vary depending on whether a soil is wet, moist or dry and it is measured by applying pressure to a sample between the thumb and forefinger to calculate it's ability resist deformity and it's stickiness. This characteristic of soil is important to the landscape construction professional in that it can help determine the suitability of soil for a base and the difficulty that can be expected when working the soil. Unlike sandy soils, when loamy and clayey soils become wet they can expand and lose strength and stability. Conversely, when the soil dries it becomes plastic and shrinks. The chart below shows the relationships between soil types and consistency (Table 12-1)

SOIL TILTH

With the many factors that can influence the health of the soil and the ability to support plant growth, one concept that combines the many properties related to plant growth is soil tilth. Tilth can be defined as the suitability of a soil to support a crop. Other related definitions include the soils ease of tillage and the soils fitness as a seedbed and ability to allow root penetration and growth. In total, soil tilth considers the properties of structure, moisture, aeration and ability of water to move within the soil. A very ephemeral condition, good soil tilth is critical for those intending to grow plants in the soil. To obtain and maintain good soil tilth requires a regimen of sound soil practices including:

- Avoiding over tilling.
- Avoid screening soil.
- Avoiding tilling at improper times (when soil is wet or frozen)
- Adding organic matter
- Providing amendments that encourage good structure
- Maintaining proper soil moisture levels

SOIL WATER

Soil is the primary conduit of water to the plant material on a site.

Types and Stages of Soil Water

Water in the soil exists in several states. Some water is moving freely through the soil while some is tightly bound to the particles of soil. Some water is stationary while some moves from location to location. Depending on environmental conditions, several states of water and stages of plant dehydration can exist in a soil profile. Some important definitions and concepts related to water movement in the soil are described below.

Saturation. Saturation is the state where water from irrigation or rainfall has infiltrated into the soil and filled all of the pores. The state of saturation is typically temporary in soils with good permeability and will lasts for a short period of time until gravity and other forces move the water through the soil. Extended states of saturation create problems for plants and the microorganisms that are present in the soil.

Table 12-1. Soil Consistency.

	WET SOILS		MOIST SOILS	DRY SOILS	CLASSIFICATION*	MANUAL INDEX FOR CONSISTENCY*	SOIL TYPES
	STICKINESS	PLASTICITY					
INCREASING COHERENCE ↓	Nonsticky	Nonplastic	Loose	Loose	Very Soft	Extrudes between fingers when squeezed	Sandy
	Slightly sticky	Slightly plastic	Very friable	Soft	Soft	Molded by light to moderate finger pressure	to ↓
	Sticky	Plastic	Friable	Slightly hard	Medium Stiff	Molded by moderate to firm finger pressure	
	Very Sticky	Very plastic	Firm	Hard	Stiff	Readily indented by thumb, difficult to penetrate	Clayey
			Very firm	Very hard	Very Stiff	Readily indented by thumbnail	
			Extremely firm	Extremely hard	Hard	Indented with difficulty by thumbnail	

Chart adapted from lecture notes, Rob Harrison, University of Washington: http://soilslab.cfr.washington.edu/uhf475/notes/UHF475phys.html

*From the "Cohesive Soil" table in Uniform Field Soil Classification System, Michigan Dept. of Transportation: http://www.michigan.gov/documents/mdot/MDOT_SoilClassification_189904_7.pdf

Gravitational. Water in the gravitational state will drain from the soil by force of gravity. Gravitational water is typically flowing through the pores in the soil and is being held only by the irregularities in the pore space arrangement.

Field Capacity. Field capacity is the point where the soil has been fully wetted and gravity has removed the rest.

Hygroscopic water. When environmental conditions remove free water from the soil, water will still exist by clinging to the outer layer of soil particle molecules. This water is called hygroscopic water and is not available to plants for uptake.

Temporary wilting point. The temporary wilting point is a situation when a plant cannot absorb water fast enough from the soil due to environmental conditions. Plants recover from this situation when evening hours reduce the plants transpiration rate or plants receive water.

Permanent wilting point. The permanent wilting point occurs when plants attempt to absorb water from the soil but the soil is depleted of available water. This is a condition from which plants may not recover if not corrected.

Forces Moving and Holding Water in the Soil

Water within the soil uses a number of forces to move from point to point. When the soil is saturated, gravity will pull downward on water that is not attached to soil particles. After rainfall or irrigation the soil will be saturated with water molecules and, depending on the type of soil, this water will be pulled down and through the soil until all excess free moving water has passed. Water that is moved by gravity moves quickly through most soils and as it passes through the soil it can remove with it nutrient molecules, salts

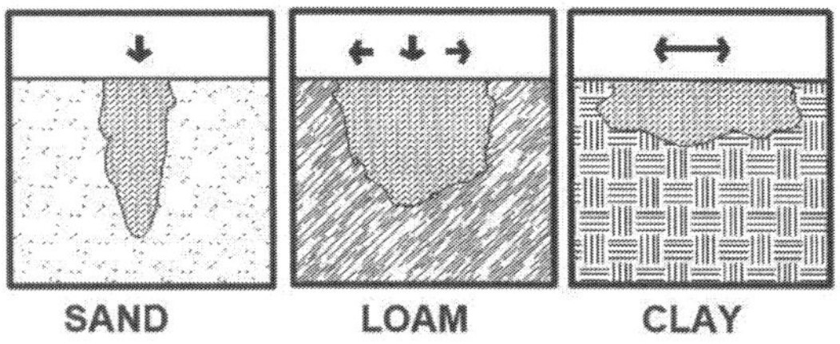

Figure 12-5. Wetting pattern in various soil textures.

and smaller soil particles. This process, called leaching, is responsible for the majority of particle movement downward in soil horizons. Water pulled by gravity may be utilized by plants if the water comes in contact with a root while passing through the soil. The water remaining is being held by soil particles or is nested in the pores of the soil peds so that it cannot be removed by gravity.

Water movement also occurs in the unsaturated state. This movement of non-free water occurs at a much slower pace and is prevalent during the periods between irrigation or rainfall. Water becomes bonded, or adsorbed, to the outer molecules of soil particles by a force called adhesion. This water, termed hygroscopic water, holds water tightly and is not available to plants. Bonded to the hygroscopic water are additional molecules of water held by a force called cohesion. Cohesive water resists gravitational forces and can be held in layers several molecules thick. The larger the surface of a soil particle the greater the amount of water that can be held. Cohesive water is available to plants and can move from particle to particle via a force called capillary action. Capillary action is a chain of linked water molecules pulled towards plant roots. Another force that moves water through the soil is potential. Water is attracted to the drier areas, called areas of lower potential, from areas that are wetter, or areas of higher potential. As plants lose moisture from transpiration through the leaves, a negative pressure is created throughout the plant and the roots use this negative pressure to draw water in. When exposed surface areas of soil are dried by the sun the water is drawn towards these areas from moister regions in the soil.

Available Water. With all these forces holding and moving water through the soil, how does the plant obtain this needed water. Within the soil there is water that can be absorbed by plants just by coming in contact with the roots. This water, which may be freely moving after irrigation or rainfall or may be loosely bonded by cohesion, is readily taken in by the plant. This type of water is considered available water because of its ease of availability to the plant. In addition, as plant roots grow they come in contact with water being held on the surface of soil particles and will absorb that moisture. Lastly, water can be drawn to the plant through potential and capillary action.

Water holding capacity of various textural and structural types. Soil texture will impact the ability of water to remain in the soil. Textures that are composed with high amounts of clay provide significant surface area and small pore spaces that hold large amounts of water. This water may be held so tightly that it becomes unavailable to plants through the traditional water movement forces. Alternately, soils that are sandy that have large pores will allow water to pass easily, allowing them to dry quickly. Soils that are silty and/or loamy and soils with a granular structure have a mixture of pore sizes and surface area that allow adequate amounts of water to be stored, while also making that water available to plants. Water flow through soils that have a granular structure is typically greater than the infiltration and percolation of water through platy and structureless soils. The infiltration and percolation rates through blocky and prismatic soils is intermediate.

Water Movement in the Soil

When water moves through the soil its directional movement is subject to the many forces described above. As irrigation or rainfall wets the soil the boundary between the saturated soil and the dry soil below can be unusual, but is predictable. The ability to predict the wetting front is predicated on the soil texture and structure and how the water is applied. Soils that are granular and composed of loamy or sandy soils will wet in a pattern that is even and representative of where the water is applied (Figure 12-5). Evenly applied water will form a horizontal front while water applied to a specific point will fan out in an inverted cone shape directly below the point of application. Sandy soils will form an almost vertical downward column of drainage. Soils that are platy or clayey will experience a wetting front that is more horizontal, regardless of where the water is applied. This is due to the clay pulling the water into its network of small pore spaces. Block and prismatic structures will drain in a downward manner with horizontal movement if the texture is clayey, with clay based soil structures pulling the water horizontally before releasing water to a more granular soil below. In any situation, recognize the difficulty in wetting soils that are clayey or granular soils that have a boundary adjacent to clayey soils.

SOIL CHEMISTRY AND FERTILITY

Among the properties exhibited by soil, chemistry and fertility are among the most important for plant growth. Soils are impacted by numerous chemical processes that add nutrients and create structure. Most important to the landscape professional is the process of supplying nutrients to plant material. This effectiveness of this process is dictated by the structure and texture of the soil and by the presence of the elements that can enhance or inhibit fertility.

Nutrients Required by Plants

Plant growth can be broken down to the elemental level by studying the compounds that the plant produces to initiate, maintain and regulate growth. Each of these compounds have basic molecular components that can be found in various quantities in the soil. Plants are known to require a minimum of 16 elements to grow, and each of these elements are provided, either wholly or partially, through the soil. These elements are available to the plant in the ionic form, meaning that they have either a positive or negative charge. This form of the element allows the nutrient molecule to remain in the soil attached to colloids and water. Certain elements are in compounds with other elements and many are pure forms of the element. The elements essential to plant growth include those listed below.

Carbon (C), Oxygen (O) and Hydrogen (H). These three elements make up the backbone of the compounds essential to plant growth. Few of the products produced in the plant are without at least one of these three elements. Despite their importance, it is rare to fertilize for any of these elements. Water and the atmosphere (both subsurface and surface) provide adequate supplies of C, H and O under normal circumstances.

Nitrogen (N), Phosphorus (P), Potassium (K), Magnesium (Mg), Calcium (Ca) and Sulfur (S). These six elements are considered macronutrients due to the quantities required by plants for normal growth. Provided from decomposing minerals in the soil and common basics of fertilizers, these elements form many of the plant compounds such as chlorophyll and regulating compounds.

Boron (B), Copper (Cu), Iron (Fe), Chlorine (Cl), Manganese (Mn), Molybdenum (Mo) and Zinc (Zn). This last group of elements are considered micronutrients because they are required in lesser amounts for plant growth. Despite the small quantities required, shortages of each may leave the plant vulnerable to deformities or environmental extremes.

These elements are provided to the soil through the decomposition of minerals and organic matter and through fertilization (covered below). The nutrients, in ionic forms and compounds, move through the soil by attaching to water molecules and are held in the soil by being adsorbed onto the many colloidal clay and humus particles present.

Cation Exchange Capacity

Without assistance from the chemistry component of soil, most nutrients that are decomposed in or added to the soil would be washed away by soil water. Fortunately the soil has numerous particles with high numbers of bonding sites for nutrients Mentioned earlier in this text, these particles are called colloids. The predominant colloids in the soil are certain clays and humus. "Soil colloids usually have a net negative charge and will attract and hold positively charged ions (cations) on or near their surface. Other cations in the soil solution that approach the held cation might be able to replace it, thus exchanging for it. This replacement of one adsorbed cation by another cation from solution is called cation exchange. ..Cation exchange takes place on the surfaces of certain clays and humus colloids and on the surfaces of plant roots."[6] Several nutrients are among the most common found on exchange sites in soils, including calcium, magnesium, and potassium. Cation exchange, or CEC, measures the total of exchangeable cations that a soil can adsorb. This measurement is expressed in centimoles of charge per kilogram of soil (CMOLc/KG). In addition to impacting fertility, CEC plays a role in the alteration of soil pH and soils with a high CEC can adsorb some of the cadmium, zinc and nickel pollutants from wastewater.

Soil pH

The primary soil factor that will impact the availability of nutrients in the soil is pH. In practical terms, pH is the measure of how acidic (acid) or alkaline (base or basic) the soil. In more scientific terms, pH, or power of hydrogen, is a measure of the number of hydrogen (H+) or hydroxyl (OH-) ions are present in the soil. Soil that has a balance of hydrogen and hydroxyl ions is considered neutral, and when balance or near balance is achieved, the nutrients in the soil are more available to plants. An excess of H ions will bond with nutrients in the soil and prevent them from being absorbed by plant roots.

pH chart and explanation of logarithmic scale. pH is measured on a logarithmic scale ranging from 0 to 14, with 7 the neutral point where H and OH ions are in balance (Figure 12-6). When reading the scale it is important to know that the values are logarithmic, or that each step on the scale is 10 times the previous step. Numbers below 7 indicate a soil that is more acidic. Other substances that are acidic in the order of least to most acidic would include coffee, orange juice and battery acid. If the number is above 7 the soil is considered to be alkaline, or basic. Substances that are alkaline in the order of the least to most alkaline would include baking soda, ammonia and bleach.

Affect of pH on nutrient availability. Understanding the measurement of pH is critical to helping the landscape professional prepare soil for successful plant growth. Soil can be tested to determine the pH using simple test kits available at a garden center or by having a laboratory test performed. Results are typically presented as a single number between 0 and 14 for each test performed. The result of the test and the types of plants being installed will determine if and what treatments are necessary. Most plants require a pH of between 6.0 and 7.5 to successfully pick up nutrients from the soil. Some plants prefer soils that are slightly acid or slightly alkaline. If the soil in which you are planting does not match the requirements for the plants then the soil must be amended to correct the problem. Note that soil pH can be altered in small areas for specialty plants (e.g a planting bed for rhododendrons) while the remainder of the site can be held at another pH.

Adjusting the pH. Correcting soil pH is a common practice for landscape construction professionals. After soil testing a determination can be made regarding the type and magnitude of the treatment. Remember that when changing the pH the soil will buffer against (resist) rapid pH changes and the amount of lime required to raise the pH increases as the CEC increases. pH modification is typically a process that will

[6]SOILS IN OUR ENVIRONMENT, pages 110-1), Duane T. Gardiner, Raymond W. Miller

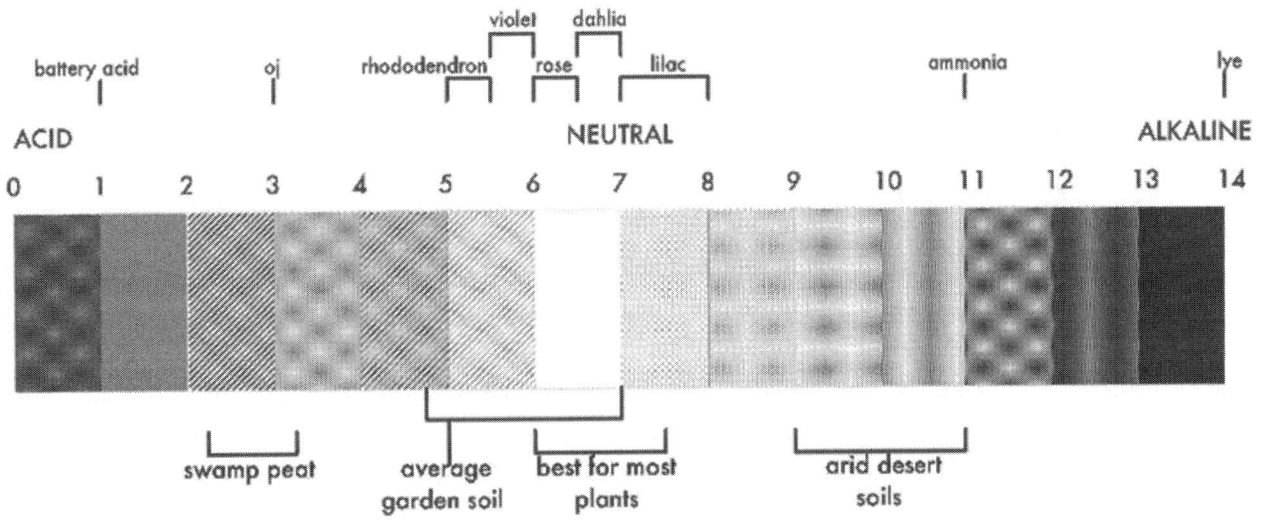

Figure 12-6. pH scale

require a number of treatments rather than a single application of soil amendment.

To adjust an acidic soil higher on the pH scale will require the addition of lime. Lime, and other calcium products bond with the H ions in the soil to bring the balance closer to neutral. The approximate amounts of lime added are shown on the following chart (please note these numbers are approximate and should be adjusted based on your individual site):

- Sandy soils: 10 to 25 lbs lime per 1000 square foot to raise pH by 1 point
- Loamy soils: 50 to 60 lbs of lime per 1000 square foot to raise pH by 1 point
- Clayey soils: 100 lbs of lime per 1000 square foot to raise pH by 1 point

To adjust an alkaline soil lower on the pH scale will require the addition of sulfur. Sulfur can be in elemental form and blended in as a soil amendment. The approximate amounts of sulfur added are shown on the following chart (please note these numbers are approximate and should be adjusted based on your individual site):

- Sandy soils: 20 lbs sulfur per 1000 square foot to lower pH by 1 point
- Loamy soils: 50 lbs of sulfur per 1000 square foot to lower pH by 1 point
- Clayey soils: too variable to estimate

Saline and Sodic Soils

In areas where salts are in large quantities in the water supply, plants may suffer from problems due to salinity and sodicity. Salinity is the presence of any type of soluble salt in the water (this could be potassium, nitrate or sulfate salts) and sodicity is the presence of sodium chloride salts in the water. Each of these conditions can be caused by the aquifer from which irrigation water is drawn of from the lack of leaching excess salts through the plant root zone. Another potential cause of saline and sodic soils is a high water table that retreats, leaving behind deposits of salts near the surface. Saline and sodic ions create problems by replace nutrient ions on CEC sites. In high concentrations in the soil water these ions can actually draw water out of the plant roots (exosmosis). Several plants, including ornamental plants and fruit trees are intolerant of saline and sodic soils and the presence of salts can cause soil structure to break down into a massive soil type.

Measuring Salt Problems. The presence of salts in the soil will require a laboratory test to measure the extent of the problem. Measures of salt may include a rating of EC, or electrical conductivity. Low numbers in this exam suggest few problems with salt, while high numbers can indicate severe problems. Another measure is SAR, or sodium adsorption ratio. This indicates the percentage of cations that are sodium. As with EC, higher numbers indicate severe sodic problems. Field indicators of salinity and sodic problems are a white crust forming at the surface of the soil (saline) or soil that has a black greasy surface (sodic).

Correcting Salt Problems. Correction of both conditions will require addressing the internal drainage of the soil, either with organic matter additions in minor cases or with the installation of sub-surface drainage in severe cases. Following the correction of drainage the soil should be thoroughly flushed to leach the salts through the soil. Sodic soils will require the additional step of adding gypsum (calcium sulfate) to bind with the salts prior to flushing.

ORGANIC MATTER

Soil would not be as attractive a growing medium were it not for the organic component. Organic matter plays a number of roles in the soil and each is nearly essential to the sound performance of the plants we install.

Breakdown In The Soil

Organic matter begins as the cover material that is growing or living on the surface. As plants and animals die, the organisms responsible for decay work to slowly break that matter down into the basic components of molecules and molecular chains. Decaying plants and animals are reduced to a layer of biomass that is barely recognizable as its original form and is called organic matter. Organic matter is composed of carbon chains that may be simple, such as sugars, or more complex such as carbohydrates, cellulose or lignin.

As the organic matter continues to decay it moves to a state where the parent material is no longer recognizable. This state of decomposition produces what we know as humus. With the many benefits of organic matter, when decomposition reaches the humus state it provides a significant colloidal presence in the soil. Colloids are soil particles ringed with negative electron charges that hold nutrient ions (humus and clay particles are the primary colloids in the soil).

Nutrients provided by soil decomposition and added through fertilizer are primarily positively charged (cations, see below), and the presence of colloids will aid in the retention of these nutrients until taken in by plants. Unfortunately, humus is short lived and will continue decomposition and quickly move into the soil matrix.

Carbon to Nitrogen Ratio. When encouraging the process of decomposition, such as in composting, materials are sought out that are high in nitrogen. These products are typically plant material that is still green (a result of high nitrogen levels) such as plant leaves and stems. The green products are balanced by brown materials (a result of higher levels of carbon) such as branches and dead materials. The relationship between the brown materials (carbon rich) and green materials (nitrogen rich) is expressed as the C:N ratio, or carbon to nitrogen ratio.

Materials that have a ratio similar to fresh lawn clippings (1:30) or clover (1:20) will decompose faster than products with a ratio similar to sawdust (1:500). The organisms that perform the decomposition process that turns dead plant and animal matter into organic matter and humus are power by nitrogen. During the decomposition process these organisms consume the nitrogen in the decaying matter and later release it back to the soil after they themselves die. This consumption of nitrogen can leave decomposing organic matter deficient in nitrogen until the process is complete. Eventually the situation will correct itself, but the speed of the decomposition can be significantly slowed if the levels of nitrogen in the decaying matter is low at the onset of the process.

Value Of Organic Matter In Soil

Organic matter is a high value substance in any soil that will support plant growth. The benefits of organic matter serve many functions related to plant growth and supporting life in the soil.

Some of the benefits are as follows:

- Release of Organic Compounds. Organic compounds are building blocks of plant life and the fuels plants use for energy. Plants take in simple organic compounds and create more complex compounds that provide 90 to 95% of nitrogen, phosphorus and sulfur needed for plant growth.
- Creating Chelates. Organic matter creates ligands (chelates) that bond the metals iron, zinc, copper and manganese. These soluble chelates make metals more available to plants.
- pH Buffering. Organic matter buffers soil from rapid pH changes.
- Glues. Microorganisms that create the organic matter secrete fluids and glues that create structure (polysaccharides), particularly in clayey soils.
- Plant Hormones and Chemicals. The microorganisms responsible for producing organic matter produce IAA (indole acetic acid), vitamins, gibberellic acid and auxins, all essential compounds for plant growth.
- Water Holding. Organic matter improves water holding capacity and available water in soil.
- Soil Temperature. Organic matter moderates soil temperature (on the surface).
- Colloidal Action. Organic matter and humus serve as an important colloid, providing 30 to 70% of CEC in soil.
- Erosion Reduction. Organic matter reduces erosion by holding soil particles together. With this extensive list of benefits from organic matter and humus, the value of maintaining at least a minimum level in the soil should be obvious.

Applications Of Organic Matter

The average amount of organic matter in a healthy soil is typically 5%. In North Carolina it is not uncommon to find soils with less than 2% organic matter content. This number can range from zero in desert situations to as much as 20% in peat bogs and highly organic soils. In normal conditions a soil typically loses approximately 2% or more of its organic matter per year due to the following reasons:

- Plant use
- Erosion; wind and water
- Climate; higher temps decompose faster
- Tillage practices can reduce organic matter
- Texture; coarser textures speed decline

Preventing the removal of organic matter is nearly impossible. It is a natural process of creation and consumption that would have dire consequences if halted. The replenishment of organic matter is part of the natural process that the landscape professional can enhance through supplemental applications. Organic matter can be added to the soil by providing materials that are already in the process of decay or have the appropriate C:N ratio described above. Such sources can include the following:

- Mulch. Many additional benefits are provided by mulch, including weed control, maintaining moisture, and protecting plants from mechanical damage
- Organic Soil Amendments. Amendments such as manures, meals, and plant and animal by-products will add to the organic component of the soil as well as the microorganisms available.
- Compost. Compost will make an adequate organic amendment when selecting materials with low C:N ratio (soil 10:1, alfalfa 12, manure 20, crop residue 40, straw 60).

The last item on this list, compost, is one of the most effective methods of increasing organic matter content of the soil. Compost is the decomposed residue of plant and animal matter. It is created by layering recently living plant matter (greens) and dead material (browns) and adding moisture. Regularly mixing a compost pile and maintaining proper moisture speeds the decomposition process. Available on a small scale from home gardeners, to large volumes from commercial ventures, the addition of a 1/2 inch layer of compost tilled into the top 10 inches of soil raises the organic matter content approximately 5%.

LIFE IN THE SOIL

Within the soil matrix of water, air, minerals and organic matter lives a complex web of life. Woven into the peds and particles is a vast array of small and microscopic organisms that are at work turning minerals into nutrients, compounds into alternative compounds and mixing, blending and protecting the soil. This network is a fragile complex of interrelated organisms that perform vital functions that make soil what it is and cause many of the problems associated with soil. Despite the negatives of various organisms, without this network the functions of breaking down organic matter, releasing and converting nutrients, fixing nitrogen, controlling disease and aerating the soil would go unattended. Included in this mix are the following:

- Viruses. Non-living strands of RNA with a coating. Some cause diseases like mosaic and wilts, enzymes attack and perform limited beneficial roles.
- Actinomycetes. Threadlike bacteria that prefer warm dry soils with oxygen. Actinomycetes decompose tough products like chitin and cellulose, fix N similar to legume. There are over a billion per gram and may require inoculation. Actinomycetes are responsible for the aromas we smell in soil and certain medicines
- Bacteria; residue decay and nitrogen fixing, warm, moist, neutral soils, nitrogen fixation takes atmospheric N and converts it from gaseous to useable by plants, turn nitrites into nitrates using nitrosomas and nitrobacter bacteria, **rhizobium** bacteria nitrogen fixation performed by bacteria in root nodules of legumes (peas, alfalfa, alder, locust, beans…). bacteria also oxidize many chemicals, nitrite into nitrate, carbon monoxide into carbon dioxide, sulfide into sulfate
- Algae. Single cells or strands of cells that carry on photosynthesis including green (diatoms) and yellow/green algae. Algae fix nitrogen, produce organic matter and organic substances at a very high rate. Algae refer wet soils and are found near surface where there is light or on bodies of water.
- Protozoa. Found in water, in the soil and around plants moving by flagella or cilia. Protozoa break down plants and feed on bacteria, but also cause many diseases like malaria, dysentery, sleeping sickness, and often contaminate drinking water
- Slime molds. Single cell organisms that move and break down organic matter and control diseases.
- Lichens. Lichens (fungi and blue/green algae also known as cyanobacteria) extract minerals from rocks.
- Fungi. Mycelium (a mass of threads or slender filaments) that are vital to soil in helping roots absorb nutrients and water. Most fungi require oxygen but are tolerant of acid soils. There are several harmful fungi that are predatory such as smuts, rusts, wilts, molds, and mildews on plant material and aflatoxins (carcinogens) that can be caused by some molds growing on grain and peanuts, but in soil there are several beneficial fungi. One of the most important is **mycorrhizae** (actually a term referring to the association of a fungus and the root). There are several strains of this fungus, including VAM (vesicular arbuscular myco), ecto (works between

cells) and endomycelium (penetrates cells) that help with water absorption and extend roots to pick up hard to reach nutrients such as phosphorus, zinc, copper, and molybdenum. Mycorrhizae functions best in highly weathered and leached soils low in CEC and acidic. Mycorrhizae also protects seedlings and new roots from pathogens and can extend the reach of roots from 10 to 1000 times. This fungi works by excreting chemicals that dissolve ionic bonds and forming webs that capture and store nutrients and moisture. The mantle formed by web blocks entry of diseases and emits antibiotics targeting specific plants pathogens.

- Nematodes. Microscopic jointed worms that feed on dead plants (saprophytic or omnivorous). Most are parasitic and harmful and ease entry of other pathogens into plants, but certain species are parasitic towards other nematodes.
- Earthworms, night crawlers (middens), red worms. Organisms that are constantly mixing and aerating soil and producing nutrient rich castings. Worms exist best in organic soils between 5 and 8.5 pH with reduced salt and high calcium and no pesticide use and predators.
- Arthropods and gastropods; insects, mites, ants termites, snails, slugs. This group of organisms consume and decompose dead plant parts, mix and aerate soil; and create as many problems as benefits.
- Centipedes (poison), earwigs, springtails, mites. These insects are both herbivores and predators and they decompose dead plants by shredding.
- Vertebrates. Moles, mice, ground squirrels, gophers, prairie dogs. While often not welcome in the soil, these creatures aerate and mix soil and can rehabilitate dry sites.

Encouraging beneficial organism growth in the soil requires the adjustment of many of the typical management practices traditionally used. Practices recommended to maintain a healthy soil with significant benefits to plants include the following:

- Moisture. Maintain the soil in a moist (field capacity) condition, avoid long term wet or dry conditions.
- Ph. Adjust the pH of the soil to between 6 and 7 through the addition of lime or sulfur.
- Amendments. Add organic matter and natural sources of nitrogen, phosphorus, sulfur and calcium.
- Contamination. Avoid contamination and minimize pesticide use and over fertilization. Using fertilizers that are low in salts and synthetic components will also aid beneficial organisms.
- Tillage. Limit tillage to improve fungi populations. Constant tillage will reduce the opportunity for fungal nets to develop.
- Mulching. Adding mulch to help hold moisture in the soil and to keep the surface temperature of the soil cooler.

While not every organism in the soil is beneficial, maintaining sustainable practices such as those listed above will allow the professional in the landscape field to reduce the amount of harmful chemicals that are used and to keep the environment healthy.

FERTILIZERS AND FERTILIZATION

Keeping plants alive and healthy often involves the addition of fertilizer to the soil. Fertilizers provide the basic nutrients needed by plants in a variety of forms and formulas. When fertilizing plants the landscape professional can choose from synthetic or naturally occurring materials, liquids or powders, single nutrients or blended fertilizers and an almost infinite variety of choices. Regardless of the fertilizer selected for the project, the plant is only looking for the nutrients. Choices for more naturally occurring fertilizers may provide protection for the environmental quality and be more sustainable than synthetic products but the plant has little regard for the form, it is only seeking the nutrient.

Several factors will influence the application of fertilizers. Landscape professionals should familiarize themselves with the signs of nutrient deficiency in plants. Symptoms often occur in the foliage and new growth of the plants, but can also be found in fruit, flower and growth habit. Testing the soil or plant foliage for deficiencies prior to planting is a standard practice when developing a fertilization and soil amendment program. As with pH, simple test kits can be purchased at garden centers or ordered online, and more sophisticated laboratory tests are available. If the project is of high value, the expense of the laboratory tests is worth the investment.

Before engaging in a fertilization project the landscape professional must know the basics of fertilizer terminology and be able to understand the labeling of the product they apply. Among the items that should be studied are the ratios, analysis and grade of the fertilizer, as well as the recommended application methods. The landscape professional should also understand the concept of pH and its impact on the availability of fertilizers and be familiar with the affects that fertilizer applications can have on soil pH.

Fertilizer Basics

Much of the information needed to properly fertilize can be found on the container that carries the fertilizer.

Fertilizer ratio – NPK. There are typically three numbers located on the front of most fertilizer bags. These numbers represent the percentage of nitrogen (N), phosphorus (P) and potassium (K) in that order, by weight in the fertilizer. If a label indicates a 10-10-10 fertilizer, then the weight of each nutrient in the bag is 10% of the total weight, or if the bag contains 100 pounds of fertilizer then 10 pounds would be nitrogen, 10 pounds phosphorus, and 10 pounds potassium (Figure 12-7). The remainder of the bag would be a carrier agent (often pulverized clay) and possibly other nutrients. This labeling system makes it easy to determine the amount of nutrient available by simply multiplying the ratio number by the total weight.

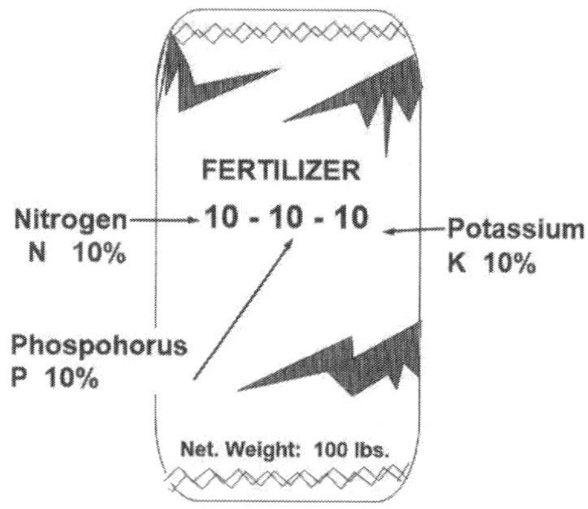

Figure 12-7. Example fertilizer label.

Fertilizer analysis and grade. There is a twist to the ratio shown on the front of the fertilizer bag. This twist is that the three numbers said to represent the percentage of N, P and K are actually wrong. The current labeling system presents these numbers in a manner that suggests that is the amount of actual nutrient present, but the nitrogen is often ammonia or nitrate, the phosphorus often a compound that is not pure phosphorus, and the potassium carrier is the same. In most 10-10-10 fertilizers the actual amount of N, P and K is most likely 10-4-8. This difference is the difference between ratio and grade. The grade represents the actual amount of useable element in the fertilizer while the ratio is the amount of the nutrient compound by weight. To determine the actual percentage of each useable nutrient in the fertilizer the analysis printed on the label must be examined. This will identify what nutrients are available, their percentage in the blend, and if the nutrient is present in a compound or as a pure element.

Complete fertilizers. Fertilizers can be formulated to address specific plant types or can be blended to assist a full range of plants. Examples of specific fertilizers would be one for turf, which might have a higher nitrogen ratio (25-10-10) or a fertilizer blended to improve flowering in plants (10-20-20). It is even possible to find or have formulated fertilizers that contain only one or two of the macronutrients to address specific nutrient deficiencies. Complete fertilizers provide all of the macronutrients and may include almost all of the nutrients necessary for plant growth. Of the 16 necessary elements it is not unusual for complete fertilizers to have 14 to all 16 of the elements. Complete fertilizers are useful for improving the overall fertility of soil, particularly prior to planting or as part of an ongoing fertilization program.

Affects of fertilizers on pH. As described in an earlier section, most plants thrive when the pH of the soil is between 6 and 7.5. When the pH is maintained in this range the majority of nutrients are available to plants. Repeated fertilization with certain fertilizers can have an impact on the pH, slowly moving the soil towards the acid or alkaline side of the scale. Several synthetic fertilizers use sulfur compounds as the carrier for the nutrients, and the repeated use of the same fertilizer could eventually make the soil acidic enough to disrupt nutrient availability. It is important to check the pH of the soil often when regularly fertilizing, particularly with the same synthetic fertilizer over long periods of time.

Fertilizer Forms. Fertilizers are available in a variety of forms. The most common forms used in the ornamental landscape are liquids, dry granules and time release capsules, but the full range of forms available include:

- Pressurized liquids. Materials stored under pressure, typically at low temps. Primarily used in large scale agriculture and injected into soil with special equipment.
- Liquids. Fluids not under pressure that may start as a liquid or as a dry mixed with water. Also available as solutions that don't settle (water soluble powders) and as suspensions, or non-dissolving chemicals coated with clay that will settle if not stirred.
- Dry. Several forms including powders and pulverized that can create dusty powders and cake during storage. Also as granules or larger grains which spread easily and without dust but also cake when exposed to moisture. Prills are finely ground granules which are coated and flow smoothly without dust or caking.
- Slow release. Coated capsules which slowly dissolve, releasing chemicals as coating breaks

Methods of application. In most ornamental landscapes the fertilizer is broadcast over the areas to be addressed, but there are situations where the fertilizer needs to be applied in a more accurate method. Options include the following:

- Broadcast. Common in hort applications, broadcast application spreads the fertilizer evenly over the soil surface and incorporates it into ground. Typically done before planting, this method is good for newly seeded turf or sod and some ornamental applications.
- Pop up. Fertilizer is placed above seed so plant intercepts after germination.
- Fertigation. Common in greenhouse work, fertigation is working its way into the landscape through newer irrigation systems. Fertigation injects small amounts of fertilizer into the irrigation water supply.
- Injected. Fertilizer is placed below surface of soil directly into root zone, usually using hydraulic applicators. Used for trees and landscape plants that have immediate fertilization needs or have competing ground covers like turf in the root zone.
- Foliar. Fertilizer is applied directly to foliage with intake through stoma on the leaves. This application method has limited effectiveness since most is overspray or placed on surfaces with few stoma.
- Topdress. Topdress fertilizer is spread over existing beds and near existing plants and not incorporated into soil.

Organic fertilizers

The sustainability movement has increased awareness of fertilizers that are organic and derived from naturally occurring products. Such products as kelp, meals and by-products have gained in popularity due to the limited impact such fertilizers have on the environment. Generally low in grade, these fertilizers have the added benefit that the carrier typically provides some addition of organic matter to the soil.

Fertilizer calculations

Determining the quantity of fertilizer to be applied can be approached using at least two method. The first method, and the most common among most homeowners, is to use the instructions on the fertilizer container and apply nutrients when the plant exhibits deficiency symptoms. The downside to this method is that the actual presence of nutrients in the soil and the needs of the plant are not taken into account.

The second method in more involved and more appropriate for a high value landscape maintained by a professional. The process would start with soil and/or tissue analysis to determine the amount of nutrients currently present. This would require a laboratory analysis of the full range of necessary plant nutrients to obtain specific amounts of each nutrient present in the soil. This amount is compared to the type of plant growing in the area to be fertilized. Plant groups have varying needs due to their growth structure and methods. Grasses tend to be heavy nitrogen consumers while flowering plants need greater quantities of phosphorus and potassium. The nutrient need is also influenced by the time of year the fertilizer is to be applied. Spring fertilizations tend to be heavier in nitrogen to support the new active growth of the plant, yet nitrogen applied in large quantities in the fall may lead to tender growth that will freeze in a temperature change. The applicator needs to carefully determine what type of nutrient is needed and what amount are required. Lacking this information, the applicator should seek professional assistance when making those decisions.

Once the type of fertilizer and the quantity has been determined, the applicator can then use the container labels to determine how much to apply. The need should be expressed by a certain number of pounds per unit (typically per 1000 square feet or per acre, occasionally it will be expressed per plant). Read the ratio of the fertilizer on the container and perform the following calculation. Note that this calculation is for only one nutrient, and if the fertilizer contains several nutrients a calculation must be performed for each. Use the largest quantity to determine the application amount. If the amounts differ significantly, seek a fertilizer with a ratio more closely matching the quantities needed. For example, if you calculate you need 4 pounds of nitrogen, 3 pounds of phosphorus and 5 pounds of potassium, look for a fertilizer that has a ratio of 4-3-5 or a multiple of this number (eg: 8-6-10).

Fertilizer application calculations:

- Identify the fertilizer need (per area unit)
- Calculate the area to be fertilized and divide by the unit from the first step
- Multiply these two to obtain the total weight of fertilizer required
- Divide this number by the ratio on the bag for the appropriate nutrient
- Multiply the result by 100 to determine how much of the selected fertilizer that should be applied

An example calculation:

- Need is for 5 pounds of nitrogen per 1000 square feet
- The area to be fertilized is 8000 square feet, divided by the unit from the first step equals 8
- Multiply 8 time 5 to obtain the fertilizer required, or 40 pounds
- Divide 40 by 12 if you have an 12-5-5-fertilizer, or 3.33
- Multiply 3.33 by 100 to obtain the amount of fertilizer to be applied, or 333 pounds

CHAPTER 13

SITE GRADING

OBJECTIVES

By reading and practicing the techniques described in this chapter, the reader should be able to successfully complete the following activities:

- Recognize the size and scope of grading required for a project
- Change the grade on a site.

Most landscape projects require moving soil to accomplish design goals. A simple concept of grading could be described as removing soil from where it is not needed and placing it where it is desired. **Grading** a site requires background knowledge about soils and the grading process, the ability to calculate quantities of cut and fill, judgments about the size of the project, and what approach should be taken.

Grading is accomplished through a process called *cutting and filling*. Cutting is the removal of unneeded or undesirable soil from a location, and filling is the placement of appropriate soil where it is needed. Although this concept seems simple, conditions exist that complicate the process. If soil with plant matter, such as turf, is reused when filling, it would later decompose and settle. The desire to save topsoil and place it in the area where it will benefit plants adds complexity to the **cut and fill** process. Respreading topsoil and smoothing the finish grade complicate the idea of cut and fill even further.

The amount of soil moved and the types of landforms required by the landscape plan will determine whether landscape contractors can accomplish the project using typical landscape equipment, or whether the project should be subcontracted to grading contractors who have special equipment and expertise in large earthmoving projects. Determining the size of project that can be effectively graded with a skid-steer and dump truck is a matter of experience. Because heavy equipment can do the job more efficiently, many landscape contractors subcontract larger projects to grading specialists. When considering the grading portion of a project, contractors should base their decision on their equipment and capabilities.

RELATED INFORMATION

Information in this chapter is supplemented by instruction provided elsewhere in this text and in other sources. Before undertaking the activities described in this chapter, read the related information in these sources:

- Safety in the Workplace, Chapter 7
- Construction Layout, Chapter 9
- Erosion Control, Chapter 16

> **CAUTION**
>
> North Carolina Landscape Contractors are limited by law to performing site work on projects under one acre. They may perform finish grading on any sized site. Information included in this section related to grading is beyond this scope of work and is included here as reference.

STEPS TO GRADING A SITE

When working on small projects, contractors can use a simplified grading approach of pushing the soil and sod away from a project and pushing them back when construction is completed. When

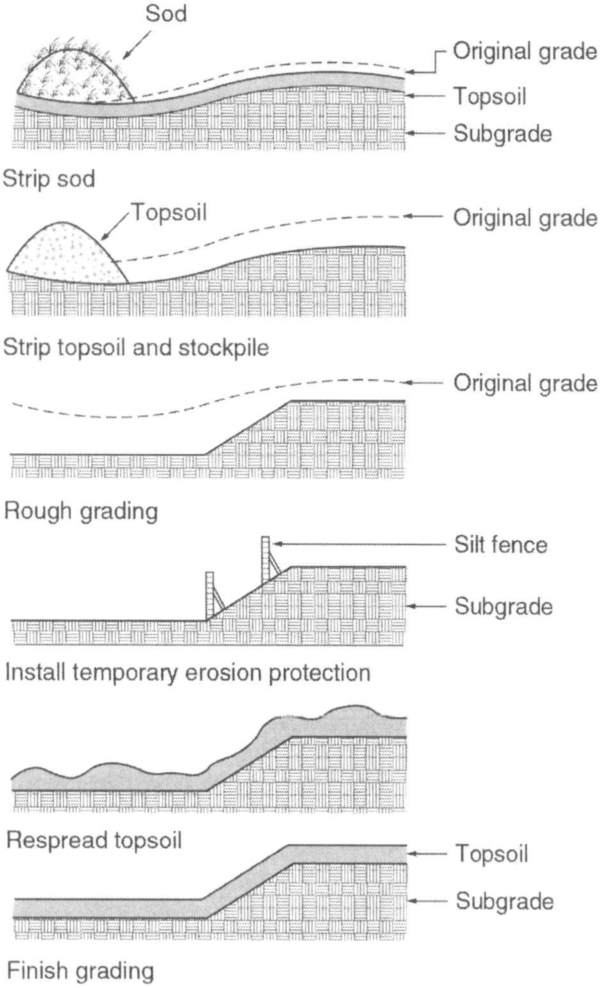

Figure 13-1 Steps of the grading process. A. Strip sod. B. Strip and stockpile topsoil. C. Perform rough grading. D. Install temporary erosion protection. E. Respread topsoil. F. Finish grade.

major grade changes are required, however, contractors must use a process that accommodates the orderly completion of all steps (Figure 13-1). Each step of this process is accomplished using specialized grading equipment, ranging from a skid-steer on a small site to bulldozers, scrapers, motor graders, power shovels, backhoes, compaction equipment, and dump trucks on larger sites.

Strip Sod

Because vegetative matter decomposes over time, ground covers such as sod should be removed separately and either disposed of, composted, or stockpiled separately from topsoil for use in noncritical areas. The site should be stripped to a depth of approximately 4 inches to remove the densest layer of vegetative matter. In some areas, this depth may be decreased or increased based on the type and maturity of the covering plant material. In small grading operations, this step can be completed using a skid-steer with a toothed bucket, passing over the site with the bucket set at a depth just below the root zone of ground cover plantings. On larger sites, a bulldozer will be required, setting the blade at a shallow depth and blading the organic layer into piles that can be loaded into dump trucks by backhoes or endloaders for transport to a disposal area. Areas where tree stumps were located should be excavated with a backhoe to a depth of 24 inches in a 10-foot diameter circle centered on the stump.

Strip Topsoil and Stockpile

Following the removal of vegetative matter from the site, strip enough topsoil to cover all areas where topsoil is to be respread in the final grading step. Include an additional 15% in this stockpile to cover settling, erosion, and compaction losses. When calculating areas to receive topsoil, include all turf and ground cover areas, as well as planting beds. A shortage of topsoil indicates that topsoil will need to be imported to cover planting areas. If possible, save all healthy topsoil from areas of a site that are disturbed and avoid disrupting areas where no construction is to take place.

Stripping topsoil on small sites can be done using a skid-steer with a toothed bucket. Set the bucket depth so that it scrapes the topsoil layer to the depth of the subsoil; then transport it to a storage area. Larger sites will require a scraper pass over the site, often using more than a single pass. The scraper blade is set to the depth of the topsoil layer (or the maximum depth), and the topsoil is removed to the depth of the subsoil. The scraper can carry the topsoil to a storage pile and deposit it for storage. Alternatively, a bulldozer can scrape the topsoil layer into piles that are emptied into a dump truck by a backhoe or power shovel for deposition in a storage area. Because of the energy required for hauling and the damage that harvest sites can incur, recycling topsoil from the existing site is preferable to importing topsoil from outside sources. To achieve this goal, contractors may have to request adjustment of the cut and fill areas to balance the soil available. Place this topsoil in a stockpile that is located away from construction areas, yet is easily accessible both for immediate needs and at the end of construction.

Excess topsoil can be stockpiled or, if low in organic matter, used to establish **subgrade** on the site. Most topsoils are stable enough to serve as the subgrade for **berms,** lawn areas, and other areas without permanent improvements. Soils high in organic matter are not recommended as subgrade for paved areas or structures because of the possibility of soil settlement. Soils that are high in sand content or have poor structural qualities, such as high shrink/swell clay, should also be avoided as fill material.

Rough Grade

Rough grading involves cutting and filling the site to establish proper subgrade elevations. This adjustment of grade should always be done on subsoils, rather than by manipulating healthy topsoils. If topsoil still exists in an area where grades are to be changed, strip the topsoil before grading to new elevations. These elevations are obtained by subtracting the required topsoil layer, pavement and pavement base, or other nonsoil subgrade improvements from finish grade.

Within the scope of rough grading are establishing platforms on which paving and structures can be built, establishing turf and landscaped areas, trenching for utilities, and excavating for piers/posts for structures. Staking for rough grading is typically placed slightly offset from the area being graded, with markings on the stake that indicate to the equipment operator the cut or fill required in the area of work. If grading changes are significant, restaking of the site after each step of the grading process may be necessary. Although it does not require the precision of finish grading, subgrading should be as accurate as possible to reduce grading work later in the project.

During this process, contractors should also be aware of area soils that are unsuitable for construction. These areas appear wet or spongy, have a foul smell, or are differently colored. If such areas are encountered, excavate the entire depth of unsuitable soils and replace it with suitable soils. If the depth of unsuitable soils exceeds 24 inches, a soils engineer should be consulted to recommend a solution. Also review the causes of the soil problem in that area. **Tile** installation may be required to remove excess water. Providing stable subsoil is important to the long-term stability of all paved areas and structures. Rock can also pose a problem for rough grading operations. Unless the rock is loose and can be moved with excavation equipment, an expert in blasting may have to be contracted before continuing excavation.

Areas where fill is to be deposited should be first prepared by scarifying the soil's surface. Using a tractor pulling an agricultural disk or using a motor grader with a scarifier attachment, you can accomplish scarifying. In fill areas on steep slopes, you may need to bench, or terrace, the slope before adding fill. Benching can be done either by using bulldozers that scrape away level terraces from a hillside or by using power shovels that excavate soil from hillsides and load it into dump trucks for transport to a storage area.

Cutting will take place in all areas where the current grade is higher than the desired sub grade. Bulk excavation is accomplished on small sites by hand using shovels and wheelbarrows or by using a skid-steer equipped with an excavation bucket. The soil is removed from areas where the grade requires lowering and transported to fill areas and deposited. By loading cut material into a truck and transporting it to fill areas, rather than transporting the soil with a skid-steer, contractors can improve productivity on some sites. When filling, place soil in 6-inch lifts (layers) and compact the lift before adding more fill. This method provides more stability to a fill than when compaction is completed only after placing all fill. To assist compaction, you may need to lightly spray water on the lifts.

Bulk excavation of larger sites is typically accomplished using scrapers or bulldozers. The scraper would make several passes over a cut area, removing soil with each pass to the maximum depth allowed by the equipment. Suitable soil is then transported to storage areas or fill areas and deposited in lifts that can be compacted after placement. As an alternative to a scraper, a bulldozer can push and cut material into piles, and a loader can fill dump trucks for transporting the material to fill or storage areas. During this excavation process, operators are guided by offset grade stakes. As operators pass a stake, they can observe if they need to remove more soil. This excavation process is continued until the platforms on which structures and pavement are to be built have reached the specified grade and slope.

Successful cutting leaves a platform with a consistent and relatively smooth surface on which further work can proceed. If there are irregularities in the surface, a motor grader can provide more detailed grade manipulation. In areas of rolling topography, the motor grader will typically be required to create the desired slope and elevations.

Excavated materials are deposited into fill areas and typically placed in lifts by the scraper, or these materials are emptied into windrows or piles by dump trucks and spread into lifts with a motor grader. Between placing lifts, the soil is compacted using motorized compaction equipment. Clay or clay-like soils are typically compacted using 10 to 12 passes over the lift with a sheep's foot roller. Granular soils are typically compacted using 5 to 6 passes over the lift with a rubber-tired roller or vibratory steel drum roller. If fill material is dry, water it by using a spray truck to consolidate soil particles before compaction.

To minimize the amount of erosion after rough grading, terrace long slopes, rather than leaving the site as a series of long exposed slopes. Grades can be adjusted to required elevations prior to respreading topsoil.

Following the establishment of rough grade, excavation for utility trenches and pits and for footings, piers, and piles can be started. For deep trenches, excavate by using backhoes; for shallower installations, chain trenchers. Depending on the utility, the alignment is staked and grade stakes may be added. Utilities such as sanitary and storm sewer will require a consistent grade at the bottom of the trench, regardless of the surface grade. This often requires an on-site surveyor to verify that the excavator has attained the necessary trench depth. Soil is excavated from the trench location and placed alongside the trench for future backfill material. Utilities typically maintain a consistent depth below the surface grade; therefore, they are better suited to excavation using a chain trencher. The chain trencher can be self-propelled or attached to a tractor or skid-steer. The trencher works backward along the desired alignment, with a screw mechanism that automatically piles soil to the side of the trench to use for future backfilling.

When utility installations are complete, backfill is pushed into the trench using a skid-steer or endloader. In instances where trenches are wide and/or deep, fill may be required in separate lifts and compaction of the backfill using a sheep's foot roller, vibratory plate compactor, or rammer compactor may be required. Unless properly compacted and backfilled, trenches will settle over time and leave a depression running through the site; these depressions are difficult to correct.

Install Temporary Erosion Protection

In most projects, grading work halts after rough grading to allow construction of walls, paving, and other site improvements. Some projects may be small enough to allow the grading process to proceed from beginning to end; but as a project's size and complexity increase, grading must be completed in stages. If grading halts after rough grading, temporary erosion control measures (see Chapter 13) should be installed.

Respread Topsoil

When most heavy traffic over the site has ceased and all walls, pavement, and structures have been installed, grading operations can continue. Prior to spreading topsoil, insure that all construction debris has been removed. Scarify the surface of the existing soil to allow for better bonding of the topsoil layer to the existing soil layer. Topsoil from the stockpile is removed and spread over the site to the required depths. Small areas can be respread using skid-steer equipment with a bucket and grading attachment, whereas larger areas will require the use of a scraper to deposit a lift of topsoil over the entire site. Depths of topsoil vary depending on project specifications, but lawn areas typically require a minimum of 6 inches up to 12 inches. Planting beds may require a minimum of 12 inches up to 24 inches. The topsoil is laid in and roughly spread to the finish grade as specified in the site grading plan.

Finish Grade

The final step prior to seedbed preparation or planting is to smooth the surface to the exact grades stated on the grading plan. This step involves manipulation of the soil to the desired finish grade. For large operations, a motor grader or tractor-mounted blade performs this work; for smaller operations, a skid-steer and shovels. Regardless of project size, performing hand work with shovels and rakes in tight areas is often required to obtain the desired or accurate grades. Begin finish grading by setting hub grade stakes with the top of the stake at finish grade. Place these stakes every 20–30 feet in a grid pattern in large areas to provide adequate reference for soil placement. Existing improvements can also be used as reference points for finish grading, with soil placed a consistent depth around curbs, pavements, and building foundations.

For large projects, finish grading operations are typically implemented using a motor grader. To assure quality in this operation, verify that the grader's tires are matched and in good working condition and that the grader's blade is angled all the way forward to scrape, rather than to cut. The grader should work in sections, windrowing any excess soil out of each section to be picked up by other equipment. The site should be rough graded and compacted prior to beginning this step. In this operation, it is preferable to make small increments of cuts rather than fill. Make multiple passes if necessary, cleaning the excess off the tops of the grade stakes after each pass.

If no grading plan exists, finish grading will need to maintain proper elevations next to paved areas and permanent improvements and to achieve proper drainage direction and slope. At this stage, soil is often lightly compacted with a drum roller. Further surface manipulation, such as rough leveling, is performed as part of the preparation for turf and areas. Permanent erosion protection should be installed immediately after finish grading to protect the site.

CHAPTER 14

WATER MANAGEMENT

OBJECTIVES

By reading and practicing the techniques described in this chapter, the reader should be able to successfully complete the following activities:

- Identify ways that water impacts the landscape
- Select appropriate methods to manage water in the landscape
- Determine the water demands of a landscape

Recent movement of the landscape industry towards sustainability has required that many of the common past practices in landscaping a site be changed. One of the most challenging, yet important, aspects of creating a "green" site is to manage water. Whether it is water that is used in irrigation, water that runs off a site during a storm or water used in building a landscape, to be sustainable requires the contractor to utilize the least amount necessary. The landscape contractor must integrate the principles of water conservation into the planning, design, execution and maintenance of their projects to consider their work sustainable. Current technologies and processes make the possibility of water conservation in the landscape a reality rather than a myth.

RELATED INFORMATION

Information in this chapter is supplemented by instruction provided elsewhere in this text and in other sources. Before undertaking the activities described in this chapter, read the related information in these sources:

- Basic Soils for Landscape Contractors, Chapter 12
- Site Drainage, Chapter 15
- Concrete Paving, Chapter 25
- Water Features, Chapter 31
- North Carolina Manual of Professional Horticultural Practice

CAUTION

Always call for a utility locate (NC811) at least 73 hours before performing *any* work at a site.

CAUTION

Irrigation construction is a trade which is licensed separately by the State of North Carolina. Any discussion of irrigation installation is done for reference only and should not be construed as work to be performed by a licensed landscape contractor.

PLANNING FOR WATER MANAGEMENT

The initial step in water management is planning. As with so many other aspects of construction, attempting to incorporate ideas while the project is underway invites failure. Including the concepts of water management as part of the planning effort before beginning work will make the impacts more effective. Part of the planning effort will rest with the design professional as they do irrigation and planting design, but the contractor may also find themselves involved in creating an environment that reduces the use of water to the bare minimum required to complete a job.

Purpose

As landscape contractors we must understand and embrace the fact that our water resources must be preserved and protected. When addressing the needs of our clients we must take an approach that efficiently uses this precious resource. In every aspect of the landscape process exploration of low water alternatives must be included.

Approach

Water in the landscape can be managed during several phases of the project. From design to maintenance, any step that utilizes water has the potential to bring water savings.

Landscape Design. Design of the landscape should include analyzing the site soils, slope and climate to determine what impacts the site characteristics will have on water consumption.

Activities planned for the site should be carefully reviewed to determine if they will require hardscape or softscape solutions. Ideally, plant material selected for the job should be drought tolerant and be placed in hydrozones.

Installation and Planting. Preparing the site for planting will require that soils be dry and workable, amendments be added to improve soil texture, structure and water holding capacity and that the site remain covered until planting is ready to proceed. Proper plant installation techniques should be followed to assure maximum plant survival.

Watering and Irrigation Water Management. Irrigation systems designed for water conservation should include equipment selected that meets all codes and requirements, and are designed for efficient and uniform distribution of water. Water budgeting should be prepared and shared with clients to avoid excessive water use due to lack of knowledge regarding the system.

Managing Storm water Runoff. Rainfall can create issues in almost any landscape, but in both wet and dry areas of the country, runoff from rainfall can be controlled. In dry areas it may be beneficial to capture and reuse storm water runoff to offset water demands for irrigation. In areas with excessive rainfall, detaining the runoff on site will ease the pressure of storm water collection systems downstream. Methods to perform both of these tasks are increasing in use as the move to sustainability grows.

Landscape Maintenance. Once installed, maintenance techniques that keep soil health at an optimum and engaging in cultural practices that maintain plants in good health work with the systems installed to maximize water conservation.

Contractors Responsibilities

Of the many activities for which the landscape contractor will be responsible during the installation of a project, few are more important that understanding the requirements under which a project must be built. Extensive codes and regulations exist to guarantee the health, safety and welfare of the public, and conservation of water is no exception. Landscape projects that utilize water have the potential to be governed by many codes. It will be a joint responsibility of the design professional and landscape contractor, as well as other professionals involved in a project, to know and understand the content of these codes, and to apply them appropriately to a project. Common codes include standard Plumbing Codes, Building Codes and land use regulations.

More recently a growth in Water Conservation and Use codes has significantly impacted the landscape industry. For instance, landscape irrigation in the State of North Carolina is licensed separately from landscape construction. In certain municipalities, projects may be limited in the amount of water allowed to irrigate plants and/or operate water features. Meeting these codes may require extensive calculations and an understanding of what types of plant material are allowed. Examination of the Environmental Protection Agency (EPA) website regarding Water Sense Landscaping provides valuable guidelines and processes to reduce water use in the landscape.

LANDSCAPE DESIGN

The steps of the landscape design process include many variables that require review before decisions are finalized. Like the choice of hardscape materials, the selection of plants, the layout of use areas, incorporating the concepts of water conservation into the design process is part of the new standard of design. Analysis and plant selection are key parts of the design process that impact the level of water conservation on a site, so they are reviewed in more detail in this section.

Site analysis

Careful review of site conditions will make the process of planning the irrigation system an easier and more effective task. Unlike the design process, key elements of the land should be evaluated before determining plant choices and irrigation system components. Listed below are elements that are critical review elements for water conservation.

Regional and local microclimates.
Understanding the daily and seasonal weather patterns of a site can drastically alter the plant choices and irrigation system. What are the temperature extremes of the site, what is the seasonal rainfall average, what parts of the site are exposed to constant sun or shade. Each of these questions need to be answered in order to properly select plant material. Answer these questions for the overall site, then review the site to see if there are areas where the conditions are even more extreme than the overall site. Each of these areas should be identified with potential plants, and then the irrigation developed to support them.

Soil conditions. Take soil samples throughout the site to determine the texture, structure and permeability of the soil. Samples should be taken that differentiate slope changes and cover crop types. A key consideration for soil that relates to water management would include the amount of water that infiltrates into the soil after rainfall or irrigation. Soil that does not have good infiltration may pond water on the surface to evaporate or allow the water to drain off the site before entering the soil. Neither of these conditions is beneficial to water management because the water does not enter the root zone to be taken up by plant material. After the samples are analyzed, indications as to what soil modifications may be necessary to provide improved effectiveness of standard irrigation equipment. In instances where the soil is very sandy or has a percentage of clay over 5 percent, the soil may required additions of organic matter to improve structure and texture. In loamy soils the need for modification is typically minimal. Soils that indicate high salt levels will require treatment with gypsum and may also require subsurface drainage be installed.

Preparing a landscape water budget. In areas where water resources are limited it is advisable, and often required, that a landscape water budget be prepared. The landscape water budget is an estimate of how much water a landscape in any particular location should be using during a given period. Preparing a landscape water budget allows the designer/contractor/client to design a landscape that uses an appropriate amount of water, or pay for excess use with higher water rates.

This concept is used in different ways depending on how critical the water resources are in a particular area. In some areas the water budget is determined for a site in order to calculate the billing for water use. This amount may be either the actual need calculated for the landscape installed, or a percentage of the actual need if conservation measures have been implemented.

Water use over the allowed amount is billed at a higher rate to discourage waste. Another use of the process is to calculate how much water the site is allowed to use (sometimes referred to as the baseline), and then calculating the estimated use based on the type of landscaping proposed. If the estimated use exceeds the allowed use, adjustments must be made in the landscape to reduce water requirements. In water challenged areas a municipality or water district may limit the amount of high water use plants and, require that plants selected for the landscape be low water use materials.

Calculating the landscape water budget considers factors such as the evapotranspiration rate (amount of water lost due to soil evaporation and plant transpiration), rainfall, the amount of area that is landscaped, and the type of plants installed to determine how much water should be applied to the landscape. This number is typically adjusted to account for irrigation system inefficiencies and converted to a volume measurement for design and billing purposes. In more sophisticated locations, the types of plants may be separated into groups with varying water demands such as turf and shrubs/ground covers.

Evapotranspiration (ET or ETo) is calculated by a local weather station that measures such factors as rainfall, solar radiation, air temperature, wind speed and humidity. These weather stations are positioned in geographic areas appropriate for measuring local conditions. To obtain ETo information, contact local water districts or municipal governments that regulate water consumption.

Several variations of formulas are used to calculate landscape water budgets, but most have similarities in that they consider the basic factors noted in the explanation above. An example of the formulas used to calculate water budgets that is adapted from the Environmental Protection Agency is outlined below. Alternative formulas are shown at the end of this section.

EPA Water Budget Calculations. The EPA tool for developing a water budget involves three steps, the first is to establish a baseline for typical water demand of a typical landscape, the second is to establish an landscape water allowance based on required water conservation techniques, and the third step is to calculate the landscape water requirement of the proposed landscape. The figures in step two and three are then compared to determine if the landscape will have adequate water or if the plan needs to be adjusted to fit within the allocated water.

Calculations for each step are as follows:

Step 1. Baseline establishment

Use this answer in the second formula.

Baseline = ETo × A×Cu

Where:

ETo = Local reference evapotranspiration (inches/month) A = Landscaped area (square feet)

Cu = Conversion factor (0.6233 for results in gallons/month)

Step 2. Landscape water allowance

Use this answer to compare to step 3 to see if you are exceeding water allowance.

LWA = 0.70× Baseline

Where: LWA = Landscape water allowance (gallons/month)

Step 3. Landscape Water Requirement

Use this answer to determine how much water the landscape design will use.

LWRh= DUlq x [(ETo × Kl) − Ra] × A×Cu

Where:

LWRh = Landscape water requirement for the hydrozone (gallons/month) DUlq = lower quarter distribution uniformity (dimensionless)

ETo = Local reference evapotranspiration (inches/month)

Kl = Landscape coefficient for the highest water-using plant in that hydrozone (dimensionless) Ra = Allowable rainfall, designated by WaterSense as 25% of the site's peak monthly rainfall A = Area of the hydrozone (square feet)

Cu = Conversion factor (0.6233 for results in gallons/month)

Source: EPA Water Sense, December 9, 2009

Plant Selection

Picking the plants that are used to populate the landscape is a significant element in reducing the amount of water required to maintain the site. While all designs must meet certain aesthetic requirements, searching for alternative plants that provide the same visual impact but with reduced water demands will aid in the long term water consumption. Plants that are native to the area and adapted to seasonal rainfall typically are sound choices. Plants that use reduced water and are drought tolerant are also excellent additions to the palate. When installing plants, place them in appropriate hydro-zones so that irrigation can be designed to match the water needs of plants.

Amenities

The landscape designer has many choices to make when articulating designs. One choice is the use of amenities that utilize water. Water features such as fountains, pools and streams are exciting and valued components of any landscape design, but each has the potential to waste water if designed inappropriately. Features that recycle water, capture overspray and minimize the loss of water from evaporation and loss of containment will reduce the overall consumption of water. Consideration can also be given to utilizing water captured from storm water runoff as the water supply for such features in the landscape.

INSTALLATION AND PLANTING

Numerous activities are available to assist in water management when constructing the landscape. Some possibilities include:

- Use practical techniques when installing the landscape and plant material.
- Avoid damage to the site and minimize compaction.
- Mulch plant material after installation.
- Avoid working sites in rainy conditions that will damage soil structure.
- If soil is in poor condition either amend the soil or consider a cover crop until site grading is necessary.
- Protect the site from erosion and utilize hand operations to build if equipment operation is not necessary.
- Protect all existing plant material to be preserved by fencing, mulching and providing temporary irrigation.

> **CAUTION**
>
> Perform only those tasks allowed through the irrigation licensing law exemptions. Irrigation Contractors are licensed separately and should perform work reserved by that licensure law.

IRRIGATION

An obvious location to begin water management is with the irrigation system for a site. The items listed below are critical steps to managing water consumption on a site:

- Begin irrigation planning with a water budget and perform a water audit on an annual basis.
- Perform an evaluation or pre-audit of selected controller zones and irrigation heads.
- Have the irrigation system program and schedule calibrated on a weekly or monthly basis.
- Accurately match irrigation needs with precipitation rates for irrigation heads.
- Consider watering with gray water or water stored from rainwater storage.
- Install a smart controller that will adjust the watering cycles based on plant needs and site conditions.
- Replace older spray heads with high precipitation rates with sprinklers with

lower rates if the plant material, use and soils dictate a change.

- Consider drip and micro-spray systems for ground covers and shrub plantings.
- Set cycles to water in the morning to reduce loss from evapotranspiration.
- Set controllers for multiple short watering cycles rather than a single long cycle to allow the water to infiltrate.

STORMWATER RUNOFF

The loss of rainfall from a site creates two problems. First is the loss of a resource and second is the addition of rainwater to storm sewer systems downstream. Addressing both issues requires that rainwater previously allowed to run off a site and into the storm sewer system be captured and either reused in the garden or allowed to slowly dissipate into the ground. The systems designed to perform these tasks range from a simple planted swale to complex underground storage systems. Regardless of the method chosen, the management of storm water runoff has moved to the forefront of considerations when designing and building a landscape.

Collection of Runoff

With barrels, cisterns and drywells, storm runoff from roofs and paved areas can be captured and reused or allowed to dissipate back into the ground. Barrels are drums that are positioned under and connected to downspouts to collect runoff directly from the roofs of structures. Cisterns and drywells are containers of varying volumes, some as small as 5 gallons and others as large as several thousand gallons, that are buried underground on a site. Details for installation of these collection methods can be found in Chapter 15 following. A single large cistern/drywell can manage runoff; also available is a series of small drywells connected to roof drains around a site to accommodate runoff dissipation. Permits are required for most cistern and drywell installations, and specialty contractors will be required for electrical connections and deep underground construction.

One simple method for capturing runoff from roof drains is to empty the drain into a barrel designed for such methods. Disconnected from piping leading to storm sewers, the roof drain is diverted and connected to a large barrel or drum, typically around 50 to 55 gallons in size. The barrel must be completely enclosed to eliminate mosquito habitat. Position the barrel next to a roof drain. Barrels should be installed on a stable base, preferably one that is a foot or two above ground level. This base can be constructed of wood timbers or concrete block and should have a 4-inch thick layer of base rock below. Cut the roof drain and install elbow pipe to direct the water to the drain barrel. Installing an open wire mesh between the elbows will help capture debris that washes down the drain, or a more elaborate screening system can be constructed or purchased if significant debris is anticipated.

Where the drain connects to the barrel, place an overflow valve in the event the barrel fills beyond capacity. This can be a valve inserted into the elbows or a 2-inch diameter, 90- degree elbow installed through a hole drilled in the barrel's side near the top rim. At the bottom of the barrel, a hose spigot should be installed; this allows connection to a garden hose for reuse of the water.

Cisterns are typically the term used for containment that stores water for reuse, whereas drywells generally refer to containment that dissipates water back into the ground. Both containers are buried, with the top of the container below ground, and are fed storm water runoff through tiling and piping systems that empty into the top of the container. Cisterns are often constructed of cast-in-place concrete with a concrete bottom. Precast concrete, plastic, and fiberglass cisterns are also available. To reuse the water stored in a cistern, a submersible pump with a line connected to the irrigation supply system is required. A filtering system is also essential to prevent plugging of the irrigation system with debris from the cistern, and an access to the cistern may also be required to allow maintenance.

Drywells can be premanufactured out of plastic or fiberglass, or they can be perforated plastic or concrete panels that are set into a hole excavated in the ground. Drywells can also be constructed of stacked stone with a concrete slab for a cover. A modular open-celled storage system allows a storage area to be variable in size. Many drywells have perforated walls to allow dissipation of water into the soil, and many also are filled with large drain rock for structural stability. A modular system will require placing the modular units within a jacket of filter fabric to allow percolation of stored water.

Installation of either system requires excavating an area large enough to place the container, placement of base rock to provide a level and stable base for the container, connection of the inlet piping, and backfilling around and over the container. If a surface access is required, you can place a sleeve over the opening in the container; then connect a secure hatch at surface level over the sleeve.

CAUTION

Use caution when excavating and installing cisterns in areas with high ground water.

CAUTION

Falls into or entrapment in a cistern or drywell can cause injury or death. Both during and after construction, protection should be provided for cisterns and drywells to prevent unlawful or accidental entry into the structure. Secure covers should be provided.

Discharge of Runoff

Detailed information regarding the construction of many of the discharge methods discussed here can be found in Chapter 15 following.

Bioswales. Another application of the concept of storm water detention, the bioswale is a gradually sloped drainage channel with shallow sides lined with plant material and, in certain situations, rip-rap. Used to slow runoff and trap pollutants and sediment, the bioswale allows water to percolate into the soil, rather than running off the site. The bioswale can be used as a decorative landscape element, is typically placed to capture polluted runoff from parking and paved areas, and is most effective in areas where runoff is intermittent. not constant.

To construct a bioswale, grade a channel with side slopes not exceeding 3:1 (3 feet horizontal to 1 foot vertical) and a center line slope that is as gradual as the site will allow (1% is desirable). The bioswale's cross-sectional shape can be either parabolic (curved) or trapezoidal (angled). If the native soil is primarily clay and impervious, the top 12 inches of soil should be amended with approximately 50% sand and compost. Seed or plug the area with grasses native to the area that can tolerate temporary inundation by floodwaters. Place an erosion mat or jute netting over the area to limit erosion while the plant material cover is being established. If the swale experiences high volumes of water, the bottom may be covered with a 4-inch rip-rap.

The plant material in the bioswale is only periodically trimmed and is allowed to grow to full height to assist in trapping sediment and slowing the drainage. At the end of the bioswale, place an outlet that is sized to allow drainage from the swale during periods of heavy rains.

French Drains. French drains are gravel trenches covered with a thin layer of soil and ground cover. The gravel in these trenches stores water in the open spaces between each stone. A closed drainage system that requires no outlet point, a French drain would be properly placed in low areas that collect water or in locations where poor soils slow the percolation of surface water.

Begin by using the formula identified in Appendix D to calculate the length of French drain required. When you have calculated the length of French drain, mark the location of the trench on the site. If the site will not accommodate a single trench, you may split the required length into separate trenches placed at least 36 inches apart. To be effective, the majority of the trench should be located directly under the area that floods. Excavate a trench 12 inches wide and 42 inches deep along the lines marked. In turf areas, remove the sod set it aside for reuse. Save approximately 10% of the soil excavated from the trench for cover.

For each trench, cut two lengths of 48-inch wide landscape fabric 2 feet longer than the trench length. Place the first piece of landscape fabric up one side of the trench. Fold the top over the outside edge of the trench. You do not need to cover the entire bottom of the trench. Repeat the process with the other piece of landscape fabric on the opposite side of the trench. Fill the trench to within 6 inches of the top of the trench with 1–2-inch diameter washed river rock. When filling the trench, use care not to disturb the landscape fabric. Fold the remaining landscape fabric over the top of the river rock. Backfill the trench with the soil set aside earlier and compact. If you saved the sod, replace it over the fill.

The average life of a French drain is approximately 5–10 years. After that time, the storage capacity of the pores between the river rock will be reduced from silt that has worked into the drain. A faster alternative is to construct the French drain without placing landscape fabric around the river rock. However, this alternative has a typical life of fewer than 5 years because silt will form more quickly.

Rain Gardens. An alternative to simple managing the storm water runoff is to design a garden that celebrates the presence of rainwater and its return to the soil to continue the water cycle.

Similar to bioswales, rain gardens provide an opportunity for water to percolate into the soil and recharge the groundwater rather than run off the site. When properly constructed, rain gardens will manage the excess rain from a typical storm without long term ponding, while at the same time provide a location for plants typical of the local region.

LANDSCAPE MAINTENANCE

If a landscape is designed and constructed properly, the majority of the cost of the landscape will be maintenance during the many years that the client enjoys the project. Design and construction will be short term compared to length of time that gardeners must care for the project. During this extended maintenance period, using methods that are efficient and sustainable will be recognized in lower project costs and better health of a garden for the entire life of the garden.

Among these practices would be minimizing the use of pesticides (or engaging in Integrated Pest Management), caring for the soil and managing water. This final item requires minimal input and will yield maximum return.

Maintenance Techniques to Manage Water Use

For the gardener, working water management into routine activities requires only minor adjustment of their daily/weekly routine. Adding a few moments to one task and observing as well as acting will aid in producing a garden that sparkles despite minimal water consumption.

Plant Care. The fine gardener or landscape professional should endeavor to maintain plantings and soil at optimum level in order to reduce the amount of water needed. Proper and timely pruning can reduce the stress on plant material and limit transpiration loss when the growing season heats up. Plants that are stressed take in more water and nutrients to maintain growth than plants that are healthy, so keeping plants healthy by using preventative actions for diseases and pests will maintain their metabolism at a normal level.

Mulching. Maintaining an even 2 to 3 inches of compost or organic mulch over planting beds and in root zones will reduce the amount of water loss to evaporation. As the soil heats up, water is drawn from lower zones and evaporates into the atmosphere, so keeping the surface cool and protected from the sun will limit this loss. Additional time-release nitrogen fertilizer may be required to offset the loss from decomposing mulch.

Soil Health. As much effort should be put into keeping the soil healthy as is put into keeping plants healthy. Regular additions of organic matter, using naturally occurring fertilizers and organic fertilizers, avoiding pesticides and minimizing tilling will help improve soil conditions. A healthy soil with good structure and texture will maintain water at field capacity longer than an unhealthy soil, and make irrigation more effective when it is needed.

Irrigation System Maintenance. Keeping irrigation systems finely tuned is a necessity to managing water while keeping plants alive. Avoid overspray and make sure leaks are repaired immediately. Set timers to match the climatic needs and adjust them seasonally as the weather changes.

Additional issues to consider during irrigation system maintenance are utilizing a rain sensor to automatically turn off the irrigation during a rain event and matching heads and their precipitation rates to the infiltration rate of the soil in the area covered by the heads. Within a site the soil types and infiltration rates can vary widely, requiring examination of the site for those areas where water is running off rather than entering the soil. In these locations the head and/or precipitation rate should be adjusted or changed so that the water is applied at a rate that matches the infiltration rate in that area.

Maintenance Practices. To support the activities noted above, gardeners can utilize on site composting, mulch mowing, recycling of wastes and directing storm water to garden areas to enhance the water management efforts.

SUPPLEMENTAL INFORMATION

Calculations for landscape water budgets are a new addition to most community requirements, therefore a standard formula has not been established nationwide. Additional formulas for calculating landscape water budgets are shown below.

> **CAUTION**
>
> Before performing calculations for landscape water budgets, verify that calculations can be performed by a landscape construction professional and also verify what, if any, formula has been adopted for the jurisdiction in which the work is being performed.

ALTERNATIVE 1

Landscape (Site) Water Budget = ETo x Cwb x A

Cu

Where:

ETo = daily reference EvapoTranspiration (inches per month)

Cwb = water budget adjustment factor (the species factor divided by the irrigation system efficiency)

ER = effective rainfall (portion of usable daily rainfall)

Area = measurement of the square footage of turf and non-turf

Cu = Conversion factor to put result into water volume per time period (.6233 for gallons per month) irrigation and green industry

ALTERNATIVE 2

Another variation of the landscape water budget formula takes into account the differences in water demand between turf areas and other landscaped areas (shrubs and ground covers). This formula is stated as follows:

Landscape (Site) Water Budget = (Actual ETo x Kl) - ER x Area / IE x Cu

Where:

ETo = daily reference EvapoTranspiration

Kl = landscape coefficient (this will adjust the ETo for turf or non-turf landscaped areas)

ER = effective rainfall (portion of usable daily rainfall)

Area = measurement of the square footage of turf and non-turf

IE = Irrigation Efficiency (increases water budget to account for system inefficiencies.)

Cu = Conversion factor to put result into water volume per time period (.6233 for gallons per month) Contra Costa CA water district

CHAPTER 15

SITE DRAINAGE

OBJECTIVES

- By reading and practicing the techniques described in this chapter, the reader should be able to successfully complete the following activities:
- Describe how water impacts a construction site.
- Drain water away from improvements on the surface.
- Drain water away from improvements with a subsurface system.

> **CAUTION**
>
> Stormwater management is an important environmental concern and is highly regulated. In North Carolina Storm drainage design must be performed by a licensed design professional. Information in the chapter regarding stormwater management is presented solely as a guide to draining small landscaped areas. Consult state and local codes and ordinances for additional information.

Much of landscape construction today addresses the issue of water. Irrigation systems combat drought; footings and pavement design strengthen improvements against frost; and grading, tiling, and other drainage work are implemented to reduce flood and water damage. Of all the elements that can cause problems on a site, water is the one element that can single-handedly wreak the most havoc. Whether the problem is an excess of water from flooding or poor drainage, a shortage of water from drought or frozen water that heaves pavement or ices walks, proper management of the many potential impacts that water can have on a site will minimize construction and long-term problems. In this chapter, we examine ways to control water by draining it from improvements on a site.

Two general concepts are incorporated into making site drainage improvements. The first concept is draining water from the site on the surface. Surface drainage consists of shaping the ground to direct runoff where desired. When preparing a site for proper surface drainage, the intention is to slope the ground from important features that water can damage, such as structures, walls, and paved areas. In addition, the contractor attempts to avoid low areas that will collect water and make spaces unusable after rains or irrigation. This method of removing water is typically the most cost-effective and easiest to construct. It is applicable on most sites to some degrees and, on many sites, is the only technique needed for draining.

Basic to surface draining a site is the principle of maintaining a low point, or a series of low points, that is lower than the elevation of structures and important site features. These low points are sometimes referred to as **free outs** or **swale high points.** These low points guarantee that if rains continue and reach flood stage, water will flow away before entering a structure. This principle is easy to maintain on sites with hilly or rolling topography, but it is a challenge on sites that are flat. Sites that limit surface drainage possibilities or make locating low points difficult require drainage systems that are more complex than surface treatments.

When the volumes of water are great or the site's topography is not favorable to effective surface drainage, subsurface drainage systems must be employed to maintain positive drainage. Subsurface systems involve collecting the water on the surface and then allowing gravity to draw it into a piping system for removal. Although more expensive and time-consuming to construct than surface drainage, subsurface systems can be effective in draining problematical sites.

Also discussed at the end of this chapter is the concept of storm water **detention,** dissipation, and mitigating polluted runoff from a site. Many projects incorporate the idea of retaining rainwater for a period after a storm in detention ponds to minimize the impact on downstream areas. Storm water can also be detained and pollutants and sediment can be filtered using a **bioswale.** On selected sites, storm water runoff can be collected and reused or returned to the soil by using drainage structures to dissipate the water into the ground. Construction and finishing of a detention area or bioswale, as well as other storm water management fixtures, may become the responsibility of grading or landscaping contractors.

Regardless of the method they select to drain a site, landscape construction professionals must respect the character of natural waterways that run through and near a site. Development of a site typically diverts, increases, or changes the runoff that passes into the existing drainage network. When this happens, the environment beyond the site is changed, often for the worse. Responsible water management for a site includes protecting downstream waterways from disturbances, such as silt from erosion, contamination from chemicals used in construction, and flooding from diverted runoff.

RELATED INFORMATION

Information in this chapter is supplemented by instruction provided elsewhere in this text and in other sources. Before undertaking the activities described in this chapter, read the related information in these sources:

- Safety in the Workplace, Chapter 7
- Basic Construction Techniques and Small Equipment Operation, Chapter 8
- Site Grading, Chapter 13
- Concrete Paving, Chapter 25

SURFACE DRAINAGE

In any proper grading and drainage scheme, positive surface drainage should be the first consideration. Surface drainage can best be described as draining water from locations where it will be a problem. Drainage is achieved by shaping and sloping surfaces. More specific techniques involve the grading of swales, or shallow ditches, and the use of diversion berms to direct runoff where the designer desires. Surface drainage is the predominant method for sites that are small or have limited amounts of runoff. As a site increases in size, surface drainage may be limited to directing the runoff to more permanent drainage structures such as tile or storm sewers. Another factor that may limit the effectiveness of surface drainage is the amount of runoff. Sites that have many structures and much pavement limit the amount of water that the ground can absorb, leaving large amounts of water that must be removed to protect these improvements. During torrential rains on these sites, surface drainage methods can be quickly overwhelmed.

GRADING SLOPES

Sloping surfaces away from permanent improvements is a simple technique that is also essential to good site drainage. Structures, walkways, patios, walls, and other intensive-use areas of the landscape benefit from having the ground slope away for a short distance, allowing water to drain away from these structures. This shaping process should be addressed during site grading, especially during the rough and finish grading steps.

The percentage of slope graded for a site is dictated by construction drawings or, in the absence of a grading plan, is determined by standards and site conditions. Standards for most sites recommend that a minimum slope of 2%–3% be maintained across turf areas to provide positive drainage. Pavement areas drain well if a 2% slope can be maintained. Athletic fields and sporting surfaces have required slopes recommended by the authority governing that type of activity. Grade around buildings should be maintained at least 6 inches below the structures finish elevation, and the ground outside the structure should fall an additional 6 inches in the first 10 feet away from the building.

Grading Drainage Swales

Drainage swales are shallow ditches designed to intermittently carry water through and away from a site. If a site has adequate slope and area to accomplish drainage without swales, none should be used. Although swales are drainage channels, they are typically constructed with side slopes that are gradual enough to mow. As with all surface drainage, the general slope of swales can be completed during rough grading and the detailed slope completed during finish grading steps. The highest point of a swale should be at least 6 inches lower than the finish elevation of any paved area or structure. From that high point, a minimum of 2% downstream slope should be maintained, with grades of up to 3%–5% allowed for short distances. Although the side slopes are maintained at grades that allow mowing, water volume or occasional steep slopes may require permanent channel erosion protection in some cases.

Swales should be used where they will be most effective. Placement around structures and through low areas of lawns allows the swale to perform the function of collecting water from downspouts and lawns and transporting it away (Figure 15-1). When a hillside with high runoff abuts an improvement, a swale should be placed between the hillside and the improvement to intercept runoff. Water carried in swales can be directed to storm sewer **inlets** or emptied into drainage channels, streams, or unused lawn areas. This latter choice will create wet areas that are unusable for periods of time.

Grading Diversion Berms

Occasionally, a site will have a slope that directs runoff toward structures and other improvements. If a swale cannot be constructed to intercept this runoff, a diversion berm may be an alternative. A swale lowers the surface elevation, whereas a diversion berm mounds soil upward to direct

Figure 15-1 Drainage swale constructed to direct runoff away from improvements.

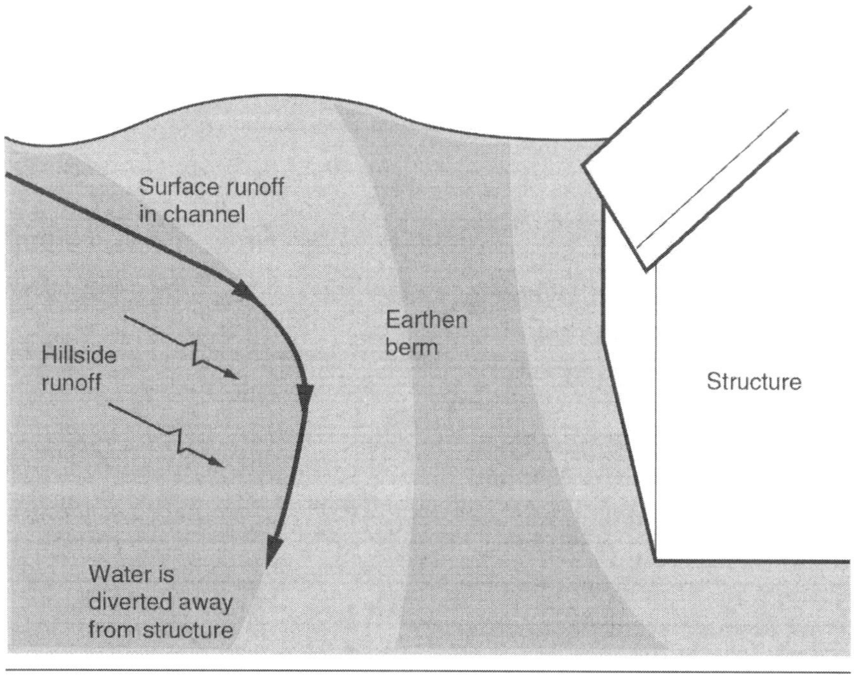

Figure 15-2 Diversion berm to direct surface runoff.

water (Figure 15-2). By mounding soil a short distance from an improvement, and continuing that mounding around the improvement, water can be directed to the point below the improvement.

Diversion berms should be constructed during site grading. To be effective, the berm must create a small swale on the upslope side to carry water, and it must continue around the improvement being protected until the highest point of the berm is level with the improvement's finish elevation. Exercise caution when using diversion berms near structures. The space between the berm and the structure will continue to drain toward the structure; and if water from downspouts, roof drainage, or other large quantities of runoff land in this zone, the structure could flood. If this is the situation, consider using a tile or storm sewer system to handle drainage.

SUBSURFACE DRAINAGE

Although the first consideration for site drainage should be surface drainage, contractors may have to construct subsurface drainage systems on certain sites. Among these sites are those that have variable grades, are not conducive to the construction of swales, are subject to temporary flooding, have high volumes of runoff, or a high percentage of site coverage by structures and/or paved areas and a critical need to channel runoff away from structures.

Three approaches to subsurface drainage are available, with the first two considered within the scope of the landscape contractor's work. The first approach is using a **dry well, or Closed French Drain,** to draw excess water off the surface and to store the runoff until it percolates into the surrounding soil. The second approach is using an underground tile to transport runoff to an outlet point. This system requires that the surface be graded properly to direct water to the system collection points, typically a surface inlet, and then transported to an outlet point through nonperforated pipe. Combining these two surface drainage techniques is termed a **French Drain**, or **Open French Drain**, which is discussed under Installing Subsurface Tile Systems. Subsurface water can be removed from a site with the use of a **perforated tile** system, which collects underground water without using surface inlets. The third approach is the construction of storm sewers, a system of drainage structures and underground piping engineered to collect high volumes of runoff at surface low points and carry the water to an outlet point.

> **CAUTION**
>
> Never connect storm drains to sanitary sewer lines.

> **CAUTION**
>
> Verify that the location where you intend to direct water collected in a tile or storm sewer system is a legal location to empty runoff.

Constructing Dry Wells (Closed French Drains)

French drains are gravel trenches covered with a thin layer of soil and ground cover. The gravel in these trenches stores water in the open spaces between each stone (Figure 15-3). A closed drainage system that requires no outlet point, a closed french drain would be properly placed in low areas that collect water or in locations where poor soils slow the percolation of surface water.

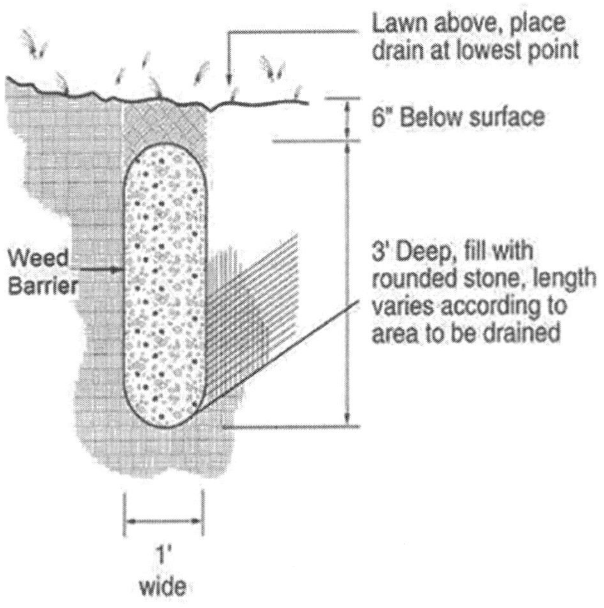

Figure 15-3 Cross section of a closed french drain.

Begin by using the formula identified in Appendix D to calculate the length of closed french drain required. When you have calculated the length of closed french drain, mark the location of the trench on the site. If the site will not accommodate a single trench, you may split the required length into separate trenches placed at least 36 inches apart. To be effective, the majority of the trench should be located directly under the area that floods. Excavate a trench 12 inches wide and 42 inches deep along the lines marked. In turf areas, remove the sod set it aside for reuse. Save approximately 10% of the soil excavated from the trench for cover.

For each trench, cut two lengths of 48-inch wide landscape fabric 2 feet longer than the trench length. Place the first piece of landscape fabric up one side of the trench. Fold the top over the outside edge of the trench. You do not need to cover the entire bottom of the trench. Repeat the process with the other piece of landscape fabric on the opposite side of the trench. Fill the trench to within 6 inches of the top of the trench with 1–2-inch diameter washed river rock. When filling the trench, use care not to disturb the landscape fabric. Fold the remaining landscape fabric over the top of the river rock. Backfill the trench with the soil set aside earlier and compact. If you saved the sod, replace it over the fill.

The average life of a closed french drain is approximately 5–10 years. After that time, the storage capacity of the pores between the river rock will be reduced from silt that has worked into the drain. In addition, using landscape fabric to line the closed French drain will eventually accumulate clay and fine silt particles on the surface of the fabric and restrict the flow of water into the trench. Because of this limitation, an alternative is to construct the closed french drain without placing landscape fabric around the river rock. This alternative will also, eventually, fill with silt but the useful life span may equal that of the unlined trench in silty or clayey soils.

Installing Tile Systems

Tile systems can be used to drain both surface and subsurface water. Surface water is drained away through inlets or trench drains that allow water to drain into a pipe and be carried to an outlet point. Tile also can be used to intercept the water table (subsurface water that is moving up toward the surface) and to reduce damage from frost. Installation of each of these systems is described in the following sections.

Installing Tile Systems with Surface Inlets. Installing a tile system to drain surface areas begins with flagging inlet points and an outlet point. Inlets should be located in paved areas and lawns, near roof downspouts, and in any location where significant runoff is expected. Between inlet locations, a simple network of connecting tile lines should be marked leading to the outlet point. This network should avoid uphill runs.

Beginning at the outlet point, excavate an 8–12-inch wide trench along the entire length of the collection system (Figure 15-4). The trench should be deep enough that the grade can fall at a 1% rate from the highest inlet to the outlet point. Excavating the trench 1–2 inches deeper will allow a sand setting bed to be added and make adjusting the trench to keep a downhill grade easier. Add this sand layer before placing the pipe. Beginning at a point just before the highest inlet, lay 4-inch diameter **nonperforated** tile or pvc pipe that exits at the surface and drops to the bottom of the trench. At this beginning of the system, cut the tile flush with the surface and install a cap (Figure 15-5). This cap will serve as a cleanout in the event the system becomes plugged with debris. Continue running tile along the bottom of the trench's length. Large numbers of inlets or heavy runoff areas will require increasing the tile size to 6 inches or larger on the lower portions of the drainage system.

At each location where an inlet is planned, cut the corrugated plastic tile or pvc pipe and insert a T connection. Insert a vertical pipe (**riser**) (Figure 15-6), running from the T to approximately 12 inches above the surface for future connection to an inlet. Continue laying pipe and inserting Ts until you complete the entire system. Premanufactured Ts, angles, and Ys are available to make branching and connecting systems easier. Cut and join tile and pipe as described in Small Equipment Operation

Figure 15-4 Trenching and placing plastic drain tile.

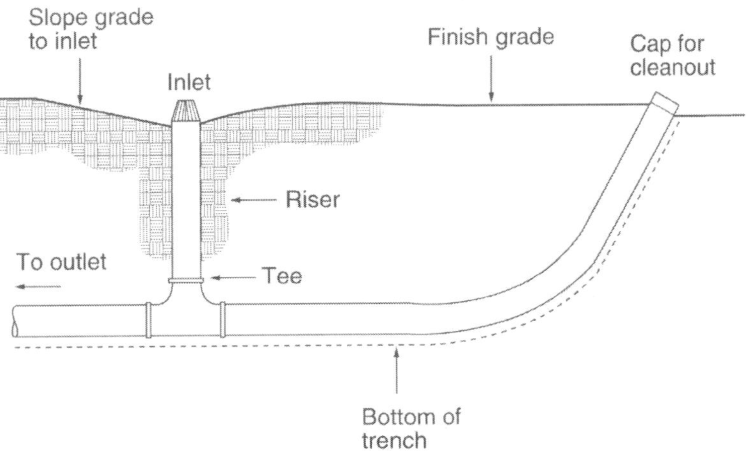

Figure 15-5 Cross section of tile riser and cleanout.

Figure 15-6 Tile riser before being trimmed for inlet installation.

Chapter. As you complete pipe and fitting installations, add enough soil or granular backfill to fill in on both sides and just cover the tile or pipe before moving to the next fitting. This fill, called **haunching,** will hold the tile or pipe and fitting against movement as you work on other portions of the project. Backfill the system to the surface, lightly compacting the backfill after every 12-inch layer.

Fiberglass inlets with flanges that fit into the risers are premanufactured for tile systems (Figure 15-7). Landscape contractors can choose from a wide variety of sizes and styles, including deep and shallow inlets, square and round inlets, and parabolic grates to reduce plugging from surface debris. To install inlets, excavate the finish grade around each location where a riser was placed. Cut the riser at this elevation and place the inlet into the end of the riser. Position the riser flush with the surrounding ground. Backfill the hole and adjust the finish grade to create a low point at the inlet.

Figure 15-7 Prefabricated inlet box with grate. Beehive or domed grates can clog when used in areas with mulch or debris.

See the storm sewer section below for alternate piping and inlet methods for tile systems with inlets.

Installing Surface Trench Drains. Capturing runoff on sloped pavement and around structures often requires installing a trench drain.

The **trench drain** is a formed/molded linear channel with a grate that sets in a frame on top of the channel. This drain is intended to be placed with paving on both sides of the drain or along the edge of a paved surface. Depending on the manufacturer, these channels can be installed in connected links that are approximately 2 feet in length or in longer sloped channels that are up to 10 feet in length. Installation methods will vary as well; depending on whether the channel is being installed before or after the surrounding paving has been completed.

To install the trench drain prior to installing surrounding paving, first mark the drain's location and elevation. If necessary, excavate a trench that is at least 4 inches deeper than the channel's bottom and at least 8 inches wider than the channel's width. Set a stringline along the trench's length at the finish elevation and alignment of the grate. Pour a foundation of concrete along the trench's length. Install the end cap and outlet for the channel's low point. Beginning at the lowest point, insert the channel into the bedding, pushing down or lifting the channel to match the stringline. Adjust the alignment of the channel to match the stringline.

Trim the end of the last piece of channel and install the end cap before placing in the bedding (Figure 15-8).

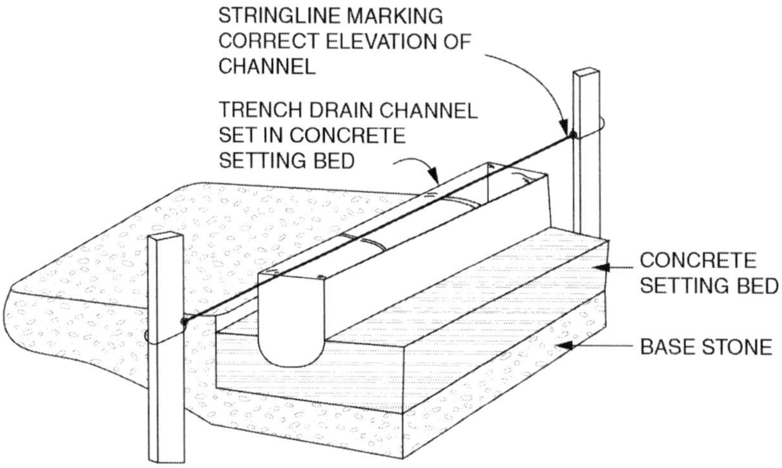

Figure 15-8 Trench drain channel placed in concrete setting bed. Pavement to be placed up to channel.

After the channel is in place, mask the grate to protect it from concrete spills or other damage. Install the grate into the frame, and attach the frame to the channel. You may now install the paving material along both sides of the channel, using the frame and grate to hold the top of the channel in proper position. If concrete is placed adjacent to the frame on both sides, you may need to apply expansion joint material along one or both sides of the channel's frame.

An alternative installation method is to install forms alongside the channel and pour the paving on both sides of the channel separate from the pour around the drain. When using this alternative, be certain to install a keyway or reinforcing bar that extends from the drain pour into the paving pour.

To install the trench drain after surrounding paving has been poured, proceed with the paving pour and box out a channel for the trench drain that is at least 8 inches wider than the channel (Figure 15-9). After the surrounding paving has been completed, excavate a trench in the boxout that is at least 4 inches deeper than the assembled drain. Assemble the drain channel and frame. Mask the grate and attach the grate to the center of 2 × 4s that are 2 feet wider than the boxout. Place these 2 × 4s every 4 feet along the length of the drain. Attach expansion joint, if necessary, along one or both sides of the boxout. Assemble the grate to the frame and place the entire assembly into the trench, centering the drain in the boxout. Carefully pour concrete along the entire length of the drain. Use care to tamp the concrete under the channel and to completely fill the voids of the boxout. Finish the concrete and remove the 2 × 4s. Alternatively, there are drain systems that provide brackets to support the drain assembly in the boxout without using 2 × 4s. These brackets mount on the channel and/or frame and typically are left in the pour; however, provide support for the channel while the concrete is being poured around the drain.

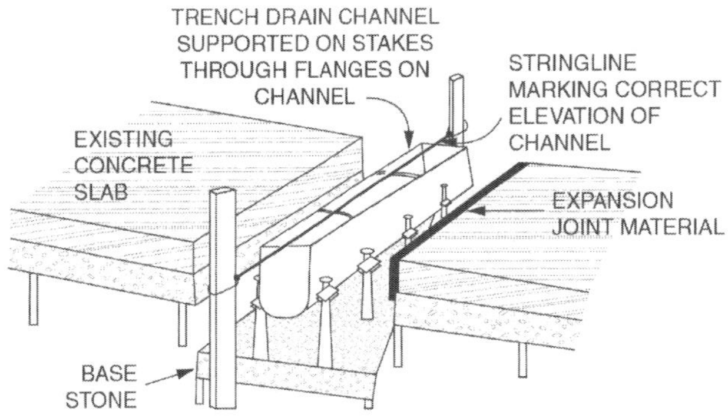

Figure 15-9 Trench drain channel supported on stakes in trench. Channel is installed in a trench through existing pavement. Pavement to be placed around channel.

Installing Subsurface Tile Systems. Tile used to intercept subsurface water is laid out in a pattern to cover the entire area that requires drainage (Figure 15-10). These systems may also be referred to as French drains. Tile line locations are marked out in a parallel line pattern with a connecting tile that runs perpendicular to these lines at the low end. A single tile leads from this connecting tile to the outlet. Soil type, rainfall, and severity of existing water problems determine the spacing of the parallel lines, which may range from 5–40 feet apart, depending on the conditions. The more severe the conditions, the closer the spacing. Consult an engineer if you are uncertain about spacing tiles for a particular

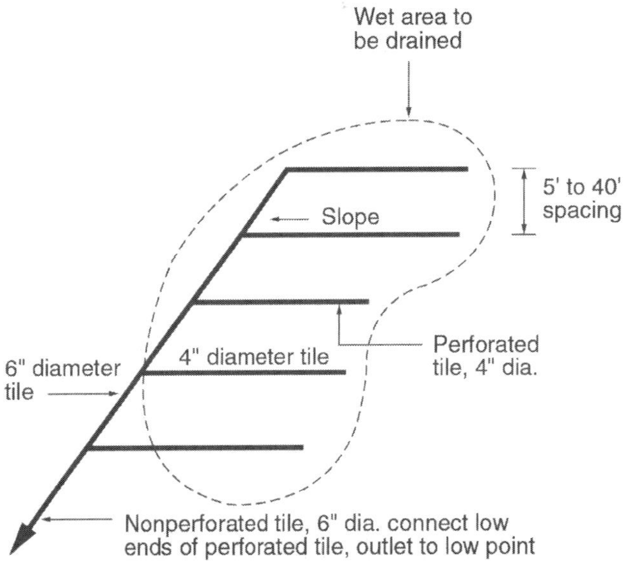

Figure 15-10 Plan view of tile layout for intercepting subsurface water in a wet area.

application. Inlets are rare on this type of tile system.

Excavate and place tile in the pattern used for surface drainage tile systems, except use *perforated* tile. To prevent fines from filling a perforated tile, backfill with coarse backfill material, such as pea gravel, or use a perforated tile with a **geotextile** sock wrapped around the tile. Even with the precaution of a geotextile sock covering, in areas with clayey or silty soil the geotextile may eventually become plugged with fine soil particles and block water from entering the tile so one may choose to eliminate its use. If intended to protect structure footings from frost, the tile must be slightly deeper than the footing's bottom. When used to drain wet areas, the effectiveness of this system is significantly increased by backfilling the trenches with crushed drainage stone rather than soil (Figure 15-3).

Installing Storm Sewer Systems

Specialized contractors must construct large storm sewer systems. Operation of the heavy equipment needed to install storm sewers and the hazardous conditions of trench work place this work beyond the typical landscape contractor's expected scope of responsibility. Landscape contractors will, however, be required to grade surfaces around storm sewer inlets and possibly connect tile systems they install to the storm sewers. Because of this relationship, the components of the storm sewer system will be reviewed.

Storm sewers are permanent subsurface drainage systems composed of two major parts: inlets and piping. Inlets, underground concrete (either precast or cast-in-place) or masonry-built boxes with openings in the top, perform the water collection for a storm sewer. Water is directed to the inlets on the surface and then falls through these openings. Different types of inlets are used, based on where the water is being collected. Having a **sump** in the bottom, **catch basins** are designed to catch debris and sediment that fall into the inlet. **Curb inlets** are concrete boxes with metal frames shaped to match roadway curb lines. Openings along the curb allow water to enter the inlet from

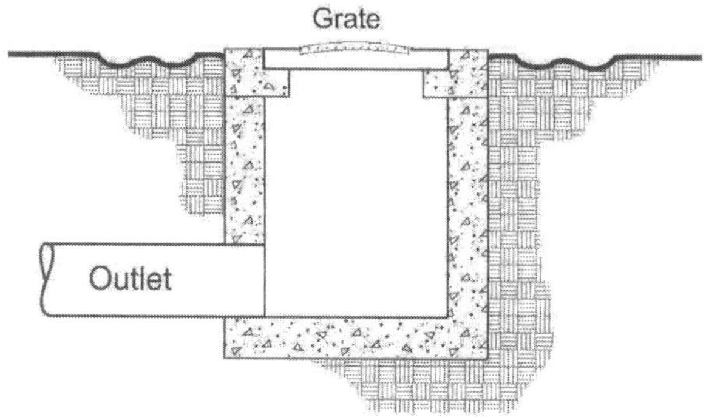

Figure 15-11 Drain inlet.

the side. Once inside the inlet, water flows into rigid (pvc, concrete, and HDPE are most common) piping and is conducted to outlets at streams or rivers. This pipe is typically laid at a minimum slope of 2% to maintain flow (Figure 15-11). Surface grades that lead to storm sewer inlets should be maintained relatively flat because steep slopes adjacent to the inlet may cause erosion. Also, the adjacent finish grade should be flush with the inlet to avoid water ponding.

With approval from the storm sewer owner, you may connect tile systems to inlets as an outlet point for small drainage systems. To make the connection, knock a hole into the inlet with a sledgehammer and push the tile through the hole into the inlet. The space around the hole should be filled with mortar so that soil does not wash into the inlet (Figure 15-12). When you use this outlet method for tile systems, verify that the tile line can be emptied no lower than halfway down in the inlet. Tile entering near the bottom of the inlet may have surcharge, or water running back up the tile when the inlet is full.

Treating Outlet Areas

Outlet areas for surface and subsurface drainage systems require special treatment to prevent erosion. End points of swales, channels, tile systems, and storm sewers typically carry large volumes collected from the site (or several sites), and the water at these locations is also moving quickly. The combination of these two factors makes the locations prone to severe soil erosion.

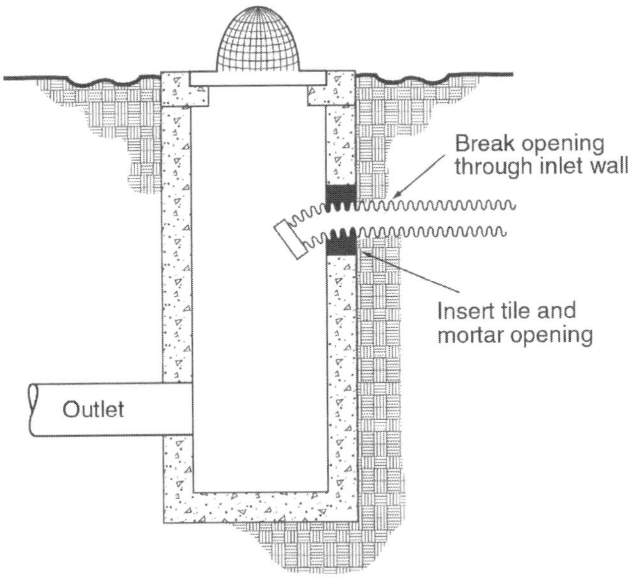

Figure 15-12 Connecting drain tile to existing storm sewer inlets. Perform this connection only with permission from the storm sewer owner.

To reduce the impact of erosion, treat each of these locations with rip-rap.

Rip-rap, large stone, is used for lining drainage swales to reduce erosion. Composed primarily of 4–8-inch rock, rip-rap reduces erosion by slowing the water as it strikes the rock's surface. The weight of rip-rap holds the surface contour in position so that it is not washed away like soil or smaller stone. The rip-rap at outlets should be placed over geotextile fabric centered on the outlet. The geotextile should be placed in a square with dimensions twice the outlet's width (Figure 15-13). Clients should be advised to monitor this area periodically to watch for erosion problems.

With tile systems, consider covering the outlet opening with landscape fabric to prevent small animals from entering the pipe. Cut a large piece of fabric and wrap it around the pipe end. Secure the fabric with duct tape to prevent water from washing off the fabric.

TEMPORARY STORAGE, DISSIPATION, AND REUSE OF STORM WATER RUNOFF

Previous sections have described methods of managing storm water runoff by directing the

Figure 15-13 Treatment of drain outlet with 4"–8" rip-rap to reduce erosion.

water off of the site and into regional water systems. Concerns over flooding and water shortages in highly developed areas have led to development of several methods of addressing storm water runoff before it even leaves the site, including detaining runoff in a basin and slowly releasing it into regional systems, retaining water on-site and letting runoff dissipate into the ground, or even capturing runoff and reusing the water to supplement site irrigation.

> **CAUTION**
>
> Some of the following drainage components must be designed by licensed professionals in North Carolina, including level spreaders and detention basins. Consult state and local codes and ordinances for additional information.

Level Spreaders

In areas where large volumes of water need to be channeled and then directed onto the surface for slower discharge, a level spreader can be utilized. A level spreader diverts storm water from a channel and directs it into a holding pond, or forebay. From this forebay, the runoff flows over a level weir, or lip, onto a protected section of surface where it percolates into the ground. Level spreaders are effective at mitigating normal volumes of storm water runoff that would otherwise be directed into regional drainage systems. Engineers or landscape architects should design level spreaders to obtain proper dimensions for storage and dissipation of runoff.

To construct the level spreader, begin by excavating the diversion structure and the forebay. This is typically done by grading the earth to create a detention pond with a diversion berm running to the channel from which water is being diverted. The forebay can be of any shape, but linear dimensions typically match the lip dimensions better than rounded or freeform shapes.

The channel can be emptied directly into the forebay, or a premanufactured diversion "gate" can be inserted into the channel to direct the runoff into the forebay. Line the bottom of the forebay with 3-inch rip-rap. Along one or more sides of the forebay, construct a level lip that will allow water to flow out of the forebay at the same rate at all points along the lip. This lip can be a cast-in-place or precast concrete curbing or a metal gutter that is built with the top perfectly level along its entire length. Alternatively, some designs empty a water channel directly into a precast forebay that is placed at the outlet of the channel. In this design, the precast forebay needs to be placed level on stable base rock (Figure 15-14).

In front of, and along the entire length of the lip, place an area of filter fabric that is covered with 3 inches of rip-rap. The design will determine the dimensions, but this area typically extends no less than 5 feet in front of the lip. The rip-rap area should be constructed at a gradual grade sloping away from the lip, should be a minimum of 4–6 inches below the lip, and should match the natural grade around the outside perimeter. This rip-rapped slope allows the water to dissipate over the site's natural grade, rather than run at high velocity down the original channel. In some designs, this dissipation area is seeded with native grasses that will assist in slowing the runoff's velocity.

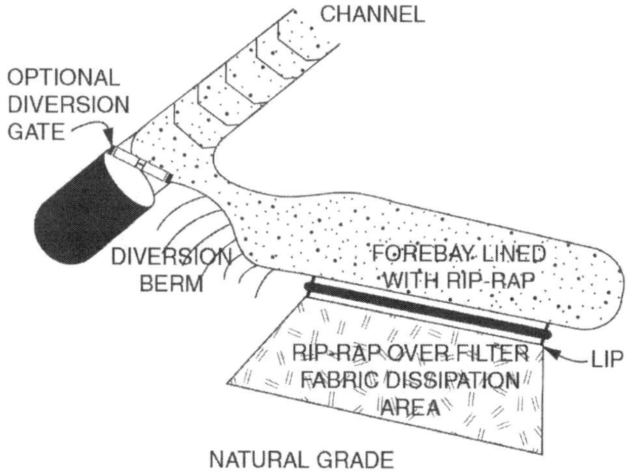

Figure 15-14 Diagram of a level spreader used to dissipate runoff from a drainage channel.

Storm Water Detention Basins

Storm water detention is based on a simple concept. Before a site is developed with paving and structures, most rainwater is absorbed, or percolates, into the surface. After the site is developed, a majority of the water runs off the site instead of percolating into the ground. Storm water detention plans design a pond on the site that will hold storm runoff from a developed site and release it at the same rate as on an undeveloped site. If the detention of storm water is properly practiced in developed areas, flooding that occurs from runoff during heavy storms should be reduced.

Constructing detention areas usually involves specialty contractors but sometimes falls under the landscape contractor's responsibilities. On-site detention ponds can be placed in turf areas and, when open space is restricted, are occasionally placed on paved parking areas. Turf-lined ponds must be built to exact dimensions to detain the proper amount of water. Rim elevation (elevation where the water will reach its highest level) is critical when grading for a detention pond. Low points in the rim elevation will allow water to exit the detention structure, rather than being retained. Most detention ponds also have an overflow to accommodate rains that exceed design capacities. This overflow may be a grassed or paved channel similar to those discussed in Chapter 16, Erosion Control.

Ponds also require an outflow pipe in which the size of the opening, called an **orifice,** is determined by extensive calculations. Whether plastic or metal, the orifice may require that openings in the surface be covered to reduce the outflow. When sizing the orifice for detention, the most common method is to have a metal plate welded over the required percentage of a metal grate or to glue a covering over plastic grates. Design professionals should calculate the sizes of the detention area and the orifice opening.

Bioswales

Another application of the concept of storm water detention, the bioswale is a gradually sloped drainage channel with shallow sides lined with plant material and, in certain situations, rip-rap. Used to slow runoff and trap pollutants and sediment, the bioswale allows water to percolate into the soil, rather than running off the site. The bioswale can be used as a decorative landscape element, is typically placed to capture polluted runoff from parking and paved areas, and is most effective in areas where runoff is intermittent, not constant.

To construct a bioswale, grade a channel with side slopes not exceeding 3:1 (3 feet horizontal to 1 foot vertical) and a center line slope that is as gradual as the site will allow (1% is desirable). The bioswale's cross-sectional shape can be either parabolic (curved) or trapezoidal (angled) (Figure 15-15). If the native soil is primarily clay and impervious, the top 12 inches of soil should be amended with approximately 50% sand and compost. Seed or plug the area with grasses native to the area that can tolerate temporary inundation by floodwaters. Place an erosion mat or jute netting over the area to limit erosion while the plant material cover is being established. If the swale experiences high volumes of water, the bottom may be covered with a 4-inch rip-rap.

Figure 15-15 Bioswale planted with native grasses.

The plant material in the bioswale is only periodically trimmed and is allowed to grow to full height to assist in trapping sediment and slowing the drainage. At the end of the bioswale, place an outlet that is sized to allow drainage from the swale during periods of heavy rains.

> **CAUTION**
>
> When performing maintenance on cisterns, drywells or ANY underground facility, always follow safety guidelines for underground and confined area work. Have proper safety equipment and NEVER work alone when working underground.

Cisterns and Drywells

With cisterns and drywells, storm runoff from roofs and paved areas can be captured and reused or allowed to dissipate back into the ground. Cisterns and drywells are containers of varying volumes, some as small as 5 gallons and others as large as several thousand gallons, that are buried underground on a site. A single large cistern/drywell can manage runoff; also available is a series of small drywells connected to roof drains around a site to accommodate runoff dissipation. Permits are required for most cistern and drywell installations, and specialty contractors will be required for electrical connections and deep underground construction.

Cisterns are typically the term used for containment that stores water for reuse, whereas drywells generally refer to containment that dissipates water back into the ground. Both containers are buried, with the top of the container below ground, and are fed storm water runoff through tiling and piping systems that empty into the top of the container.

Cisterns are often constructed of cast-in-place concrete with a concrete bottom. Precast concrete, plastic, and fiberglass cisterns are also available. To reuse the water stored in a cistern, a submersible pump with a line connected to the irrigation supply system is required. A filtering system is also essential to prevent plugging of the irrigation system with debris from the cistern, and an access to the cistern may also be required to allow maintenance. An overflow allows excess water to drain when the cistern is full. Drywells can be premanufactured out of plastic or fiberglass, or they can be perforated plastic or concrete panels that are set into a hole excavated in the ground. Drywells are often constructed from a trench lined with geotextile, then filled with loose, coarse stone. This type of drywell is called a closed French drain and it's construction is described earlier in the section. Subsurface drywells can also be constructed by burying a large cube of loosely stacked flat stone with a concrete slab for a cover or using prefabricated storage systems. A prefabricated modular open-celled storage system allows a storage area to be variable in size. Many drywells have perforated walls to allow dissipation of water into the soil, and many also are filled with large drain rock for structural stability. A modular system will require placing the modular units within a jacket of filter fabric to allow percolation of stored water.

Installation of either system requires excavating an area large enough to place the container, placement of base rock to provide a level and stable base for the container, connection of the inlet piping, and backfilling around and over the container (Figure 15-16). If a surface access is

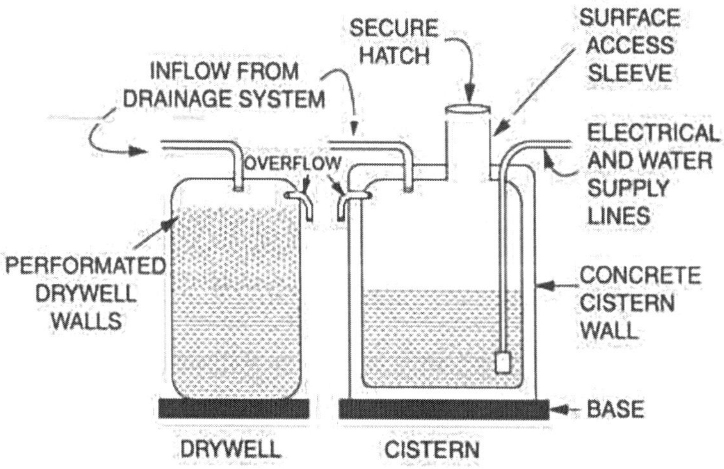

Figure 15-16 Diagram of a cistern and a drywell.

required, you can place a sleeve over the opening in the container; then connect a secure hatch at surface level over the sleeve.

> **CAUTION**
>
> Failure to properly install a backflow prevention valve when connecting an irrigation system to a potable water supply is unlawful and may result in contamination of the water supply.

Soaker Trenches

Runoff from roof and surface area drains can be redirected into the soil through soaker trenches. Similar in nature to a shallow closed french drain and septic leaching fields, the soaker trench is a subsurface trench filled with coarse gravel that holds large volumes of water until it can percolate into the surrounding subsoil. Trenches may also be designed to make use of modular retention cells that are wrapped in filter fabric. In their designs, soil engineers or landscape architects can determine the effective length of the trench, which may also require a permit for construction. If the runoff is diverted directly into the soaker trench, the problem of the filter fabric being plugged by silty or clayey soil is mitigated.

To build the soaker trench, locate the area where the trench is to be installed. Ground that is level is preferable. If on a sloping site, the trench should run perpendicular to the grade.

Excavate a trench that is 2–3-feet deep and 2–3-feet wide and slightly sloping from one end to the other. The actual width, depth, and length will be determined by the design of the trench, based on the soil type and the amount of impermeable surface to be drained. General guidelines for a trench in good draining soil would require a 2-foot wide by 3-foot deep trench, with 15 feet of length for every 1,000 SF of surface being drained. Poorly draining soil would generally require a 3-foot wide by 3-foot deep trench, with 25 feet of length for every 1,000 SF of surface being drained. An engineer or landscape architect should verify these dimensions.

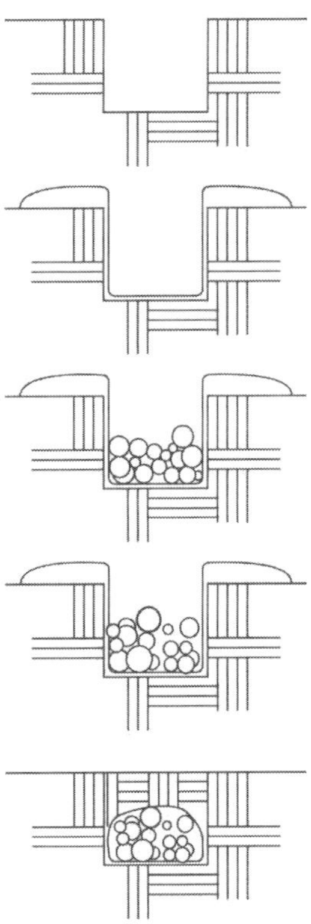

Figure 15-17 Step-by-step construction of a soaker trench.

Line the bottom and sides of the trench with an 8-foot wide piece of filter fabric. Fold the excess fabric off to the side for later covering of the trench. Fill the trench to within 1 foot of the surface with 1–2½-inch rounded drainage rock. Lay a socked perforated drain tile down the center of the trench for the entire length. Connect the end of this tile located at the higher end of the trench to your drainage system, and cap the tile at the lower end. Fold the remaining filter fabric over the top of the drain tile and backfill the trench (Figure 15-17).

Storage Barrels

One easier method for capturing runoff from roof drains is to empty the drain into a barrel designed for such methods. Disconnected from piping leading to storm sewers, the roof drain is diverted and connected to a large barrel or drum, typically around 50–55 gallons in size. The barrel must be completely enclosed to eliminate mosquito habitat.

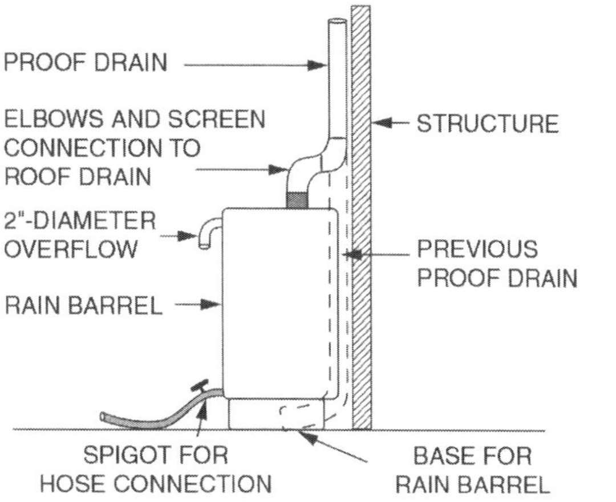

Figure 15-18 Diagram of a rain barrel.

Position the barrel next to a roof drain. Barrels should be installed on a stable base, preferably one that is a foot or two above ground level. This base can be constructed of wood timbers or concrete block and should have a 4-inch thick layer of base rock below. Cut the roof drain and install elbow pipe to direct the water to the drain barrel. Installing an open wire mesh between the elbows will help capture debris that washes down the drain, or a more elaborate screening system can be constructed or purchased if significant debris is anticipated (Figure 15-18).

Where the drain connects to the barrel, place an overflow valve in the event the barrel fills beyond capacity. This can be a valve inserted into the elbows or a 2-inch diameter, 90- degree elbow installed through a hole drilled in the barrel's side near the top rim. At the bottom of the barrel, a hose spigot should be installed; this allows connection to a garden hose for reuse of the water.

Runoff to Lawns and Gardens

The easiest method to reduce site runoff is to disconnect roof drains from piping that leads to storm sewers and redirect that runoff to lawns and garden areas. This technique is easy to implement but difficult to control. Runoff from roof drains must be directed to planted areas, or the drains should be rerouted to discharge directly above or into the area to be irrigated.

Gravity will do the work of directing the runoff downhill. Before implementing this system, verify that runoff will empty into areas that are planted and not into structures or paved areas. Many roof drains are installed to prevent flooding of structures and paved areas, and drains that are performing that function should not be disconnected. To contain the runoff in desired areas, you may have to grade a small berm around the garden to temporarily hold the water.

A continuing issue with this method is the runoff's consistency. Often a support irrigation system is required to balance the times when there is no storm runoff.

CHAPTER 16

EROSION CONTROL

OBJECTIVES

By reading and practicing the techniques described in this chapter, the reader should be able to successfully complete the following activities:

- Identify locations on a construction site that require erosion protection.
- Reduce soil erosion from the surface of a construction site.
- Install erosion control measures.

One goal of most landscape designs is to provide positive drainage throughout a site with stable surfacing that will remain in place during all conditions. However, to change a site from its existing conditions to the shapes and forms desired requires various levels of disruption.

The period between existing conditions and finished product provides a window for one of the most challenging problems facing the landscape contractor—site erosion. Improvements to sites such as structures and paved areas may increase the amount of water exiting a site, complicating the goal of maintaining stable surfacing. When construction is complete, the potential for erosion still exists on slopes that remain unprotected. Stabilizing these slopes and channels is an important part of the erosion protection concept.

Erosion is the removal of soil from a site as a result of the action of water and wind. Conditions that exist during the landscape construction process, particularly site grading, make most sites vulnerable to erosion. Several factors influence the process of erosion, including soil type, vegetative cover, soil particle size, slope of the site, exposure of the site, and the amount and speed of water and wind over the site. Changing or disrupting these factors is the focus of most erosion protection methods. At each construction site, an important technique for reducing erosion is to cause minimal disturbance to the existing vegetative cover. Additional control methods typically involve covering the soil, reducing or diverting the amount of water and wind passing over disturbed soils, anchoring the soil with plant roots, or slowing the water and wind speed to reduce their capacity to move the soil particles.

Erosion control may be part of a contractual agreement between contractors and clients, or landscape contractors may make their own decisions to provide control measures. Contract documents may specify measures that must be taken to protect the site from erosion, but occasionally they provide only a clause stating "Contractor shall protect site from erosion." Keeping soil on the site protects a valuable resource and reduces cleanup efforts during the project. Erosion protection can also provide protection from liability by preventing the disruption of adjacent properties from out-wash soil. In either situation, whether contracted or through the independent judgment of the contractor, erosion protection provides a valuable preventative service to the landscape project.

The techniques presented in this chapter will use the methods just identified to address erosion on three fronts. Erosion controls are identified for the site's perimeter and exposed surfaces and for drainage channels that carry runoff water from the site. Techniques are identified as temporary or permanent control methods, with use and installation methods provided for each. The majority of erosion control measures address the problem of water erosion and, unfortunately, have minimal effect on wind erosion patterns.

As with all steps of landscape construction, calculations need to be performed to order materials and complete the steps identified in the following sections. Refer to Chapter 5, Construction Math, to review methods of linear, area, and volume measurements required by this chapter.

The design of erosion control plans and structures is highly regulated in North Carolina. In most cases, designs must be completed by engineers or landscape architects and approved by local or state authorities. Consult local codes for more information.

RELATED INFORMATION

Information in this chapter is supplemented by instruction provided elsewhere in this text and in other sources. Before undertaking the activities described in this chapter, read the related information in these sources:

- Safety in the Workplace, Chapter 7
- Basic Construction Techniques and Small Equipment Operation, Chapter 8
- Site Grading, Chapter 13
- Site Drainage, Chapter 15

PROTECTING THE SITE FROM PERIMETER EROSION

Protecting the site's perimeter tackles two fronts: preventing eroding soil from washing onto neighboring properties and reducing runoff entering the site. To prevent water from flowing across a site, landscape contractors can install buffer strips around the site in low-volume situations or interceptor channels if the volumes of water are higher.

Installing Buffer Strips

Preserving a buffer of vegetation around the site is an initial step to reducing runoff that enters a site and causes erosion. Existing plant material, including grasses, ground covers, shrubs, and trees, has root systems that can slow and dissipate water that passes into the site. The wider the buffer strip, the better. A minimum of 2–3 feet can have an impact in areas where there is only sheet surface runoff. For areas where greater volumes of runoff are expected, a wider buffer of 10–20 feet would be more appropriate. Channels that direct runoff onto a site will most likely need more structural methods to control the larger volumes of water.

Installing Interceptor Channels

In areas where any amount of runoff can potentially harm a site, a more reliable method of reducing the volume of water entering it is to construct an interceptor channel. The **interceptor channel** is a shallow swale lined with concrete or a heavy-grade vinyl liner (similar to a decorative pool liner) that is placed along the site's perimeter on the high side. This channel is continued along the site's perimeter to an outlet point that is unlikely to compound the erosion (Figure 16-1). Water coming from higher off-site elevations and running into the construction area falls instead into this channel and then flows to the outlet without passing over the areas prone to erosion.

With the aid of trenching or excavating equipment, landscape contractors should install interceptor channels before other construction begins. The sides should be approximately 2:1 slopes with a flat, level surface at the bottom of the channel. Following excavation, a vinyl liner is placed in the channel and secured to the subgrade, or the subgrade is surfaced with a 3–4-inch thick layer of concrete. These channels typically intercept small amounts of runoff. An engineer should size larger interceptor channels to assure proper function for erosion control. A concrete-surfaced channel is a semipermanent structure and can be left in place after construction to deal with long-term irrigation issues, whereas the vinyl-lined channel is only a temporary structure.

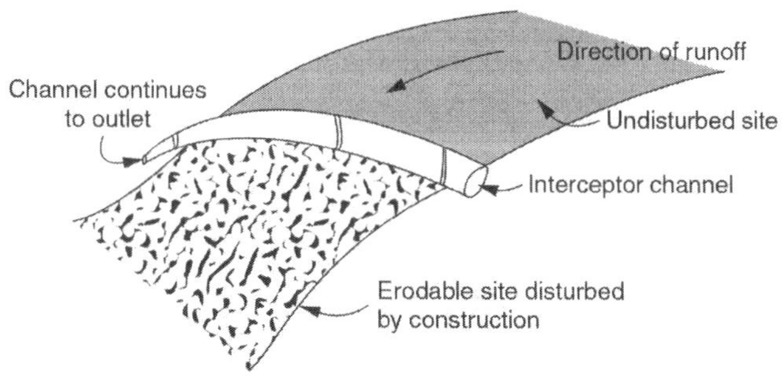

Figure 16-1 An interceptor channel designed to capture runoff before it enters a site.

Two techniques have been used with varied degrees of success to prevent soil erosion— straw bales and silt fences. An erosion control technique, the silt fence is constructed of **landscape fabric** attached to and suspended vertically between posts or stakes that are driven into the ground. Water strikes the landscape fabric and slows, dropping its load of sediment. Both straw bales and silt fences slow the velocity of water leaving the site, and the sediment is dropped on the upstream side of the protection and stored in 18–24-inch basins. Both techniques are more effective when existing ground cover vegetation is left in place for at least a 10–20-foot strip along the site's entire perimeter. Wattles, covered in "Protecting the Site from Surface Erosion," will also provide some degree of protection on shallow slopes or on surfaces that have been minimally disturbed. More recently, compost filled socks have been used for these same purposes.

Placing these devices in the proper location greatly increases their effectiveness. Areas to be treated are those below a site's disturbed areas, particularly locations downstream from these areas. Lower areas of sites and channels (see "Protecting the Site from Channel Erosion" later in this chapter) are other potential areas for protection. Both silt fences and straw bales are temporary structures and should be removed after construction ends and when permanent erosion control is functioning properly.

Maintenance of these devices is also critical to proper functioning of the systems. Whichever method they select, contractors should periodically remove the sediment in front of silt fences and straw bales to allow water to run through, and not over, them. Both silt fences and straw bales should be kept in an upright position. Bales that have tipped over and silt fencing that sags reduce the effective area of protection.

Installing Straw Bale Perimeter Protection

Contractors have used straw bales for many years to hold eroded soil on a site. Although inexpensive, bales are prone to washout and have a limited life. Their use should be limited to short-term projects, in which maintenance of bales can be performed. Materials required for straw bale perimeter protection include enough bales (measured along the longest dimension) to cover the perimeter and 2–3-foot wood or metal stakes for each bale placed (Figure 16-2).

Figure 16-2 Surface erosion control measures with straw bales and wattles on the slope.

Begin installation by marking the locations where you will provide perimeter protection. Clear weeds and debris for a 2-foot wide path along the perimeter identified for protection. Level the surface within this cleared path; the bales must make continuous contact with the surface to prevent leakage under them.

Beginning at the lowest point along the perimeter, place a bale on edge and push stakes into the top of the bale 12 inches from each end and centered in the bale. Drive these two stakes into the ground until the stakes are flush with the top of the bale. Place a second bale snug with the end of the first bale and repeat the staking procedure. Continue placing and staking bales until the bales line the entire perimeter.

Figure 16-3 Silt fence installation for perimeter erosion control.

Installing Silt Fence Perimeter Protection

Silt fences are the most effective protection method to reduce washout. Materials required for silt fence perimeter protection include enough premanufactured silt fence and stakes to cover the perimeter to be protected.

Begin installation by marking the locations where you will provide perimeter protection. Clear weeds and debris for a 2-foot wide path along the perimeter identified for protection. In a straight line along the low side of this cleared strip, excavate a 6-inch wide by 12-inch deep trench along the entire perimeter (Figure 16-3). Using a trenching machine for large projects will save both time and labor.

Beginning at the site's low point, place the bottom of the silt fence in the trench. Drive the wood stakes into the ground, leaving 24 inches of stake above the top edge of the trench. With each successive stake, stretch the fabric taut between the stakes. Tuck fabric into the trench and backfill. If more than one length of fabric is required, overlap the first length of fence with the second by 5 feet. Fasten both lengths together using nylon ties. Complete the installation by backfilling and compacting the trench.

An alternative to silt fence with preinstalled stakes is to hang weed barrier from an existing fence at the site's perimeter. The bottom edge of this installation should be buried in the same manner as the silt fence. If using an existing fence for support, excavate a trench along the upstream (high) side of the fence. To fasten to an existing fence, push nylon ties through the silt fence 2 inches from the top of the fabric and wrap them around the fence wires or surfacing. Stretch the fabric taut and place a tie every 2 feet.

PROTECTING THE SITE FROM SURFACE EROSION

Once the plant material cover has been removed from a surface, the process of erosion begins. Water droplets hit the surface and dislodge a particle of soil. Several particles are eroded away and rills, or small valleys, are formed. If left unchecked, the rills eventually form a network of gullies, and soil is systematically and continually eroded. Steep slopes and soils highly susceptible to erosion speed the process. To reduce erosion, surface protections are designed to either hold the soil in place with plant roots or cover the soil to limit the dislodging of soil particles. The best protection methods combine both of these techniques.

Protection methods used to reduce surface erosion include terracing, establishing **cover crops, mulching**, using wattles, applying soil stabilizers, covering sites with erosion prevention mats, and installing structural coverings on steep slopes. Each of these methods can be used as both temporary and permanent control measures. Most effective among these controls are ones that combine establishment of a cover crop with mulching, **erosion mats**, or permanent structural controls. Areas best suited to these protection methods include any surface that has been disturbed, but particularly disturbed areas with slopes greater than 2% (2 feet of fall in 100 feet of horizontal distance) and soils highly susceptible to erosion.

Applying Soil Stabilizers

The same products that bind aggregate to create a paved trail surface can also be applied to soil to reduce erosion. Although these products bind soil particles, they are only effective on gradual slopes, typically 1% slope and less, and should not be considered a long-term solution. Stabilizers may also reduce or eliminate the germination of cover crops applied before or after stabilization.

Soil stabilizers used for erosion control include polyurethane products, pine tree resin emulsions, bituminous emulsions, and ground seed hulls in powdered form. The liquid polyurethane stabilizer is poured directly over soil and blends into the top 1 inch of the surface. This product is most effective in preventing soil spreading or spilling into surrounding areas and contaminating other surfaces. For example, polyurethane is used in a golf course sand trap to keep the sand and soil separated. Liquid resins and emulsions must be blended into the top 3 inches of the soil by hand or by using mechanical equipment such as tillers or tractormounted blades. Once the resins or emulsions are incorporated, use heavy rolling equipment to compact the area. Powdered mixtures are blended into the top 3 inches of soil in the same matter and are moistened before compaction.

Terracing

When landscape contractors have control over grading of the site, they can adapt terracing to reduce erosion. Generally used in agricultural applications, terracing involves sculpting slopes into a series of nearly level, flat areas separated by steeper slopes. Planting cover crops or constructing retaining walls will maintain stability of steep slopes, but the terraced areas are less susceptible to erosion if the grade between the walls is nearly level. Although not appropriate in all areas, and expensive to implement, terracing can make a site more productive, as well as less susceptible to erosion.

To create terraces, "bench" the site during the rough grading phase of construction into a series of flat areas that are a minimum of 8–10-feet wide up to several feet wide. Steep slopes, typically no more than 4 feet high, separate these flat areas. Walls are then constructed to hold back the steep slopes, or the steep slopes are graded at a 2:1 slope and heavily planted and covered with erosion control blankets. After the slopes are completed, the flat areas are then planted with cover crops or permanent vegetation.

Using Cover Crops

Roots of plant material provide an effective method for holding soil in its place. Seeding a disturbed site with a quick-growing crop will both buffer the impact of rain and hold the soil. Selection of a cover crop requires knowledge of locally available crops that germinate quickly. Common selections include oats, wheat, annual ryegrasses, and buckwheat. The most serious limitation of this method is the time required for plant material to germinate. This limitation suggests combining a cover crop with another method that provides immediate abatement of erosion.

Many designs rely on vines, herbaceous ground cover, and woody plant material as a permanent cover to protect slopes from erosion. Because these plants take time to establish, it is necessary to combine their planting with temporary erosion control measures. Suggestions for minimizing the effects of erosion during the establishment period include spacing the plants closer, using erosion mats, and mulching.

Mulching

An inert covering over a disturbed surface reduces the impact of rain on soil particles.

Using mulch reduces the energy with which the water strikes the soil, limiting the disturbance of soil particles and the potential for erosion. A labor-intensive process with limited effectiveness on steep slopes, mulching functions best when combined with seeding of a cover crop under the mulch.

Mulching begins with selecting a suitable mulch material for the project site. Common choices are straw, wood chips, and shredded wood, with straw being a more cost-effective solution for construction protection. Spread the mulch evenly over the entire disturbed area by hand or mechanical means (spreader). Binding the mulch with the surface using a roller or a disk will slightly improve the durability and effectiveness of the mulch. This treatment requires periodic reapplication during construction. Expect some minor erosion and gullying that should be repaired prior to respreading topsoil. If gullying becomes a serious problem, consider channel protection for those affected areas.

A variation of mulching is hydraulic mulching, or **hydromulching**. This process, which requires special equipment, mixes mulch with water and a **tackifier** (sticky substance). The mixture is then sprayed on the site's surface. Hydromulching is typically accomplished by feeding the materials into a trailer-mounted hopper and spraying evenly over a site using a large hose. If desired, seed can also be mixed with the mulch, although the seed's germination and survival rates are reduced when this mixture is used. Hydromulching allows use of more durable mulches and reduces the labor required to evenly spread the mulch over the site.

Hydromulch formulas, called *bonded fiber matrices* (BFMs), chemically bond the materials and provide a durable, papier-máché-like coating over an exposed area. Water, starch, or a guar-based tackifier, and either cellulose (recycled paper) or wood fibers are blended and sprayed on the exposed surface. In some applications, synthetic fibers are added to increase bonding capabilities, and dyes are added to simulate vegetation colors. A few products have introduced water-absorbing gels into the mix to assist in holding water. Application of BFMs is best accomplished if the mixture can be sprayed so that it descends in an almost vertical angle similar to rainfall. Applying the material from opposing directions will improve coverage. BFMs require a drying time of up to 48 hours to be effective, and any rainfall or irrigation that occurs prior to curing may erode the surface.

Caution should be used in selecting BFMs if you plan to establish vegetative cover. The materials used to bond the product and the hard covering created after it is applied may restrict the germination and growth of cover crops. If combining seeding with BFMs, prepare the seedbed and sow or drill the seed prior to applying the matrix.

Installing Wattles

Wattles are tubular-shaped nylon nettings filled with straw fibers or small sapling branches such as willow. Installed on a slope perpendicular to water flow, wattles slow the water and force sediment to drop (Figure 16-4). Wattles are also used around the rims of storm drains and in locations where it is desirable to reduce

Figure 16-4 Wattle installation.

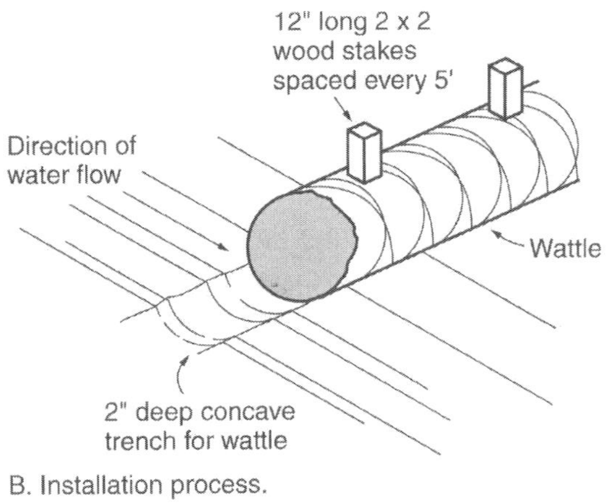

Figure 16-5 Trenching and staking of wattles.

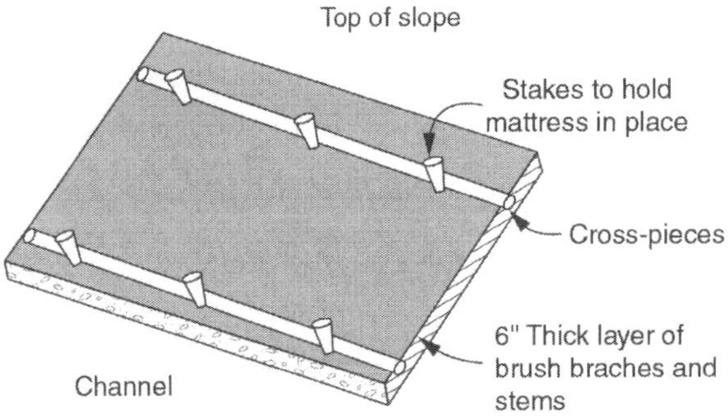

Figure 16-6 Diagram of a brush mattress.

sedimentation. Wattles are measured for length by laying out the material near the location of installation. Cut the wattle using tin snips or a knife and reseal the cut end of the netting using a twist tie. Along the alignment where the wattle is to be placed, excavate a shallow, concave trench approximately 2 inches deep. Place the wattle in this trench and stake it into place using 12-inch long 2 × 2 wood stakes spaced every 5 feet (Figure 16-5). Although wattles degrade over time, they are not intended to be left after permanent cover or erosion control is in place. Compost filled socks are similar to wattles and used in a similar fashion.

Installing Brush Mattresses and Pole Plantings

For lakefronts, channels, and streambanks in areas where fast-growing plant material can be harvested, brush mattresses and pole plantings can be used to reduce streambank and channel erosion. Brush mattresses are 6-inch thick layers of thin-diameter brush branches and stems that are arranged vertically along an embankment or channel side. Willow or other fast-growing plant material are preferred for this application. At the top and bottom of the smaller branches, horizontally lay 2–3-inch diameter cross branches. Drive stakes 2–3 feet into the embankment; wire the stakes to the cross branches to hold the branches in place. Then place soil over the mattress to encourage rooting (Figure 16-6). In moist environments, pole plantings, or stakes of fast-growing plant material such as willow and dogwood, can be driven into the embankment and allowed to sprout. These poles should be at least 2 inches in diameter and 4 feet in length and driven at least 2 feet into the embankment. With the buds of the poles facing upward, space the poles every 2 feet horizontally and vertically.

Installing Erosion Control Blankets (Erosion Mats)

Erosion control blankets (ECBs), or erosion mats, are a layer of biodegradable materials sandwiched between two layers of lightweight netting. Materials commonly used for netting are slowly photodegradable, and some manufacturers produce nettings that slowly biodegrade. Mats are intended to be anchored to a disturbed surface that has been seeded, either below or on top of the mat, and left to degrade over time. The lightweight netting is ground up by mowers or imbedded into the ground cover, which eventually covers the site. The mat material, often wood fibers, excelsior, coir (coconut husks), straw stems, or other wood by-products, degrades over one to two seasons and allows any seeded ground covers below the mats to grow.

Not all ECBs are biodegradable. Some use nonbiodegradable synthetics and plastics for the netting or core, and the products do not break down as readily as the natural or lightweight products. Some erosion mats are intended to remain in place for long periods and are sold as turf reinforcement mats, or TRMs. These and similar products, which are difficult to remove once vegetative cover is established, will remain in or under the plant material cover for long periods of time. This variety of material choices requires that the selection of a product be based on careful review of the situation for which the material is being used. Although they are more costly than mulching, mats provide better cover and a more stable form of protection for slopes up to 5%.

Installation begins with identifying the area to be covered. Prepare the entire seedbed below the area where the mat is to be placed. Starter fertilizer and seed may be placed on top of the mat, but placement below the mat provides better success for seed germination rate. Beginning at the site's high side, excavate a trench 6 inches deep and bury the top edge of the mat. Staple the fabric to the bottom of the trench (Figure 16-7). Backfill and compact the trench. For improved stability of installation, the mat can be wrapped around a ½-inch wood dowel or piece of #3 rerod, with the stakes placed straddling the dowel or rerod (Figure 16-8).

Roll out the mats in the same direction that water will run across the surface (top to bottom). Verify that there is good mat-to-soil contact. Where two mats are adjacent to one another, overlap the mats 12 inches. Mats can also be overlapped if there is excess material in odd-shaped areas. If mats are placed on a sloped surface, overlap them by placing the mat from the higher side over the mat on the lower side. Using metal staples or stakes (usually provided by the mat manufacturer), secure the mat every 12 inches around all edges and at overlap joints (Figure 16-9). Place staples in staggered rows every 18 inches for the length of the mat. For installations where the slope length is more than 20 feet top to bottom, install an additional row of stakes across the width of the mat every 10 feet (Figure 16-10).

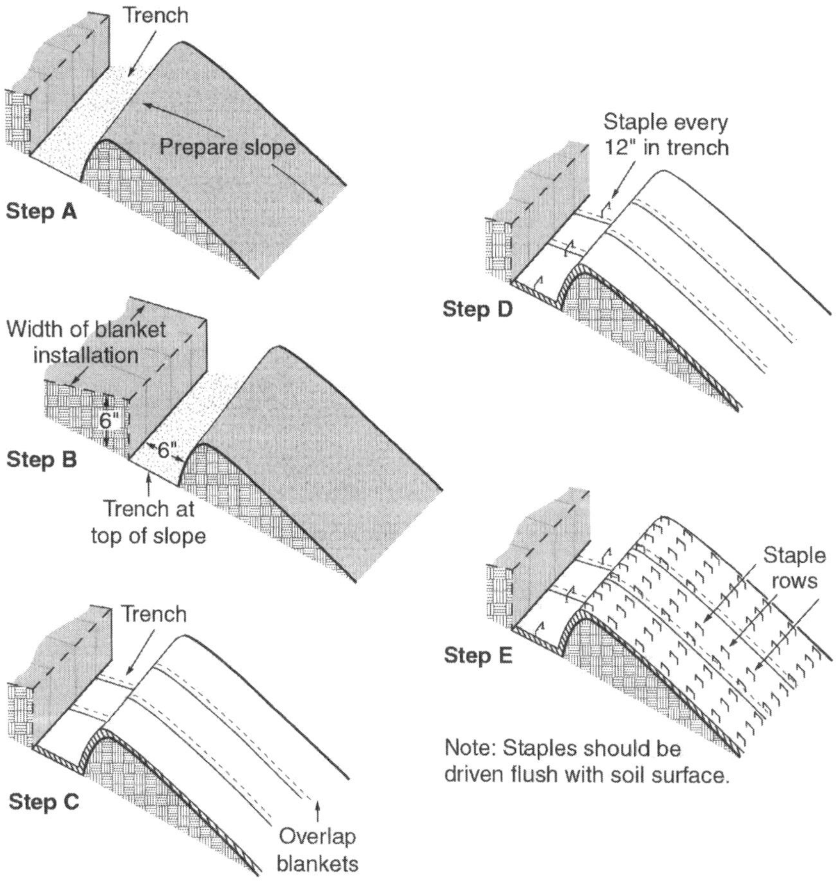

Figure 16-7 Installation of an erosion control blanket. The blankets are oriented with the long dimension running in the same direction. as surface runoff.

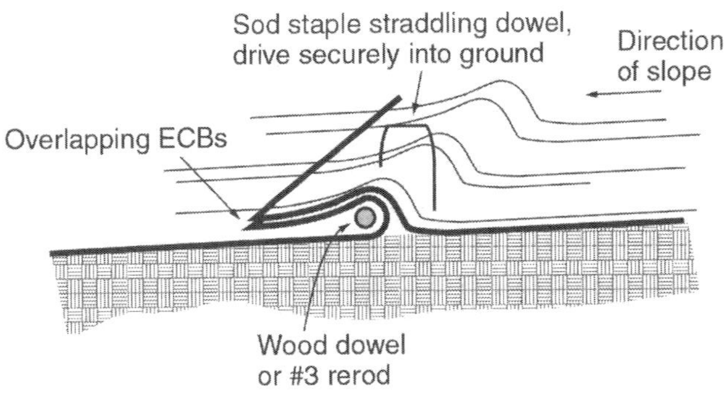

Figure 16-8 Using a dowel or rerod to improve stability of ECB installation.

Figure 16-9 Anchoring an erosion mat using metal staples. Photo shows overlapping ECBs and stapling before installation.

In applications where the possibility of water running under the mat is high, "check slots (Figure 16-11), or two closely spaced rows of anchors may be used transverse to flows at intermittent points down a slope or along a channel."[1] Construct a check slot by excavating a 6-inch deep by 6-inch wide trench along the entire width of the slope. Roll the blanket into the trench and staple at the bottom; then fold the blanket uphill on top of itself and fill the

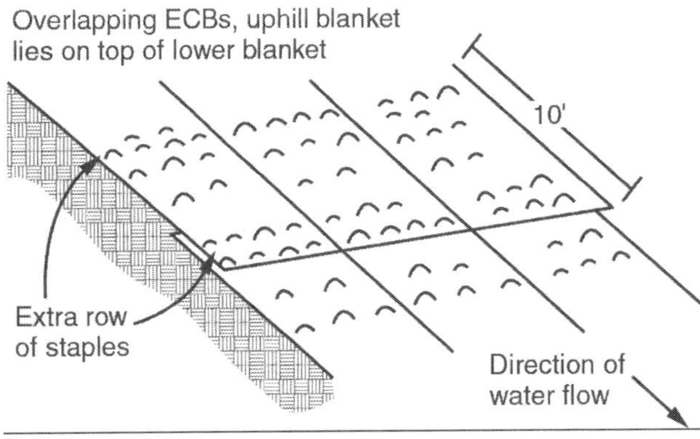

Figure 16-10 Overlap of ECBs secured with a double row of staples.

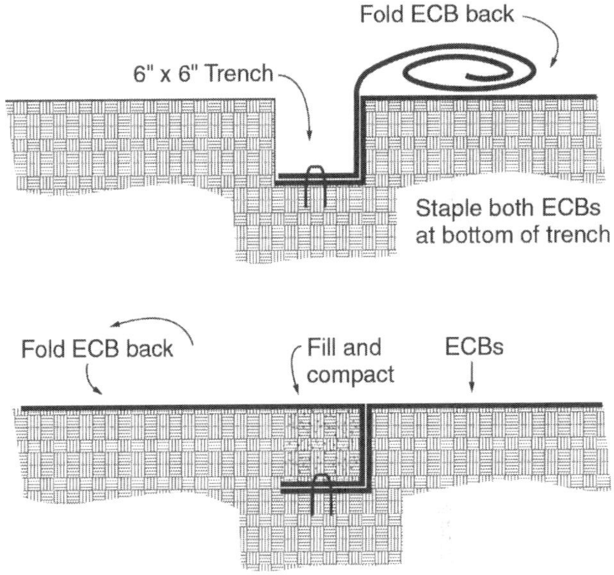

Figure 16-11 Securing ECBs with a check slot.

trench. When the trench is filled and compacted, continue rolling the blanket down the hill. After the ground cover is established and prior to the first mowing, remove all stakes and staples that can be located. This will reduce the chance of mowers "throwing" loose stakes as projectiles and will protect mowing equipment from damage.

[1]Greenfix America, Technical Data, http:// www.greenfix.com.

Controlling Structural Erosion on Steep Slopes

Steep slopes may need a more durable installation alternative for reducing surface erosion. Three choices of structural controls are available for a variety of situations—cellular confinement systems, slope retaining blocks, and rip-rap.

Cellular Confinement Systems. Cellular confinement systems use a web of geotextile pockets spaced down a slope to hold surface materials in place against erosion forces. These pockets function similarly to small dams that hold back material while slowing the water running down a hillside (Figure 16-12). Materials perforated with holes approximately ¼-inch in diameter are used for most installations, but nonperforated cells are available when filling with fine aggregates that may wash through the openings. When properly installed, the cellular confinement system stabilizes steep slopes and can be used for soil and granular fill, as well as for concrete.

Before installing a cellular confinement system, remove all debris and surface irregularities; the slope must be smoothed. Excavate a 12-inch wide by 12-inch deep trench along the entire top edge of the slope. Place a geotextile cover over the entire slope and fold the cover into the trench (Figure 16-13). Geotextile

Figure 16-12 Cellular confinement system.

© Delmar/Cengage Learning.

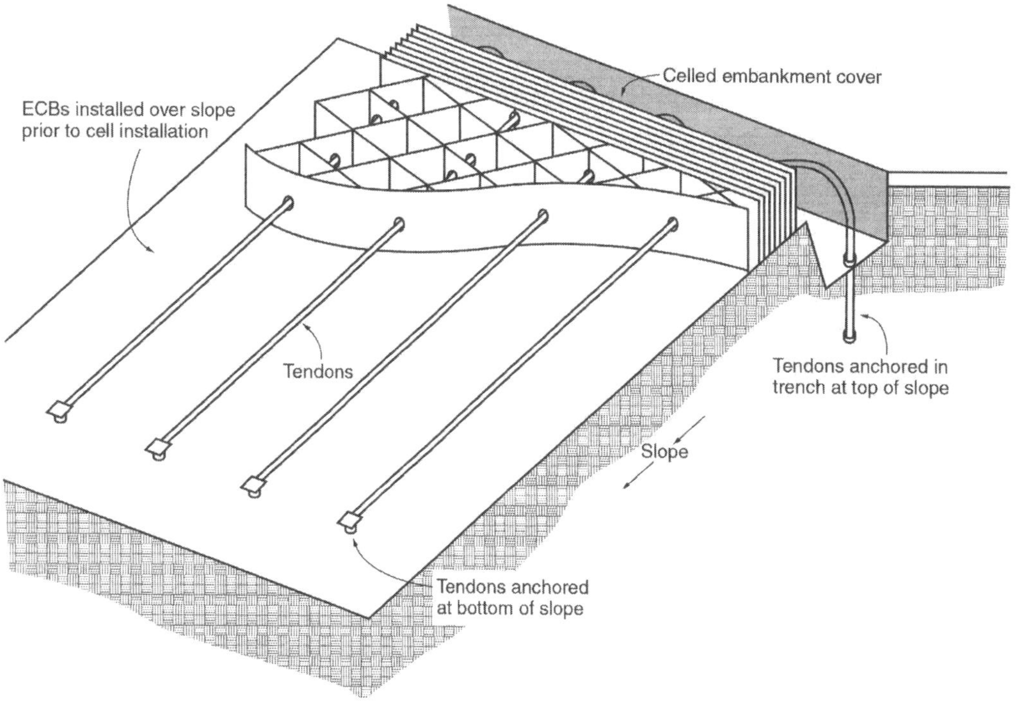

Figure 16-13 Installation of cellular confinement system.

© Delmar/Cengage Learning.

should be placed with the long dimension running down the slope the same direction as runoff. Staple the geotextile into the soil surface every 12 inches along all seams and edges and every 18 inches throughout the center of the material.

Supporting lines, or tendons, are anchored in the trench at the top of the slope using rerod, stakes, tree anchors. These tendons should be spaced to match the openings in the cellular confinement system. Place an unexpanded section of the confinement system fabric next to the trench on the slope side. Using a tube or a hook placed through the openings, thread the tendons through the openings in the unexpanded cellular confinement system. Pull the tendons down the slope and space them parallel to each other. Expand the cellular confinement system down the slope. If the slope is irregular, the cells can be compressed or tapered to match the slope direction. Secure the bottom of the cellular confinement system by knotting the tendon just past the last cell and anchoring the tendon just beyond the last cell. Fasten runs of cellular material to each other by stapling cells along the edge of the material. Anchor the installation internally by staking the tendons at 5-foot intervals down the slope.

Fill the cellular confinement system from the top of the slope working downward. Gently place fill material by hand or, if using excavation equipment, dropping the load from under 3 feet above the material. Evenly distribute the material throughout the cells.

Slope Retaining Blocks. Interlocking precast concrete block can be used to structurally stabilize a steep slope. Although similar to retaining wall block, these blocks are installed with a steeper **batter**, or backward lean, and with open voids between units. Slope retaining blocks anchor a slope by creating a loose wall that holds the soil at its natural **angle of repose** and allows plant material to establish in the voids.

To install slope retaining block, excavate a 12-inch wide by 6-inch deep trench along the entire length of the slope. Place the base course in this trench. The base course is laid by leveling the blocks side to side in the trench. Slope the base toward the hillside to provide the batter recommended by the manufacturer (typically 2-inch batter for every 1 foot height of wall). Blocks in subsequent courses should be placed straddling the two blocks below. Backfill with soil and continue adding courses until you reach the top of the slope. As you construct the wall or after you complete the installation, you may add ground cover plants in the voids.

Rip-Rap. In cases where plant material is not a reliable or practical choice for protecting embankments from erosion, permanent protection can be obtained by placing rip-rap (loose rock surfacing) over landscape fabric. Install the landscape fabric running in the same direction as the slope, and staple the fabric in place with sod or fabric staples. In instances where significant water is running onto the slope from above, excavate a 6-inch deep trench along the top of the slope, and bury the top edge of the fabric in this trench. Staple the fabric to the bottom of this trench, backfill, and compact. Beginning at the bottom of the slope, place rip-rap of at least 4–8-inch diameter over the fabric. Material choices may include rounded or angled stone or other locally available stone. Rip-rap must be large enough and heavy enough to counter the force of water washing down the slope. Carry the rip-rap 18 inches beyond the fabric's edges at the top and sides to help hold the fabric in place.

PROTECTING THE SITE FROM CHANNEL EROSION

Unless a site is extremely flat, water will collect in lower areas to drain away. This runoff is often heavy enough to form channels in areas with high volumes of runoff. If the channels are disturbed or have no protection, severe erosion can result. To provide temporary protection from erosion, techniques such as silt fences are used to slow down the runoff and to trap soil washed from higher elevations. Erosion mats can provide longer term protection because they help establish well-rooted ground covers on the channel's surface. In locations where water volumes and speeds are high, paved surfaces or rip-rap is used.

Determining the proper technique to use, as well as the proper location of the treatment, varies greatly from site to site. If the site is still under construction and more grading or construction activities are planned in the channel area or in those areas more susceptible to erosion located above the channel, temporary silt fences along the entire channel route are recommended. Spacing of silt fences depends on the slope and volume of water. However, a standard is to place the fences 50 feet apart for a channel that has a slope of 2–3% or drains an area that is primarily covered by impermeable surfaces. Steeper slopes and greater permanent coverage will require closer spacing. In channels with a flat slope, it is possible to place the erosion mats as described in "Protecting the Site from Surface Erosion" above.

Channels in areas where all construction is completed may be addressed with one of the permanent solutions. A ground cover is acceptable if the flow in the channel is intermittent enough to allow seeding to germinate. Maximum slopes of 2–3% and drainage areas that are less than 50% permanent cover approach the upper limits of channel erosion control using living plants. Channels above these limits should have rip-rap installed or be paved to limit erosion.

Installing Silt Fences

Silt fence for channel protection is installed in a manner similar to silt fence installation for perimeter protection. Materials required for channel silt fence will include lengths of the premanufactured silt fence with stakes that are 50% longer than the channel width (e.g., 10-foot wide channel requires 15-foot fence lengths). Begin installation by marking the locations where fences are to be located. Silt fence should be placed across the channel perpendicular to the direction of the water flow. Position the silt fence in a *V* configuration with the point of the *V* at the channel's low point and facing downstream (Figure 16-14). Clear weeds and debris for a 2-foot wide path along the path identified for the silt fence. Excavate a 6-inch wide by 12-inch deep trench along the path.

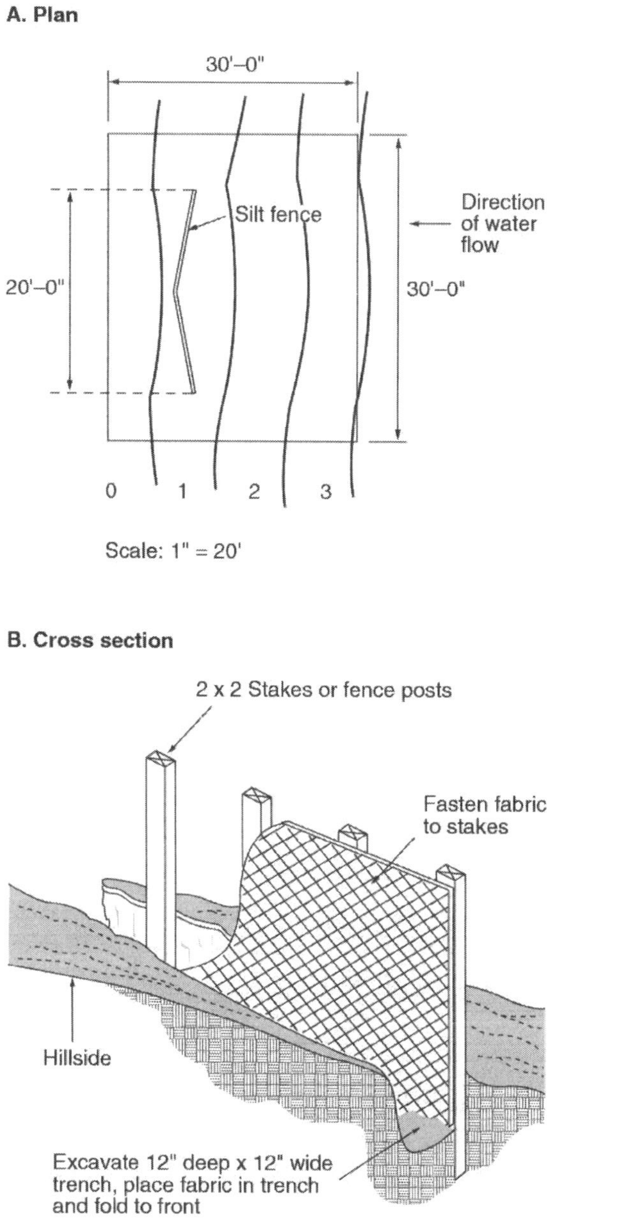

Figure 16-14 Silt fence. A. Layout. B. Installation.

Beginning at the edge of the channel, drive in place at the bottom of the trench the first stake of one of the previously cut silt fence lengths. Leave half of the stake/fabric above the top edge of the trench, and place with the fabric on the upstream side. Stretch the silt fence out along the length of the trench, driving wood stakes into the ground. With each successive stake, stretch the fabric taut between the stakes. The silt fence should be completed using a single piece of material. Complete the installation by backfilling and compacting the trench (Figure 16-14).

Similar to the procedure for perimeter protection, the silt fence must be maintained by periodically digging the trapped soil out of the reservoir. Failure to clean out in front of the fence may allow water to flow over the fence, making it nonfunctional. If the reservoir fills up rapidly, consider placing more fencing between existing installations or addressing surface erosion above the channel with a temporary control.

Installing Erosion Mats

Erosion mats can also be used for protection of channel surfaces. Installation is the same as that described in the previous paragraph, with the following exceptions. Beginning at the channel's low end, roll out the mats in the same alignment that water will flow in the channel (Figure 16-15). Where two mats are adjacent to one another, make certain the mats overlap 12 inches. Overlap by placing the mat from the higher side over the mat on the lower side and securing them with staples. Using metal staples or stakes (usually provided by the mat manufacturer), secure the mat every 12 inches around all its edges and across its center. Place staples in staggered rows every 12 inches for the length of the mat. In instances where significant water is running into the channel from above, excavate a 6-inch deep trench along the top of the slope and fold the edge of the mat in this trench. Staple the mat to the bottom of the trench, backfill, and compact. After ground cover is established or prior to the first mowing, remove all stakes and staples that can be located. Place rip-rap at either end of erosion mats in areas of high water volumes.

Figure 16-15 Placement of erosion mat along length of a channel. Note that the mat is placed with its long dimension running the same direction as the water flow.

Installing Rip-Rap

Rip-rap erosion protection is accomplished by lining a channel with large, loose stone that water, when passing through the channel, cannot pick up and wash away. This permanent installation performs the functions of slowing the water as it strikes the stone and holding the soil beneath the stone in place. Some contractors use a variation of this application by laying landscape fabric below the rip-rap before placing it.

The success of rip-rapping is entirely based on selecting the proper size of stone. For most small channels, 4–8-inch stone will provide adequate weight to slow the water and to hold the soil. Larger channels may require larger stone to perform this same function. Consult a design professional if you are uncertain about what size of stone to select. Place the stone beginning at the lower end of the channel and evenly cover all surfaces (Figure 16-16). To be effective, the stone must extend from the bottom of the channel to the top, with no gaps in coverage.

Figure 16-16 Swale protected with 4–8-inch rip-rap.

The owner must periodically maintain the rip-rap. Sediment dropped in the channel creates an ideal environment for grasses and weeds to germinate. Manual, mechanical, or chemical weed control will be needed to control growth in the channel.

Installing Paved Channels

Paved channels provide the most reliable protection against channel erosion. Unfortunately, they are also the most expensive and difficult to construct. The reader is referred to Chapter 23, Concrete Paving, for details regarding preparation, forming, and pouring cast-in-place concrete. Following are some special considerations for review before selecting and pouring paved channels as a permanent erosion protection.

Pouring slabs for channels that will carry large volumes of water requires special preparation and finishing to ensure an effective installation. First consider whether the channel can be paved without being disturbed by the amount of drainage through it. If flows through the channel are not intermittent, explore other methods to divert or stop the water to allow construction. Because the slabs that form the channel may not be completed in a single pour, contractors will need to provide joints that are solid and impermeable. Any water that works under the slab will cause erosion, resulting in failure of the channel. The channel's surface should be "distressed," or textured, to slow the water as it moves through the channel. To distress the surface, drag a rake across the finished concrete perpendicular to the direction of water flow or embed 4–6-inch diameter angular rock into the concrete, leaving half of the rock exposed. Other methods of distressing the surface are available; however, these methods may require that the slab be thickened by 1–2 inches to avoid weak areas.

Treatment of outflow areas should be considered when providing channel protection. The area where water passes out of a channel is a potential area for significant erosion. The grade in this area should be flattened and covered with rip-rap to prevent the installed channel protection from being undermined (see "Treating Outlet Systems" in Chapter 12).

SECTION 3

SUMMARY

Creating attractive landforms and effective site drainage requires grading the soil on the site and protecting it from erosion. Section 3 discussed the process for grading a site, installation of basic drainage structures, and temporary and permanent erosion protection measures. Each of these components works together to create interesting site features, to effectively remove unwanted water from a site, and to keep valuable soil in place.

Grading is a logical process of removing, sculpting, and replacing the layers of soil on a site. Initial steps in grading include stripping sod and vegetative matter from the surface, stripping and stockpiling topsoil, rough grading to approximate elevations desired, and placing of or installing temporary erosion control. At the conclusion of rough grading, the process is suspended until drainage systems, utilities, walls, paving, and structures are in place. When intermediate construction activities are completed, the grading process resumes with the respreading of topsoil and grading to desired finish elevations. Additional smoothing and shaping of the finish grade may be undertaken before establishing turf areas. Permanent erosion control measures follow either finish grading or completion of turf areas.

Managing the amount of water that drains from the site can be addressed by surface drainage or subsurface drainage systems. Surface drainage involves the shaping of grade to direct water to desired locations. On sites with little existing topography, the construction of drainage swales or diversion berms may be required to direct surface runoff. When surface techniques do not provide effective drainage, subsurface systems such as open or closed french drains, tiles, and storm sewers may be required. Open and closed French drains are temporary storage trenches that drain and hold small amounts of water in low, undrainable areas. Closed French drains let the water slowly percolate into the surrounding subsoil, while open French drains allow both percolation and provide a subsurface tile to drain water away from the trench. Tile systems involve the trenching and laying of pipe that will intercept water and carry it to an outlet point. Storm sewers work in the same manner as tile systems, with the exception that water is collected at concrete structures set at low points throughout the site and carried in large, non perforated concrete pipes. In areas where flooding is a problem, temporary storage, reuse, or dissipation of storm water runoff in detention ponds, bioswales, cisterns, soaker trenches, and rain barrels may be required. With outlets sized to slowly release detained water, detention ponds are open basins into which storm water is directed, whereas bioswales filter water that is moving along a channel. Soaker trenches allow the slow percolation of runoff from underground trenches into the surrounding soil. Cisterns and rain barrels allow the storage of rainwater runoff until it can be used for other purposes.

Keeping valuable soil on the site is the function of erosion protection measures. Erosion can be addressed at the perimeter of the site, over surfaces in areas more susceptible to erosion, and along channels that carry runoff. Perimeter protection is accomplished by burying straw bales or silt fences at the construction boundaries and other required locations. Measures typically used over surface areas include terracing, establishing fast-germinating cover crops, mulching, placing wattles, brush mattresses, erosion mats, cellular protection, and rip-rapping of steep embankments. Channel erosion protection ranges from installation of erosion mats and silt fencing to the rip-rapping and paving of high-volume channels.

SECTION 4

SITE UTILITIES

INTRODUCTION

Drainage systems are not the only utility systems for which the landscape contractor may have responsibility. Preparation of the site for an electrical contractor's work, kit installation of direct current (DC) or low-voltage lighting systems, and custom installation of DC lighting systems are the most likely utility systems that landscape contractors may also need to address. Because general contractors or project owners often retain separate utility contractors to perform related utility work, only reference information is provided for other utilities.

Whether engaging in a simple or complex utility installation for a site, landscape contractors must exercise caution when working with underground utilities. Call 811 for location of lines or cables before digging, and use extreme caution when using equipment and digging trenches for utility work.

> **CAUTION**
>
> Most utilities require design by registered design professionals and installation by specialty licensed contractors. Confirm these legal qualifications prior to considering any utility construction.

> **CAUTION**
>
> ALWAYS contact NC811 at least 72 hours before any excavation begins.

SUSTAINABILITY SUGGESTIONS

When working on a project, landscape contractors should follow these suggestions for sustainability:

- Select lighting components, particularly lamps, that are high efficiency. Light emitting diode (LED) lamps provide maximum lighting for the energy input and are preferred over incandescent lamps.
- Place lighting circuits on photocells and timers to limit energy consumption to the times when lighting is needed rather than having circuits that are on all the time.
- Utilize the most efficient irrigation equipment available. Select controllers that use smart technologies, such as ET (evapotranspiration) control of the irrigation times, and sensors that limit over irrigation after rain. If a choice is allowed by the construction documents, drip irrigation systems are more efficient than spray systems. Remember that Irrigation Construction in North Carolina is a licensed trade and that landscape irrigation systems must be installed by a North Carolina Licensed Irrigation Contractor.
- If permitted by project documents, use of recycled water (gray water) can be maximized for site irrigation.
- Choose materials that have reduced toxicity, including those that are toxic in their manufacturing processes and uses. Minimize use of polyvinyl chloride (PVC) products, pesticides, synthetic fertilizers, and wood preservatives.

PHONE, TV, AND TELECOMMUNICATIONS SYSTEMS

Most people underestimate the impact of phone, TV, and telecommunications systems on the landscape. Any deck or gazebo can be "wired" for technology with simple preparation during the construction phase of landscaping. Installing a phone line communications wiring or coaxial cable to an outdoor structure expands the idea of the virtual office into the virtual garden. Specialized contractors must install private phone or TV lines; however, installation of empty conduit is recommended even if service lines are not initially placed.

Please note that utilities may regulate who makes the connections to their service lines and may charge for additional outlets connected to a single service. Inform clients that there is also a security issue with phone and TV connections in exterior applications. If access points have no locking covers or security measures, then anyone could plug a phone into the client's line and make unauthorized calls.

GAS SYSTEMS

Gas systems can be either natural gas or liquid propane (LP). Gas used in exterior applications is typically reserved to supply lines to outlying structures for outdoor cooking and occasionally for lighting or for firepits. As with other utility systems that pose health and safety risks, gas systems require specialized contractors for installation and connection.

PLACEMENT OF CONDUITS FOR FUTURE USE

When installing permanent landscape features, particularly those adjacent to buildings, it is advisable to install empty conduit under the feature. Conduit can be placed under walks, patios, decks, and similar structures to avoid the necessity of digging up these elements at a later date to install utilities. Consider placing two oversized Schedule 40 conduits (4–6 inch) through which electrical, gas, water, and other lines can be pulled in the future. Conduit can be placed through a basement wall or left just outside the wall if there are concerns about moisture or insects entering the structure. The conduit should be capped to prevent moisture from filling the pipe and possibly flowing back into the structure. Sloping the conduit away from a structure is also advisable. Check applicable codes and ordinances for rules that dictate minimum separation distances from certain utilities such as water and electricity.

CHAPTER 17

LOW VOLTAGE AC LIGHTING AND RELATED ELECTRICAL WORK

CAUTION

- As prescribed by North Carolina Law (89D-11), landscape contractors may design, install or maintain low-voltage landscape lighting systems, provided (i) the work does not exceed the scope of the exception set forth in G.S. 87-43.1(7) and (ii) the low-voltage lighting systems do not exceed 50 volts and constitute a Class II or Class III cord and plug connected power system. The exception noted above is as follows:
    - 87-43.1 Exceptions.
    - The provisions of this Article shall not apply (7) to the replacement of lamps and fuses and to the installation and servicing of cord-connected appliances and equipment connected by means of attachment plug-in devices to suitable receptacles which have been permanently installed or to the servicing of appliances connected to a permanently installed junction box. This exception does not apply to permanently installed receptacles or to the installation of the junction box.

OBJECTIVES

By reading and practicing the techniques described in this chapter, the reader should be able to successfully complete the following activities:

- Install a custom low-voltage site lighting system.
- Install low-voltage lighting kits.
- Install footings for alternating current (AC) lighting installations.

In this chapter, the installation of a custom and kit **low-voltage alternating current (AC)** and **direct current (DC)** electrical systems is presented, along with a summary of site-related alternating current electrical installations that may become the landscape contractor's responsibility.

RELATED INFORMATION

Information in this chapter is supplemented by instruction provided elsewhere in this text and in other sources. Before undertaking the activities described in this chapter, read the related information in these sources:

- Safety in the Workplace, Chapter 7
- Basic Construction Techniques and Small Equipment Operation, Chapter 8
- Site Amenities, Chapter 32

CAUTION

- Installation of 120 and 240 volt supply wiring must be provided by a licensed electrician.
- Licensed landscape construction professionals are limited in the types of lighting systems they may install. See the caution noted in the OBJECTIVES heading earlier in this chapter

- Permits may be required to install landscape lighting.
- All work must be performed according to National Electrical Code, applicable codes and manufacturer's specifications.
- All circuits for outdoor lighting must be protected with ground fault interrupter circuit breakers.
- Approved GFCI circuit breakers or receptacles will be used to protect all transformers and circuits.
- All fixtures shall be UL 1838 approved.
- Transformers are to be UL 1838 approved and Pool and Spa rated.
- All GFCI circuit breakers and/or receptacles will be installed by a licensed electrician.

Many parts of the landscape work together in improving the esthetic quality of a site, but few are more dramatic during the evening hours than landscape lighting. Plants, water features, hardscape and the other built portions of a project provide interest while the sun is casting light over the garden, but when the sun goes down they all blend into a dark, amorphous mass. Only through illumination by landscape lighting can the character of plants and the intricacies of textures be truly enhanced. Past lighting systems have offered a limited range of options when adding this evening dimension to the site, but advances in lighting technology have greatly enhanced the choices in lighting styles, reliability, placement of lights and the cost of operation. As improvements continue to evolve the character of landscape lighting, adding lighting to a project has steadily moved from a luxury to a necessity.

Low-voltage AC lighting is so named because the electrical power used is reduced from a high level (typically 110 to 120 volts and occasionally 220 volts) to a lower level (typically 12 volts or 24 volts) to operate the lights installed in the system. Although the concept is simple, the parameters of designing a low-voltage AC lighting system can often confuse the typical layperson and even the occasional contractor. For simplicity sake, one can visualize the low-voltage lighting system as being a collection of components that produce decorative effects for the landscape. An electrical source provides the power to operate the system, a transformer reduces the voltage to a level that matches the fixtures on the system, electrical **controllers** such as timers and photocells turn the system on and off based on desired conditions for light, fixtures with lamps provide the illumination, and electrical cable distributes the electrical current from the transformer to the fixtures.

The effective operation of this system is based on mathematical relationships among a defined set of electrical parameters that are standards throughout the electrical industry. Although more concerned with system installation, contractors can improve their work and understand why systems are laid out in a particular manner by learning some of the basic design guidelines, electrical basics and components of lighting design.

PLANNING A LIGHTING PROJECT

Successful lighting requires planning before fixtures are installed and illuminated. Before digging into the details of circuit layout and fixture selection, begin the project with identifying what tasks are to be performed with lighting, understanding electrical concepts, and learning the mathematical relationships of electrical components. Each step of the implementation must be completed using the principles of exterior illumination and the laws of electricity. Failure at any point of the planning will lead to results that are less than desirable and can even put the safety of the contractor or site visitor at risk.

Steps to planning will include determination of what purpose the lighting needs to perform, which will assist in selecting and placement of fixtures. Carefully determine what tasks need to addressed through lighting, whether it is strictly decorative or if there are serious safety or security issues to be addressed. Once the purpose(s) for lighting your site have been determined, select fixtures and determine their placement to perform the tasks. Follow with the calculation of circuits for the lighting, including wire sizing and length of runs to adequately supply the lights with power. Once circuits have been determined, controllers can be selected to support the system circuitry. When all components have been selected the installation of the lighting system can begin.

LIGHTING DESIGN WITH EXTERIOR FIXTURES

Providing quality exterior illumination involves determining the purpose for light, and that requires knowing what types of lighting fixtures are necessary, where they should be placed, where they should be aimed and if the beam should be altered. Lighting can perform the tasks of safety, security, mood and esthetic enhancements, and while these tasks sound basic, the combination of light alteration, techniques and effects create several choices that must be considered in order to properly illuminate a landscape.

Uses for Landscape Lighting

Lighting a landscape project can be completed for several reasons. Some clients may choose to enhance plant material or create a special ambiance, while others are simply hoping to deter problems or make an area safer. Regardless of the choices, special lighting types are often required to completely address the lighting needs of a landscape. Using available lighting techniques provides an almost infinite range of methods to highlight landscape elements.

Landscape Feature Lighting using Focal or Spot Lighting. Lighting is the landscape element that works the best when calling attention to a particular part of a project is necessary. A beam of light, whether in front of, beside or behind a plant, sculpture, fountain or wall will accent the element and its color or texture. And being a night time element, lighting has the added benefit of being both functional and dramatic. Spot lights, either with narrow or wide beams, are the primary fixture choice in creating the dramatic esthetic effects known to most. Other effects can be achieved with flood lights. A summary of typical features that can be lit is below, while the specific lighting techniques are described in the following section.

Trees. Plants take on a new dimensions when the trunk, branching pattern and foliage are illuminated. When lighting trees avoid the temptation to use a single fixture placed by the trunk. Instead, use enough fixtures distributed around the plant to light the entire canopy. Add a single fixture focused up or down the trunk (or possibly both) to connect the tree to the ground.

Paths. Path lighting is one of the basic requirements of illuminating a site. Path lighting is typically done with fixtures mounted on stems of various heights, the taller the stem the wider the circle of light cast. Placement should alternate on either side of the path and create a continuous swath of light along the path. When a path curves the fixture should be placed on the outside radius of the path.

Boulders and Rocks. Natural features are almost mystic when illuminated at night. Use the cross-lighting technique with lights to the sides of the boulder, or with the light of each fixture just glancing the edge of the boulder. Use wide flood lights or optical lenses.

Fences and Walls. Even typically boring elements such as fences and walls come alive when light is added to the equation. Use up-lighting placed far enough away from the fence/wall to avoid "hot spots". It may take several fixtures to light an entire wall, or fixtures can be spaced randomly to light up dark spots in the background.

Water From Above. Recommended for turbulent water and waterfalls, placement of fixtures near or behind where water and air mixes will provide the most dramatic effects.

Water From Below. Special fixtures designed for underwater use create dramatic effects when placed under aquatic plants and in turbulent water right under the areas of impact.

> **CAUTION**
>
> Understand the electrical codes when placing fixtures in or near water. Special transformers and fixtures are required for lights in the water. Lights near water that flows into pools or spas must be placed a minimum of 10' from the water even when using underwater transformers.

Arbors, Trellises, Pergolas and Gazebos. As primary features of the landscape during the day, it follows that lighting these elements after dark would be a landscape priority. Lights for these special places need to perform the functions of creating volume and focus on detail. This can involve using up-lights to focus attention of posts, down-lights hidden in overhead structures and up/down light fixtures mounted to walls other vertical surfaces. Separate switching for lights in these areas allow for low-level full time illumination of the general area with additional task and decorative lighting when the area is being used.

Stairs. Beyond the aspect of safety, highlighting the change in grade created by stairs provides a sense of grounding to the landscape. Lighting in stairs may be placed directly in the riser (during construction) or placed beside or above the stairs. When placing light beside or above the stairs make certain that the light is high enough to illuminate each tread. Failing to do so will create an unsafe tripping hazard.

Atmosphere/Romance Lighting. To create atmosphere for exterior spaces create a composition of different types of lighting, with those lights in use areas like patios and decks placed on a switch.

Mood lighting. In one sense, all lighting is mood lighting due to changing darkness to light, but techniques can be used to create special feelings on a site by lowering the intensity and using the beam in a diffuse manner to create mood effects. This lighting is often created using low intensity flood lighting that is mounted above or below plants and aimed to blanket a site with low level light or aimed to cast character shadows of plants on walls and structures.

Seasonal Lighting. Low-voltage lighting can add seasonal interest by adding colored filters to fixtures. In addition, providing GFCI outlets in key locations around a landscape create opportunities to enhance the landscape with seasonal lighting.

Safety. Helping visitors identify entry points or navigate stairs and paths are examples of lighting for safety purposes. Well placed lighting can also help homeowners find the proper key for entries, perform evening tasks and navigate pathways. Lighting for safety purposes does not need to overwhelm the site, but instead should be of the correct intensity and focused on the task that needs to be lit. Tasks such as active outdoor events may require a more widespread distribution of light. Careful selection and placement of safety lighting is the key to effectiveness.

Security. While safety lighting is often subtle and carefully placed, security lighting takes a more intense and broad tact. Security lighting is typically completed using flood lighting that casts a wide beam over areas that need to be illuminated in order to prevent unwanted activity. Using the principle that those who wish to harm us prefer to operate in the shadows, filling an area with light provides the protection we desire. Creating a site that feels safe and discourages crime will often include a combination of low-voltage fixtures and 120 volt lighting. Any type of low-voltage fixture can perform the task of illuminating areas where unwanted visitors could hide, however it may take more low-voltage fixtures to accomplish the task when compared to 120 volt fixtures. Careful selection is still required in placement of security lighting in order to truly cover the areas where safety is a priority and to avoid intrusions into the privacy of others.

Lighting Techniques

Basic light fixtures can be combined and placed in a wide array of techniques to achieve effects that enhance the esthetic and functional purpose of the landscape. While many techniques use similar fixtures, the range of effects can be altered by the types of lenses, the placement of the fixtures and the aiming of the fixtures. Listed below are the primary lighting techniques used by the industry.

Up-Lighting: Front, Cross and Back. One of the most common methods of illuminating exterior objects, up-lighting involves placing fixtures at or in the ground aimed upwards at the object you plan to illuminate. Forms of up-lighting are based on the placement and aiming of the fixtures.

- Front. Placement of multiple fixtures focused on the front of plants, structures, walls and other vertical elements minimizes textures and shadows while downplaying the lit objects dimensions (Figure 17-1).

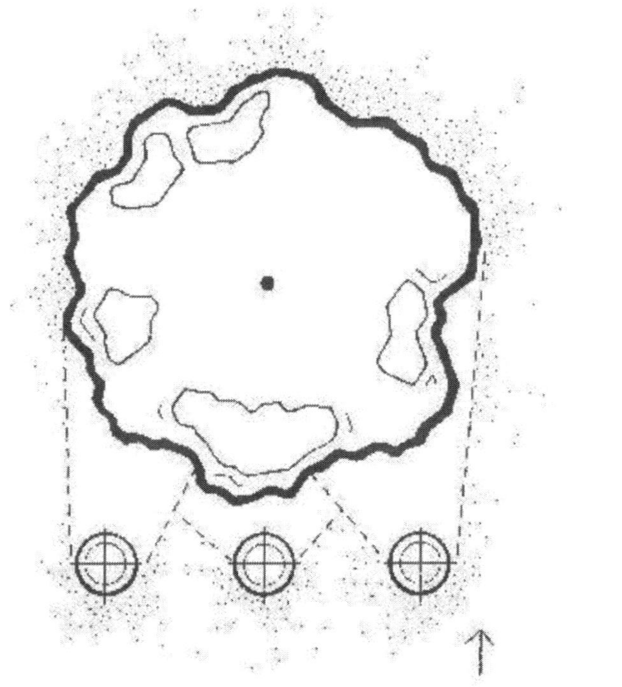

Figure 17-1. Front lighting, plan view. Symbol shows fixture location.

- Cross. See text below.
- Back. Placement of multiple fixtures behind open/airy and translucent plants will produce a halo effect with few shadows, texture, and light intensity but provides sharp contrast and establishes depth. Different effects are created when the fixtures are placed at various distances from a wall used for back-lighting. Close placement (6”) will create a V pattern and distant placement (24”) a Scallop pattern, while moderate placement (12”) will create a grazing effect that highlights wall textures.

Down-Lighting. Placing a fixture above an object and casting a light downward at a steep angle (less than 30 degrees outward angle) can provide a soft method for illuminating detain and texture of objects (Figure 17-2). Lights can be placed under eaves, on walls or in trees to highlight outdoor living areas, water features, and create moonlight effects. Care must be taken in the selection and placement of the fixture to hide the source and not create “hot spot” glare where the observer can see the lamp. Placement of the wiring may also create challenges.

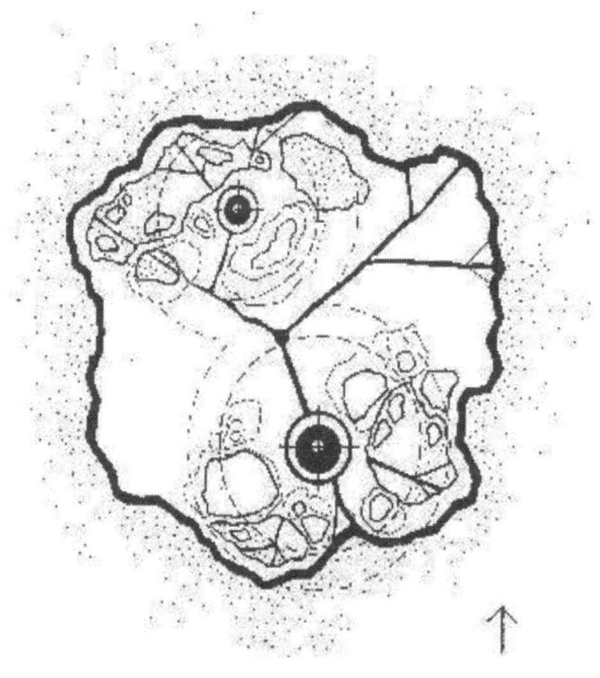

Figure 17-2. Down-lighting, plan view.

Silhouette-Lighting. The textures and unique forms of shrubs and small trees can be enhanced using silhouette-lighting if a wall behind the plants is present. Placing a fixture similar to the back up-lighting method will silhouette the branches and foliage of the plant(s) against the wall behind (Figure 17-3).

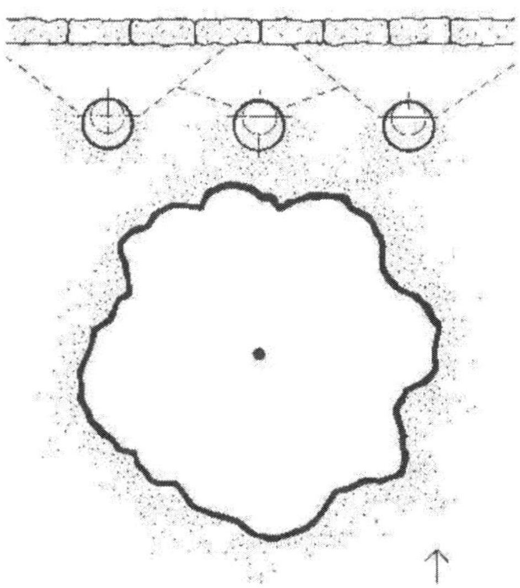

Figure 17-3. Silhouettelighting, plan view. Symbol shows fixture locations.

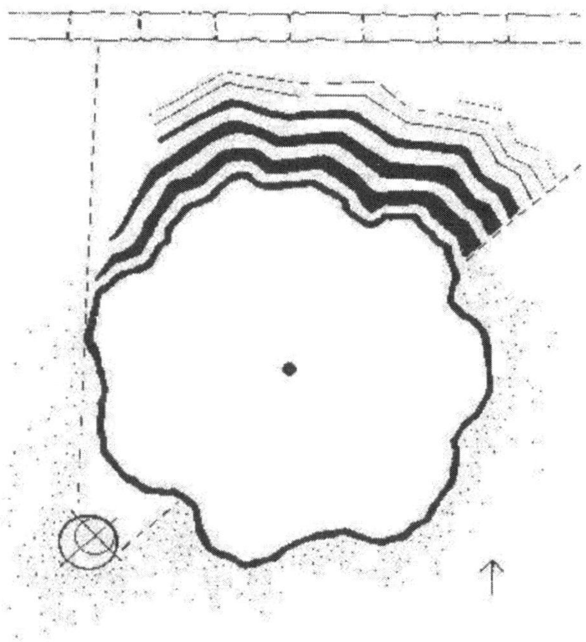

Figure 17-4. Shadow-lighting, plan view. Symbol shows fixture location.

Shadow-Lighting. Using an object's shadow to create interest can be accomplished by placing one or two fixtures on the ground directly in front of the object and casting the light through/past the object onto a wall or structure behind. Aim lights carefully so no "hot spot" occurs on the object (Figure 17-4)

Cross-Lighting. Placing fixtures to the sides of rocks, multi-trunk plants and fountains will emphasize the textural details of the object (Figure 17-5).

Moon-Lighting. One of the more difficult effects to obtain, moon-lighting can involve placement of several fixtures in a properly selected tree to give the impression of the moon casting a gentle light over the open surface below. Plants that have open canopies with adequate branching and interesting bark make the best candidates. Make certain the ground plane below the plant is an open surface (lawn, hardscape) since lights cast on shrubs and other plants will diffuse the effect. Lights are placed using a stand-off bracket, typically in a downward aimed cross-lighting pattern. Placing a down-light on the trunk will make the connection of the tree with the ground (Fixture 17-6).

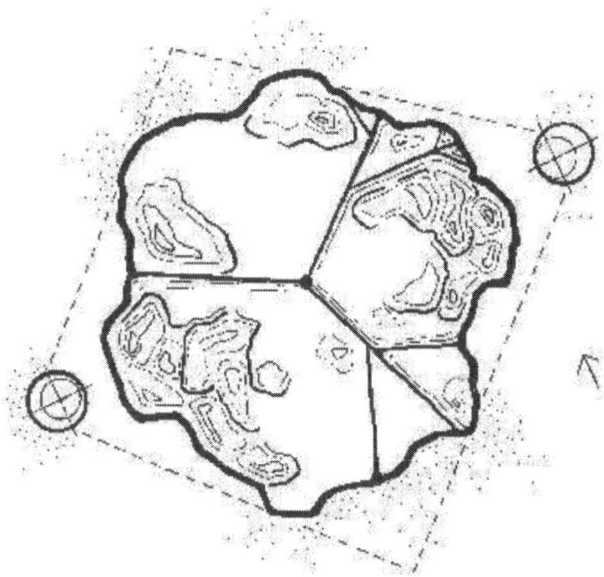

Figure 17-5. Cross-lighting, plan view.

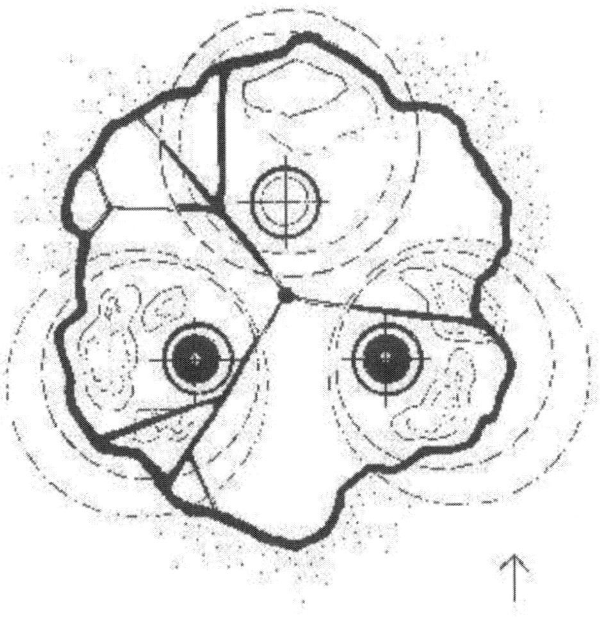

Figure 17-6. Moon-lighting, plan view.

Mirror-Lighting. If your landscape has a still-water feature (pool or pond), mirror-lighting can enhance the visual effect of any object that is lit. When the viewer is positioned across the water from an illuminated structure or plant material the inverse perspective creates a strong visual. For maximum effectiveness the water should not be a feature that has disruption or underwater lighting.

Graze-Lighting. To emphasize the texture of structures and walls, graze-lighting can be used. Placing fixtures, aimed either up or down, 12 inches from the face of the surface will create shadowing effects that call attention to stone, brick, stucco or other rough surfaces. Lights may have to be tilted slightly to avoid "hot spots".

Beam Alteration. Along with determining the type of placement and aiming of the fixtures in the landscape, the designer must also recognize the value added to the project by selecting the proper lamps and altering the beam to enhance the visual product. Beam alterations include items such as optical corrective lenses and diffusers used create the final visual touches for a site.

Vi-Op Lens. Visual optical lenses spreads the and slightly softens (less than De-Op) the light beam. Good for moon lighting, boulder lighting and when a wider softer pattern is necessary.

Ax-Op Lens. Alters the light pattern from circular to rectangular and slightly softens the beam. Use for fences or when a rectangular pattern better fits the object(s) being lit.

De-Op Lens. Defused optical lenses soften the intensity of the light beam. Use them on down-lights, under eaves and to reduce "hot spots".

Blue-Op Lens. Blue optical lens creates a special softer look and is good in underwater and moon lighting situations.

Tru-Light Filter. Used to change the yellow color of a halogen light to white.

Eclipse Glare Shields. Louvers or shields that reduce off glare to approximately 45 degree angles. They are used to help hide the light source and eliminate the direct view at the lamp.

Hex Louvers. Used to cut the angle of glare from the viewpoint.

LOW-VOLTAGE COMPONENTS

General

A variety of components are necessary to create an effective landscape lighting scheme. A wide range of manufacturers and qualities of equipment is available to the landscape contractor, so it is important that the contractor understand the goal of the project and the desired effect in order to make the proper selection of components. All cables, wire, transformers and fixtures must meet all applicable code requirements and be tested by an approved laboratory.

Transformers

Transformers reduce the voltage of typical household circuits so that low-voltage systems can work. Transformers are weather tight electrical boxes that are either wired directly to a household circuit or plugged into a household outlet. Inside the transformer is special circuitry that reduces the voltage from 110 or 120 volts to circuits that carry from 12 to 24 volts. Transformers are also available that reduce 120 volts to 24 to 30 volts. 240 volt transformers are also available. This lower voltage is typically adequate for powering a run of light fixtures for the landscape.

Some transformers only supply a single circuit connection (tap) for exterior lighting circuits, while more complex transformers may offer multiple circuits (taps) with varying voltages. This multi-tap approach provides flexibility for the designer to allow for varying wire lengths and attages. Accessory equipment for transformers include timers and photocells. **Timers** turn a circuit on and off based on time, whereas **photocells** allow a circuit to be turned on and off based on the amount of light present on a site. Any transformer used must be sized to match the electrical demands of the exterior lighting system proposed and must be sized to supply even amperage to all fixtures on a circuit.

Transformers are typically available in a range of wattages and with varying numbers of circuits that can be installed. Because of the variability of lighting fixtures, number of fixtures, and length of lighting runs, installation of a transformer that has multiple circuits (or voltage taps) will aid in providing adequate power to multiple wire runs (Figure 17–14). The actual size of a transformer will be determined by the total watts required and the ability to supply uniform voltage to each lamp on a circuit. Transformers will require connection to an AC current circuit and installation in a location with easy access and according to manufacturer's recommendations.

In some projects it may be beneficial to establish multiple transformers located at various locations around the property. When home runs, or the lines from the transformer to the hub or first fixture, become exceedingly long the voltage drop may exceed the capacity of the system. Placing transformers on opposite sides of the house will shorten the runs to reduce voltage problems.

Conduit

All wiring and cable placed in conduit for mechanical and/or code compliance should be placed in PVC conduit. In standard applications a Sch. 40 PVC can be used, but in locations where there are potential hazards such as digging or underground work, Sch. 80 PVC should be used. Select conduit as specified by code or written specifications. All joints must be securely connected and waterproofed to prevent entry of soil, water, or other debris into the conduit.

Cable

Wiring for exterior lighting differs significantly from wire typically used for interior applications. Within most exterior wires are two multi-stranded copper wires. These wires allow the electricity to be conducted to, and returned from, the fixtures on the system. Various wire gauges, or wire sizes, utilize the same dimension of wire but change the gauge by placing together different numbers of strands. The coating of most low-voltage wires is thicker than household wires to minimize damage from landscaping activities and is treated to withstand ultraviolet (UV) light deterioration. Cable used in exterior settings must be type UF (Underground Feeder), stranded, properly sized AWG (American Wire Gauge) minimum, of direct burial quality and covered with insulation treated to inhibit actions of oil, water, Salt, UV radiation and to repel rodents.

Wire Splice Protectors

All connections used in exterior lighting must be water tight and make positive contact. While there are many ways to make connections, specialty equipment will be needed to prevent corrosion and failure of connections from natural elements. Various types of connections are available and can, if properly installed, protect connections from faulty operation. In each method the use of dielectric grease to lubricate wires and connectors will assist in reducing corrosion. Some of the typical connections include those listed below.

Waterproof Wire Nuts. Waterproof wire nuts are similar to standard wire nuts with the exception that they are filled with a waterproof grease on the inside and include a plastic seal over the bottom. The wires are twisted together in a clockwise direction and then inserted into the hole in the seal. The wire nut is then tightened over the wires. If wire nuts are used, they should be properly sized for the wire used and should have an approved watertight connection.

Splice Gel Connections. Splice gel connections are plastic housings into which wires are inserted, then the housing is depressed and a gel spreads around the wires. The gel eventually hardens into a waterproof protective covering for the connection. When selecting gel connections verify the connectors are for use with stranded wires. Install only according to manufacturer's instructions.

Heat Shrink. Heat shrink coverings are plastic sleeves that are slid over a connection and then heated to mold around the connection. Successful in preventing most weather related elements from fouling the connection, heat shrinking requires placing the sleeve before the connection is made and use of a heat gun or torch to seal the tubing. Install only according to manufacturer's instructions.

Hub Connections. Making wire connections inside a weatherproof hub that is mounted above ground will reduce the failures associated with natural elements.

Controls and Switches

Within the circuits of the exterior lighting system there may be a need for switches, timers, photocells and other control devices. All controls must be approved for the application, meet electrical codes and conform to system requirements. Typically, switching and junction materials are the same as those used for exterior high voltage systems and are sealed and weatherproofed to protect the circuitry. Exterior lighting switches may also be integrated switching with irrigation systems if the system provides such opportunities.

Fixtures

The luminaries used in custom low-voltage systems are primarily made of cast metals with heavy-duty housings that can withstand the abuse of an exterior application. Most **fixtures** provide a sealed chamber, where the bulb is located, and a secure method of anchoring the fixture. All fixtures must provide two wire leads that are spliced into the wiring system with weatherproof connections. All fixtures used must be weatherproof and match the intended design use and/or specification. All fixtures must be supplied with the proper lamps.

Lamps

Several lamp types are available for exterior illumination. Incandescent, Halogen, Xenon, and LED are typical types of bulbs available in low-voltage lighting systems. Once the standard for lighting, incandescent lamps are being phased out because of their inefficiency and short lives. **Halogen**. Halogen is an advanced form of incandescent lighting, provides a bulb with a longer life, brighter light, and higher efficiency of operation.

Xenon. Yet another form of high-intensity discharge lighting for low-voltage systems are **Xenon** lamps. In Xenon lamps, electrodes replace the filament of the incandescent lamps and produce light that mimics natural light with a high level of efficiency.

LEDs (Light emitting diodes. LEDs use diodes to produce a light that is extremely efficient with and produces a white light with some color correction. Specialized manufacturing of LEDs provides greater flexibility in the design of low-voltage circuits for exterior illumination, allowing many more fixtures on a single circuit with lamps that are less sensitive to changes in voltage. Selection of the proper lamp will be based on factors such as initial cost, life cycle costs, quality of light, and the desired durability of the product. Limitations include the number of components that are required for the LED, leading to multiple possibilities for lamp failure.

Voltage will also have a limiting effect on the life of lamps used in exterior lighting. Tables L-1 and L-2 show the effect of various voltages on lamp life for halogen and non-halogen bulbs. LED lights would be excluded from these tables.

UNDERSTANDING ELECTRICAL CONCEPTS AND TERMS

Although the concept appears simple, the parameters of designing a low-voltage DC lighting system can often confuse the typical layperson and even the occasional contractor. While the contractor is primarily concerned with the installation and proper functioning of the exterior lighting, an understanding of basic electrical concepts will improve their insight into why certain fixtures are selected, how circuit design impacts lamp performance and why various wire sizes are necessary. The contractor does not necessarily need to become an expert in low-voltage electricity to complete their work; but they can become more knowledgeable by understanding basic electrical terms and concepts. The terms *voltage*, *amps*, *watts*, and *ohms* are common to the design of electrical circuits, and the following explanations can help relate these terms to low-voltage lighting systems.

Current.

Current is the flow of electricity through a conductor, such as wire, and is measured in amperes.

Circuit.

A completed path of electrical current.

Voltage.

Voltage is the electrical potential of a circuit, or the circuit's ability to do work. A volt is a measure of electrical pressure; a volt has the potential to produce a current of 1 ampere through a resistance of 1 ohm. To use an analogy from irrigation, voltage is similar to pressure. An irrigation line that has pressure can operate irrigation heads, whereas a circuit with voltage can illuminate lights. Voltage is provided throughout a household using electrical circuits with circuit breakers or, in the case of low-voltage systems, transformers. Voltage is slowly lost over the length of the system through resistance from the wire and by fixtures in use on the circuit. This loss of voltage is termed **voltage drop** and is one of the factors that controls the length of a wire run, the size of the wire, the size (or wattage) of lamps on a circuit, and the number of lamps that can be placed on a circuit. Sources of voltage drop include the following:

- Electrical source: electrical outlets
- Transformers: the conversion of line voltage to low voltage
- Gauge of wire being utilized with low voltage lighting system
- Length of wire being utilized with low voltage lighting system
- Lamp load being utilized with fixtures on system
- Connections at each of the following locations:
    - hubs
    - fixtures
    - Transformers
- Fixtures

Amps.

Amps are the "flow rate" of electricity in a circuit. Amperage is the measure of the flow of electrical current through a wire or other conductor. Using the same irrigation analogy, if volts represent the pressure of an irrigation line, amps represent the gallons per minute that the line can deliver. Higher amperages for a circuit increase the amount of electricity that can flow to the lights connected to the circuit. Amperages for circuits are controlled by circuit breakers, which limit the amount of flow based on the size of the wire. If too much amperage is drawn into or available to a circuit with a wire that is too small, heat will build up and the potential for fire or circuit failure is increased.

Watts and Ohms.

Watt is a unit of electrical power. A watt is a measure of the amount of electricity being used, whereas an **ohm** is a measure of electrical resistance. Ohms are the property of a conductor which opposed the flow of an electrical current, resulting in the generation of heat in the conducting material. Wattage will typically be listed on electrical appliances and also on lamps of a low-voltage lighting system. This wattage rating tells the designer how much of the electrical current that lamp will use. The wattage allowed by a circuit will depend on the length of the wire and the size of the wire in the circuit. Each of these factors consumes electrical current and must be balanced by the correct voltage and amperage of a circuit. Again, using the irrigation analogy, just as irrigation heads discharge water, using up the pressure and gallons per minute, lamps on an electric circuit discharge heat (in the form of light), using up the voltage and amperage.

The maximum wattage of lamps that can be placed on a circuit is based on the size of the wire. As an example, using 12-gauge wire on a 12 volt system, a lighting run of up to 30 feet could have 150 watts of lamps, whereas a lighting run of up to 150 feet could have 30 watts of lamps. If the wire is larger, the wattage allowed increases; and if the distance decreases, the wattage allowed increases. As noted above, when using LED lights, the number of fixtures on a run can be significantly increased, and the voltage can have a wider range.

Ohms Law. The flow of electrical current is governed by Ohms Law. Ohms law is a set of mathematical formulas used to calculate the amount and strength of electrical current flowing through an electrical system. The formulas show the relationship between amps, watts and volts in an electrical system. Amps are the flow of electricity (using the irrigation example, the gallons per minute). Volts are the measure of the electrical pressure/current strength (using the irrigation example, this would be the pressure of the water in pounds per square inch) with one volt having the power to produce a current of one amp through a resistance of one ohm. Watts are a measure of electrical resistance.

Expressed as formulas, the relationships are as follows:

- Watts / volts = amps (watts divided by volts equal amps)
- Volts x amps = watts (volts multiplied by amps equal watts)

Examples of these formulas applied to electrical calculations would yield:

- Watts / volts = amps:
- 100 Watts / 120 Volts = .833 AMPS
- 100 Watts/ 24 Volts = 4.16 AMPS
- 100 Watts / 12 Volts = 8.33 AMPS
- Volts x amps = watts
- 120 Volts X 20 Amps = 2400 Watts
- 24 Volts X 20 Amps = 480 Watts
- 12 Volts X 20 Amps = 240 Watts

These relationships form the guiding principles when determining the size and configuration of circuits in electricity. Design principles and calculations shown below are an application of Ohms Law.

Transformer.

A transformer is a device that converts current of one voltage into current of another voltage (120v to 12v or 24v in the case of low voltage lighting)

CIRCUIT DESIGN AND CALCULATIONS.

Knowledge of basic electrical concepts is necessary to understand the functioning details of exterior lighting, and in order to make exterior circuitry properly function the correct relationships between voltage, current and resistance must be calculated. If the calculations are not done properly a lighting system may not work at all, or may have lights that dim or lamps could burn out prematurely. To properly calculate circuit design, the contractor must familiarize themselves with the basics of circuit calculations and circuit layout.

Establishing Lighting Circuits

Circuit layout begins by laying out the fixtures desired for your lighting design (see techniques in the previous section), and identifying the location, purpose and wattage of the bulb for each fixture (Figure 17-7) In order to make the fixtures perform their task the designer must make sure that the proper amount of electricity is flowing to each lamp. The first step in this process will require grouping fixtures together by:

- Special lighting purpose (timed lights for a sign or switched lights along a path). Certain fixtures may be performing a special lighting purpose and need to be turned on/off with other light fixtures or at specific times. Fixtures in this category should be grouped together to form one or more circuits that are attached to a timer, photocell or other control device. The calculations for fixtures in this situation will be the same as fixtures on other circuits, but they are separated because of required control needs.

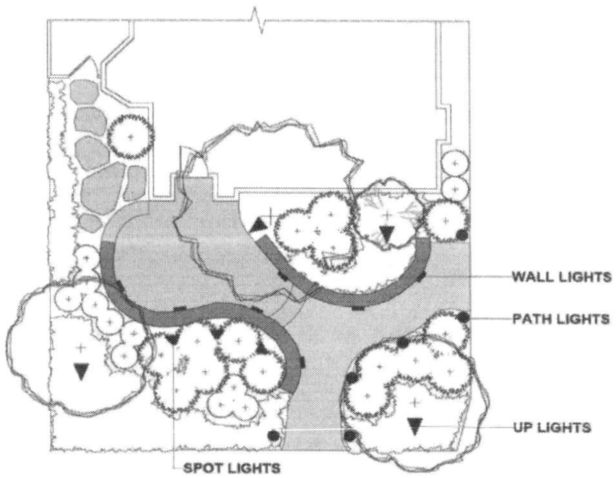

Figure 17-7. Locating light fixtures according to site and design requirements.

- Geographic locations with a total wattage that does not exceed the maximum (see chart based on wire size in the next paragraph).
- Limiting circuit length by calculating the load on a circuit. Lengths will vary depending on wire size, lamp type, total wattage of lamps and the distance from the transformer.

Low voltage lighting lamp loads are a critical factor in determining the voltage on a given gauge and length of wire. Each circuit must have a total lamp wattage that does not exceeds the NEC standard for the size of wire being used. When selecting cable for a project the National Electric Code (NEC) limits the number of watts that can be loaded onto various wire sizes. These limitations are further reduced by the electrical standard of not loading a wire to more than 80% of the wires capacity. The following list shows three standard electrical wire sizes and the wattages allowed:

- 16 ga wire (16/2): Can support 120 watts at 12 volts, but is limited by the NEC to 80% of that total, or a maximum of **96**. A 24 volt system would have the capacity of 240 volts, but is limited by the NEC 80% rule to **192** watts.
- 12 ga wire (12/2): Can support 240 watts at 12 volts, but is limited by the NEC to 80% of that total, or a maximum of **192**. A 24 volt system would have the capacity of 480 volts, but is limited by the NEC 80% rule to **384** watts.
- 10 ga wire (10/2): Can support 360 watts at 12 volts, but is limited by the NEC to 80% of that total, or a maximum of **288**. A 24 volt system would have the capacity of 720 volts, but is limited by the NEC 80% rule to **576** watts.

- ***8 ga wire (8/2) is limited by NEC to 25 amps, so the limitations for 8 ga wire would be **300** watts for 12 volts and **600** watts for 24 volts.

Putting this in layman's terms, a 12 volt circuit using 12/2 wire cannot carry more than 192 watts of bulbs, while 10/2 wire can carry 288 watts and 8/2 wire can carry 300 watts. While this suggests that using a lower gauge wire can carry more fixtures, most circuits are still composed of 12/2 wire because of costs and because the variety of voltages available at the transformer. Increasing the voltage of the circuit to 24 volts will allow additional wattage of bulbs to be added to circuits. When fixtures have been assigned to groups based on loads (Figure 17-8), calculations can begin that will determine the electrical flow through the circuit and the necessary voltages and wire sizes, or to identify where the circuit must be adjusted to meet design parameters.

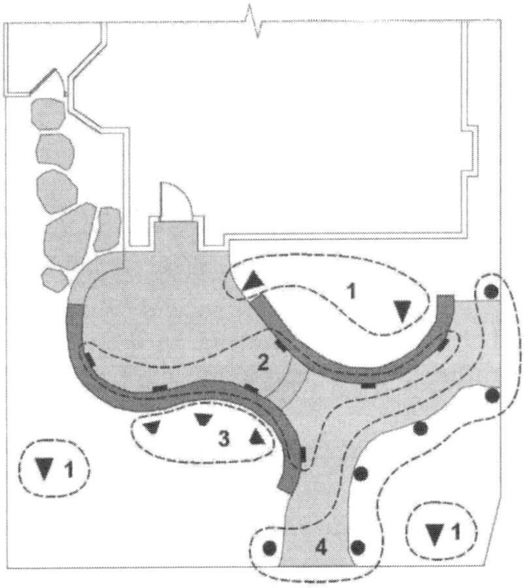

Figure 17-8. Grouping fixtures into circuits based on total wattage of lights in the group and fixture type.

Circuit Loading Calculations

In addition to the limitation of wattage on each circuit, the circuit must deliver between 10.8 and 11.5 volts to each lamp in order for the lamp to properly operate in a 12 volt system, and 21.6 to23 volts to each lamp in a 24 volt system. While the transformer connection to which the circuit is connected may provide adequate voltage, some of the voltage is lost while travelling to the fixtures and through the connections along the way (voltage drop, see description above). Part of this voltage drop is due to the gauge of the wire used and an additional drop is due to the distance of the wire run. The longer the wire run the higher the voltage drop when using the same gauge wire and lamp load. The standard voltage drop per foot of wire for each of the three typical gauges is as follows:

- 16 ga wire (16/2): .00409 of voltage drop for every foot of wire.
- 12 ga wire (12/2): .00162 of voltage drop for every foot of wire.
- 10 ga wire (10/2): .00108 of voltage drop for every foot of wire.
- 8 ga wire (8/2):.00064 of voltage drop for every foot of wire.

The designer can select the initial voltage for each circuit by choosing the appropriate voltage connection in the transformer, but they also need to calculate the voltage drop in with wire and connections to assure the proper voltage is delivered to each fixture. To calculate the voltage drop between two points on a circuit will require two steps.

- The first step is to divide the wattage load on the circuit by the voltage of the lamp voltage (12 or 24 volts) of the circuit to obtain the amperage of the circuit. The second step is to use this amperage in the following formula to obtain the voltage drop.

***NEC code limits the maximum amperage on a secondary circuit to 25 amps for 8 ga wire, limiting the wires total amperage.

- Amperage (from above calculation) x distance in feet between the two points x 2 x the constant for voltage drop for the wire type = voltage drop for that segment of wire.

In the hub circuit, this total voltage drop can be subtracted from the previous voltage to obtain the actual voltage at the next fixture. If the voltage at any lamp is not adequate then a higher voltage tap in the transformer must be used or larger wire with less voltage drop substituted for the 12/2 wire. In daisy chain and T layout circuits, the loading at each lamp should be calculated to verify that voltage at each lamp is neither inadequate or excessive. One solution for this situation is to create a new circuit when the lamp wattage exceeds the maximum.

The design of the circuit layout will also assist in compensating for this voltage drop to fixtures. As described later in this chapter, certain circuit designs have significant voltage drop (daisy chain and T designs) because the electricity must past through each fixture along the circuit. This additional connection and load causes the drop to increase for each fixture along the length of the circuit. Other designs (Hub designs) route the electricity to a central point and then distribute it evenly to the fixtures on the circuit (Figure 17-9). This limits the voltage drop to the loss in the wire and the central connection, allowing for more even distribution of voltage to fixtures.

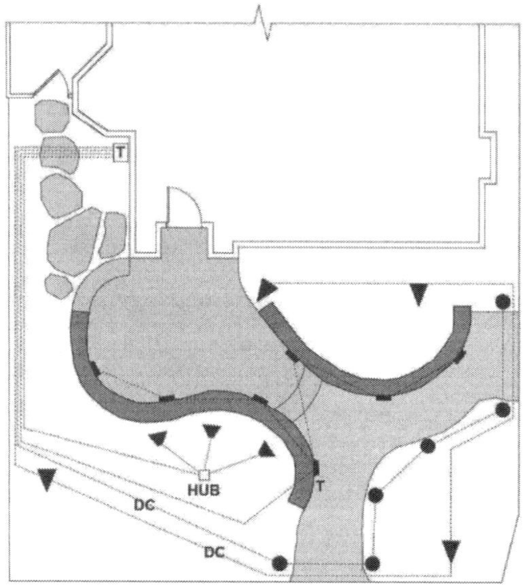

Figure 17-9. Common Lighting Circuits. Selecting circuit type, wire size and number of fixtures requires calculation of electrical loads.

Avoiding Common Errors

Landscape lighting is a specialized aspect of landscape construction, and if a construction professional undertakes a lighting project with limited experience there is a good chance they will make some of the mistakes common in the industry. To forewarn those individuals, listed below are a list of items that should be considered before installing exterior illumination:

- use electronic amp probe and voltage meter (use an RMS electronic amp probe for LED lighting)
- use adequate number of fixtures in proper locations
- make installations flexible
- understand electrical concepts such as voltage drop, maximum wattage load and circuit layout before attempting to install a system
- never use more than 80% of a transformers capacity
- use waterproof connections
- Conclude the installation by making three verifications:
- verify proper voltage at the lamps
- verify the primary amperage at the transformer
- verify the amperage on secondary runs.

LAYOUT AND CALCULATIONS FOR TYPICAL CIRCUITS

The design of lighting layouts begins with selecting the type and placement of fixtures desired for the site. After making the choices as to where lighting fixtures should be distributed throughout the site, the work of circuit layout begins. There are several alternative circuit designs available to power exterior lighting, including the hub, linear (daisy chain) and T methods. The process described in this text emphasizes a hub approach to circuit design due to the many advantages of hub circuitry. While each of the circuit layout methods have advantages and disadvantages, the hub approach provides the most efficient layout in terms of voltage distribution, number of connections and ease of adjustment when the fixtures need to be moved.

When planning a lighting system, the designer uses some standard guidelines and mathematical formulas to determine the parameters of a lighting circuit. These guidelines will help the designer determine how long the lighting run can be, how many lights can be placed on a circuit, and whether the lights will function properly. Add these factors to the decisions about the style of fixture and esthetic function of the lighting, and the design of a system can become a challenge. Some of the common guidelines used for low-voltage lighting systems are identified below:

- Unless the lighting needs are small enough to warrant a single circuit, lights that perform similar functions work best on separate individual circuits. For example, path lights are best on the same circuit, rather than being grouped with several different lighting styles.
- Lights are grouped in zones that are about the same distance from the transformer. Instead of being on the wire supplying the circuit, lights are placed on a branch line that is then connected in the center of that branch line to the wire supplying power to the circuit. This evens out the voltage drop among all of the fixtures on a circuit.
- To achieve maximum and even light and to maintain maximum bulb life for a low-voltage halogen lamp system, each circuit should deliver between 10.8 and 11.5 volts to each lamp in a 12 volt circuit, and between 21.6 and 23 volts for a 24 volt circuit. LED circuit voltage can have a much wider range, between 6 and 18 volts per circuit depending on the manufacturer, without losing lighting quality or lamp life. LEDs also allow many more fixtures to be placed on a circuit than do traditional lamps.
- Because of voltage drop on long circuits, wire runs can be limited in length. This keeps the lights on the circuit from dimming because of the lack of voltage. An example is limiting 12 volt circuits with halogen lamps to 100 watts for 100 feet of circuit length. This will create a voltage drop of between 3 and 4 volts over the length of the circuit. Unlike other lamp types, many LED lights can be placed on a longer circuit because of their low wattage and compensation for voltage differences.
- When using transformers that have taps with different voltages, use higher voltage taps for the longer wire runs and lower voltage taps for shorter runs.
- The interrelationship among volts, amps, and watts determines how many lights can be placed on a circuit in low-voltage lighting. To determine how many watts of lighting can be placed on a circuit, use the formula Watts = Volts x Amps. For example, a 10-volt circuit at 15 amps would support 150 watts of lighting, or 15, 10-watt bulbs. The actual number of lamps on a circuit would be even fewer when the loss of voltage for every foot of the wire run is subtracted. Although this is a simple example, calculating the size of a more complex low-voltage lighting circuit follows the same basic tenets of this formula.

Alternative voltage layouts

The system and associated math described above is for 12 volt circuitry, the standard in the industry. Because the National Electrical Code defines low voltage as systems that are below 30 volts, other electrical systems are available for exterior illumination. One such system is the 24 volt system. Using a 24 volt system has an advantage of lower voltages in that is provides more efficient delivery of power to the fixtures.

Hub Circuit

Multiple circuits layout utilizes a series of hubs, all powered by the transformer to 12 or 24 volts. Connected to this hub are fixtures, each with their own 16/2 wire, that are no more than 25' from the hub. Within the hub the connections are made in above ground waterproof conditions in order to extend the life of the system. Individual fixtures on their own wire lead make adjusting the fixtures after a project changes possible. Connecting fixtures individually allows the mixing of fixture types and wattages on the same hub. The number of fixtures connected to a hub is limited only by the total wattage of lamps.

To prepare the circuit layout for the hub method, mark the location of all proposed fixtures and their wattage on a scaled plan. Identify the locations where power will be supplied to the transformer, or multiple transformers if necessary. Beginning anywhere on the plan, identify a group of fixtures that are within a 25' radius (50' diameter) circle. Circle those fixtures and total the wattage of all the fixtures. If the wattage does not exceed 192 watts (for a 12 volt system, or 384 watts for a 24 volt system), then draw a box at the center of the circle equidistant from all fixtures and label it hub 1. If the wattage exceeds 192 watts, then drop one or more fixtures to lower the wattage below 192 (or 384 if using a 24 volt circuit) and leave the dropped fixtures for another hub zone. Continue grouping fixtures and identifying hub locations until all fixtures on the site have been included in a circuit. Selecting fixtures that are within the same geographic area makes the preparation of circuit layout more efficient. If there is reason to place lights on separate circuits because of photocells or timers, use additional hubs to separate the lights by geography and by control needs. When completed all fixtures should be connected to a hub that is no more than 25' away.

Calculate the voltage drop for each circuit to determine what voltage tap and wire size are necessary to power the circuit. For purposes of example, the following graphic and calculations illustrate how to determine the circuit details (Figure 17-10).

Hub Circuit Calculations:

Beginning measurements and assumptions: The system is set up as a 12 volt circuit with a 100 foot home run from the transformer to the hub. There are 5 fixtures, each with 35 watt lamps for a total of 175 watts. Each fixture is 25 feet from the hub. The second set of calculations are for a24 volt system with the same number of fixtures, dimensions and wire sizes. The calculations for the circuit would be as follows, with a chart for all calculation in Tables L-1 and L-2

Multiple hubs will require a transformer with multiple taps, typically ranging in amps in order to power all hubs. If fixtures require grouping because of timer or photocell connections, place those fixtures on their own circuit(s).

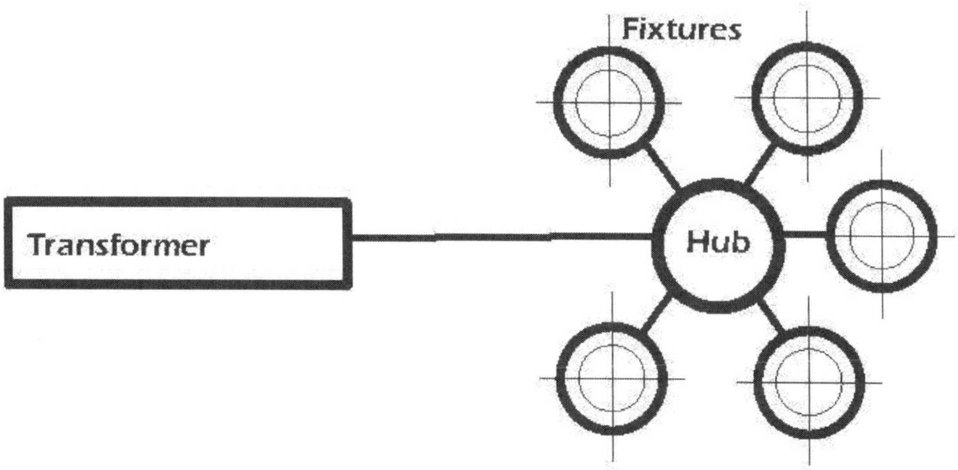

Figure 17-10. Hub circuit layout schematic, plan view.

Table L-1. Calculations for 12 volt hub circuit

CALCULATIONS FOR 12 VOLT HUB CIRCUIT

A	B	C	E	F	G	H	I	J	K	L	M	N
circuit name	circuit type	wire size	total lamp wattage on circuit	amp load (total lamp watts/12) X	circuit length in feet X	con-stant 2 X	resistance for wire size =	resulting voltage drop +	circuit voltage =	tap to be used -	voltage drop (col. J) =	voltage at hub
CALCULATION 1												
transformer to hub/first fixture calculation	hub	12/2	175	14.58 X	100 X	2 X	0.00162 = from chart	4.7 +	12 =	17 -	5 =	12 MIN= MAX=
			total lamp watts past hub							hub voltage (N above)	voltage drop (J)	voltage at lamp
CALCULATION 2												
voltage drop to each fixture connected to hub	hub	16/2	35	2.92 X	25 X	2 X	0.00401 = from chart	0.6		12 -	0.6 =	11.4 MIN=10.8 MAX= 11.5

ADAPTED FROM: THE PROFESSIONAL GUIDE TO LANDSCAPE LIGHTING by NATE MULLEN

Table L-2. Calculations for 24 volt hub circuit

CALCULATIONS FOR 24 VOLT HUB CIRCUIT

A	B	C	E	F	G	H	I	J	K	L	M	N
circuit name	circuit type	wire size	total lamp wattage on circuit	amp load (total lamp watts/24) X	circuit length in feet X	con-stant 2 X	resistance for wire size =	resulting voltage drop +	circuit voltage =	tap to be used -	voltage drop (col. J) =	voltage at hub
CALCULATION 1												
transformer to hub/first fixture calculation	hub	12/2	175	7.29 X	100 X	2 X	0.00162 = from chart	2.4 +	24 =	26 -	2 =	24 MIN=21.72 MAX=24.12
			total lamp watts past hub							hub voltage (N above)	voltage drop (J)	voltage at lamp
CALCULATION 2												
voltage drop to each fixture connected to hub	hub	16/2	35	1.46 X	25 X	2 X	0.00401 = from chart	0.3		24 -	0.3 =	23.7 MIN= 21.6 MAX= 23.0

ADAPTED FROM: THE PROFESSIONAL GUIDE TO LANDSCAPE LIGHTING by NATE MULLEN

For the 12 volt circuit:

Calculation 1. Begin by calculating the voltage drop from the transformer to the hub:

- 175 watts (total amps on circuit)/12 volts (circuit voltage) = 14.58 amps.
- 14.58 (amps) x 100 (feet of wire from transformer to hub) x 2 x .00162 (constant for voltage drop per foot of 12/2 wire) = 4.7 volts (voltage drop from transformer to hub).
- Select the electrical tap by adding the voltage drop to the circuit voltage, so 4.7 plus 12 would lead to the use of the 17 volt tap.
- This voltage drop of 4.7 volts would leave 12 volts at the hub (17 volts - 4.72).

  Using a smaller or larger voltage tap would leave the voltage at the hub outside the 10.8 to 11.5 range necessary for optimal performance.

Calculation 2. Calculate the voltage drop from the hub to each fixture:

- 35 watts (any of the lamps) /12 volts (voltage at the poc) = 2.92 amps.
- 2.92 (amps) x 25 (feet of wire to each light) x 2 x .00401 (constant for 16/2) = .6 voltage drop from hub to each fixture.
- This voltage drop of .6 leaves 11.4 volts at the each fixture, which is within the desired range.

Daisy Chain Circuit

Historically the most common circuit layout, the linear connection of fixtures is still popular despite its inefficiencies and drawbacks. A Daisy Chain circuit connects the first fixture to the home run, then sequentially connects all following fixtures. Daisy

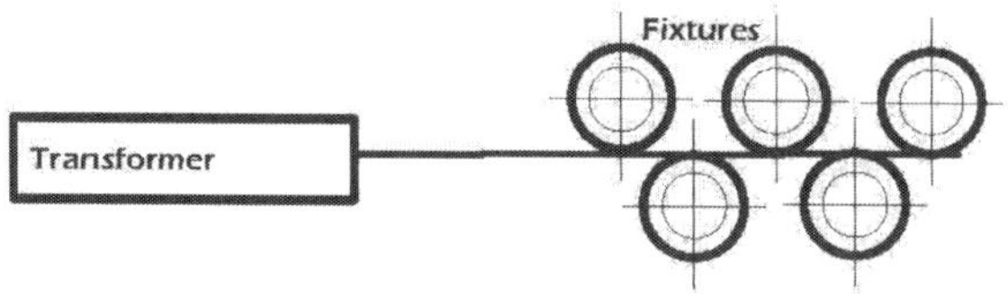

Figure 17-11. Daisy chain circuit layout schematic, plan view

Chain circuits are limited to 50' from the first to last fixture, and will experience voltage drop from fixture to fixture.

To layout Daisy Chain circuitry, identify the location of all proposed fixtures and their wattages on a scaled base map. Locate fixtures that can be easily connected with a single run of wire. Calculate the wattage along the run and limit the total to 192 watts or 50' of wire.

Calculate the voltage drop for each circuit to determine what voltage tap and wire size are necessary to power the circuit. For purposes of example, the following graphic and calculations illustrate how to determine the circuit details (Figure 17-11).

Daisy Chain Circuit Calculations.

Beginning measurements and assumptions: The system is set up as a 12 volt circuit with a 100 foot home run from the transformer to the poc (point of connection for the first fixture). There are 5 fixtures, each with 35 watt lamps for a total of 175 watts. The distance between fixtures is 12.5 feet with 50' from the poc to the last fixture. The second set of calculations are for a 24 volt circuit with the same parameters. The calculations for the circuit would be as follows, with a chart for all calculation in Tables L-3 and L-4.

The net result of these calculations is that the 17 volt tap leaves the voltage too high at the first light, despite being within range for the remaining fixtures. If the calculations are redone using the 16 volt tap the voltages are adequate at only through the first two fixtures. The last 3 are too low. Ultimately, the only solution will be to shorten the circuit or reduce wattages of the lamps. This disadvantage is the primary reason the hub circuit is being selected over the daisy chain circuit.

Table L-3. Calculations for 12 volt daisy chain circuit.

CALCULATIONS FOR 12 VOLT DAISY CHAIN CIRCUIT

A circuit name	B circuit type	C wire size	E total lamp wattage on circuit	F amp load (total lamp watts/12)	X	G circuit length in feet	X	H con-stant 2	X	I resistance for wire size	=	J resulting voltage drop	+	K circuit voltage	=	L tap to be used	-	M voltage drop (col J)	=	N voltage at first fixture
CALCULATION 1												0								
transformer to first fixture calculation	daisy chain	12/2	175	14.58	X	100	X	2	X	0.00162	=	4.7	+	12	=	17	-	5	=	12 MIN=10.8 MAX= 11.5
CALCULATIONS 2 THROUGH 5			total lamp watts past first fixture													first fixture voltage (N above)				
voltage drop to fixture 2	daisy chain	12/2	140	11.67	X	12.5	X	2	X	0.00162	=	0.5				12	-	0.5	=	11.5 MIN=10.8 MAX= 11.5
			total lamp watts past second fixture													second fixture voltage (N above)				
voltage drop to fixture 3	daisy chain	12/2	105	8.75	X	12.5	X	2	X	0.00162	=	0.4				11.5	-	0.4	=	11.1 MIN=10.8 MAX= 11.5
			total lamp watts past third fixture													third fixture voltage (N above)				
voltage drop to fixture 4	daisy chain	12/2	70	5.83	X	12.5	X	2	X	0.00162	=	0.2				11.1	-	0.2	=	10.9 MIN=10.8 MAX= 11.5
			total lamp watts past third fixture													voltage (N above)				
voltage drop to fixture 5	daisy chain	12/2	35	2.92	X	12.5	X	2	X	0.00162	=	0.1				10.9	-	0.1	=	10.8 MIN=10.8 MAX= 11.5

ADAPTED FROM: THE PROFESSIONAL GUIDE TO LANDSCAPE LIGHTING by NATE MULLEN

Table L-4. Calculations for 24 volt daisy chain circuit.

CALCULATIONS FOR 24 VOLT DAISY CHAIN CIRCUIT

A circuit name	B circuit type	C wire size	E total lamp wattage on circuit	F amp load (total lamp watts/24)	X	G circuit length in feet	X	H con-stant 2	X	I resistance for wire size	=	J resulting voltage drop	+	K circuit voltage	=	L tap to be used	-	M voltage drop (col J)	=	N voltage at first fixture
CALCULATION 1												0								
transformer to first fixture calculation	daisy chain	12/2	175	7.29	X	100	X	2	X	0.00162	=	2.4	+	24	=	26	-	2.4	=	23.6 MIN= 21.6 MAX= 23.0
CALCULATIONS 2 THROUGH 5			total lamp watts past first fixture													first fixture voltage (N above)				
voltage drop to fixture 2	daisy chain	16/2	140	5.83	X	12.5	X	2	X	0.00401	=	0.6				23.6	-	0.6	=	23.0 MIN= 21.6 MAX= 23.0
			total lamp watts past second fixture													second fixture voltage (N above)				
voltage drop to fixture 3	daisy chain	16/2	105	4.38	X	12.5	X	2	X	0.00401	=	0.4				23.0	-	0.4	=	22.6 MIN= 21.6 MAX= 23.0
			total lamp watts past third fixture													third fixture voltage (N above)				
voltage drop to fixture 4	daisy chain	16/2	70	2.92	X	12.5	X	2	X	0.00401	=	0.3				22.6	-	0.3	=	22.3 MIN= 21.6 MAX= 23.0
			total lamp watts past third fixture													voltage (N above)				
voltage drop to fixture 5	daisy chain	16/2	35	1.46	X	12.5	X	2	X	0.00401	=	0.1				22.3	-	0.1	=	22.2 MIN= 21.6 MAX= 23.0

ADAPTED FROM: THE PROFESSIONAL GUIDE TO LANDSCAPE LIGHTING by NATE MULLEN

For the 12 volt circuit:

Calculation 1. Begin by calculating the voltage drop from the transformer to the poc, or the first fixture:

- 175 watts (total amps on circuit)/12 volts (circuit voltage)= 14.58 amps.
- 14.58 (amps) x 100 (feet of wire from transformer to poc/first fixture) x 2 x .00162 (constant for voltage drop per foot of 12/2 wire) = 4.7 volts (voltage drop from transformer to first fixture).
- This voltage drop of 4.7 volts requires the use of the 17 volt tap (system voltage of 12 plus voltage drop of 4.7) at the transformer to maintain the voltage at the first fixture within the acceptable range (10.8 to 11.5 volts), with a 4.7 voltage drop leaving 12 volts at the poc/first fixture.

Calculation 2. Calculate the voltage drop to the second fixture, using the amperage calculated after the poc/first fixture:

- 140 watts (wattage of the remaining lamps on the circuit, lamps 2 through 5)/12 volts (voltage at the poc) = 11.67 amps.
- 11.67 (amps) x 12.5 (feet of wire to 2nd light) x 2 x .00162 (constant for 12/2)= .5 voltage drop from poc to 2nd lamp.
- This voltage drop of .5 leaves 11.5 volts at the second fixture.

Calculation 3. Using the voltage at the second fixture, calculate the drop to the third fixture.

- 105 watts (lamps 3, 4 and 5)/12 volts (at the second lamp) = 8.75 amps.
- 8.75 x 12.5 x 2 x .00162= .4 voltage drop from the second to the third fixture.
- This voltage drop of .4 leaves 11.1 volts at the third fixture.

Calculation 4.. Using the voltage at the second fixture, calculate the drop to the third fixture.

- 70 watts (lamps 4 and 5)/12 volts) = 5.83 amps.
- 5.83 x 12.5 x 2 x .00162= .2 voltage drop from the third to the fourth fixture.
- This voltage drop of .2 leaves 10.9 volts at the fourth fixture.

Calculation 5. Using the voltage at the second fixture, calculate the drop to the third fixture.

- 35 watts (lamp 5)/12 volts = 2.92 amps.
- 2.92 x 12.5 x 2 x .00162= .1 voltage drop from the fourth to the fifth fixture.
- This voltage drop of .1 leaves 10.8 volts at the fifth fixture.

T Circuit

T layout connects several fixtures in a linear circuit, then utilizes a single wire home run from the transformer to the center of the wire connecting the fixtures. When operated the power is delivered to the center of the circuit, halving the lamp load on the wire compared to a strictly linear (daisy chain) circuit. Circuit run lengths and run wattage are variable based on circuit calculations.

To layout T circuitry, identify the location of all proposed fixtures and their wattage on a scaled base map. Identify fixtures that are geographically grouped together and of similar wattage, then connect them with a line that matches the calculations for each side of the T.

Calculate the voltage drop for each circuit to determine what voltage tap and wire size are necessary to power the circuit. For purposes of example, the following graphic and calculations illustrate how to determine the circuit details (Figure 17-12)

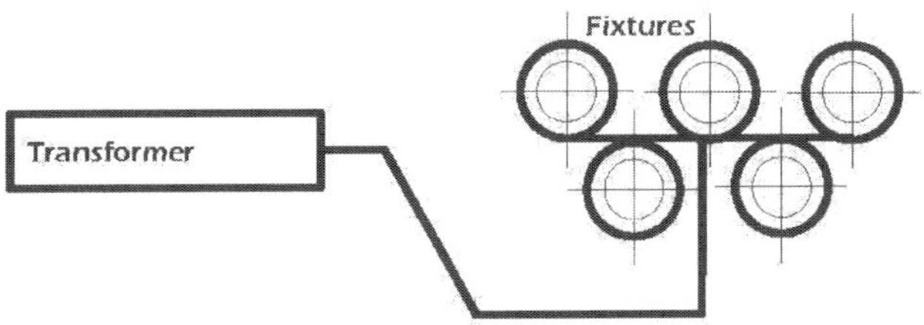

Figure 17-12. T circuit schematic layout, plan view.

T circuit calculations:

Beginning measurements and assumptions: The system is set up as a 12 volt circuit with a 100 foot home run from the transformer to the poc (point of connection for the first fixture). There are 5 fixtures, each with 35 watt lamps for a total of 175 watts. The distance between fixtures is 12.5 feet with 50' from the poc to the last fixture. The calculations using 12/2 wire would be as follows. The calculations can also be viewed in Tables L-5, L-6 and L-7.

Calculations for the 12 volt circuit:

Calculation 1. Begin by calculating the voltage drop from the transformer to the poc, or the middle fixture:

- 175 watts (total amps on circuit)/12 volts (circuit voltage)= 14.58 amps.
- 14.58 (amps) x 100 (feet of wire from transformer to poc) x 2 x .00162 (constant for voltage drop per foot of 12/2 wire) = 4.7 volts (voltage drop from transformer to hub).
- This voltage drop of 4.72 volts suggests the use of the 17 volt tap at the transformer and leaves 12.3 volts at the poc.

Calculation 2. Calculate the voltage drop to the fixture on either side of the poc:

- 70 watts (2 lamps to either side of poc)/12 volts (voltage at the poc) = 5.83 amps.
- 5.83 (amps) x 12.5 (feet of wire to 2nd light) x 2 .00162 = .2 voltage drop from poc to the lamps on each side of the poc.
- This voltage drop of .2 leaves 12.1 volts at the second fixture.

Calculation 3. Calculate the voltage drop to the fixture on either side of the poc:

- 35 watts (1 lamps to either side of 2nd fixture)/12 volts (voltage at the poc) = 2.92 amps.
- 2.92 (amps) x 12.5 (feet of wire to last light) x 2 x .00162 = .1 voltage drop from 2nd fixtures to the fixtures at the ends of the T.
- This voltage drop of .01 leaves 12.0 volts at the last fixtures on either side of the T.

The net result is that with the 17 volt tap used for the circuit, the voltages are too high to each lamp. Recalculating the voltage drop using a 16 volt tap leaves each fixture with voltages within the desired range. Table L5 shows the calculations for the 17 volt tap and Table L-6 shows the calculations for the 16 volt tap.

As with other circuit designs, if fixtures require grouping because of timer or photocell connections, place those fixtures on their own circuit(s).

T systems have the disadvantage of numerous connections, often in the ground, that have the potential to fail. The linear nature of the circuit also creates voltage drop each successive lamp creating lights that dim towards the end of the circuit. The most appropriate use of the T method is for circuits that have 3 fixtures with lamps of similar wattage and the fixtures are close to the home run connection.

CUSTOM LOW-VOLTAGE ELECTRICAL SYSTEM PLANNING

When the needs of the project require exterior illumination for aesthetic or safety purposes, landscape contractors can craft custom low-voltage lighting installations from the many components available. Lighting of many styles can be designed using the variety of fixtures, lamps, transformers, controllers, and wiring available to the competent lighting installer. A custom installation offers a better quality product and more satisfaction than lighting using a stock kit.

Another difference is the piece by piece installation required for a custom system. Beginning with a dedicated power supply, rather than an electrical outlet, and ending with fixtures that are set either with heavy-duty anchors or in footings and wired with waterproof connections, completion of a custom lighting job requires far more effort than does the installation of a packaged kit system. The result of this extra effort, however, is a lighting system that is more durable, far more effective, and more aesthetically pleasing than the less expensive system.

Guidelines for Planning a Custom Lighting System

When planning a lighting system, the designer uses standard guidelines and mathematical formulas to determine the parameters of a lighting circuit. These guidelines will help the designer determine how long the lighting run can be, how many lights can be placed on a circuit, and whether the lights will function properly. Add these factors to the decisions about the style of fixture and esthetic function of the lighting, and the design of a system can become a challenge. Use the information in the "Layout and Calculations for a Typical Circuit" section previously to guide the planning of the custom lighting system, with the following considerations regarding the various components of the system.

Electrical Source. For a custom DC electrical system, a licensed electrician must provide a circuit to the location where the transformer(s) will be located. This supply line should be on a separate ground-fault circuit interrupt (GFCI). GFCI circuits are designed to shut off electrical power to the circuit when voltage fluctuations from short circuits are sensed, providing protection from accidental shock. When routing the electrical supply to an exterior location, the contractor should place all components in conduit a minimum of 18 inches deep and ensure that all components are waterproofed and grounded. This circuit, which may have multiple sub-circuits, depending on the scope of the project, should have a dedicated circuit breaker on the electrical panel. This circuit can have a switch, but it is often best to avoid switches, photocells, timers, and other control devices on this circuit and place such controls on the individual circuits coming out of the transformer.

CAUTION

Working with electrical systems poses serious risk of shock, burns, or electrocution. Only a licensed electrician should perform electrical connections.

Transformers and Hubs. Electrical sources for custom low-voltage systems typically follow one of three distribution methods. The first is mounting a single transformer and wiring each circuit from that transformer. Requiring the positioning of only one control point, this method can suffer from poor lighting performance because long runs of cable must serve the fixtures. The second method is to mount a single transformer that feeds a number of hubs positioned around the site (Figure 17-13). Multiple hubs allow shorter runs of cable to the lighting fixtures, thereby reducing voltage drop and improving lighting performance. Hubs can also equalize voltage among lighting runs or for feeding to other hubs. The third method is to run separate electrical circuits to multiple low-voltage transformers located close to the lighting fixtures the transformer will serve. Although this method increases the cost because AC circuits are running to various locations throughout the site, lighting quality is typically better because wiring runs for each low-voltage circuit are shorter.

Any of these three methods will require a transformer sized to handle the electrical demands of the system. Transformers are typically available in a range of wattages and with varying numbers of circuits that can be

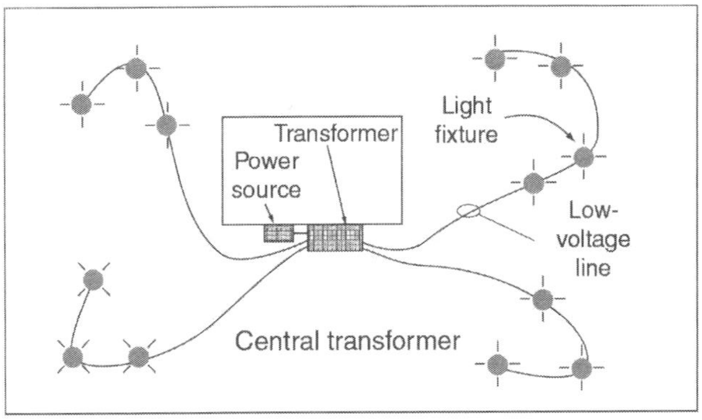

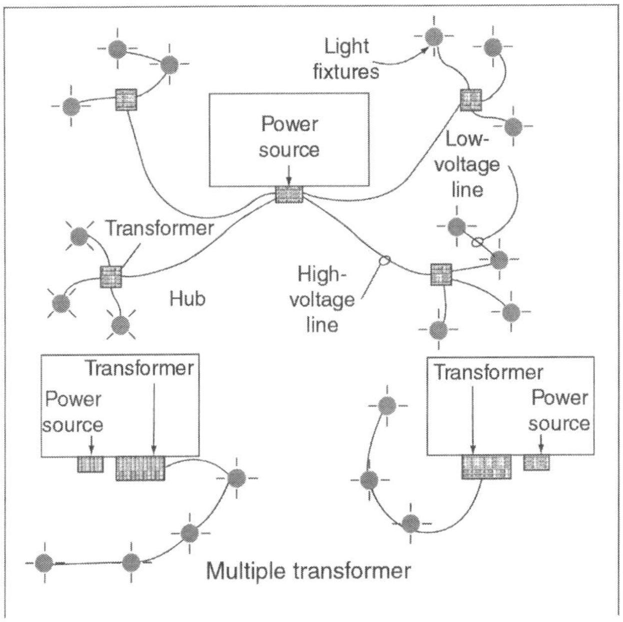

Figure 17-13 Transformer and wiring options for DC lighting.

Figure 17-14 An FX PotenzaX low-voltage transformer with multiple wire taps and timer.

installed. Because of the variability of lighting fixtures, number of fixtures, and length of lighting runs, installation of a transformer that has multiple circuits (or voltage taps) will aid in providing adequate power to multiple wire runs (Figure 17-14). Multiple taps can also aid in programming different operating systems such as photocells, timers, and remote controls to specific lighting circuits. When mounting the transformer and controller, position the equipment in a location that is accessible but not visible to the public. Transformers should be mounted a minimum of 18" above grade or per local code, with higher installations making wiring and connections easier. If space within the transformer has been allowed for adding timers or photocell controls, install those features at the beginning of the circuit. Separate weatherproof boxes may be necessary for installing circuit control features.

Fixture Placement. The wide range of lighting types suggests a variety of fixture types and installation methods. However, most decorative lighting is accomplished by using either an appropriately placed spot or flood fixture. Spot fixtures focus a narrow beam of concentrated light at an object, whereas flood fixtures cast a wide beam of diffused light. Placement will require an understanding of the lighting's purpose. In most applications, the light being cast, not the fixture, should be the focal point. This suggests that the contractor locate the fixture so that it is hidden from view without compromising the beam of light. Placement behind plants, signage, and site structures and on the backside of plant branches and trunks are common ways to hide the fixtures. The intensity and spread of the light beam for each fixture is controlled by a reflector installed inside the fixture behind the bulb. Bulb and lens choices will also determine beam intensity and spread.

INSTALLATION OF CUSTOM EXTERIOR LIGHTING SYSTEMS

The installation of the electrical system relies on attention to detail and quality workmanship to assure proper operation. Follow any specifications prepared for the system and electrical guidelines defined in codes and ordinances. One primary difference between the packaged kit lighting systems and custom low-voltage Low voltage AC electrical systems is product quality. A custom installation offers a better quality product and more satisfaction with that product. Another difference is the piece by piece installation required for a custom system. Beginning with a dedicated power supply, rather than an electrical outlet, and ending with fixtures that are set either with heavy-duty anchors or in footings and wired with waterproof connections, completion of a custom lighting job requires far more effort than does the installation of a packaged kit system. The result of this extra effort, however, is a lighting system that is more durable, far more effective, and more aesthetically pleasing than the less expensive system. In most situations the system installation will follow the steps outlined below.

> **CAUTION**
>
> Verify North Carolina Law 89D-11 and with local building code administrators which lighting work can be performed by the landscape contractors. See the exceptions noted in the OBJECTIVES section at the beginning of this chapter.

Ground Fault Interrupter Installation

All exterior low-voltage must be connected to a GFCI circuit. If a separate GFCI circuit is not present a licensed electrician will need to install the protected circuit with either a direct connection to the transformer(s) or provide a protected outlet into which transformer(s) can be plugged. This supply line should be on a separate ground-fault circuit interrupt (GFCI). When routing the electrical supply to an exterior location, the contractor should place all components in conduit at the depth required by local codes and ensure that **all components are** waterproofed and grounded. This circuit, which may have multiple sub-circuits, depending on the scope of the project, should have a dedicated circuit breaker on the electrical panel. This circuit can have a switch, but it is often best to avoid switches, photocells, timers, and other control devices on this circuit and place such controls on the individual circuits coming out of the transformer.

Fixture Layout and Assembly

Begin the installation of the lighting system by flagging, assembling and placing fixtures according to the design. The wide range of lighting types suggests a variety of fixture types and installation methods. However, most decorative lighting is accomplished by using either an appropriately placed spot or flood fixture. Spot fixtures focus a narrow beam of concentrated light at an object, whereas flood fixtures cast a wide beam of diffused light. Placement will require an understanding of the lighting's purpose. In most applications, the light being cast, not the fixture, should be the focal point. This suggests that the contractor locate the fixture so that it is hidden from view without compromising the beam of light. Placement behind plants, signage, and site structures and on the backside of plant branches and trunks are common ways to hide the fixtures. The intensity and spread of the light beam for each fixture is controlled by a reflector installed inside the fixture behind the bulb. Bulb and lens choices will also determine beam intensity and spread. Pre-assembly of fixtures will reduce working time and improve quality if done in a controlled work situation. For hub systems, 25' 12/2 lead wires can be connected to the fixture using a secure waterproof connection.

Anchoring the fixture to the ground and the cable to the fixture is another factor that will influence the success of the installation. Some fixtures have direct burial stems that are inserted into the ground to stabilize them. Other fixtures may require the pouring of a small concrete base, or even a concrete footing, to properly anchor them. Installing fixtures so that frost, erosion, soil settling, and other disturbances do not shift the fixture (and the resulting light) should dictate the anchoring method.

Still other connection methods include those that bolt directly to fences, walls, and other permanent objects that can provide support. Routing cable to fixtures can often be accomplished underground or on the surface as described below; but in some installations, the wire needs to be routed behind walls, across the tops of structures, or even up the trunks of plant material. Regardless of the cable routing choice, consider a location and method that will protect the cable from damage and hide the cable from view.

Hub Location

When using the hub method, locate the center of a grouping for the placement of the hub. Securely mount the hub in the ground

Transformer Placement

Locate the correct position for the transformer. This location should be near GFCI power supply and in an area that allows for installation and maintenance. When mounting the transformer and any controllers, position the equipment in a location that is accessible but not visible to the public. Transformers should be mounted a minimum of 18 inches above grade, with higher installations making wiring and connections easier. If space within the transformer has been provided for adding timers or photocell controls, install those features at the beginning of the circuit. Separate weatherproof boxes may be necessary for installing circuit control features.

Laying Cable

Begin cable layout by starting with your home-runs. Check the design for the proper size and type of cable. Wire gauges for kits are often 18-gauge; whereas for custom applications, the installer may choose 14-gauge or 12-gauge to reduce voltage drop. When laying out wire runs, leave slack line along each run to allow for adjustment of fixture and cable locations. Unless you are using conduit, do not bury the wire until the system has been completely laid out, **documented** and tested. Lay the longest first and mark the ends of the cable run #1. Leave extra cable at each end of the run for connections, but do not exceed the lengths required to provide proper operating voltage to each fixture. If connecting runs directly to fixtures, lay additional cable in the area of the fixtures to allow for adjustment and place cable in the pattern based on the circuit design (hub, T, daisy chain, loop). At hubs, leave additional cable for connections.

Continue the process of laying home-runs from fixtures/hubs until all of your circuits are laid and marked. Grouping the runs together as they move closer to the transformer will save on trenching and reduce confusion. Placing runs near edgers and walkways may also reduce the chance of lines being severed by digging operations. When laying cable to eaves look for drain pipes that can serve as conduit for wiring. Crossing walkways can be done through drainpipes or by expanding joints between slabs and sealing wire in place with self leveling pour stone.

Anchoring the fixture to the ground and the cable to the fixture is another factor that will influence the success of the installation. Some fixtures have direct burial stems that are inserted into the ground to stabilize them. Other fixtures may require the pouring of a small concrete base, or even a concrete footing, to properly anchor them. Installing fixtures so that frost, erosion, soil settling, and other disturbances do not shift the fixture (and the resulting light) should dictate the anchoring method.

Still other connection methods include those that bolt directly to fences, walls, and other permanent objects that can provide support. Routing cable to fixtures can often be accomplished underground or on the surface as described below; but in some installations, the wire needs to be routed behind walls, across the tops of structures, or even up the trunks of plant material. Regardless of the cable routing choice, consider a location and method that will protect the cable from damage and hide the cable from view.

Fixture Connection

Note: If burying cable in conduit, pull the cable through the conduit prior to making fixture connections.

If not pre-assembled, connect wires to fixtures along the wire run or to fixture that is run from hubs. All connections must be installed according to applicable codes and manufacturers specifications. Connections should be directly to the fixture, or to pigtails leading from fixtures. Use proper connection techniques that provide secure and weather proof protection.

Connect wires with similar polarity. Wire strands can be distinguished by checking for identification, typically a white stripe, white lettering, or ribbing. For splicing use the following guidelines. When making electrical connections always apply dielectric grease to the connection, and cover nuts and screws with anti-seize to make future maintenance easier.

Wire Nuts. Strip wire back far enough so that the throat of the wire nut does not run up on the insulation. If joining wires of different size, hold the smaller wire slightly in front of the larger wire when beginning the connecting process. Use dielectric grease on all connections. Twist the wire nut on clockwise until the wires begin to wrap around on themselves. Pull on the nut to verify it will not come off the connection. Use the proper size nut according to this following chart:

- Orange: 18 or 16 ga. wire, max 2 wires
- Yellow: 14 ga wire, max 2 wires
- Red: 12 ga wire, max 3 #12 or 2 #12 and 1 110
- Gray: 10 ga wire, lug wire nut recommended over plastic
- Large Blue: 8 ga wire, lug wire nut recommended over plastic

Lug Connection. Strip wires back 1.25". Separate leads into hots and commons, with like leads being connected. Hold the common wires together and twist clockwise two loose turns. Place brass lug over wires and twist clockwise while sliding hub up to insulation. Crimp the lug and trim the excess wire. Slide the grease cap over the connection.

Compression Crimp. Strip wires back 1". Place crimping tool over wires and compress. Cover with grease cap.

Waterproof wire nut. This connection is a wire nut filled with a waterproofing compound that holds the wire connection in a moisture-resistant seal (Figure 14–8). Installation is similar to other wire nuts: Simply strip the last half inch of each wire to be joined, give the two wires a slight clockwise twist together, then slip the nut on and turn in a clockwise direction until snug. Test the connection by pulling on the nut to verify it will not come off.

Splice Gel Connector. Splice gell connectors make a more permanent waterproof connection. Follow the manufacturer's specifications and local codes for this application.

Heat-shrink connectors. Heat shrink connectors are another way to provide a weatherproof connection. Again, follow the manufacturer's specifications and local codes for this application.

Transformer Connection

Mount the transformer and make all home-run connections to the appropriate taps. The final Strip adequate wire to allow the set lug to secure firmly on the wire and not the insulation, and that no copper wire extends beyond the connection.

Perform System Tests

Testing and adjusting the custom installation will require multiple steps. Initial tests should come when the wiring runs are established in the form of voltage checks at the splicing points and ends of runs. After the wires have been connected to the transformer and to the fixtures, use a digital voltmeter. Touch each of the two leads with the voltmeter to measure the voltage at the splicing points, where a maximum of 11.5 volts should be registered (with the exception of LED where the minimum and maximum voltage varies by manufacturer), and at the end of the fixture run, where a minimum of 10.5 volts should be registered (again, with the exception of LED lighting where the minimum and maximum voltage varies by manufacturer). Voltages above 11.5 at the beginning of the run create the risk of burning out lamps prematurely, and voltages below 10.5 anywhere along the circuit create problems with obtaining even lighting along the entire run of fixtures. Should voltages exceed these limits, adjustments can be made to the length of the wire run, the size of the wire, adjustment of the transformer or the number of fixtures on a circuit. In addition to checking voltages, perform a nighttime check of fixture placement to assure that the desired effect is being obtained. Fixtures that are not creating the lighting patterns desired should be adjusted.

Bury Cable

Wire for low-voltage lighting can be placed underground in conduit, directly buried into the ground, or placed on top of the ground and hidden under mulch. Although using conduit is preferable to protect the installation and to reduce maintenance problems, direct burial is often used for low-voltage systems. Bury cable to a minimum depth of 6", with a preferred depth of 12" to 18". Trench by hand areas near utilities, irrigation piping and plant roots.

Cover trenches and compact soil, then restore sod, mulch or other cover over trench. Cable placed in trees must be run up the side away from normal viewing and fastened securely to the tree using staples.

For conduit installations, the conduit and fixture installation require coordination, as listed below, to place each fixture properly.

- Excavate a 4-inch wide trench to the depth required by applicable code from the supply to the first fixture in the run.
- Lay out a lightweight metal or schedule 40 plastic electrical conduit and fittings along the trench location. At each fixture a curved piece of conduit should turn toward the surface at the fixture location. A separate curved piece of conduit should lead back down into the trench to start the conduit run to the next fixture.
- Cut the conduit to fit between fixtures and join.
- Place the conduit in the trench and backfill.
- Install light fixture bases, if required. If no base is required, mount a waterproof junction box on top of the two curved conduits. Install the light fixture either on the installed base or, as direct burial, next to the junction box (Figure 17-15).
- Pull the wire from the source to the first fixture using a lubricated electrician fiber extension pole or wire snake fed through the conduit. Leave extra wire at the fixture location to make connections and slight adjustments. Continue to pull cable for all fixtures in the run.

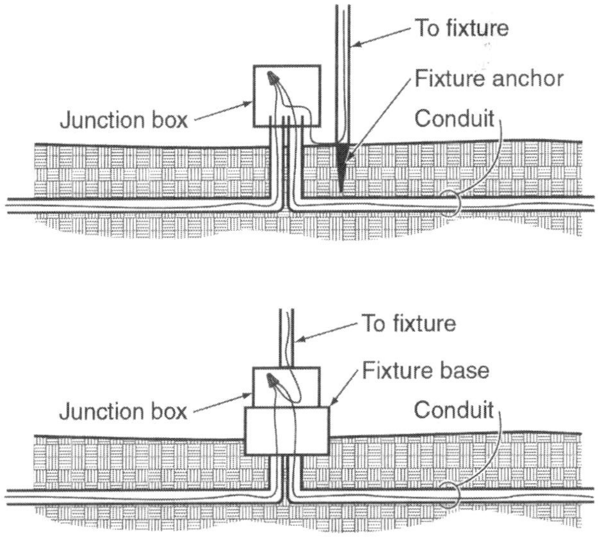

Figure 17-15 Connections for a DC lighting fixture.

- Make connections at the fixtures, and then make connections at the power source. Connections for LOW VOLTAGE AC fixtures are often accomplished within the fixture, either in the bulb housing, a built-in junction box, or a base. When making connections, even inside a junction box, use the guidelines noted below to reduce connection problems and failure.

Verify your work has not damaged any site improvements

Before completing the project review the planting beds, lawns and other site improvements to verify that your work has not damaged any of the existing landscape. Turn on the irrigation system to locate any pipes or heads that may have been damaged by trenching or fixture installation. Drip irrigation tubes and heads can also be easily buried or cut by lighting operations.

Perform Night Adjustments

To verify the effectiveness of the lighting, review the installation after dark to check voltage levels and light aiming. Daytime electrical load is often different than evening loads, which could require changes in the system. Beam alignment and "hot spots" are difficult to locate during the daytime hours. Make all final adjustments before declaring the project complete.

Prepare Record Drawings Prior to burying the cable, prepare the as-built drawing showing the locations and sizes of all system fixtures, hubs, cables and transformers. Performing this work before burying makes it easier to identify the location and number of cables in a run.

LOW-VOLTAGE ELECTRICAL SYSTEM KITS

Exterior low-voltage electrical system kits are used primarily for powering small-scale decorative lighting schemes. Spotlights, stair lights, low-level walk lights, uplights, and downlights in plant material are examples of low-voltage direct current (DC) lighting applications that the landscape contractor can install. Installation of basic DC lighting fixtures may vary slightly from manufacturer to manufacturer, but the steps undertaken for system assembly are similar.

Locating Electrical Sources and Controllers

DC electrical systems require an AC outlet to provide power. Typical AC sources are 120volt outlets located in garages, basements, or exterior locations. Identify an outlet in a weatherproof location where a transformer can be placed. It is necessary to select an outlet that is a GFCI circuit.

Most transformers are designed so they can be mounted on a post or wall with a grounded plug for an outlet. The transformer, typically supplied with a single or double tap, reduces the AC current so that the low-voltage system may use that current. A low-voltage electrical cable plugs into the transformer and must be fed to the locations where lights are located. If the transformer is inside, drill a hole through an exterior wall and feed the lighting cable through to the outside. Plug the hole with insulation or steel wool and fasten the cable to a nearby stud with a wire staple.

Some DC lighting systems have controllers that turn on lights at dusk or allow the user to control the on and off times. These controllers may be built in with the transformers or may be separate units placed along the cable. Either method requires that the controllers be located where the owner can gain access to the equipment. In the case of photocells, controllers must be located in an area that receives ample sunlight. Therefore, transformers with built-in controllers must be located outside a structure, and the cord that connects to the AC outlet must be fed in a conduit through the wall to the outlet.

Fixture Installation and Cable Connection

Fixtures require some level of assembly according to the manufacturer's instructions and applicable codes. Locate the fixtures in the areas where they are to be placed before stringing the cable. Lay the cable from the transformer to where the first fixtures are located. Provide ample cable to allow for adjusting the fixture locations after they are connected. Typical fixture assembly and connections are performed as follows:

1. Insert bulb into lamp base socket (Figure 17-16).
2. Attach lens to lamp base. Lenses will snap or twist into the base (Figure 17-17).
3. Run a loop of cable through the mounting stem bracket (Figure 17-18).
4. Connect the lamp base to the cable by pressing the cable onto the metal prongs projecting from the lamp base (Figure 17-19). These prongs puncture the cable and make contact with each conductor in the wire. One metal prong must make contact with the wire inside each side of cable. Use care not to bend the prongs.
5. Attach a threaded cap, which will hold the cable in place (Figure 17-20).

Figure 17-16 Inserting bulb into lamp base socket.

Figure 17-17 Attaching lens to lamp base.

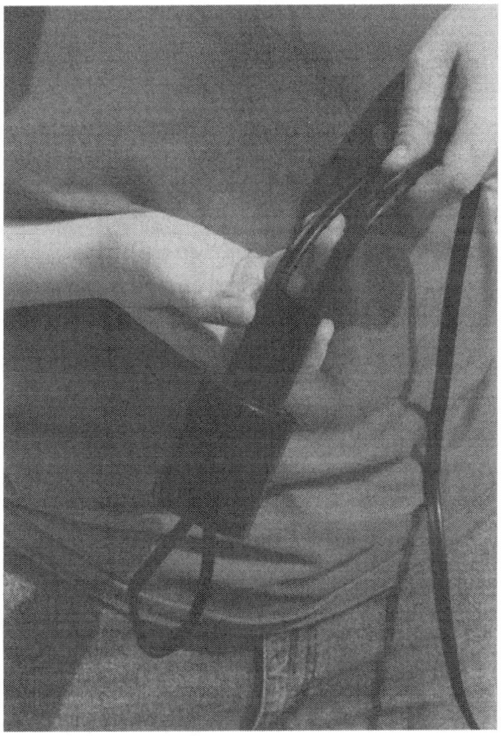

Figure 17-18 Running loop of cable through mounting stem.

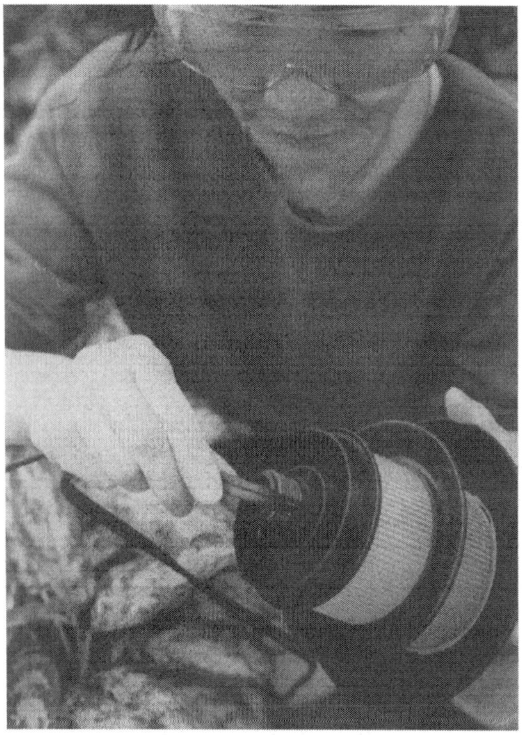

Figure 17-19 Connecting cable to lamp base. A metal prong must penetrate each side of the cable for light to work. Do not bend metal prongs.

Figure 17-20 Attaching threaded cap to lamp base.

Figure 17-21 Sliding mounting stem over threaded cap.

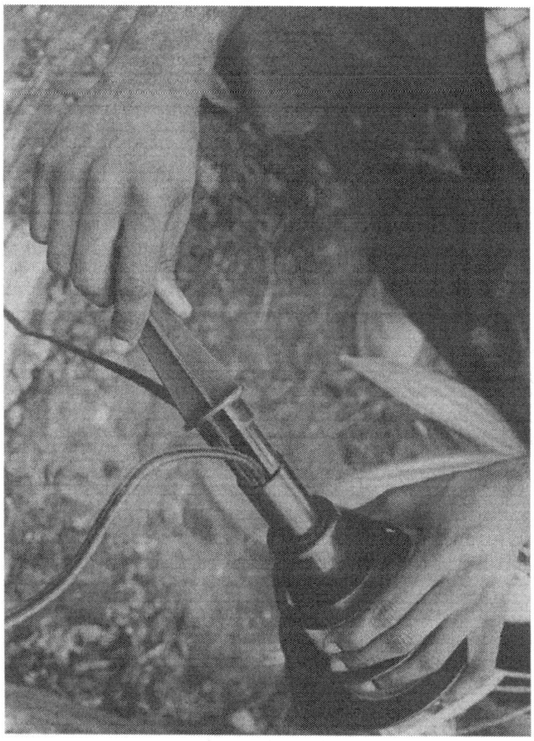

Figure 17-22 Inserting mounting stem.

6. Slide the mounting stem bracket into place over the threaded cap (Figure 17-21).
7. Insert the mounting stem into the mounting stem bracket (Figure 17-22).
8. Gently push the fixture into the ground (Figure 17-23).

Figure 17-23 Gently pushing fixture into ground.

(Note: This assembly procedure is general and may not apply to every style and manufacturer of light fixtures. Review manufacturer's instructions and follow all applicable codes and standards before assembling any light system.)

Ground-level lights may have the stem and fixture in a single unit, allowing the installer to connect the light and insert the mounting stem into the ground in a single operation. Mounted lights may require that the fixture be snapped or bolted to a mounting base.

Continue installation of fixtures at each location along the cable where a light is planned following NEC low voltage standards and local codes.

INSTALLING CONDUIT FOR FUTURE USE

Placement of empty conduit that the electrician, irrigation contractor, or other utility installer may later use is another task that may be assigned to the landscape contractor. Conduit installation requires the trenching and placement of weatherproof PVC or metal conduit to locations where future utility service is planned and to unserviced areas that could require future irrigation or electrical service. When determining empty conduit locations, consider running conduit from structures with utility service under paved terraces and walks, from open lawn areas to smaller planting beds that are isolated by hardscape or property lines, and at regular intervals under paved pathways. Additional areas where empty conduit may be beneficial are isolated side yards and areas that link front yards to back yards.

Check construction documents and local codes for allowable types of conduit and proper burial depths. If no plans or codes are applicable, bury **Schedule 40** conduit a minimum of 18 inches deep. Installing two conduits that are either 2 inches or 3 inches in diameter should provide adequate dimension to route future irrigation mains, controller wires, low-voltage or AC electric, or gas lines. For locations where only electrical is anticipated, a single 2-inch diameter conduit should suffice. Trenching for conduit and piping of all types should be executed after the rough grade has been established and deep utilities such as drainage, water, and sewer service have been completed. Trenching before paving and finish grade have been established reduces disturbance of completed parts of the project.

Leave a stub of conduit projecting 6 inches beyond the edge of any hardscape. If surface connections are desired, extend the conduit to finish grade at each location where a fixture or other electrical service is located. Cap or place duct tape over the open end, and mark the location with a colored flag for visibility. It is also helpful to mark the location of empty conduit on a plan to make future location of the conduit easier. Although it is not recommended to extend empty conduit through foundations at the time of installation, if it is necessary to do so, such installations should be securely capped and sloped so that any moisture trapped in the conduit runs away from the structure. Leave additional length on the end extended through the foundation so the cap can be cut off and still leave room to install a fitting.

SECTION 4

SUMMARY

While a majority of the utilities designed to serve a site are installed by specialized contractors, the landscape contractor may be assigned responsibility for some portion of the site lighting and asked to perform minor utility tasks while coordinating activities with other utility installers. Section 4 described the site lighting tasks that are typical for a landscape project.

Installation of the Low Voltage Alternating Electrical systems require an understanding of the purposes and techniques for lighting a site. Using light to enhance the features of the landscape throughout the day and throughout the seasons can be accomplished by using fixtures that light up, down, in front of and behind landscape elements. While plug and shine light kits still are sold, the level of quality of landscape lighting has advanced exponentially over the past decade. New tools are available to treat the observer with a variety of effects, and the contractor that installs the systems must be knowledgeable and artistic. Exterior illumination has moved beyond the simple path light to safety and esthetic lighting in many forms.

Creating an effective and attractive lighting installation requires more than just knowing where to place a fixture. Understanding the science and mathematics of electricity combined with knowing what components perform which tasks will lay the foundation of a solid system. Advances in lighting such as LED lights has simplified part of the circuitry design, yet the contractor must still understand how to wire, connect and power the system. Hubbed distribution points supplied with AC current and controllers can manage safety and decorative lighting for a large site.

The scope of electrical lighting that can be accomplished by the landscape contractor will be limited by codes, licensing requirements, technical knowledge and safety concerns. While the landscape contractor may not the installer of electrical systems, understanding the nature of this portion of the landscape will serve as a valuable resource.

SECTION 5

LANDSCAPE RETAINING WALLS AND STAIRS

INTRODUCTION

One of the most dominating functional and visual elements of the landscape is the **retaining wall**. Whether a single wall or several walls grouped together in **terraces**, this vertical element creates an immediate and significant change in a landscape. Walls also serve a variety of functional purposes for the homeowner, from mitigating erosion to creating space. Primary among the functions of the retaining wall is the leveling of grades to create more usable areas in the landscape. On sites that have a significant slope, normal use of open areas for lawns, gardens, play areas, or circulation routes may be restricted because of the steep grade. Retaining walls can create level areas to accommodate these activities.

Large-scale wall installations, like those seen along roadsides, may rely on techniques such as soil nailing and anchoring or building cantilever walls, but most residential and smaller commercial projects rely on what is termed gravity walls. Contemporary construction materials and techniques make walls a versatile and effective landscape element. Walls of almost any form, color, and material can be blended with other landscape elements to accomplish design goals. Despite these innovations, walls are still an expensive and time-consuming landscape element to construct; so, landscape contractors must consider all possible solutions when addressing grade problems.

The chapters of this section cover construction techniques for building walls with several common materials available to landscape contractors. Chapters cover the installation techniques used for timber wall construction, segmental wall unit (precast concrete) and structural cell construction, dry-laid stone wall construction, and gabions. Not included are retaining walls constructed of cast-in-place concrete, rammed earth, or mortared veneer materials. Both cast-in-place concrete and mortared masonry veneer retaining walls are impermeable materials that require stabilizing designs and specialized drainage systems placed behind the wall to protect them against water pressure.

In addition, the skills required and risks involved in forming and pouring large installations typically place these walls beyond the landscape contractor's scope. Specialty contractors are also required for cantilever walls and for soil nailing and anchoring, as well as for walls used in situations with dynamic water such as river or marine revetments. Nonretaining, freestanding wall construction, including mortared walls, cast-in-place concrete, stucco, rammed earth, and veneered walls, are discussed in Chapter 30.

SUSTAINABILITY SUGGESTIONS

Incorporating the following actions into your project can make your work more sustainable:

- When you have control over such choices, give careful consideration to the materials used in your project. Choose local materials before selecting materials that must be transported great distances to your site, and choose renewable materials, rather than products that cannot easily be reused.
- Select toxin-free, environmentally friendly materials. Avoid plastic materials that use harmful chemicals in their manufacturing process. When using wall materials to create planters and other areas in which consumable food is grown, do not use wall materials treated with chemicals that prevent decomposition.

WALL CONSTRUCTION GUIDELINES

The process for constructing walls and stairs can be approached a number of ways. The following guidelines provide general ideas from which a project can be started:

- Always construct walls according to applicable codes and guidelines.
- Always follow manufacturer's specifications.
- Always begin wall construction at the lowest point (Figure S5–1).
- Work from lower walls to upper walls when terracing.
- Build cast-in-place concrete stairs first and then build the wall up to the stairs.
- Locate stair and/or corner locations and plan material layout to end evenly at these points.
- To avoid delays caused by weather, install base courses for several projects, rather than beginning and completing one project at a time. Bad weather interferes with base construction but has minimal impact on stacking of subsequent courses or horizontal layers of wall material.

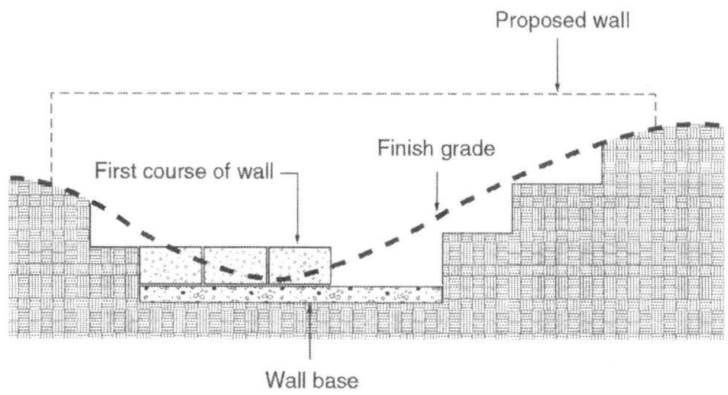

Figure S5-1 Beginning wall at low point.

- The bottom course of all walls should be buried below grade. This will enhance the wall's stability. There are manufacturer's and engineering standards for bottom course burial depths.
- Excavation of a wide trench along the wall alignment will ease access problems, allow use of a skid-steer for excavation, and provide more room for working.
- Never use pea gravel as a base, infill, or backfill materials for walls. It does not create enough friction between stones to maintain stability.

CHAPTER 18

MATERIALS AND INSTALLATION TECHNIQUES FOR RETAINING WALLS

OBJECTIVES

By reading and practicing the techniques described in this chapter, the reader should be able to successfully complete the following activities:

- Choose appropriate materials for a retaining wall.
- Plan the installation of a retaining wall.
- Install a sound base for a retaining wall.
- Drain water from behind a retaining wall.
- Stabilize a retaining wall.

Wall material selection is dictated by the construction documents prepared for a project. If the contractor or the client makes the choice, a review of available materials will help with proper selection. Regardless of the type of wall material selected, site preparation is similar. Preparing the proper base, providing for drainage behind the wall, and planning wall stabilization are required for all walls, especially for those that are taller than 1 foot.

RELATED INFORMATION

Information in this chapter is supplemented by instruction provided elsewhere in this text and in other sources. Before undertaking the activities described in this chapter, read the related information in these sources:

- Related information can be found in applicable codes and ordinances.
- Related information can also be found in manufacturer's specifications.
- National Concrete Masonry Association's "Design Manual for Segmental Walls"
- Safety in the Workplace, Chapter 7
- Basic Construction Techniques and Small Equipment Operation, Chapter 8
- Concrete Paving, Chapter 25

> **CAUTION**
>
> **LAWS REGARDING RETAINING WALL DESIGN**
>
> The North Carolina Building Code dictates that:
>
> - Retaining systems greater than 5 feet (1524 mm) in cumulative vertical relief and adjacent to a structure located closer than the vertical relief shall be designed under the responsible charge of a registered design professional.
> - NO engineering is required for retaining walls that are less than 5 feet tall and more than 5 feet from a structure.
>
> Retaining systems providing a cumulative vertical relief greater than 5 feet (1524 mm) in height within a horizontal separation distance of 50 feet (15m) or less, including retaining walls or mechanically stabilized earth walls, shall be designed under the responsible charge of a registered design professional.

SELECTION OF WALL MATERIALS

In many construction projects, the designer bases the choice of wall material on engineering and aesthetic considerations. Should the contractor have the opportunity to recommend wall materials to clients, review with them the positive and negative aspects of the many materials available. Among the variables to consider are material performance and stability, cost, appearance, ease of installation, and durability.

Although the material evaluation often focuses on new products, contractors should also consider recycled materials and those materials and techniques that reduce impact on the environment. Many of the best wall materials, including most stone and some woods, can be reused from previous applications. Old concrete paving can be reused as a dry-laid wall material. The cellular confinement material introduced in Chapter 16 for erosion control can be stacked horizontally and filled with crushed stone to create a short retaining wall. A selection that withstands the forces of nature without compromising the environment benefits all. The following sections identify several common retaining wall materials that are available to landscape contractors.

Railroad Ties and Treated Wood Landscape Timbers

Wood railroad ties are often the least expensive wall material, but availability of quality ties has been limited since the late 1980s. Ties provide a gray to dark brown color for the wall and blend well with naturalistic design themes. However, poor quality ties provide an inconsistent look to the wall surface. Workability of the ties can be difficult, considering their weight, irregular lengths, and irregular dimensions. Consistent wall building requires modular materials, and railroad ties require a great deal of sorting to match dimensions. Using either a chainsaw or cutoff saw is the most efficient way to trim ties, but the creosote, wood hardness, and buried nails and metal end ties are extremely hard on this equipment.

A more costly substitute for railroad ties is treated wood planks and **landscape timbers** (Figure 18-1). Manufactured to consistent dimensions and lengths, timbers overcome the inconsistency problems that ties present. Timbers also have a consistent wall surface color and texture. Timber weight is slightly less than that of ties, and the cost for timbers is significantly more

Figure 18-1 A wood retaining wall with vertical anchors.

than the cost of ties. Do not confuse landscape timbers with the small edging and planter timbers sold in lumber centers. Landscape timbers are typically sold in 6-inch × 6 inch or 8-inch × 8-inch dimensions, in 6–8-foot lengths, and have squared edges. The much smaller edging timber has rounded edges and is not suitable for walls. Ties and timbers treated with wood preservatives are not acceptable for use adjacent to areas where edible crops are grown. Adding sustainability to the timber and tie arena are landscape timbers manufactured with recycled plastics. Similar in workability but with an extended life expectancy, recycled plastic timbers and composite timbers can be used in many of the same situations as wood.

Segmental Wall Units

Many manufacturers now produce **segmental precast concrete units** used for constructing walls (Figure 18-2). Similar in surface area to a concrete block, these wall units come in a variety of forms, shapes, and installation methods. Segmental units create an appearance of a rough-

Figure 18-2 Segmental precast concrete unit retaining wall.

© Courtesy of Gary Pribyl, Kings Materials.

surfaced stone wall and, combined with the variety of colors, provide an attractive and consistent wall surface. Wall units can be heavy, ranging from 30–80 pounds per unit, but they weigh less than timbers and most workers can handle them. Installation requires careful layout and base course preparation, and most subsequent layers are stacked. Corners and stair incorporation can be difficult. Cost is in the mid to slightly high range when compared to other wall materials. Two common types of segmental units are **pinned wall units**, which use metal or fiberglass rods, or **lipped wall units**, which use a protrusion on the top or bottom of the unit. The primary function for the pin or lip is to maintain alignment and consistent set back.

Figure 18-3 Dry-laid stone retaining wall.

© Delmar/Cengage Learning.

Dry-Laid Stone

Used for years, **dry-laid stone** is considered a classic wall material (Figure 18-3). As the name suggests, this natural wall material is installed without mortar between the stones. Considered a highly aesthetic wall surface, the stone wall can be constructed of regular or random thickness material and with a variety of stone types. Costs vary but are typically high as a result of availability and quarrying costs, high demand in construction, and intensive labor for preparation and installation. Stone is a workable material because most cut stone weights are within a worker's lifting abilities and are available in reasonably consistent dimensions. However, stability of the material may be a concern for high walls so height is generally limited to 3 feet.

Gabions

An alternative to small, single-unit materials for retaining walls is the use of **gabions** (Figure 18-4), or heavy-duty rectangular wire baskets placed in position and filled with large stones. The size and weight of the gabions make a stable wall installation. Varying the size and type of stone inside the gabion produces different aesthetic effects, but the presence of the wire basket will always be a detraction. Because of their size, gabions require special equipment to place and fill. However, the cost is in the lower range of wall materials.

Alternative Materials

As society searches for ways to reduce consumption of materials, the efforts to find adaptive reuses for old materials has increased.

Figure 18-4 Gabion retaining wall one course high.

One such material is old concrete paving in retaining walls. Not every old paving can be reused, but if the old concrete has consistent thickness and has no reinforcement, then it can be reused successfully. With artistic application, the appearance is similar in texture and form to dry-laid stone, although close inspection will reveal the source material. From a strictly visual perspective, reused concrete paving is best when limited to applications in background locations where appearance is not the primary concern. Installation techniques are similar to dry-laid stone, with wider pieces providing more stability but more difficulty in placement. Costs for this material are primarily related to the labor involved in sorting, preparing, and installing it, hence making it a cost-effective choice.

When structural strength is not critical to a retaining wall, materials such as cellular confinement systems and irregular natural stone can be used to create installations that will serve specific purposes. These alternative materials will vary widely in their cost to install, with some ranging from minimal cost to those that are as expensive as a highly detailed wall. Although not always as efficient or attractive as other wall material choices, these alternatives may be the best choice in particular situations.

WALL LAYOUT

Prior to construction, identify the location of the front of the wall. Placing stakes and a stringline, or painting the ground along the alignment, will help in identifying potential starting points and any problems that may be encountered. Also, identify locations of stairs and corners. This layout will guide the location of the rough trenching necessary to establish an approximate grade for the wall. Offset temporary markers away from the excavation so that the wall location can be reset after rough trenching.

EXCAVATION

Excavation may be required in locations where walls are to be constructed. Sod and topsoil should be excavated from an area 2 feet in front of and 2 feet behind the entire wall alignment. Excavate to a depth that is approximately 12 inches lower than the desired finish grade along the base of the wall (Figure 18-5) or per local codes and manufacturer's specifications. This depth is necessary because the bottom, or base, course in any wall is placed below the finished grade. When excavating, remove any unstable materials encountered and replace them with **granular base**.

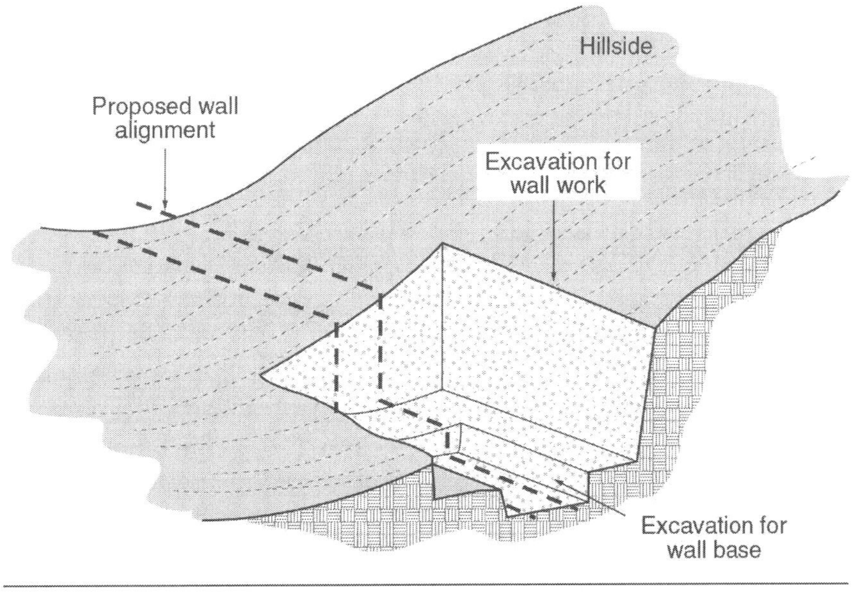

Figure 18-5 Preparing an excavation for retaining walls.

BASE PREPARATION

Wall construction begins at the lowest point of the wall (Figure S5–1). After you complete the rough trenching, replace the stringline that identifies the front of the wall. In the rough trench and along the wall alignment, excavate a trench to be filled with **base material** that is 6 inches deep and 12 inches wider than the wall material (Figure 18-6). The bottom of this trench should be level from end to end. When the depth of this level trench exceeds the thickness of the wall material, the wall should step up one level. When walls encounter embankments, this stepping may occur rapidly. Walls should never step up more than one course at a time, and the course on the bottom should always be covered by grade in front of the wall.

Fill this trench with free-draining angular ¾–1-inch crushed stone. Level the base material and compact using a **vibratory plate compactor**. Placement of a ½–1-inch layer of finer granular material on top of the crushed stone will ease the leveling of the base course of wall material. Crushed stone that passes a ⅜-inch sieve is suitable for this second layer.

Flowable Fill

A stable alternative to compacted granular base material is a medium-grade **flowable fill**, a thin concrete mixed with fly ash that will flow throughout a prepared trench. Consult premixed concrete suppliers for a suitable flowable fill formulation. To install flowable fill, excavate a base trench a minimum of 24 inches wide and 12 inches deep along the alignment of the proposed wall. Place a grade stake in the trench and mark the elevation desired for the top of the base material. Begin pouring flowable fill at one location along the trench and allow the material to fill the trench to the desired grade. Flowable fill is liquid enough that it will seek its own level without screeding or finishing. Allow the flowable fill to harden before you begin to install the wall material.

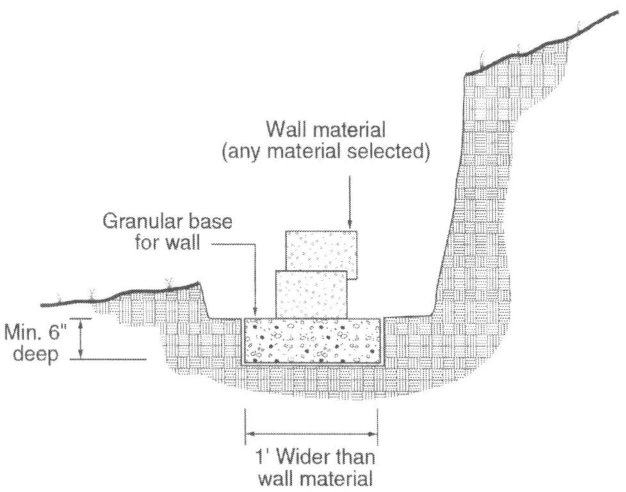

Figure 18-6 Granular base material for wall. Trench should be 12 inches wider than the wall.

Grade Beams

A design professional may require that walls in areas with highly unstable soils be placed on a **grade beam**, a reinforced concrete footing supported by concrete piers sunk to stable subgrade (Figure 18-7). Although uncommon and expensive, this application is an effective way to support a wall. Construction of grade beams begins with excavation and pouring of piers in locations and dimensions determined by the design professional. Reinforcing rod should be extended out of the top of the piers to anchor the footings. Under the alignment of the footings, excavate and place a minimum of 2 inches of sand (or whatever depth the design professional states). This will accommodate frost pushing up against the bottom of the footing.

Form the footing and place steel reinforcement that is tied to the stubs projecting from the piers. A typical grade beam is 1-foot square, but dimensions vary depending on the situation. Verify that the tops of the forms are level and at the correct subgrade elevation. Pour the footing and remove the forms when hardened. Place drainage tile behind the wall as described in the following section, backfill with **free-draining angular backfill**, and proceed with wall construction.

DRAINAGE BEHIND WALLS

Wall failure can often be traced to a buildup of **hydrostatic** (water) **pressure** behind the wall.

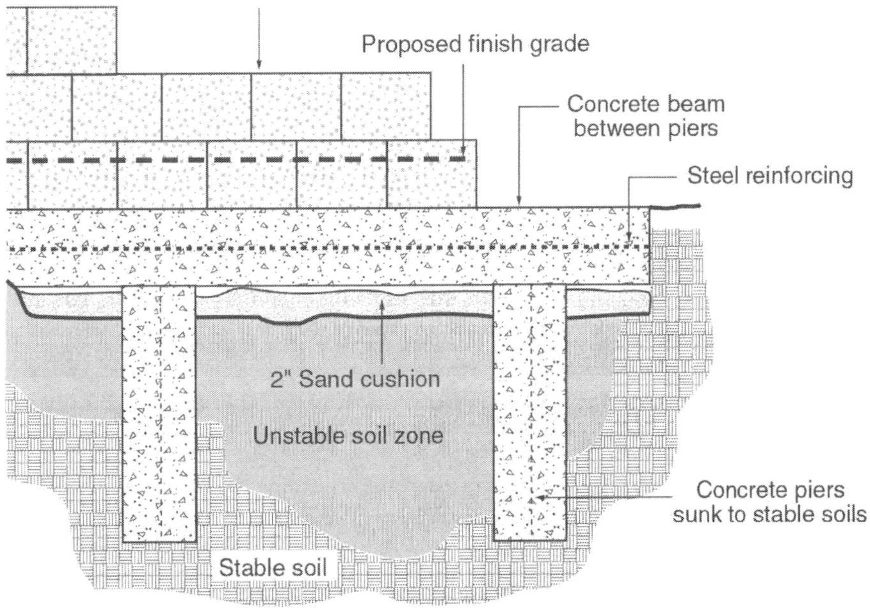

Figure 18-7 Cross section of grade beam used to support walls in poor soils.

The forces exerted by water behind a wall are strong enough to collapse even reinforced installations. If you encounter significant moisture or flowing water while preparing the wall base for construction, consult an engineer to eliminate the water problem before continuing the project. Drainage systems described in this section are proposed to handle occasional water buildup behind a retaining wall. Water problems associated with springs, high water tables, or similar types of situations may exceed the capacity of the drainage systems described in this section and lead to failure of the retaining wall.

Release of water from behind a wall is partially accomplished by placing 1–2-inch diameter Schedule 40 PVC pipes running completely through the base course of the wall every 6–8 feet. These openings, called **weepholes**, allow water to drain from behind the wall. Because many wall materials, particularly gabions, wood walls and segmental concrete units, allow water to drain through the joints and openings between materials, weepholes are often not required. Walls that are solid and without openings may require respacing or notching of wall material to accommodate the pipe.

Weepholes can also be installed by drilling a ½-inch diameter hole through the base course every 6–8 feet. A small amount of water will also pass naturally through the wall in open-joint wall materials. Weepholes and natural drainage are not acceptable substitutes for installation of proper drainage.

Although weepholes and open wall joints are beneficial, supplemental drainage is recommended in any type of wall that exceeds 2 feet in height. This is typically accomplished through the use of drainage tile placed behind the base course of the wall (Figure 18-8). A 4inch perforated **tile** placed in this location along the entire length of the wall should aid in the removal of excess water. For the tile to work properly, free-draining angular backfill should be placed above the tile to allow water to seep down to it.

Proper material selection for backfill behind the walls is critical in reducing hydrostatic pressure. A 12-inch zone directly behind the wall should be backfilled with a ¾–½-inch clean, free-draining angular granular material (also called class 57 rock or washed class 2 in some locations). This material will provide adequate compaction without disrupting water movement

Figure 18-8 Placement of drain tile behind retaining walls.

downward to the drainage tile. The tile must be sloped to the wall's low point. If the low point does not allow the tile to run around an end of the wall to daylight, you will need to cut or notch the wall material to allow the tile to pass through the wall and empty the collected water (Figures 18-9 and 18-10). Engineered walls that exceed 4 feet in height may have additional layers of tile along the wall's length to expedite collection of water.

Landscape Fabric

Certain wall materials may have open joints large enough to allow backfill material to pass through the wall. Designers may opt for a solution that places landscape fabric behind the compacted fill material to reduce the movement of soil through the wall openings. In most wall construction projects, this approach is not recommended because it can increase the hydrostatic pressure behind the wall and counter the benefits gained from drain tile and free-draining backfill. For precast unit walls, this material is not recommended because it also disrupts any wall stabilization material placement (see following paragraphs).

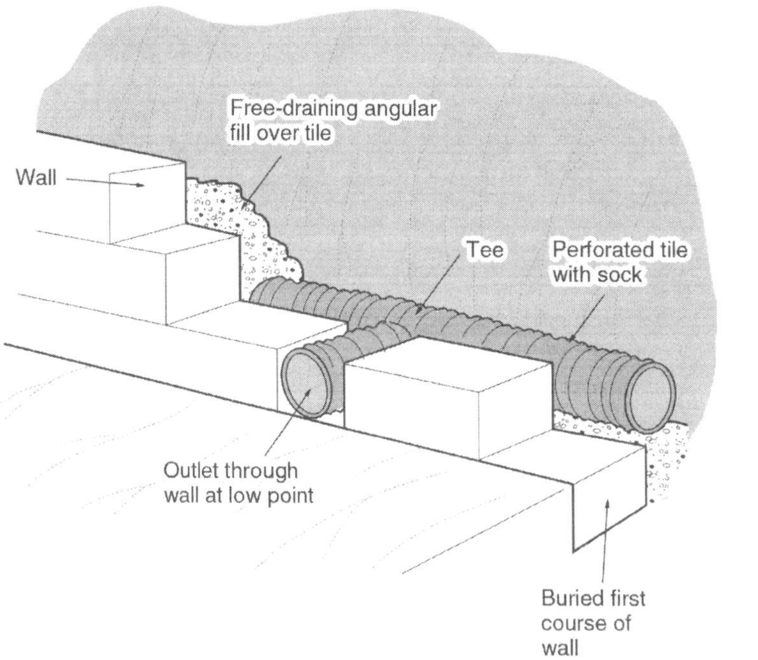

Figure 18-9 Placement of drain tile through an opening at the low point of the wall.

Figure 18-10 Drainage tile exiting through opening cut in wall.

If required by landscape plans and specifications, landscape fabric placed behind the wall should run from the base to the second-from-the-top course of the wall (Figure 18-11). Run the fabric in the long direction along the wall and place it in the trench behind the wall material before doing the first backfill. Drape the fabric over the backside of the trench until the backfill behind the wall reaches the top. Fold the fabric back over the backfill and tuck it under the top course of wall material. Then complete wall construction and backfilling.

COMPACTION BEHIND WALLS

Remaining backfill beyond the first 12 inches directly behind the wall may be original or imported soil. Backfill material should be placed in **lifts**, or layers, of no more than 6 inches before compaction. Compaction methods should be selected carefully to reduce the chance of wall collapse. For a distance of 5 feet behind the wall, compaction should be performed with a vibratory plate compactor (Figure 18-12). Beyond 3 feet, the compaction may be performed by heavier equipment. Avoid over compaction immediately behind the wall to prevent displacing wall material.

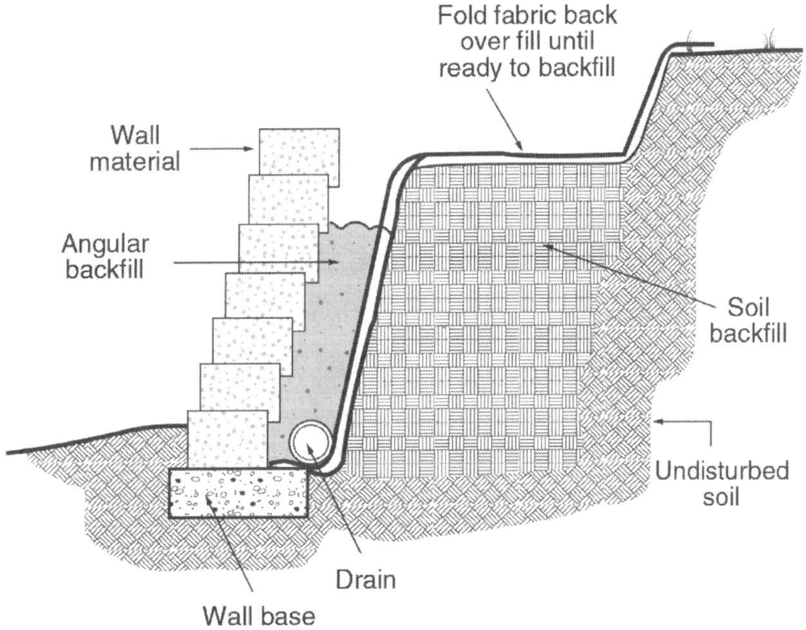

Figure 18-11 Placement of landscape fabric behind retaining walls. Note: Not all wall material manufacturers and designers recommend installation of landscape fabric behind walls.

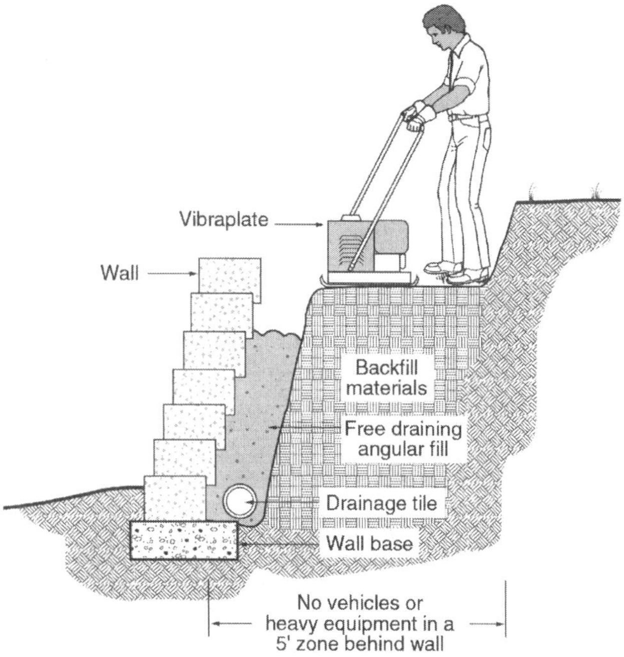

Figure 18-12 Compaction of fill behind retaining walls.

WALL HEIGHTS AND STABILIZATION

As a wall increases in height, its potential of failure also increases. Gravity and hydrostatic pressure can topple a wall, and these forces must be countered by measures that will support the wall. Typical measures used to prevent wall failure include burying or pinning the base course, **battering** the wall, placing **buttresses** in front of timber walls, installing wall anchors, and **terracing**. Detailed techniques of anchoring are explained in the chapters on specific wall materials. Please note the limitations of wall design described at the beginning of the chapter.

Burying of First Course

Burying the base of the wall provides the first measure of stability. Actual burial depth depends on engineered specifications that the design professional or manufacturer provides. At a minimum, the first course of the wall is buried; and in shorter height wall applications, the depth of one course may be adequate. With all wall materials, excavate the base trench low enough to place at least one full course of material below the finish grade on the wall's front side. Another formula used for calculating burial depth is to bury the base course 1 inch below grade for every foot of wall height, with a minimum of one course below grade. Many of the wall materials, particularly the unit wall materials, can be pinned to the subgrade using 24-inch rebars driven through holes in the material and into the base. Both of these measures anchor the base of the wall and counter pressures pushing out at the base.

Battering

Batter is the backward leaning or stepping of a wall (Figure 18-13). Batter can be built into a wall by tilting the base course slightly backward (approximately ¼-inch fall from front to back). This will cause all subsequent courses to lean in the same direction when placed. Batter can also be built into the wall by setting the front of each subsequent course back from the front of the previous course a small amount. This process, called **step-back or stairstep batter**, helps anchor the wall but keeps the materials level. Standards for step-back batter range from 1–2 inches for each foot of wall height. Most walls incorporate one of these two types of batter, particularly along a wall's straight sections and outside curves. A few wall materials may have a nonbattered vertical face on inside curves as a result of the materials from which they are constructed.

Figure 18-13 Retaining wall showing step-back batter.

Anchoring

In addition to batter, many wall systems incorporate some sort of anchor to combat overturning.

Verticals. One type of anchor used in timber or tie wall construction is **vertical** timbers, or buttresses, which are placed in front of a wall (Figure 18-14). These verticals are buried to frost depth and placed at joints in the wall to hold back the wall materials.

Deadmen. Another type of anchor used in timber and tie wall construction and occasionally in stone walls is a **deadman**, a horizontal anchor connected to the wall face and run back into the hillside. The friction from contact between deadmen and the soil behind the wall counters the forward pressures.

Figure 18-14 Vertical timber anchor for a stacked timber retaining wall. Note the vertical is placed at the joint between wall sections.

Deadmen can be constructed by placing a timber with a crosspiece into the hillside or by using rods or cables that are run through the wall face to an anchor in the hillside. Timber deadmen are typically nailed to the wall face, whereas rods or cables are connected to metal plates attached to the wall face.

Geogrid. Similar in principle to the deadman and commonly used in segmental unit wall construction, the geogrid is a newer alternative for anchoring. **Geogrid** is a gridded polyethylene or polyester fabric that is laid in contact with backfill behind a wall (Figure 18-15). The front edge of the geogrid is laid between courses of a wall or hooked over the wall pins and spread out in a flat sheet behind the wall (Figure 18-16). The friction between the backfill and fabric provides similar results to those of a deadman. Geogrid is rated according to the strength and direction of resistance. 2XT geogrid, which can be laid in either direction, is adequate for most short wall applications. Stronger geogrids typically have a higher number (e.g., 5T) and must be placed with proper orientation to have maximum design

Figure 18-15 Installation of geogrid anchoring behind precast concrete retaining wall.

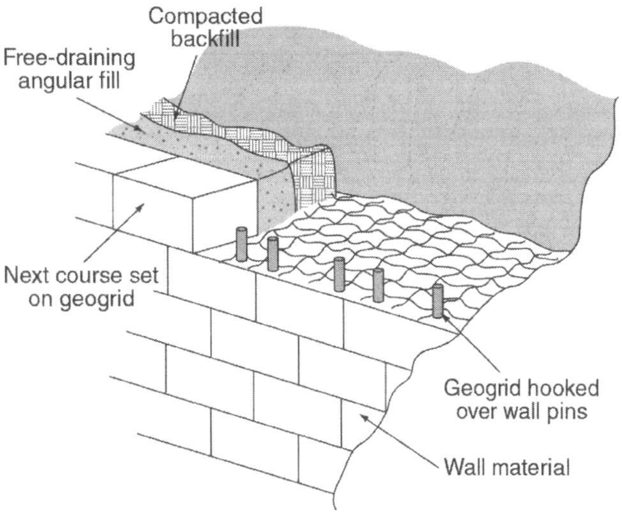

Figure 18-16 Hooking geogrid over pins in a pinned wall system.

© Delmar/Cengage Learning.

strength. Proper orientation places the loose strands of the geogrid parallel to the wall face and the bonded solid bands perpendicular to the wall face.

Terracing

One effective technique for reducing wall failure is to limit the wall's height. As mentioned earlier in this chapter, in North Carolina, retaining walls over 5 feet in height must be designed by a registered design professional. In many landscape situations, this five foot wall height is ample for accomplishing design goals. If there is a need for higher walls, either terrace the site or consult an engineer. Terracing is the construction of a series of shorter walls, each stepped back a calculated distance from the previous wall (Figure 18-17). By using terracing, you can construct a 10-foot wall as two 5-foot walls, given the proper separation between the walls, without extensive engineering. Terracing is not that useful in areas where there is extensive fill or in locations that have limited space due to the potential lack of stability in the subgrade.

All terracing activities should be performed within the guidelines of applicable building codes. In North Carolina, if the horizontal separation between walls is 50 feet or closer,

Figure 18-17 Terracing of precast concrete retaining walls for stability.

© Courtesy of Gary Pribyl, Kings Materials

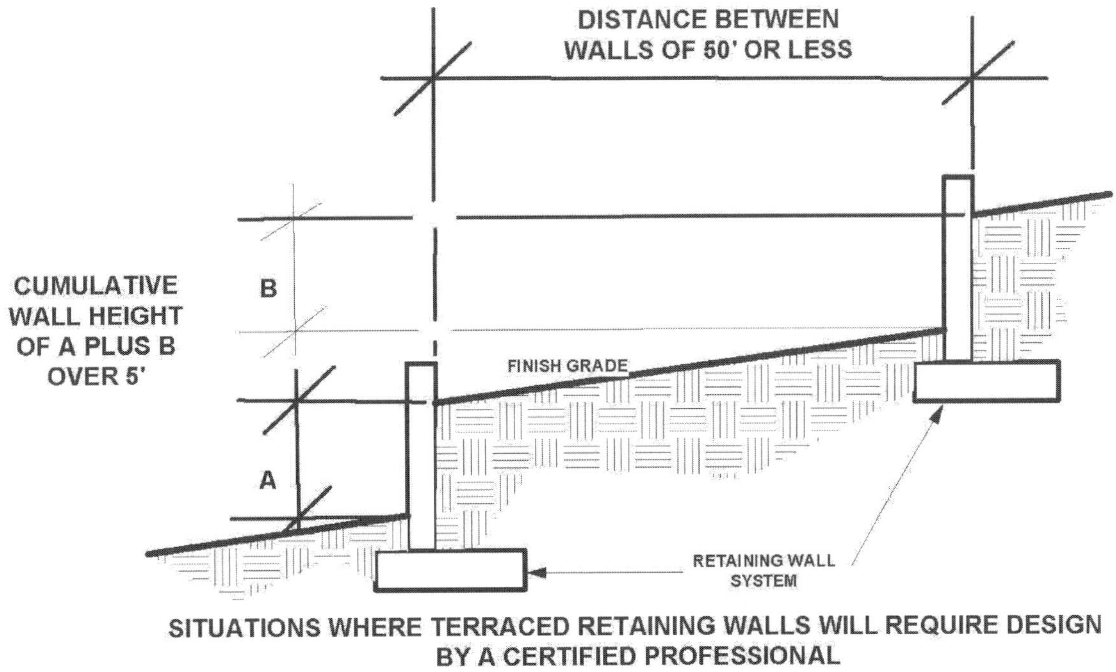

Figure 18-18 Legal Setback of Terraced Retaining Walls

measured from the back of the lower wall to the back of the upper wall, the wall must be designed by a registered professional. (see Figure 18-18).

In addition, any wall that retains earth that is greater than 5 feet in height must be designed by a registered professional, regardless of the separation. Terracing should be constructed beginning with the lower wall first, then grading an area behind the wall and constructing the next higher wall (Figure 18-19). The grade between the walls should slope forward with a minimum fall of 2 percent. Spacing between the walls depends on whether the area leveled to create the second wall is above a slope. If the wall is built on fill or has heavy traffic above, consult a design professional to determine the proper method for stabilization.

ENDING WALLS

Ending retaining walls without an abrupt stop requires some method of transitioning the grade. Methods used range from tapering the grade in front of a wall to stair-stepping the top of the wall to meet the grade (Figure 18-20). Choosing the best method depends on whether the grade behind the wall is falling or moving upward behind the wall.

Tapering Grade

The easiest method for transitioning grade is to construct the retaining wall, backfill behind it, and slope the grade from the higher elevation to the lower elevation in front of the wall at each end. Select the steepest slope possible that will allow maintenance and minimize erosion. For a wall 4 feet in height, use a minimum of 10 feet of horizontal distance in front of the wall to bring the grade down is common. Place fill carefully so that the wall is not disturbed. Taper the slope in front of the wall to accommodate grade change.

Stepping Wall Down

When the grade behind the wall is dropping, the transition to ending the wall can be accomplished by gradually stepping the top of the wall down. Execute this transition by ending the top course and extending lower courses a few units beyond that ending point. Continue stepping down until the wall matches grade or can be ended in an existing grade.

Figure 18-19 Lower wall of a terrace under construction while excavation for the next higher wall of the terrace is underway.

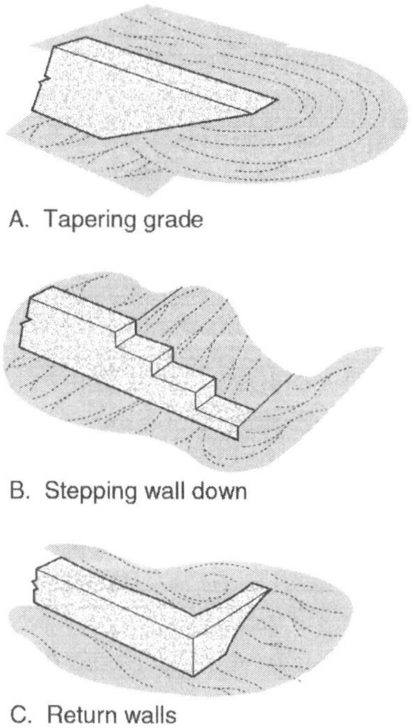

Figure 18-20 Ending retaining walls. A. Tapering grade. B. Stepping the top of a retaining wall down. C. Return walls.

Building Return Walls

If grade cannot be used for a transition, then construct a small section of perpendicular wall. This **return wall** should carry the full height of the wall until it can be stepped down or ended in an existing grade.

PREVENTION OF EXCESS RUNOFF

When a wall is constructed near the base of a slope or near a paved area, the potential for excessive runoff passing over the wall can be a problem. To reduce the potential for wall failure from this runoff, grade a shallow swale above the top of the wall that runs the entire length of the wall (Figure 18-21). This swale should empty water out at a storm sewer inlet or carry the water around to the wall's front side. An alternative to a drainage swale for paved areas is to install a curb that directs water to a location away from the wall.

CONSTRUCTION OF NONSTRUCTURAL RETAINING WALLS

If it retains soil, almost any material can be considered for a retaining wall. However,

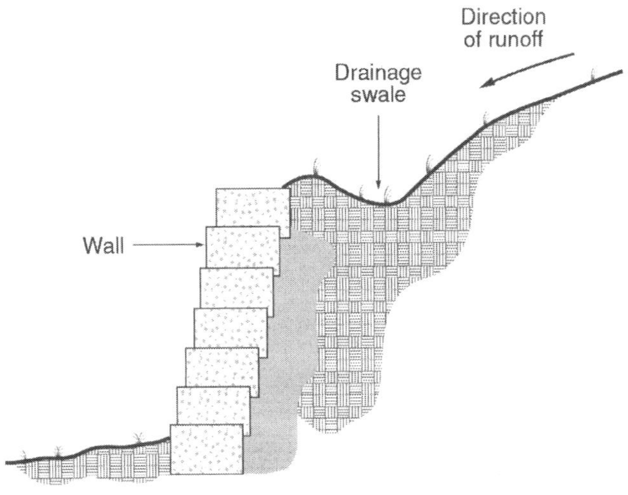

Figure 18-21 Drainage trench at top of retaining wall to intercept runoff before it can run over top and face of wall.

© Delmar/Cengage Learning.

Figure 18-22 Recycled concrete used for short retaining wall.
© Delmar/Cengage Learning.

materials that make the best walls are products that have the ability to stay upright and to support structural loads. If properly constructed, precast concrete, timbers and ties, segmental unit, dry-laid stone, and gabion walls will support calculated loads. When selecting materials for a wall that must support soil in critical situations, limit the choices to those noted above. If a short wall need not support a structural load, then you can use alternative materials to save time and money. Described below are the construction techniques associated with several types of nonstructural retaining walls for those purposes.

Recycled Concrete Installation

To install recycled concrete, use the steps for placing, leveling, and backfilling described previously for dry-laid stone. One variation in the process would be sorting the material before placement because of its irregular shape. Find the larger pieces to use for the lower courses of a wall; and for each piece, orient the flattest edge toward the front of the wall. Even with careful sorting, you will find it difficult to obtain perfection in material placement. In addition to the irregular horizontal dimensions, recycled concrete may also have inconsistent thickness. This characteristic will require shimming with pieces of stone or crushed rock to achieve stability. As with all walls, proper base and behind-the-wall drainage should be provided (Figure 18-22).

> **CAUTION**
>
> Wall construction techniques listed in this section should be limited to wall heights allowable within North Carolina Building Code and other applicable local standards. An engineer should design wall heights beyond this height. Technologies for building the walls in this section are fluid; and before constructing one of these walls, search to see if new techniques have been developed.

Cellular Confinement Wall Installation

If a wall that can support plant growth is required, cellular confinement material (see Chapter 16, Erosion Control) can be placed in horizontal layers to create an installation. The structural stability of this material requires continued research; so, this technique is only recommended for walls under 3 feet in height and without a structural load. To create a planted wall, cut a piece of confinement material that is the length of the wall with an expanded width that is at least two times the height of the wall. Steeper batters can be used, but stability will be reduced. Sizing the cut sections for a 1-foot batter with a minimum of a 1-foot wide top course provides the best stability and area for planting. Cellular materials will vary, but most will create 6-inch high wall courses after installation.

Stretch the confinement material out on a granular base and, using sod staples, anchor at the front and back edge. Fill all but the front two rows of cells with granular material. Fill the front two rows of cells with planting soil. Cut a second length of confinement material two cells, or 1 foot, narrower than the base layer. Stretch out over the base layer and anchor the front and back edges. Repeat the filling process used for the base layer, placing planting soil in the front two rows of cells and granular base in the remaining rows (Figure 18-23). Repeat laying horizontal layers of cellular material until the top course is set. Fill all cells of the top course with planting soil. Plants can be installed in voids filled with soil, eventually providing a cascade of green rather than a visually harsh wall material. Planting will be limited to ground covers, perennials, and vines because of the small planting pockets between cells.

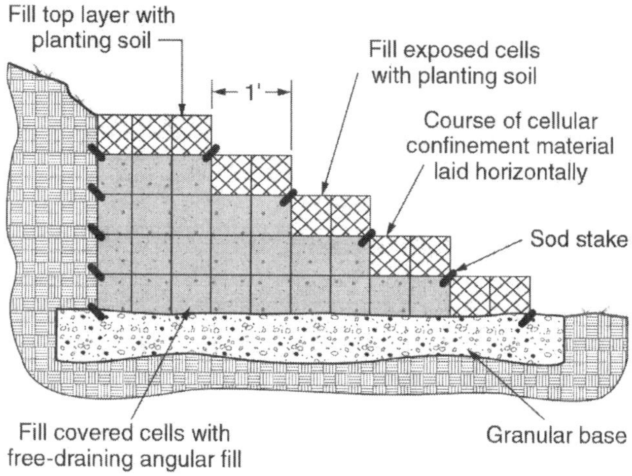

Figure 18-23 Cellular confinement wall installation.

Loose Stone Wall Installation

Using a simplified version of "piling up stone," you can use rounded and irregular shaped natural stone to create retaining walls of limited height. Unlike dry-laid stone with flat surfaces and more precise dimensions, irregularly shaped stone will require a shallower batter and a wider base to maintain stability while also retaining soil. For rounded and irregular stone, retaining wall heights should not exceed 3 feet, and stones should be a minimum dimension of 8 inches. The stability of these techniques relies on stone that is large and heavy enough to stay as placed, but they should not be used in critical situations or to protect valuable site elements. Occasional stones may break loose from the wall's surface and roll down the face into whatever improvements are placed below the wall. One significant benefit to this type of wall construction is that skill requirements are minimal. Because irregular stone cannot be fitted without a great deal of manipulation, contractors often use endloaders or skid-steers to place material.

To construct a retaining wall using irregular stone, excavate a base pad that is 1-foot deep and one and one-half times as wide as the wall's height. Place 6 inches of angular base rock into the base pad and compact using a vibratory plate compactor. Using a wheelbarrow, skidsteer, or endloader, place an initial layer of stone on top of the base pad. Spread the stone until it covers the entire base pad. The bottom layer should be partially buried along the front of the wall. Add a second layer of stone over the base layer, placing or dropping the stone near the center of the first layer. Let the stone settle to its natural angle of repose. Add additional loads of material to the top of the wall until the settled height is the desired height of the wall (Figure 18-24).

If the desired height cannot be attained without stone spreading beyond the base pad, widen the base pad. The wall's depth can be shortened if the contractor takes the additional time to hand stack the stone, rather than freely piling the stone and letting it fall to its natural angle of repose. If hand stacked, the stone

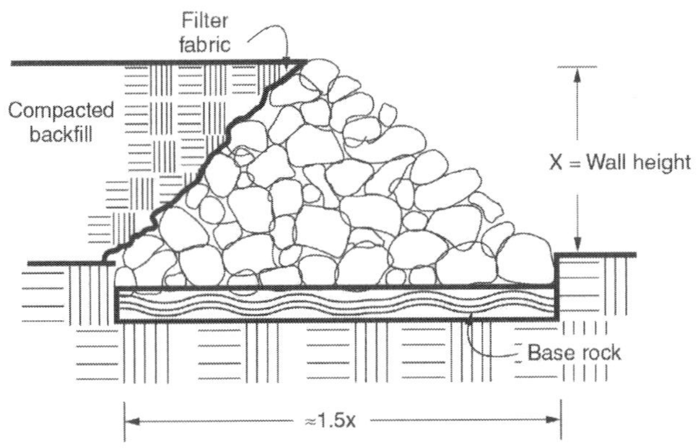

Figure 18-24 Cross section of loose fit retaining wall with irregular shaped natural stones.

should be fit together tightly. If the desired height is attained and the stone has not "spread" to the front of the base pad, remove excess stone for use elsewhere. Fill this void in the base pad with compacted soil. Although optional, drainage tile can be placed at the base of the wall on the uphill side at this time. Place a layer of filter fabric over the backside of the wall to reduce the migration of soil into the voids in the wall. Backfill the backside of the wall with soil and compact.

By hand or using small tools such as a brick set, check the stability of stone on the wall's surface. Remove any stones that are loose or could fall if disturbed by nearby soil vibrations. If aesthetics is not an issue, anchor a layer of hardware cloth at the bottom of the wall, place it over the face of the wall, and anchor it again at the top of the wall to reduce the hazard of loose material falling from the wall face.

CHAPTER 19

TIMBER RETAINING WALLS

OBJECTIVES

By reading and practicing the techniques described in this chapter, the reader should be able to successfully complete the following activities:

- Install a vertical timber retaining wall.
- Install a timber retaining wall.
- Anchor a timber retaining wall.

Retaining walls made of wood have long been a standard in home landscaping. Such walls are versatile in performing functional duties and in adding a natural look to the landscape. A former standard for wall construction, railroad ties are now difficult to locate and many people now consider them a poor environmental choice. However, newer timber materials have been introduced that produce similar aesthetic effects. A more recent addition to the "timber" family is recycled plastic formed to simulate the size and look of wood timbers. Whichever material the homeowner or contractor chooses, proper installation should produce a wall that will serve the dual purpose of retaining hillsides and adding a natural feel to the landscape.

CAUTION

Many timber and tie walls are lasting fewer years than originally anticipated. Use caution when handling and building with treated woods. Do not construct planters that are used to grow food for consumption with treated lumbers.

A variety of wall types are available for wood retaining walls, with the primary types being vertical placement, horizontally stacked timbers, or horizontally staggered timbers.

RELATED INFORMATION

Information in this chapter is supplemented by instruction provided elsewhere in this text and in other sources. Before undertaking the activities described in this chapter, read the related information in these sources:

- Related information can be found in applicable codes and ordinances.
- Related information can also be found in manufacturer's specifications.
- Safety in the Workplace, Chapter 7
- Basic Construction Techniques and Equipment Operation, Chapter 8
- Materials and Installation Techniques for Retaining Walls, Chapter 18
- Stairs, Chapter 23

PLANNING THE PROJECT

Additional preparations are required when using railroad ties as building material. Ties need to be separated according to thickness and trimmed to a consistent length. Matching the ties by thickness eases construction by allowing rows of a similar thickness. Layout of the wall location, including locating stairs, corners, and ending points, allows planning the project for minimal cutting.

VERTICAL POST OR TIMBER WALL CONSTRUCTION

For walls under 3 feet in height, timbers and even round posts can be placed vertically in a trench and reinforced to create a retaining wall (Figure 19-1). Contractors consider this method easier to construct than horizontally placed wall systems, but vertically placed timbers or posts lack stability over the long term.

Figure 19-1 Timber retaining wall with all timbers buried vertically. Elevation of tops are staggered for interest.

Preparing the Site

Initial layout and rough trench excavation are similar to the methods described in Chapter 18. Rather than excavating a trench for base material, dig a trench 12-inches wide with a depth equal to the wall's height along the entire length of the alignment. A maximum trench depth of 3 feet and maximum wall height 3 feet should be used for this installation technique.

Placement of 4 inches of granular fill in the bottom of the trench is optional.

Installing the Wall Material

Place the first segment of selected wall material into the trench. The wider trench should allow the vertical to be placed with a backward lean that will serve as the batter. Continue placing vertical segments, making sure each fits snugly against the previous segment. After installing several segments, verify that the batter is the same for all pieces; then partially backfill the trench in the front of the wall.

On the backside of the wall, anchor a treated 2 × 6 with galvanized lag screws to each vertical near the top of the timber. This 2 × 6 should be placed horizontally and connected to each of the vertical segments. When constructing curved walls, you can substitute a strip of rust-resistant metal for treated wood. Select a metal such as steel or aluminum edger and drill holes at each timber location. Connect with 4-inch lag screws as just described. As a vertical wall approaches an inside or outside corner, the batter will have to be reduced gradually until the corners are vertical. Corners may be secured using 16-inch galvanized angle brackets and lag screws on the backside of the wall (Figure 19-2).

Place drainage tile at grade level at the backside of the wall; then backfill the back and front sides of the wall. If the top of the wall is irregular, trim the tops of the wall material to the proper height. For decorative purposes, the tops can also be left with varied heights. For a more stable installation, consider backfilling the trench at the base of the timbers with concrete, rather

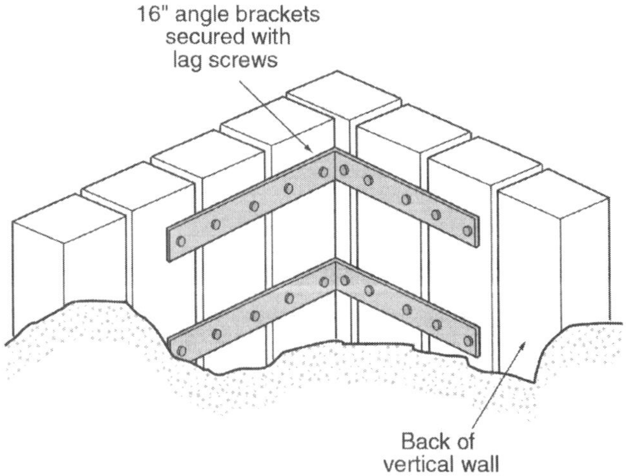

Figure 19-2 Corner connection on back of vertical timber wall.

than granular material or compacted soil. Anchoring a vertical wall is accomplished by the batter and burial of the base of the wall. Additional anchoring typically proves ineffective. **Interlocking stairs** cannot be constructed with vertical timber walls. If stairs are necessary, consult the **butt stair** installation instructions or consider pouring concrete stairs before the wall is built.

STACKED TIMBER WALL CONSTRUCTION

Stacked timber walls use the construction material placed in courses stacked directly on each other to form panels with a single vertical joint between each panel. Vertical timbers or buttresses are placed in front of this common joint, overlapping ties in each panel. Stacked walls are typically built using a tilted base course batter. This type of wall also requires trimming timbers to a consistent length.

Placing and Leveling the First Course

Installation of timbers begins with site preparation as described in Chapter 18. The first course of timbers is placed on the compacted base material in the trench. Place a timber in the trench and, using a carpenter's level, check the timber for level end to end, and for a half bubble batter toward the back of the wall. If the batter or level is not correct, lift the timber and remove or add base material as necessary. Level ties and timbers by placing small piles of granular base near each end of the timber. Once grade is established, you can gently force granular base material under the timber using a shovel. Recheck the timber and repeat until correct in both directions. If the project requires exact elevations for the bottom and top of the wall, use a survey instrument to verify elevations at this point. If the elevation is incorrect, add or remove base to adjust to the correct elevation.

Continue placing timbers the length of the first course, making sure that each timber has the same level and batter as the previous one. All timbers in the first course should be similarly placed. If you encounter a corner, trim a timber to the correct length (Figure 19-3). If an opening is placed in the wall for stairs or for other reasons, level across the opening to ensure that the wall is level on both sides of the opening. Place drainage tile behind the wall at this point and, if the tile does not outlet at the ends of the wall, leave an opening at the low point for the tile to pass through the wall (Figure 16-9). When the base course is completely set, toe-nail the timbers together using timber spikes.

Figure 19-3 First course installation for stacked timber wall.

Placing, Connecting, and Backfilling Subsequent Courses

Subsequent courses are stacked on top of the first course and backfill is placed behind the course (Figure 19-4). In instances where the lower course of the wall steps up, complete the lower course to where the step occurs. Prepare the granular base for the upper course so that it is

Figure 19-4 Placement of subsequent courses for timber wall.

level with the top of the lower timber. Set a second course of timbers straddling this base and the lower course (Figure 19-5). Timbers are anchored to the course below by drilling three, ⅜-inch pilot holes through the top timber and driving a 12-inch spike or 12-inch piece of #3 **rebar** through each hole. The three pilot holes should be located 12 inches in from each end and in the center of the timber. All holes should be centered between the front and back of the timber. Use a heavy-duty drill with a long bit to auger the holes and a sledge to drive the nails. Compact the backfill every course after you connect the courses.

When turning corners, trim the end of each tie to match the batter of the adjacent wall section. Corners of stacked walls require butting one panel against the adjacent panel. Wall panels butted together require vertical timbers on each side of the corner for stability (Figure 19-6).

Placing Vertical Timbers

Following completion of the second or third course, auger 1-foot diameter holes in the ground in front of the wall centered on the joints between timbers. The recommended depth for the holes is

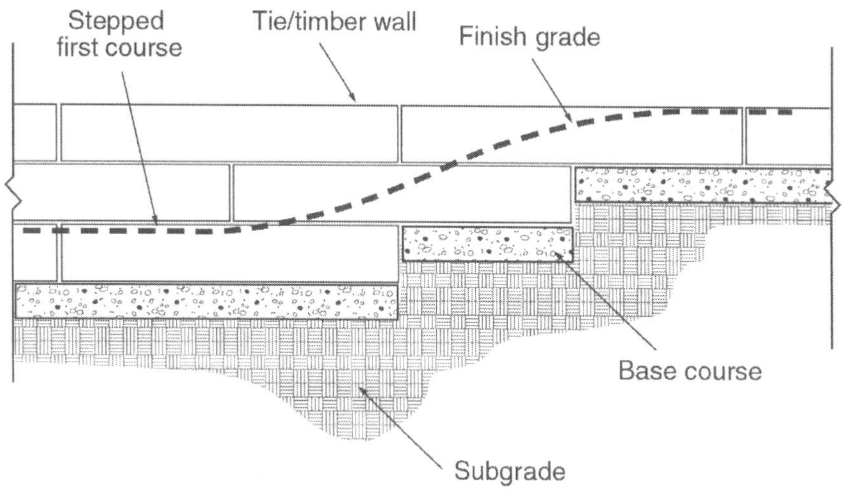

Figure 19-5 Stepping wall first course up a hill.

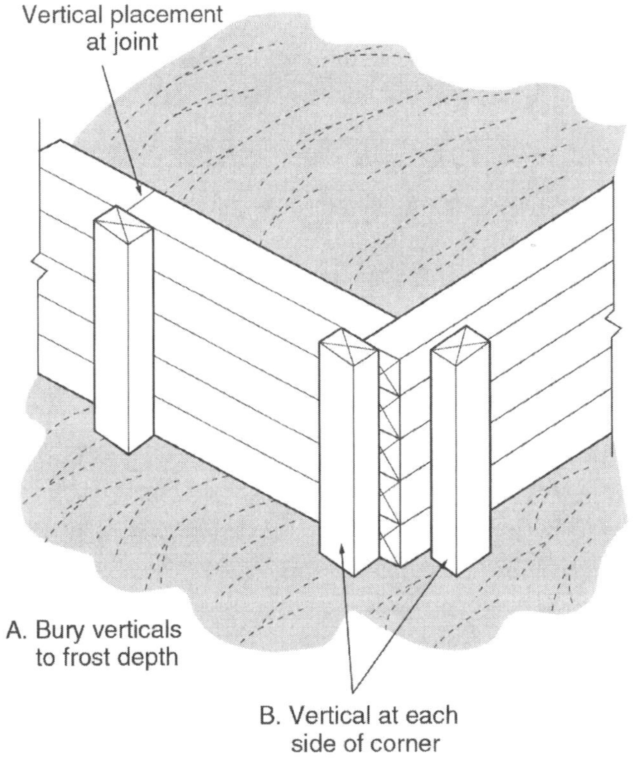

Figure 19-6 Vertical supports for stacked timber wall. A. Vertical support placement for stacked timber wall. B. Placement of vertical timber to reinforce corners.

frost depth, but they should be at least two-thirds the wall's height. (Note that this will limit the wall's height to the length of the timber minus the amount buried.) Use caution not to disturb the courses when auguring the holes. When you have placed all courses of timbers, set the vertical ties in the holes and lean them back against the wall overlapping the joint. Backfill and tamp around the vertical. For a decorative effect, you may trim the tops of the verticals at an angle.

STAGGERED TIMBER WALL CONSTRUCTION

Staggered timber walls differ from stacked walls in that the courses are staggered so that the vertical joints do not line up (Figure 19-7). Whereas stacked walls rely on batter and vertical members for anchoring, staggered walls can be built with a step-back batter and deadmen for

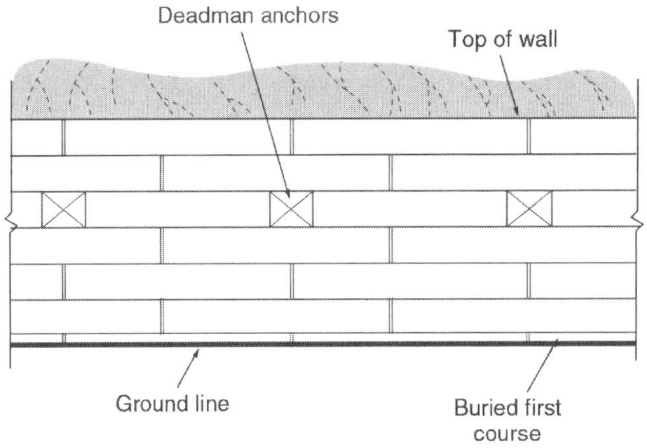

Figure 19-7 Staggered wall pattern for timber walls.

anchoring. The step-back approach allows the corners of this wall system to be easily overlapped.

Placing and Leveling the First Course

Installation of timbers begins with preparation of the base trench as described in Chapter 18. Place the first course of timbers on the compacted base material placed in the trench. Place a timber at one end of the trench and, using a carpenter's level, check it for level end to end and front to back. If the level is not correct, lift the timber and remove or add base material as necessary. If the project requires exact elevations for the bottom and top of the wall, use a survey instrument to verify elevations at this point. If the elevation is incorrect, add or remove base to adjust to the correct elevation. Recheck the timber and repeat until correct in both directions. Continue placing timbers the length of the base course, making sure that the next timber is flush with the previous one and has the same level. If you encounter a corner, trim the timber to the correct length. Place drainage tile behind the wall at this point; and if the tile does not outlet at the ends of the wall, leave an opening at the low point for the tile to pass through the wall (Figure 16-9). When the base course is completely set, toe-nail the timbers together using timber spikes.

Placing, Connecting, and Backfilling Subsequent Courses

Subsequent courses are placed on top of the first course by centering the top tie over the joint between the two timbers below. Backfill is placed behind the course and compacted after each course. In instances where the wall steps up, complete the lower course of wall to the point where the step occurs. Prepare the granular base for the upper course so that it is level with the top of the lower timber. Set a second course of timbers straddling the base and the lower course. Do not interrupt the staggered pattern when the wall steps up. If necessary, trim a timber to maintain a consistent pattern.

Timbers are anchored to the course below by drilling four, ⅜-inch pilot holes through the top timber and driving a 12-inch spike or 12-inch piece of #3 rebar through each hole (Figures 19–8 and 19–9). The pilot holes should be located 12 inches from each end and 36 inches from each end (Figure 19-10). All holes should be centered between the front and back of the timber. Use a heavy-duty drill with a long bit to auger the holes and a sledge to drive the nails. Compact the backfill every course after you connect the courses.

When you encounter a corner in a staggered wall, overlap each new course over the previous course (Figure 19-11). Drill a pilot hole in the center of the overlap area and drive a 12-inch nail or rebar through the pilot hole.

Figure 19-8 Drilling holes in timber with a cordless drill for 3/8'' × 10'' spikes.

© Delmar/Cengage Learning.

Installing Deadmen

Deadmen should be installed every fourth course of a timber wall. Measuring from the end of the wall, install the deadmen every 8 feet

Figure 19-9 Driving spikes in timber with a 2-lb. sledge.

© Delmar/Cengage Learning.

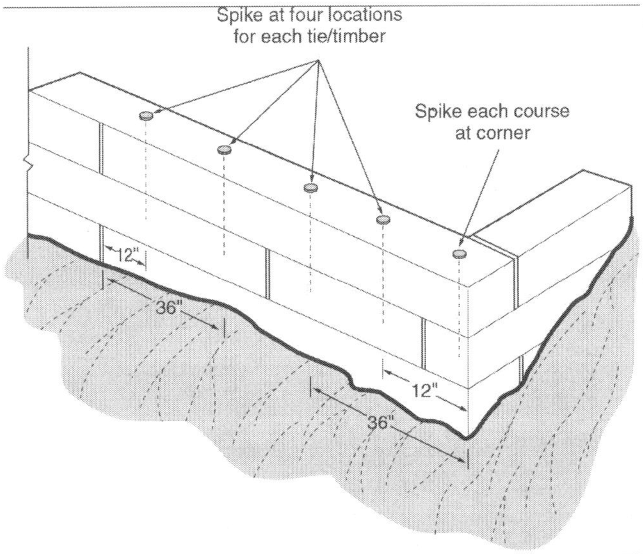

Figure 19-10 Spiking pattern for staggered timber walls.

(Figure 19-12). To install a deadman, cut an opening in the appropriate course of the wall equal to the width of the deadman. In this opening, set the end of a timber running perpendicular to the face of the wall. The length of the dead- man should extend back into the hill between 4 feet and 8 feet. If you encounter an obstacle behind the wall, you will need to trim the deadman. Excavating a trench for placing the dead- man is also sometimes necessary. At the hill end of the deadman, place a 3-foot timber cross-piece parallel to the face of the wall and under the deadman. Connect the deadman to both the wall and crosspiece by drilling a ⅜-inch pilot hole and driving a 12-inch nail through the pilot hole into the timber below. When you place the subsequent course over the deadman, fasten that timber to the deadman using a 12-inch spike through a pilot hole.

Instead of using timber deadmen, you can use the drilled cable deadman system noted in Chapter 18. This system requires less work than that required for the wood deadmen, but it leaves a visible metal plate or connector on the wall face. Anchoring a vertical wall is best accomplished using a drilled deadman placed every 6 feet horizontally. Deadmen should be placed two-thirds up the wall's height. Threaded bars or flanged wall anchors make acceptable deadmen. Drill a 1-inch diameter hole through the wall and slide a bar or cable through the hole. Anchor the bar or cable in the hillside and to the wall with 12-inch diameter plates threaded into both ends of the bar. Manufactured flanges can be used to anchor the bar into the hill.

Figure 19-11 Interlocked square corners with a stacked timber wall.

Because it is difficult to anchor to wood materials, geogrid has limited uses in timber wall applications. Some attempts have been made to drive nails through the bonded strands to anchor the geogrid or to place the grid forward far enough so it will catch on the spikes holding the timbers. However, effective results with geogrid depend on the application.

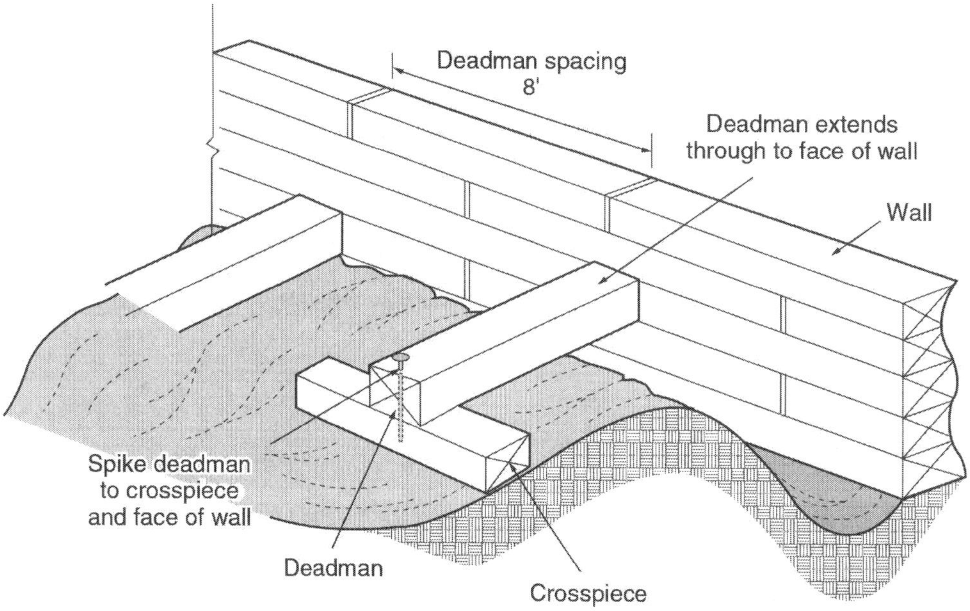

Figure 19-12 Rear view of deadman location and installation for timber walls.

RECYCLED PLASTIC AND COMPOSITE LANDSCAPE TIMBERS

Recycled plastic landscape timbers and composite timbers can be used as a nonstructural alternative to wood timbers for retaining walls and planters. Most plastic timbers are made of 100% recycled plastic and typically come in 8-foot by 5½-inch or 6-inch square dimensions. Because no preservatives are used in their manufacture and because they do not decompose, the timbers provide a long-term alternative to treated wood products. Most plastic timbers are treated for UV resistance to deter decomposition as a result of sunlight. Several product forms are on the market, but those considered typical replacement for wood are limited in color choices to earth tones and black, with additional cost for custom colors. Among recycled timber manufacturers, you will find those that add interlocking edges, predrilled holes for rebar fasteners, fitted and stackable ends, and a variety of surface textures intended to mimic wood or stone. Certain products can also be painted.

Construction techniques to install recycled plastic timbers, including base preparation, anchoring, and placement, should be the same as with wood timbers. Timbers can be cut using circular, reciprocating, or cutoff saws. Drilling should be done using a heavy-duty drill with an auger drill bit. Because this product is made of recycled content, safety equipment should be worn when working with the materials. Limited data are available regarding the strength properties of recycled plastic timbers. However, for nonstructural applications and low walls, the product seems to have performed well.

CONSTRUCTION OF STAIRS WITH TIMBER WALLS

Selection of a stair construction method is based on the type of wall constructed. Stacked and vertical wall construction methods require solid cheek walls, which will not accommodate the overlap of wall material necessary for interlocking stairs. Hence, only the butt stair method may be used for those wall types. Staggered timber walls can accommodate either interlocking stairs or butt stairs. See Chapter 23 for directions on installing butt and interlocking stairs.

CHAPTER 20

SEGMENTAL PRECAST UNIT RETAINING WALLS

OBJECTIVES

By reading and practicing the techniques described in this chapter, the reader should be able to successfully complete the following activities:

- Build a segmental precast unit retaining wall.
- Anchor a segmental precast unit retaining wall.

Use of segmental precast unit walls has increased dramatically in the landscape construction industry. Experimentation with concrete wall blocks has grown into an industry standard for construction of attractive, stable wall systems. Precast concrete units are one of the few wall materials that can be engineered for placement in vertical installations. In addition to the product's stability, its variety of surfaces and colors has enhanced the aesthetic qualities of the wall material. This chapter presents the installation of segmental wall units that use pins, lips, and anchors as stabilizing and battering systems.

RELATED INFORMATION

Information in this chapter is supplemented by instruction provided elsewhere in this text and in other sources. Before undertaking the activities described in this chapter, read the related information in these sources:

- Related information can be found in applicable codes and ordinances.
- Related information can also be found in manufacturer's specifications.
- National Concrete Masonry Association's "Design Manual for Segmental Walls"
- Safety in the Workplace, Chapter 7
- Basic Construction Techniques and Small Equipment Operation, Chapter 8
- Materials and Installation Techniques for Retaining Walls, Chapter 18
- Stairs, Chapter 23

PINNED AND LIPPED SEGMENTAL WALL CONSTRUCTION

Pinned wall units rely on metal or fiberglass pins to tie one course of segmental units to the next. Pins provide a strong connection between courses that will not slip or be dislodged by pressures behind the wall. Pins also provide a strong connection between the wall and geogrid anchoring. Lipped wall units rely on a thickened segment on the bottom or top of the block to position the subsequent courses behind units on lower courses. Although lipped units are faster to place, they do not provide as strong a connection between courses. Both solid- and hollow-core lipped units also provide a weaker connection to geogrid anchoring (Figure 20-1).

Most manufacturers recommend a level placement of segmental wall units because a setback batter is designed into the systems. In many pinned wall systems, the pins provide a means of automatically determining the setback from one course to the next. In most lipped units, the lip creates an automatic setback from the lower course. A few manufacturers may recommend that the blocks be tilted backward to create a batter for the wall. Review the literature provided by a wall material supplier to determine what method is recommended for installation.

Placing and Leveling the First Course

Chapter 18 provides important information about the preparation of the base for unit placement. As with all walls, first course installation should

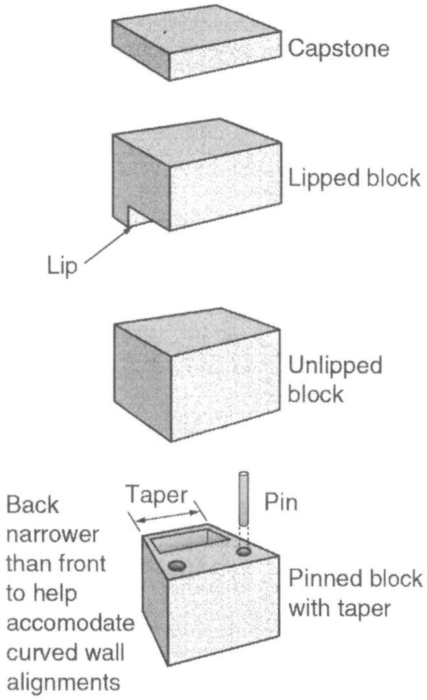

Figure 20-1 Common segmental unit types.

begin at the wall's lowest point. To minimize cutting, measure the distance between the beginning point and corners or ending points to allow for slight adjustment of the unit placement. Once you have compacted and leveled the base, set the first block. Verify which side of the block is the top side. For pinned units, the top side should have openings for placing pins, and the bottom should have openings to receive pins. For units with the lip on the bottom units, the bottom has a thickened ridge of concrete. Using a hammer, break off this lip for all blocks used on the base course. For some block types, instead of knocking off the lip, you can turn the bottom course upside down and backward for the base only. This will place the lip up and at the front of the base course. For units with the lip on the top of the block (typically on top in the front), the unit's bottom is smooth and requires no special preparation before installation.

One of the more difficult tasks in constructing walls is the setting and leveling of base stones. To speed the leveling process, place a ½–1-inch layer of fine granular material (select stone that passes a ⅜-inch sieve) over the compacted

Figure 20-2 Leveling and placing first units for precast concrete wall.

granular base. This layer provides a more workable material when making fine leveling adjustments. Place the block and check for level front to back and side to side with a carpenter's level (Figure 20-2).

If the block is not level, make minor changes by tapping it lightly with a rubber mallet. You may also make adjustments to level by tipping the block and using your fingertips to scratch away base material, if the block is high, or sprinkling handfuls of base material under the block, if it is low. These methods allow minor height adjustments and create less disturbance than striking the block with a rubber mallet. You can also adjust units by twisting the block. Major adjustments require lifting the block and adding or removing base material as required.

Figure 20-3 Fiberglass pin placement in precast concrete wall.

After setting the first block, place the second block next to it and verify that the edges are in contact and the tops are flush. Check the second block for level in both directions and adjust as necessary. Use caution not to disturb adjacent blocks that you have already set, and verify that the edges of the blocks are still in contact with each other after adjustment. Repeat this process along the entire length of the wall first course, checking periodically using a level long enough to cover three blocks. It is imperative that the first course be flush and level because any irregularity will be compounded as you add later courses. Place any drain tile behind the first course, and cut or leave an opening for the tile through the wall if drain tile is not routed around the ends of the wall. Backfill and compact the void behind the wall with a free-draining angular material.

Figure 20-4 Unit placement for precast segmental pinned units.

If you are using a landscape fabric, install it at this time (see Chapter 18 for instructions.) Fill the openings of hollow-core blocks with the same material used for backfilling behind the wall. Place backfill and compact.

Placing, Connecting, and Backfilling Subsequent Courses

After backfilling and filling cores, sweep any base material and debris from the tops of the blocks. Prior to placing further courses for pinned units, insert pins in the openings on the top of the base course blocks. Review manufacturer's instructions to determine into which holes the pins should be placed. Some block styles have pinhole locations that will create vertical walls, and others that will create a setback batter (Figures 20-3 and 20-4). Set pins along the entire length of the wall. Lipped units do not require pinning. Place blocks for subsequent courses straddling the joint between the two lower blocks, with half on one block and half on the other.

For units with the lip on the back, set the upper unit on a unit below with the lip positioned

Figure 20-5 Placement for precast segmental unit with lip located at the back of the unit.

Figure 20-6 Placement for precast segmental unit with lip located at the front of the unit.

behind the lower unit. Slide the upper unit forward until its lip contacts the back of the lower unit (Figure 20-5). For units with the lip on the front, set the upper unit on a unit below behind the lip on the lower unit. Slide the upper unit forward until its lip contacts the back of the lower unit (Figure 20-6). Continue placing blocks until you have set the entire course (Figure 20-7). Backfill behind the wall and compact; then repeat for each course until you reach the top of the wall (Figure 20-8). If geogrid is required, place it between courses.

In locations where the base of the wall must step up, fill the void beyond the end of the last block with base material and compact. This base will continue under all blocks on the upper courses, similar to the base below the lower course. Level the base flush with the top of the

Figure 20-7 Back of a wall built with lipped units showing lips protruding behind wall.

Figure 20-8 Section of segmental precast concrete wall showing backfill and drain tile.

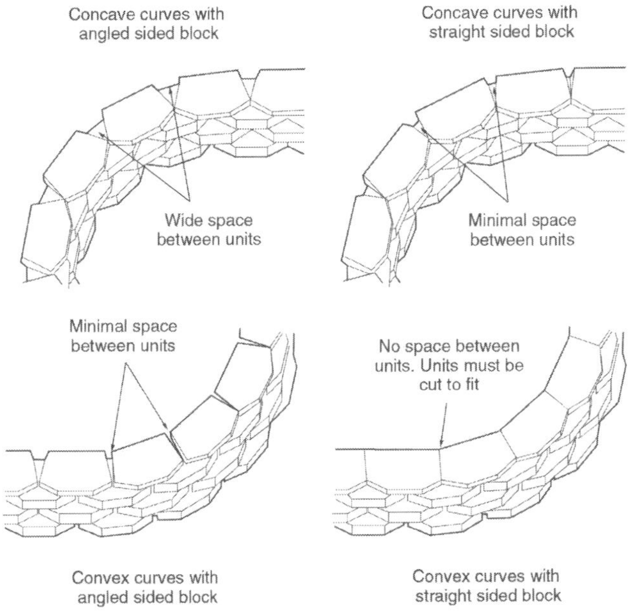

Figure 20-9 Rounded corner construction with segmental precast wall units.

lower course, and place a pin in the last block (for pinned units) on the lower course. Place a block straddling on the lower block (over the pin) and the base for the upper course. Check for level and adjust if necessary.

Different types of corners require different treatments. **Concave**, or inside, curved **corners** can typically be built by keeping the front edges of the blocks in contact and fanning out the back of the units. **Convex**, or outside, curved **corners** will also require that the block edges be in contact but may require trimming of back portions of units with a cutoff or wet masonry saw to fit the required curve (Figure 20-9). Units with the lip on the bottom side may require removal of a portion of the lip to accommodate atight radius. On long curvatures, you may need to cut a block to maintain the running bond pattern for a course (Figure 20-10). Most manufacturers have technical publications that indicate the minimum curve at which radii can be built without serious modification of blocks. Expect major cutting with radii smaller than 5 feet. Inside and outside angled corners can be difficult to construct with segmental wall units. To construct outside angled corners, begin by laying the base course so that two full units meet at the corner. If full units are not at the corner, trim an amount from units that are one or two units back from the corner so that full units are at the corner. From the two corner

Figure 20-10 Wall unit trimmed and placed on a curved section of wall to maintain running bond pattern.

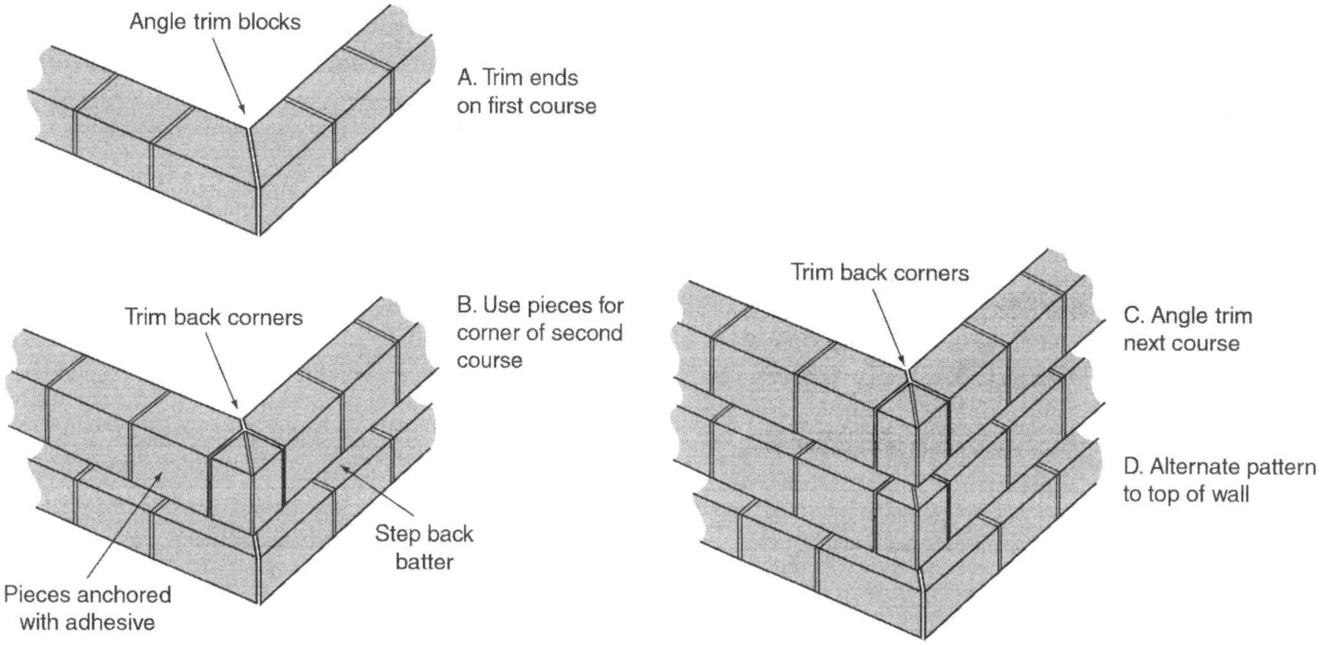

Figure 20-11 Outside angled corners with segmental units.

© Delmar/Cengage Learning.

units, trim half of the corner angle from each block (e.g., for a 90° corner, trim 45° from each block). Set the second course using the running bond pattern with the desired batter (Figure 20-11). From the two corner units on the second course, trim half the corner angle from each block. Because the batter makes these units smaller than those in lower courses, use concrete adhesive to assist in securing them to the lower course. Continue the placement and trimming until the corner blocks are smaller than half a unit. At that point, repeat the process of trimming an amount from units that are one or two units back so that full units are again at the corner. This process of trimming should continue until you reach the top of the wall. Trim the caps as required.

Inside angled corners are built by constructing base course on the left side (or whichever side you prefer) of the corner running past the right side. If necessary, trim the unit on the right side to fit flush with the left side. On the second course, reverse the order of which course runs past the other (Figure 20-12). If necessary, trim a unit so the courses fit flush (Figure 20-13). As you build the wall, continue the batter on each course. A support piece may be necessary if the passing course is not long enough to support the

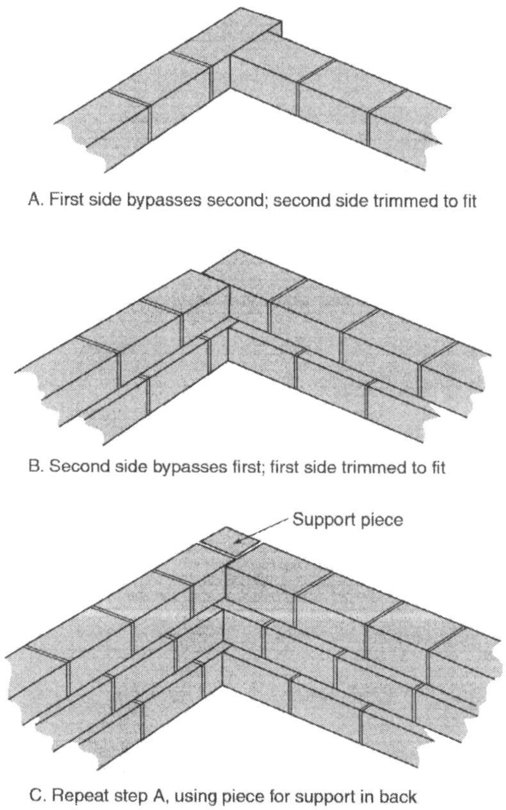

Figure 20-12 Inside angled corners with segmental units.

© Delmar/Cengage Learning.

Figure 20-13 Wall units trimmed to create an outside angled corner.

block placed in the next higher course. Trim the cap for the course that is passing to match the alignment of the back of the wall. Split solid units by hand, hydraulic block cutter, or cutoff saw with partial units placed in the wall. Hollow units can be split, but placement at a corner may expose the inside of the unit. Some manufacturers produce special corner units to address the exposure and trimming problems encountered at right-angle corners. If hollow cores must be exposed, mix mortar to match the wall color and fill the open cavity. Use concrete adhesive between courses at the corner, especially when partial units disrupt the normal placement of pins or interlocking lips.

Placing Geogrid

Manufacturers or design professionals must calculate if a wall requires anchoring with geogrid fabric. These specifications should indicate the course in which the geogrid should be placed, as well as the width of the fabric behind the wall. If the wall is tall enough to require geogrid, you will need to place it between the appropriate courses before you can build the wall any higher. Because geogrid comes in rolls, you can easily cut it to the width required by using a knife or fine-toothed saw. The required orientation must be maintained for various types of geogrid to obtain the designed strength. The direction of the geogrid's bonded and loose strands determines its proper orientation. Bonded strands are load bearing and should be placed perpendicular to the wall face. Loose strands should run parallel to the wall face.

After compacting the backfill for the course below the geogrid, roll the geogrid out flat behind the wall along the entire length of the area to be reinforced. You may need to widen the backfill area to accommodate the geogrid's width. Slide the geogrid to the front of the wall units. Pull the material back slightly if any will be exposed when you add later courses. For pinned units, place the pins for the next course so that they pass through one of the grids (Figure 20-14).

Figure 20-14 Geogrid placement between courses of precast wall units. Geogrid is oriented with the wide separated strands paralleling the wall face.

Lipped units are set in place with the geogrid resting between courses. Unpinned walls rely on the weight of the wall material, plus friction between the geogrid and the aggregate fill in the unit cores, to hold the geogrid in place. Place the next course of blocks and then stretch the geogrid away from the wall to remove any slack. Backfill and compact over the geogrid.

Capping the Wall

Most segmental units require a cap to cover open voids and spaces between the block (Figure 20-15). All cap units should be installed with pins or adhesive. Clean the top of the wall and apply adhesive generously prior to placing the caps. Pinned units require short pins to secure the cap. Push down on the cap after placement to ensure good contact with the adhesive.

Figure 20-15 Cap installation for precast concrete unit walls.

Some systems provide caps with angled ends that can be alternated for straight wall sections or placed with all angles facing in or out to cap curved walls. If a cap must be trimmed to accommodate an angle or curve in the wall, trim half the material from each side of the cap, rather than trimming all of the material from one side. Although this will require two cuts, trimming both sides will blend the cut with the wall angle.

To avoid exposing open cavities at the top of a wall that steps down, either cut a cap to fit the step or replace the unit on which the voids are exposed with two cap units stacked vertically (Figure 20-16). Bond the cut cap or stacked caps with adhesive.

Adhering and Bonding Precast Concrete Wall Materials

When wall capstones or corner units require bonding to maintain stability, thoroughly clean all surfaces to be bonded. Generously apply a flexible adhesive and place the two pieces together. Scrape any excess adhesive from the joint. Because it maintains its flexibility, a one-part urethane sealer is better to use than subfloor or construction adhesives.

ANCHORED UNIT WALL CONSTRUCTION

In addition to pinned and lipped segmental wall systems, some manufacturers produce a wall unit that uses precast anchors connected to a face piece

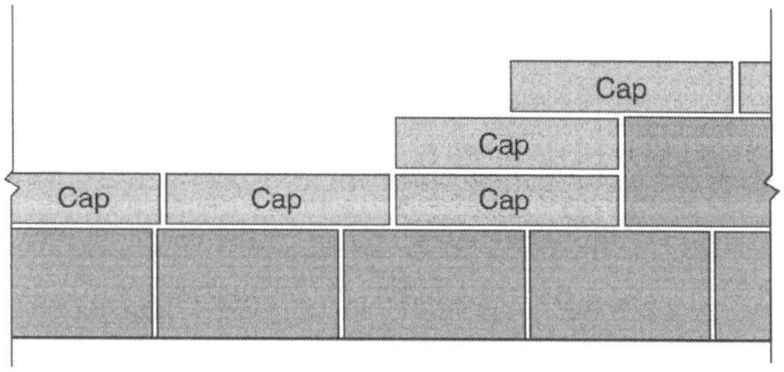

Figure 20-16 Using caps to transition a step in a wall. The caps hide any open cores or tapered backs.

and protruding back into the hillside. These anchors are covered with backfill and provide stability for the wall. Although anchored units are lighter in weight, they require more labor to assemble. The thin face piece provides a thinner profile for the wall, and the reduced anchors for the top course make planting behind the wall easier. Geogrid is installed in the same manner with anchored walls as it is for pinned wall systems.

Installation of anchor units is similar to pinned units in most aspects, except that each face piece has two rectangular precast anchors that are connected to the front with metal U pins. These anchors protrude from the back of the face piece and form a *V* shape. Pin the anchors together with a third U pin, and fill and compact the cavity. Anchors for subsequent courses rest on the anchors for previous courses (Figure 20-17). As the wall approaches the top courses, the number of anchors is reduced. The top and second-from-the-top course have only one anchor per face piece. Pin a cap to the top course to provide a finished appearance.

Figure 20-17 Anchored precast units showing anchors in place. Openings on tops of anchors are for U-shaped pins that hold anchors and face blocks together.

STRUCTURAL CELL WALLS

Placement of structural cell wall units is similar to placement of precast segmental units. A stable level base of base rock is prepared prior to installation, with the minimum dimensions established by the product manufacturer. Typically an 8-inch deep by 2-foot wide trench will be required. Place 4 inches of angular base rock in the trench and compact using a vibratory plate compactor. The wall's base course will be buried a minimum of 4 inches to improve wall stability. Any unit on the base course will require cutting the hooks off the lower back of the wall using a circular saw or reciprocating saw.

Begin placing the base course of units at the wall's lowest point. Place the first unit and level it front to back and side to side. Place the second unit and slide it against the first unit until the tabs on the side lock together. Level the second unit and continue this process for the entire base course. Place a drainage tile behind the wall and route the tile to a low point for discharge. Openings in the units for drainage or pipe outlets can be cut with a reciprocating saw. Fill the cells and an 8-inch zone behind the wall with free-draining angular stone and compact using a vibratory plate compactor. Units are designed for straight wall runs and for corners not exceeding the manufacturer's design criteria.

Subsequent courses are staggered in a running bond pattern on top of the lower courses, with each subsequent course interlocked into the course below. To place the upper courses, hold the units at an angle to lock the hooks in the back of the unit into the lower units; then lower the unit down and slide to the side to lock with an adjacent unit (Figure 20-18). After placing each course, fill and compact the cells and drainage

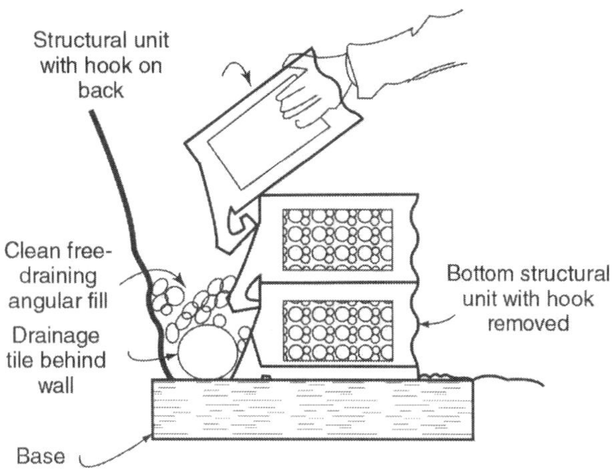

Figure 20-18 Installation of structural cell wall units.

zone behind the wall, and backfill the wall with soil and compact. If the wall exceeds 3 feet in height, you will need to place geogrid reinforcement between courses. Adjust the geogrid to one side to avoid interfering with the locking mechanism at the rear of the unit.

When corners or wall abutments are required, cut the cellular unit to fit and fill with expanded polystyrene foam for structural strength. Premanufactured end units are available that can be locked in place by setting the panel in position and striking it with a rubber mallet. To complete the structural cell wall, install capstones that are available from the manufacturer. Apply construction adhesive to the top of the unit below the capstone, set the capstone in place, and slide it forward to lock in position. Secure the rear of the unit using screws that anchor the capstone to the unit below.

STAIR CONSTRUCTION WITH SEGMENTAL WALLS

Stair construction with segmental units is accomplished in a variety of ways. Most manufacturers have engineered a solution to the stair issue by designing special stair units, producing a combination of base unit and cap units, or using standard wall units for stair construction. Most stair solutions use the butt method of placing stairs between cheek walls, but some stairs interlock with cheek walls. Stair solutions with precast units typically work best when the stair width is a multiple of the units used to construct the stairs. This requires careful spacing between cheek walls to ensure that an even number of units will fit. See Chapter 21 for directions on installing butt and interlocking stairs.

CHAPTER 21

DRY-LAID STONE RETAINING WALLS

OBJECTIVES

By reading and practicing the techniques described in this chapter, the reader should be able to successfully complete the following activities:

- Build a dry-laid stone retaining wall.
- Build a dry-laid recycled concrete retaining wall.

Successful installation of a dry-laid stone wall is as much a skilled craft as it is a construction technique. In laying the varied types of stone available to them, landscape contractors must acquire patience and vision to arrange stone in structurally sound and attractive patterns. **Ashlar** refers to stone that has been cut, or cleaved, in modular lengths and widths with consistent thicknesses to aid in placement. An alternative to ashlar is **rubble,** a stone that has natural, untrimmed edges. Techniques for laying stone are discussed in this chapter, and Chapter 30 covers the construction of freestanding walls.

RELATED INFORMATION

Information in this chapter is supplemented by instruction provided elsewhere in this text and in other sources. Before undertaking the activities described in this chapter, read the related information in these sources:

- Related information can be found in applicable codes and ordinances.
- Safety in the Workplace, Chapter 7
- Small Equipment Operation, Chapter 8
- Materials and Installation Techniques for Retaining Walls, Chapter 18
- Stairs, Chapter 23

PLANNING THE PROJECT

Stability of dry-laid stone walls is a primary concern. Most stone used today is quarried and cut into widths of 4–8 inches. This narrow width limits the weight and surface area between courses, and these two factors help in countering forces that can push the wall forward. As a result, dry-laid stone walls sometimes need both leaning batter and setback batter to provide stability. Placement of geogrid is also difficult, and using verticals in front is both unattractive and impractical. Stone deadmen can be placed, but they are of limited value because they cannot be attached to the wall or to a crosspiece in the hillside. All these factors combine to limit the effective structural height of dry-laid stone walls without a design professional's engineering expertise.

Sorting stone prior to placement speeds the process and enhances the stability of the construction. Laying several pieces out so that length can be quickly observed allows for a fast sort and selection of stone. Preparation of the site and laying of the first course is similar to that of other wall materials, but the courses above the first one require a different approach. Following are suggestions that add to the quality of a dry-laid stone wall:

- Limit wall heights to 3 feet.
- Use larger and longer stones for the base course and stairs for increased stability.
- Avoid vertical joints that run more than two courses. One of the strengths of dry-laid stone comes from the overlapping of joints (Figure 21-1).
- Maintain spacing between vertical joints that is at least as wide as the thickness of the stone.

Figure 21-1 Staggering of vertical joints in stone walls improves stability.

- Interlock all corners when possible.
- Avoid using short or small picccs of stonc near corners. Larger pieces space the joints farther apart and improve stability.
- Cut or match stone pieces a consistent thickness to eliminate one variable that makes laying a stone wall such a challenge. This practice allows the worker to concentrate on length and joint placement, not with matching both the thickness and length dimensions of the stones.

DRY-LAID STONE WALL CONSTRUCTION

The following paragraphs provide instructions on the best practices when laying a dry-laid stone wall.

Wall stability with dry-laid stone walls

Dry-laid stone is, by nature, a less stable material than other wall materials when stacked. The irregularity of the surfaces and the inconsistency in sizes make stone a greater challenge to place and stabilize than other wall materials. Stability can be enhanced by using wider stone (front to back dimension), increasing batter and limiting the height of the wall. Another method to improve stability is to add a thin layer of mortar to the back half of the stone to fill the irregular voids between

Figure 21-2 Dry-laid stone wall first course installations.

stones and increase surface contact. To maintain the dry-laid appearance, make the layer of mortar only thick enough to correct surface irregularities. If mortar is visible in joints from the front, raking the front of the joint will remove excess. This technique can be enhanced by applying mortar to the back of the wall to join courses. Capstones should be fully mortared if stability is in question. If mortar is used to stabilize a dry laid wall, allowance for water drainage through the wall via weepholes, pipes or open voids will be necessary. The need for a tile behind the wall will be even more important.

Placing and Leveling the First Course

Prepare for installation using the instructions from Chapter 18. As with all walls, laying of the first course should begin at the wall's lowest point. Setting a stringline aids in keeping the front of the wall aligned (Figure 21-2). Once you have compacted and leveled the base, you can then set the first stone. Place the stone and check with a carpenter's level for level side to side and a slight batter toward the back of the wall. A quarter bubble is often used as a standard batter. An alternative to placing a leaning batter on a stone wall is to use a step-back batter similar to that used in precast units (Figure 21-3). Although stone is not a manufactured product with built-in safeguards, a step-back batter for walls under 2 feet tall should provide enough stability to reduce the potential for failure. You can also combine both batters for increased wall stability.

If stones are not setting correctly, make minor changes by tapping with a rubber mallet. A twisting motion will also adjust the level of stones. Major adjustments require lifting the stone and adding or removing base material as required. After setting the first stone, place the second block next to it and verify that the edges are in contact and the tops are flush. Check the second block for level and batter and adjust as necessary. Repeat this process along the entire length of the wall base. It is imperative that the base course stones be flush and consistently placed because any irregularity will be visible as later courses are added. Place drain tile behind the base course, and leave an opening for the tile through the wall if you do not route the drain tile around the ends of the wall. Backfill the void behind the wall with a free-draining angular material and compact.

Figure 21-3 Dry-laid stone wall showing setback batter of 1 inch with each higher course.

Placing, Connecting, and Backfilling Subsequent Courses

Stones for subsequent courses should be placed so that the joints are staggered. Set one course at a time (Figure 21-4). Place backfill and compact. Repeat for each course until you reach the top of the wall. If you use a setback batter, move the front of each subsequent course back 1 inch from the course below.

Figure 21-4 Placement of dry-laid stone wall material.

In locations where the base of the wall must step up, fill the void beyond the end of the last block with base material and compact. This base must extend under all blocks on upper courses in the same manner as the base below the lower course. Level the base material flush with the top of the lower course. Place a block straddling the lower block and the base for the upper course. Check for level and batter and adjust if necessary. Continue placing stones for the base along the wall alignment.

Square corners should be interlocked between courses (Figure 21-5). If you use leaning batter to lay the wall, butt, rather than overlap, square corners. Concave and convex corners are typically built using shorter stones and stones that have angled ends that can be turned over to create a tight-fitting radius (Figure 21-6). For concave corners, place the shorter face of the stone toward the front of the wall. For convex corners, place the longer face of the stone toward the front of the wall. Trim stone as necessary to maintain tight joints. Maintain batter around corners. Geogrid is of limited effectiveness on dry-laid stones walls. If you use wider or larger stones, you may place the geogrid between courses and anchor it into the hillside. However, if walls are laid with narrower or smaller stone, the surface area between courses is insufficient to securely anchor the grid.

Figure 21-5 Dry-laid stone wall showing interlocking courses at corner.

The artistry of building a stone wall often comes from the pattern in which the stone is placed. It is possible to create dry-laid walls where each course is of a consistent thickness if stone of similar dimensions is available. Although this creates a stable wall, the visual interest may be lacking. To create a more aesthetically pleasing pattern with the surface of the wall, consider some of the following techniques for variation (Figure 21-7).

- Vary the thickness of the courses. Sort stone by thickness so you can insert a course that is thinner than the typical course being installed (A).
- Substitute two stones of a smaller thickness but similar length for a typical stone in the course (B).
- Occasionally insert a stone that may bridge two vertical courses (C).
- Occasionally place a collection of smaller stones in place of a typical stone on a course. The smaller stones should fill the space and may require a stone in the course above that bridges over all of the smaller stones (D).
- Insert occasional shims below the stone to raise it to a typical course height (E).
- Forego courses altogether. If your material allows you to structurally build walls without identifiable courses, begin with a bottom row of larger material; then work left to right building the wall to full height.

Figure 21-6 Rounded corners with dry-laid limestone walls. Shorter pieces are used to turn tighter corners. Stairs were in place before wall was built.

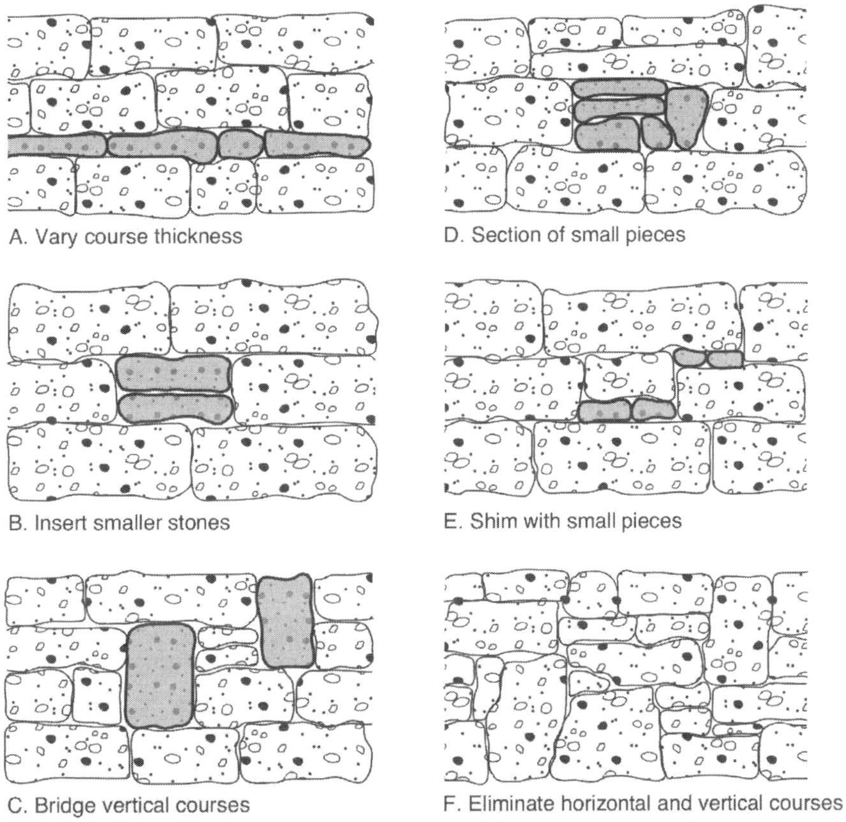

Figure 21-7 Stone pattern variations.

Utilize the full list of techniques described above. This will take longer and require you to verify the structural stability of each stone placed. The rules about avoiding long vertical and horizontal joints should be followed, with very few identifiable joints being visible when the wall is complete (F).

It is the artistic blend of solid forms and line, along with the added dimension of varying colors, that makes the difference between a wall that simply retains soil and a wall that is a work of art. Attractive walls are built with a balance of large massive stones and smaller filler stones, all surrounded by a range of more consistent sized stones, that creates the framework. Attaining mastery of stone masonry as an art form requires both an understanding of form composition and extensive practice.

Anchoring Using a Top Course

To cap a dry-laid stone wall, an anchoring course may be installed. At the top of the wall, lay a course of block with the long dimension perpendicular to the wall face. Align an end of the stone with the front of the wall and extend the long dimension beyond the back of the wall.

The capstone should be mortared in place with a heavy course of mortar in areas where it is expected that people will walk or sit on the top of the wall.

STAIR CONSTRUCTION WITH DRY-LAID STONE WALLS

Stair construction with stone is accomplished by using precut stair pieces or by selecting wider stones that can be used for treads. Both butt stairs and interlocking stairs are suitable for stone. See Chapter 23 for directions on installing butt and interlocking stairs.

CHAPTER 22

GABION RETAINING WALLS

OBJECTIVE

By reading and practicing the techniques described in this chapter, the reader should be able to successfully complete the following activity:

- Install gabions.

Gabions are an effective material for landscape walls when stability is paramount. Usually confined to large road and grading projects, the gabion is also ideal for addressing large-scale wall projects. With their wide base and heavy weight, gabions are quite stable and can be stacked three or four units high. The open nature of the material also makes hydrostatic pressure less of a problem when a wall is laid with gabions.

RELATED INFORMATION

Information in this chapter is supplemented by instruction provided elsewhere in this text and in other sources. Before undertaking the activities described in this chapter, read the related information in these sources:

- Always construct walls according to applicable codes and guidelines.
- Always follow manufacturer's specifications.
- Safety in the Workplace, Chapter 7
- Materials and Installation Techniques for Retaining Walls, Chapter 18

PLANNING THE PROJECT

Preparation for gabion construction requires that the alignment be staked and the rough grading be prepared in the same manner as described in Chapter 18. Grade preparation for gabions can be a shallow trench slightly wider than the gabion cage. Gabions are buried only 6–12 inches, rather than the depth of an entire first course.

Although they require less craftsmanship than other types of retaining walls, gabion walls do require special equipment to aid in wall construction. Caution should be used when working with gabions because of their significant weight. Although they are typically stable, gabions can slide or shift, resulting in serious injury to a worker.

GABION WALL CONSTRUCTION

The following paragraphs give instruction on the best practices when laying a gabion retaining wall.

Placing and Leveling the First Course

Leveling should be accomplished by adjusting the grade below the cages before they are placed. Mark the alignment of the first course, and place gabion cages along the alignment. Gabions should be installed with the long dimension parallel to the wall face. Note the top of the gabion and orient so that the opening edge faces the side from which material will be installed (Figure 22-1).

Carefully fill each of the cages with a consistent selection of stone that has a diameter larger than the cage openings. Stone selection should be based on availability and aesthetics. Either angular or washed river stone is acceptable. Filling operations for the first course should not dislocate the cages from their alignment. When you have filled the cages, close the tops and wire them shut (Figure 22-2). At this time, place any drainage behind the cages and fill and compact the void behind the wall with free-draining angular material.

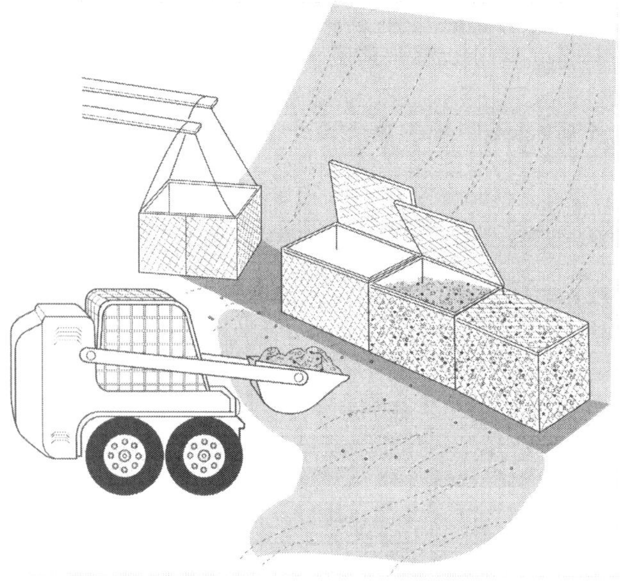

Figure 22-1 Cage placement and filling for gabions.

Placing, Connecting, and Backfilling Subsequent Courses

After placing and compacting the backfill for the first course, place the cages for the second course. Place subsequent courses straddling the joint between the two gabions below. You may use a slight setback batter of 4–12 inches for each

Figure 22-2 Gabion cages are filled with stone larger than the diameter of the cage openings. Cages are wired shut using 12-gauge galvanized wire.

Figure 22-3 Stacking gabion cages.

course (Figure 22-3). Fill the cages, close, and wire them shut with 12-gauge wire. Backfill behind the wall and compact; then repeat for each course until the you reach the top of the wall. Turn gradual corners by fanning the gabions along the proposed alignment, and overlap right-angle corners on subsequent courses.

In locations where the base of the wall must step up, fill the void beyond the end of the last gabion in the lower course with base material and compact. Level the base with the top of the lower course, and place a gabion cage straddling the lower gabion and the base for the upper course. Fill the cage and continue placing cages along the wall alignment.

STAIR CONSTRUCTION WITH GABION WALLS

Stairs used with gabion walls need to be constructed separately out of an alternative material. Although cast-in-place concrete makes a durable step, any wall material described in this section makes a suitable step for gabion applications. See Chapter 25 for forming and pouring concrete stairs and Chapter 23 for butt stair installation.

CHAPTER 23

STAIRS

OBJECTIVES

By reading and practicing the techniques described in this chapter, the reader should be able to successfully complete the following activities:

- Identify appropriate stair style for a project.
- Install stairs that abut a retaining wall.
- Install stairs that interlock with a retaining wall.
- Install freestanding stairs.

When walls are used to create levels on a sloping site, stairs are often required to traverse the different levels. Stairs are addressed as part of this section because of their relationship to walls and because many stair projects are incorporated into wall projects. Planning information presented in this chapter applies not only to stairs as part of a wall project, but also to cast-in-place concrete stairs and wood stairs built as part of a landscape structure. Specific construction techniques for cast-in-place concrete stairs are presented in Chapters 25.

The landscape also presents situations where a slope needs to be navigated with stairs even though no wall is planned. Such instances require the construction of freestanding stairs. Because the side slopes are so gradual, freestanding stairs are constructed without the benefit of retaining or cheek walls. Stairs in this situation are typically constructed with riser/tread dimensions that match the slope, rather than matching the ideal mathematical relationships for steps. This chapter also outlines the methods of planning and installing various types of materials used for freestanding stairs.

RELATED INFORMATION

Information in this chapter is supplemented by instruction provided elsewhere in this text and in other sources. Before undertaking the activities described in this chapter, read the related information in these sources:

- Always construct stairs according to applicable codes and guidelines.
- Always follow manufacturer's specifications.
- Construction Math, Chapter 5
- Safety in the Workplace, Chapter 7
- Basic Construction Techniques and Small Equipment Operation, Chapter 8

PLANNING THE PROJECT

The range of construction difficulty for stairs can be quite wide, depending on the materials used and slope on which the stairs are being constructed. Prior to beginning the project, develop a plan for materials desired and the number of risers and treads needed.

Building Codes Governing Stairs

Before beginning your project, check with local building officials to verify regulations for stairs as part of a landscape. Many communities have regulations on stair **tread** and **riser** dimensions, railing requirements, stair widths, and other stair-related attributes. Access up/down grades may also have to be accompanied by a ramp as well as stairs. Check with building officials for rules or requirements that might supersede techniques described here.

If stairs are accessible to the public, ADA (Americans with Disabilities Act) requirements will play a role in the design and construction of the project. To meet these requirements, exterior stairs must be stable, slip resistant, and noncombustible. In addition, no open risers are allowed, protection for snow and ice will be necessary, and any set of stairs with more than two treads will require handrails flanking the stairs. Other specific requirements for ADA are listed in Chapter 25 under "ADA Stair and Ramp Requirements." To meet the many requirements of ADA, exterior stairs are often constructed of cast-in-place concrete to overcome the limitations of natural materials. If the stairs are accessible to the public and if a licensed professional did not design them, seek advice to assure compliance.

Figure 23-1 Stairs built as part of a wood timber retaining wall installation.

Types of Stairs

Stairs can be constructed as part of wall systems (Figure 23-1) or be independent of walls, such as freestanding stairs traveling up a gradual slope (Figure 23-2). In certain cases, stairs may be replaced by gradual sloping ramps. The type of construction selected depends on the steepness of the slope, the distance covered, and the mobility of the user. Whenever possible, select a ramped walkway over stairs because of the ease of construction and the diverse age and physical condition of the people who will use the ramps. Building codes and access regulations may also require installation of ramps rather than stairs. When grades begin to exceed 4% longitudinal (over 4 feet of fall in 100 feet end to end), stairs should be considered as part of the project. If the slope to be traversed does not require a wall, incorporate freestanding steps to assist the client over the slope.

Figure 23-2 Freestanding stairs in a gradual slope.

Cheek Walls

Stairs constructed as part of a wall require that **cheek walls** be built on either side of the area where stairs are desired. Cheek walls are short walls that run into the hillside the stairs traverse. Perpendicular to the retaining wall, cheek walls should be the same height as the retaining wall and should extend into the hillside at least as far as the stairs will extend. Timing of cheek wall construction depends on whether stairs will be interlocked with the cheek wall or built independently and butt into cheek walls.

Material Selection for Stairs Built as Part of a Wall

A preferred choice for stair materials is the same materials used for wall construction. This provides continuity in design and dimension from the wall into the stairs. In some cases, the same material may not be possible or desirable. One popular choice for stairs is cast-in-place concrete. This material, when properly formed, can be set at any riser and tread dimension and can be poured to fit snugly with any cheek walls. Forming for stairs is covered in Chapter 25. Freestanding steps can be constructed of any wall material just identified, as well as from cast-in-place or precast concrete.

Material Selection for Freestanding Stairs

Freestanding stairs can be built of almost any material. To organize the presentation of choices and installation, materials are grouped into four categories as follows:

- Concrete Stairs. Concrete can be formed with any riser height and tread depth and can be built without the benefit of retaining walls alongside (Figure 23-3). See Chapter 25 for forming and paring concrete stairs.
- Timber Framing with Treads of Concrete, Brick, or Loose Material. Stairs along a hillside can be framed on the front and two sides with ties, timbers, or heavy-dimensioned lumber with the tread portion surfaced with a variety of materials. The front portion for each higher step rests on the sides of the lower step. For informal stairs, a tie or timber can be placed across the front of each step with the tread behind left untreated or covered with loose fill (Figure 23-4).
- Stacked Slab Materials. For informal stairs, large slab-like materials can be placed level in the ground and serve as both a riser and a tread. Each subsequent step rests on the back edge of the lower step. Materials that might be used for this type of step include precast concrete, large flat stones, tree sections, or other materials with thickness and large dimensions (Figure 23-5).

Figure 23-3 Freestanding concrete steps formed and poured as part of this entry construction.

Figure 23-4 Freestanding stairs using timbers to create risers with a loose granular material for the treads.

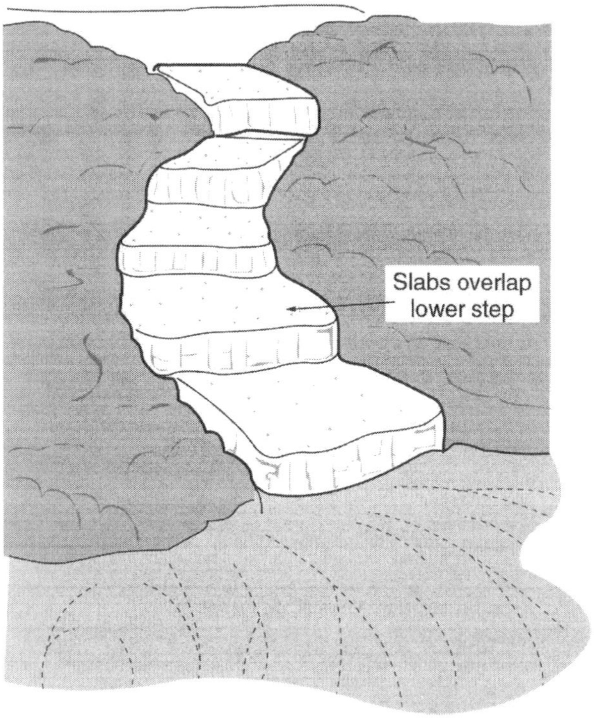

Figure 23-5 Freestanding stairs constructed from slab materials.

- Stone or Segmental Precast Concrete Wall Units. Both of these wall materials can be interlocked or butted against cheek walls to create stairs. In some precast units, the caps are necessary to cover hollow voids in the blocks.

Riser/Tread Calculations for Freestanding Stairs

Unlike those constructed as part of a deck or wall, freestanding stairs are adjusted to match the slope that is being covered. It will be a fortunate coincidence if the slope where the freestanding stairs are to be constructed matches the mathematical formula for riser/tread dimensions. Landings or cheek walls will usually have to be added to accommodate the mismatch length of the slope. To determine the number of risers and treads in a set of freestanding stairs, use the following abbreviated formula:

- Measure the length and height of the slope.
- Convert the measurements to inches.
- Divide the height (in inches) by the thickness (in inches) of the material selected for stairs. The answer will indicate how many risers are needed.
- Divide the length of the slope (in inches) by the number of risers. The answer will indicate the depth of each tread. If the tread depth is less than 12 inches, the tread depth will not accommodate a normal step pattern, creating potential safety concerns. Consider routing the stairs diagonally across the slope or extending the stairs beyond the top or bottom of the slope to provide more length for calculating tread depth.

When constructing the stairs, use the tread depth measurement to determine the placement of the front of each subsequent stair.

Building Freestanding Stairs on Irregular Slopes

When placing freestanding stairs on irregular slopes, adjusting the tread depth may be required to avoid significant excavation. If the slope is steep, shorten the tread depth to no less than 12 inches. The length cut from these treads can then be added to treads on the flatter portion of a slope. It is best to group at least three steps with short treads together. Avoid alternating a short tread depth with a long tread depth if possible. If the adjustment of treads is not acceptable, cutting and filling to create a more even slope is an alternative.

Interlocking Stair Installation

Interlocking stairs should be constructed as the wall is being erected, with the first course of the stairs installed with the first course of the wall and continuing for each subsequent course. The following steps outline how to install interlocking stairs for timbers (Figure 23-6), segmental units

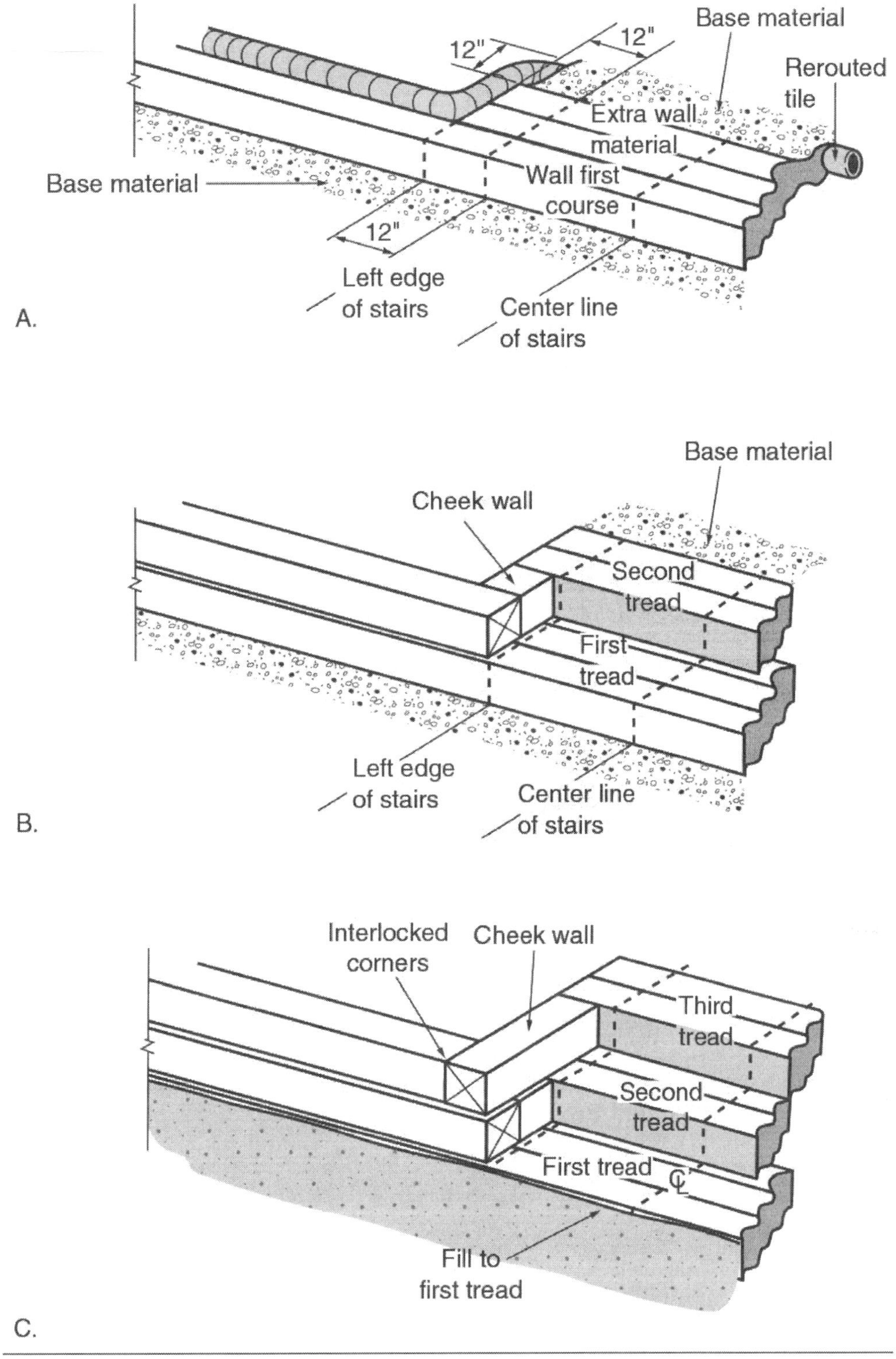

Figure 23-6 Interlocking stair construction for timber walls. A. Base trench and first course for interlock stairs. B. Second course for interlock stairs. C. Subsequent courses for interlock stairs. (Note: First course will be completely or partially buried.)

(Figure 23-7), and dry-laid stone (Figure 23-8). These instructions are prepared for stair treads that are approximately 12 inches in depth. For deeper stair treads, additional stair materials are required. If special precast or one-piece stone treads are available, use those materials for stair construction.

1. Widen the granular base trench at the stair location 24 inches in back of the entire width of the stair opening. This trench should be the same elevation as the base trench for the wall. Because the first course of the wall will be buried for stability purposes, this level will serve only as a landing and not as a riser (Figures 23-6A, 23-7A, 23-8A).
2. Route any tile around the back of the widened trench.
3. Fill this widened trench with base material and compact.
4. Place the first course of the wall up to the opening for the stairs, keeping the wall front aligned. Place the first tread behind the first wall course. This tread may be composed of multiple ties, wall units, or stones, or may be a single-piece tread. The tread should be approximately 24 inches wider than the stair opening (12 inches on each side), providing enough extra material to allow the tread to extend behind the wall on both sides of the stair opening (Figures 23-6B, 23-7B, 23-8B).
5. Construct the second course for the wall and stop short of the stair opening on each side of the stair.
6. Excavate a base trench behind the first tread for the second tread. This trench should be 18 inches wide by the length of the tread and 6 inches deep. Fill the trench with base material and compact. If a tile is present, fill over the tile without disturbing its level. Smooth the base material so that it is flush with the top of the previous tread.
7. Place the second tread across the opening for the stairs. The second tread should be 24 inches wider than the stair opening. The second tread should also overlap the back of the first tread enough to create the desired tread dimension for the first step. If using timber treads, pin the second tread to the first (Figures 23-6C, 23-7C, 23-8C).
8. Build the cheek wall between the front wall and the tread. Trim wall material as required to fit between the front wall and tread. If building the wall with wood or stone, remember that the cheek wall must interlock with the wall face at the corner and that alternate courses of the cheek wall will run to the face of the wall.
9. Backfill and compact behind the wall and tread.
10. Repeat steps 5 through 9 for each subsequent course of the wall until stairs are complete (Figure 23-9).
11. If tread coverings are used, place them for all treads.

BUTT STAIR INSTALLATION

Although easier to construct, butt stairs have less stability than interlocking stairs. Because butt stairs are not interlocked into the cheek wall, they may move up or down at a different rate than the walls next to them, causing unevenness or irregularity. Construct butt stairs using the following steps for timbers

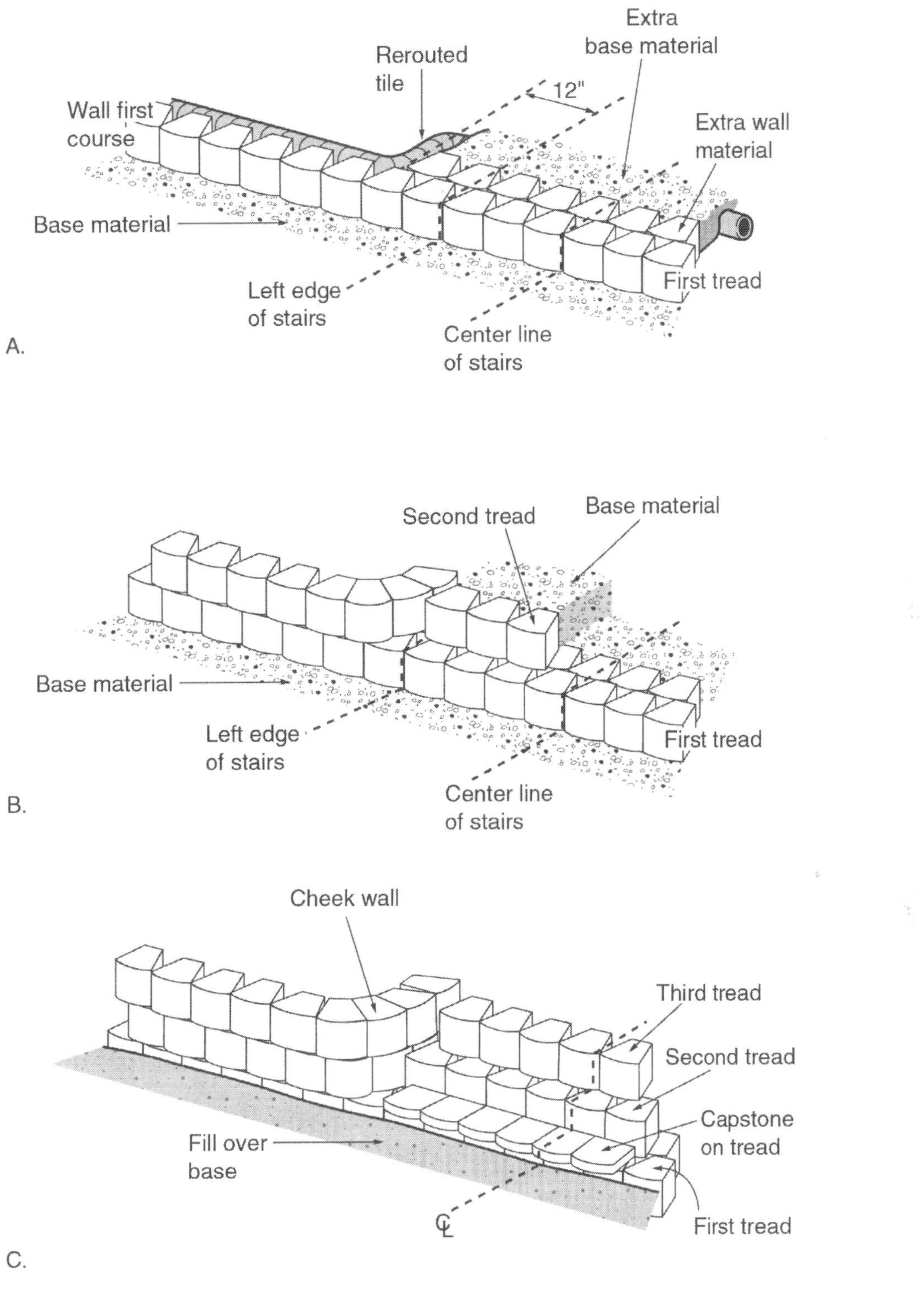

Figure 23-7 Interlocking stair construction with segmental precast units. A. Base trench and first course for interlock stairs. B. Second course for interlock stairs. C. Subsequent courses for interlock stairs. (Note: First course will be completely or partially buried.)

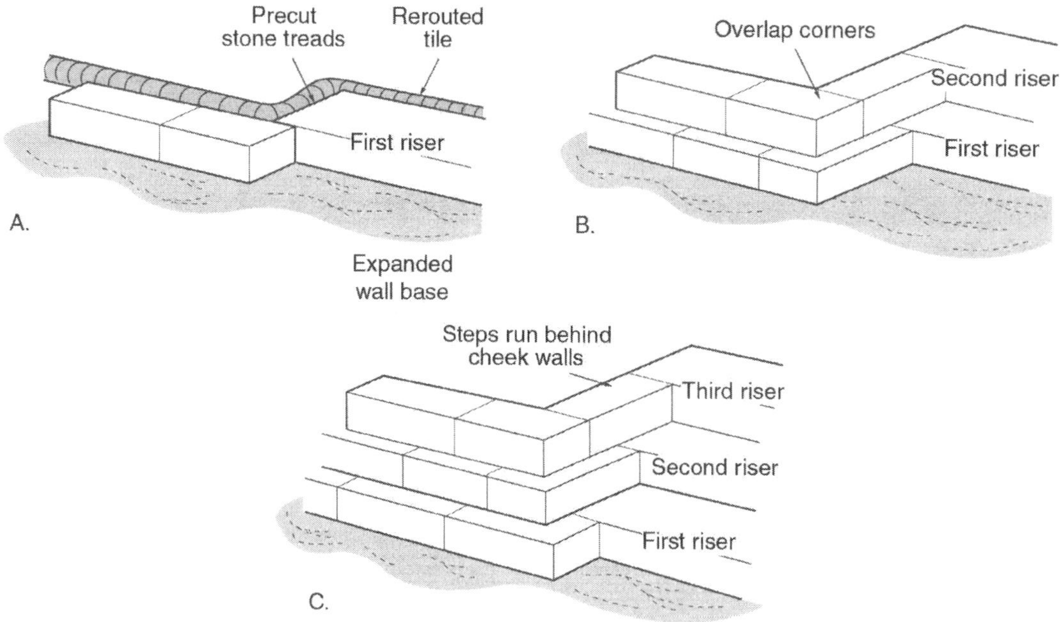

Figure 23-8 Interlocking stair construction with stone. A. Base trench and first course for interlock stairs. B. Second course for interlock stairs. C. Subsequent courses for interlock stairs. (Note: First course will be completely or partially buried.)

Figure 23-9 Completed interlocking stairs with precast units.

(Figure 23-10), segmental units (Figure 23-11), and dry-laid stone (Figure 23-12). The instructions are prepared for stair treads that are approximately 12 inches in depth. For deeper stair treads, additional stair materials are required. Precast or one-piece stone treads will simplify tread installation.

1. With butt stair construction, walls and cheek walls can be built prior to the stair installation or concurrently as the walls are assembled. If installing the walls first, leave an opening for stairs when constructing the wall and verify that the walls on each side of the opening are level and aligned. Adjusting the width of the opening to match tread material dimensions is also desirable, although use of a step-back batter on cheek walls requires cutting tread materials to fit.
2. Widen the granular base trench at the stair location 24 inches in back of the entire width of the stair opening. This trench should be at the same elevation as the base trench for the wall. Because the first course of the wall will be buried for

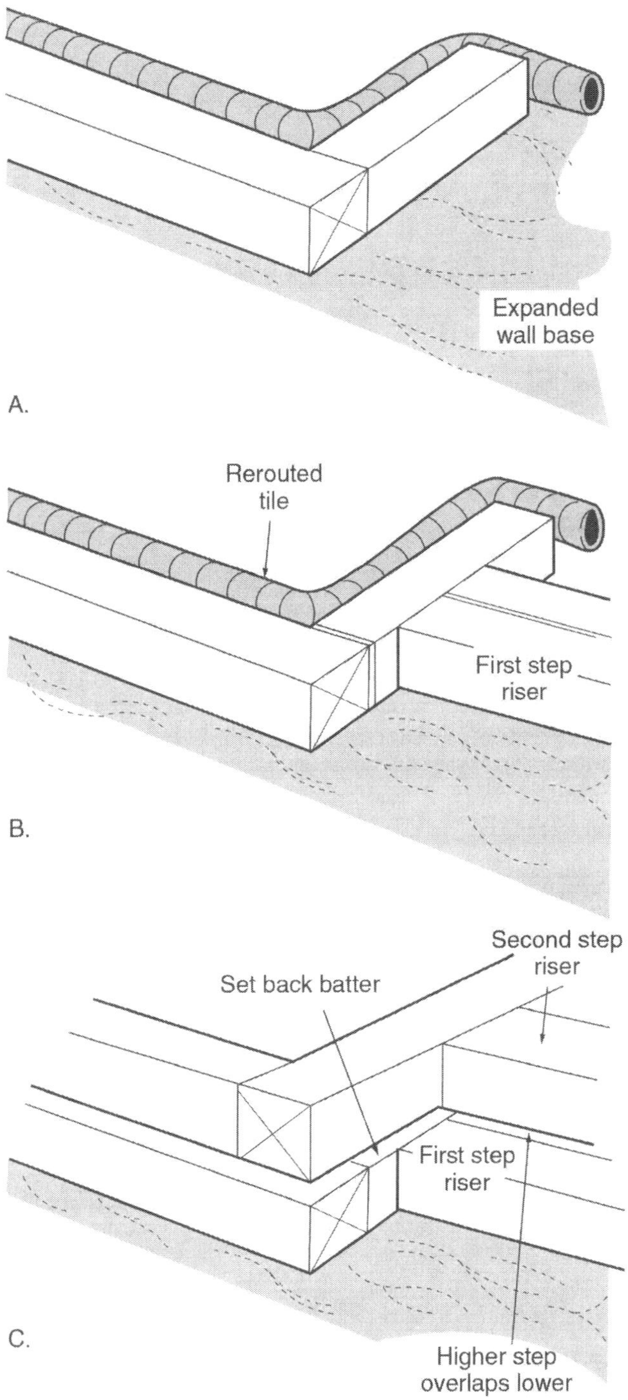

Figure 23-10 Butt stair construction for timber walls. A. First course of wall and cheek wall for butt stairs. B. First step riser for butt stairs. C. Second course for butt stairs. (Note: First course will be completely or partially buried.)

stability purposes, this level will serve only as a landing and not as a riser (Figures 23-10A, 23-11A, 23-12A).

3. Route any tile around the back of the trench where the treads will be placed.
4. Fill this widened trench with base materials and compact.
5. Place tread materials between the cheek walls flush with the first wall course. Level treads side to side and front to back. A slight (¼ inch or less) fall toward the front is desirable if it does not disrupt the riser installation. Cut and fit partial tread materials along the sides if required (Figures 23-10B, 23-11B, 23-12B).
6. If building the walls and stairs concurrently, continue construction of the second course of the wall and cheek wall before installing the second tread. With wood and stone wall materials, the wall and cheek wall must interlock at the corners. Excavate a base trench behind the first tread. This trench should be 18 inches wide by the length of the tread and 6 inches deep. Fill the trench with base material and compact. If a tile is present, fill over the tile without disturbing its level. Smooth the base material so that it is flush with the top of the previous tread.
7. Place tread materials for the second tread across the opening for the stairs. The second tread should overlap the back of the first tread enough to create the desired tread dimension on the first step. If a wall cap is used for the tread, the overlap should equal the wall unit width minus the cap width (Figures 23-10C, 23-11C, 23-12C).
8. Backfill and compact behind the tread.
9. Repeat steps 6 and 8 for each subsequent course until the wall has been completed (Figure 23-13).
10. If cap stones or tread coverings are used, place them.

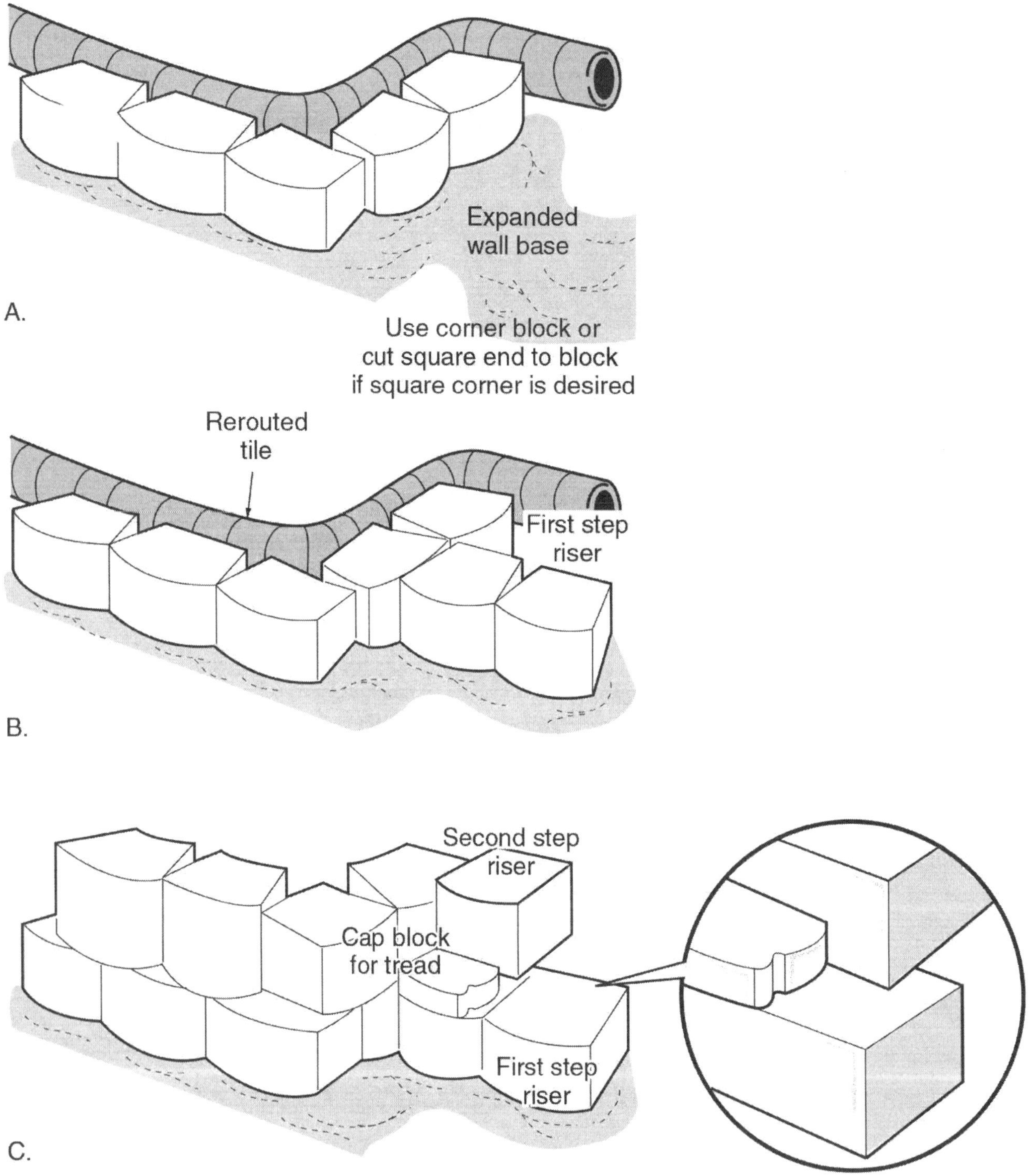

Figure 23-11 Butt stair construction with segmental precast units. A. First course of wall and a cheek wall for butt stairs. B. First step riser for butt stairs. C. Second course for butt stairs with optional tread surfacing. (Note: First course will be completely or partially buried.)

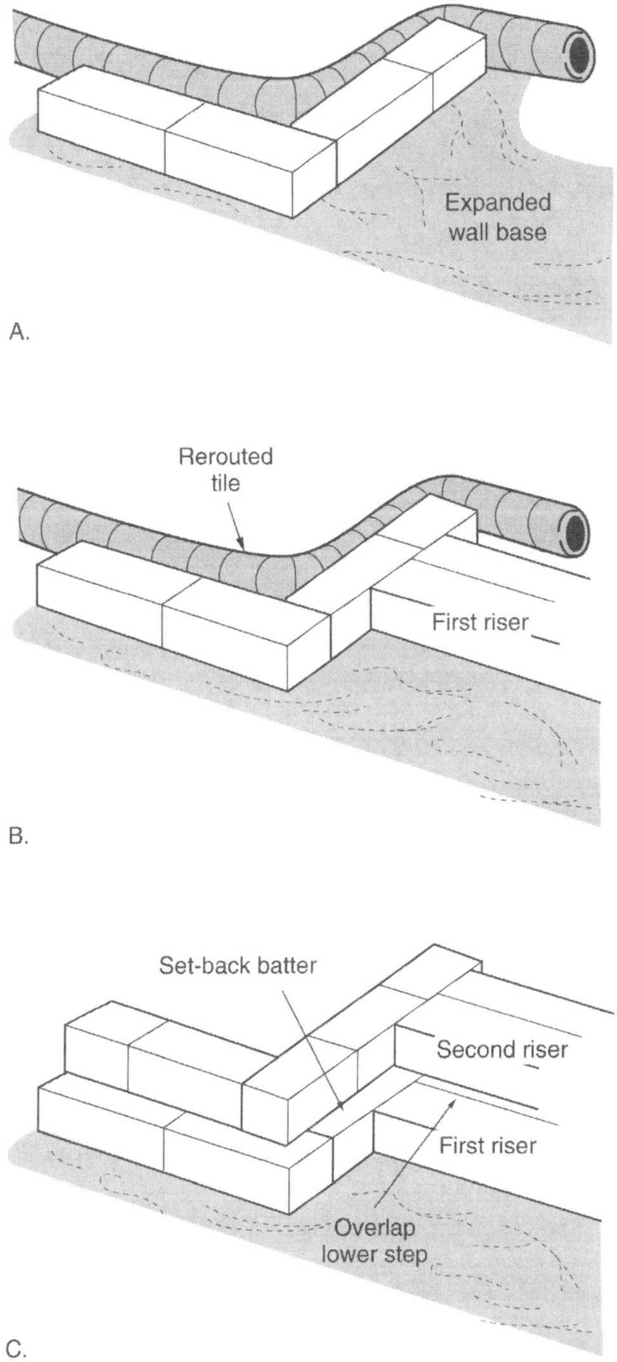

Figure 23-12 Butt stair construction with dry-laid stone. A. First course of wall and cheek wall for butt stairs. B. First step riser for butt stairs. C. Second course for butt stairs. (Note: First course will be completely or partially buried.)

© Courtesy of Paul Dykstra, Lowa City Landscaping.

Figure 23-13 Completed butt stairs with precut stone steps.

© Delmar/Cengage Learning.

FREESTANDING STAIR CONSTRUCTION

Site preparation is similar for all of the following types of stairs if placed on an even slope.

Site Preparation

Mark the location for the stairs along the slope. Cut and remove any vegetative cover and excess soil in the stair right-of-way. Add 4 inches of granular base. Except for concrete stairs, begin placement of stair material with the base step.

Concrete Stair Installation

Concrete stairs can be formed and poured similar to stairs that are built as part of a wall. After excavating the area for the stairs, fill with 4 inches of granular base material. Construct the forms and pour the stairs according to the instructions given in Chapter 25, Concrete Paving, for independent forming of stairs.

Wood-Framed Stair Installation

Stairs that have a wood framework on the front and both sides should be installed beginning with the base step. Add a small amount of granular material in the area excavated for the first stair. Cut the front piece the width of the stair. Cut two side pieces, each 1 foot longer than the depth of the tread. Place the front and two side pieces on the base material (Figure 23-14). Connect the side pieces to the front using galvanized lag

Figure 23-14 Building the base step of a freestanding wood timber installation.

screws or spikes. Level all three pieces by adjusting the base material. Fill the voids along the outside edge of the stairs with soil. Fill the tread area between the three pieces with material selected for the tread.

Cut the next set of step boards. Place the front board on the two side pieces for the step below. Position the front board so the distance to the front of the first riser creates the desired tread depth. Anchor the front board for the upper step to the side pieces for the lower step by drilling a ⅜-inch diameter pilot hole through the front board. Drive 12-inch spikes through the pilot holes into the side pieces. Connect the side board to the front pieces and repeat the filling procedure. Repeat these steps until the top of the stairs has been reached (Figure 23-15). The top stair may require an additional board opposite the front board to hold the tread surfacing material in place.

Wood Riser Stair Installation

Install a small amount of granular base material in the area excavated for the first stair. Cut the

Figure 23-15 Subsequent steps of this freestanding wood timber stair installation rest on the sides of the lower stair. Treads will be filled with granular material.

first riser piece the width of the stair. Place the riser piece on the base material and level. Fill the void behind the riser with the material selected for the tread. Fill the area along the sides of the tread with soil. Cut a second riser piece. Place the second riser piece on the tread material for the lower stair at the correct distance from the front of the first riser to create the desired tread depth. Repeat the filling operation and continue with the remaining steps.

Stacked Slab Material Installation

Place a small amount of granular base material in the area excavated for the first slab. Place the first slab on the base and level. Fill around the edges of the slab. Place the second slab with an overlap on the first slab that provides the correct tread depth. Fill around the edges of the second slab. Continue this process with the remaining slabs.

SECTION 5

SUMMARY

Construction of retaining walls is one of the major jobs of most landscape contracting businesses. Section 5 discussed the preparation for wall projects and installation of nonstructural walls, timber, segmental precast and structural cell walls, dry-laid stone, and gabion retaining walls. Also covered were the installation of stairs as part of a wall project and construction of freestanding stairs built without being incorporated into stairs. Cast-in-place concrete walls and freestanding walls are covered in Section 8.

Preparation for a retaining wall project begins with the selection of the proper wall construction material. Many choices are available, with timbers, precast concrete units, and drylaid stone being the most popular choices. A seldom-used but appropriate wall material for short walls is the gabion. When choosing wall materials, consideration should be given to aesthetics, ease of installation, and cost. Retaining walls that are cast-in-place with concrete, with or without stone veneers, are also a popular choice for walls but require special expertise to construct. Several choices are available for short walls that are not retaining any heavy structural loads. Recycled concrete, cellular confinement material, and loosely stacked irregular stone can hold back limited amounts of soil and create needed space.

Construction of all wall types requires the preparation of a sound base. Long-term stability of any wall relies on installation of the first course on solid support and with the proper level. First courses for most wall installations are buried to provide extra stability, and proper drainage is provided behind the wall to reduce hydrostatic pressure. This buildup of water is drained away from the wall using a tile placed behind and at the base with a zone of freedraining fill directly behind the wall. Stability of the wall is also maintained by building the wall with a batter, by anchoring the wall, or by doing both. Batter is the backward lean of a wall to counter the effects of gravity and hydrostatic pressure. In dry-laid stone walls the stability can be improved by applying mortar to the back of the wall. Anchoring the wall can be accomplished using vertical buttresses, deadmen, or geogrid to secure the wall to the hillside behind. Taller wall installations can be accomplished by terracing (using a series of shorter walls).

Installation techniques vary, depending on the type of wall materials selected. Wood products such as ties and timbers can be placed vertically or horizontally in stacked or staggered patterns. Vertical timbers are anchored by placing them in a trench and backfilling.

Horizontal ties are placed level with a leaning batter or step-back batter. Stacked timbers are secured using verticals buried in front of the wall at the joints. Staggered timbers walls are secured between courses using nails or pins and anchored into the hillside using deadmen.

Segmental (precast concrete) wall units are placed individually and stacked in courses. Precast units can be placed in a straight line or turn radius or angled corners. Courses are aligned using blocks with lips, pins, or blocks with special precast and pinned anchors. Most precast unit walls are stabilized using geogrid placed between courses and buried horizontally in the hill behind the wall.

Dry-laid stone walls use natural materials cut to standard or random dimensions and stacked without mortar. Stone walls rely on a batter for stability and cannot be reliably anchored with other available technologies. Because of this, the height of stone walls is limited. Gabions are metal cages filled with large aggregate and stacked to create retaining walls. Although not common in residential landscape projects, gabions are a viable alternative to other wall materials in locations where aesthetics are not a prime concern.

When addressing slopes on a site, walls are usually considered; and as part of traversing those slopes, stairs are a landscape element commonly built into retaining walls. Stairs constructed as part of a wall project can be built with the tread interlocking into the cheek walls or butting against the cheek walls. Stair material would preferably be the same material as the wall, but stairs may also be formed and poured from concrete as independent units from the wall. Special calculations are required for stair construction to obtain the ideal dimensions for risers and treads and to determine the number of risers and treads the slope requires. Freestanding stairs can also be constructed without walls from a variety of materials.

SECTION 6

LANDSCAPE PAVING

INTRODUCTION

Most landscapes rely on paving to create usable outdoor areas. By providing hard surfacing, we can create drives, walkways, patios, entry areas, and a variety of functional spaces that property owners can use in all weather conditions. In many projects, the paved area is also a source of aesthetics, introducing color, texture, and materials that enhance the overall design of a project. A paving material will work if it performs the essential function of separating your feet from the mud, but the variety of excellent paving material choices provides aesthetics as well as functionality. More recent emphasis has been placed on paving materials that reduce resource consumption and help retain water on site. Once a novelty, the desire to reuse and recycle paving materials has added a new dimension to material choices.

The chapters of this section review material selection and installation techniques for common paving materials used in today's landscape. Emphasis is on selecting a material, preparing the site, and installing the pavement. Specific paving topics covered in this section include concrete paving installation, unit paver installation, dry-laid stone paving installation, recycled concrete paving, mortared stone paving installation, granular paving, and porous paving installation. Although asphalt paving is an important paving material for many landscapes, it is not presented in this text because asphalt paving requires special equipment and contractors with paving expertise to perform this portion of the work.

SUSTAINABILITY SUGGESTIONS

- Consider paving that provides drainage through the surface instead of paving materials that are impervious or direct water off the paving surface. Permeable concrete, asphalt, pavers, and granular materials will all increase percolation of water, rather than contributing to erosion and drainage problems by increasing runoff.

- When you have control over such choices, give careful consideration to the material choices used in your project. Choose local materials before selecting materials that will need to be transported great distances to your site; choose renewable materials, rather than products that cannot easily be recycled. Examine materials carefully to understand the full life cycle cost, including the cost of production, transportation, installation, use, and disposal.

- Carefully consider your equipment needs, rather than automatically choosing power equipment over hand labor. In certain cases, it may be more cost-effective and better for the environment to perform a task using hand tools instead of hauling large pieces of gas-powered equipment to the site to perform a task.

CHAPTER 24

MATERIALS AND SITE PREPARATION FOR PAVING

OBJECTIVES

By reading and practicing the techniques described in this chapter, the reader should be able to successfully complete the following activities:

- Choose a paving material appropriate for a project.
- Prepare a project for paving.
- Install edge restraint for a paving installation.

With only minor variations, project preparation is similar for all types of **paving.** Considerations such as selection of materials, access to the site, and layout of a project should precede the start of a project. A successful paving installation, whatever the surface material used, requires a well-prepared, stable **base.** Surfacing is no better than the base on which it rests; and if the base settles or heaves, the paving will usually follow. Identified in this section are methods to prepare base and to correct drainage and soil problems that might lead to future problems.

RELATED INFORMATION

Information in this chapter is supplemented by instruction provided elsewhere in this text and in other sources. Before undertaking the activities described in this chapter, read the related information in these sources:

- Safety in the Workplace, Chapter 7
- Basic Construction Techniques and Small Equipment Operation, Chapter 8
- Interlocking Concrete Pavement Institute Standards
- National Concrete Masonry Association Standards

SELECTION OF PAVING MATERIAL

Paving material types are identified on the design documents or through discussion with clients regarding standard criteria used in determining which material will best suit the project's needs. Although selection of paving type is best done during the design phase of a project, applicable construction-related criteria should also be reviewed. The following sections identify several choices for paving materials and include a description of the pros and cons of each choice. By using this information and the installation instructions in the chapters that follow, contractors can make wise decisions about which paving material is best for a project.

Concrete

An excellent choice for surfacing outdoor spaces (Figure 24-1), **concrete** is moderate in cost and is extremely versatile in finishes and shapes. Because forms are custom-built to match the design, almost any shape of surface is possible. A variety of finishes are available, from **exposed aggregates** to **colored, impressioned** walks that mitigate the aesthetic problem of "plain" concrete. As the complexity of the forming or surface increases, concrete becomes more expensive. Yet, concrete is still one of the most cost-effective surfacing materials available. For both new and existing concrete surfaces, options of coloring concrete to create a colorful decorative surface create a cost-effective alternative to new paving. Properly installed concrete is excellent in durability and safety and is regularly used in areas with vehicular traffic and in commercial and public use areas. Maintenance is typically performed without problems unless the installation is old or cracks have formed from improper installation. Most concrete pours can be installed with moderate

Figure 24-1 Concrete paving. Shown here in an urban plaza, concrete paving is versatile and easily adapted to various settings.

difficulty if installers are experienced in preparing and completing pours.

The need for stable paved surfaces that do not aggravate excessive runoff problems has led to attempts to create porous paving surfaces. Both asphalt and concrete have been modified in selected applications to create pavement that will allow water to percolate through the surface, rather than being shed from the surface. In both material formulations, the high porosity has been created by decreasing the percentage of sand and fine aggregates in the mix, creating a pavement with continuous voids throughout the thickness of the slab. In addition to changing the formulation of the paving material, for a porous paving to have maximum effectiveness, the base layer should function as a reservoir or transport mechanism for water. In these situations, the standard base of compacted graded base stone is replaced with an 8–36-inch deep base of clean, uniform graded aggregate ranging from 1–2½ inches in diameter. This base layer is lined with a nonwoven geotextile on the bottom and sides. Applications for such surfaces range from lining drainage channels for stability to installing minor roadways, parking areas, and paths. Although effective in managing water, such surfaces also have limitations. Concrete applications in cold climates are subject to freeze/thaw damage; asphalt installations are subject to compaction in high traffic areas; and both require specialized techniques for an effective installation.

Unit Pavers

Unit paver is a collective term that includes clay **bricks, interlocking concrete paving blocks,** precast concrete units, open-cell grass pavers, permeable pavers, and modular resilient pavers. Because of their aesthetic surfaces, unit pavers have been among the most desirable and requested types of paving materials (Figures 24-2 and 24-3). This attractiveness is not without its price because unit pavers are costly and require expertise and effort to install.

Strength for properly installed unit paver surfaces is good, but failure of base/subgrade under unit pavers can create potential safety problems, breakage, and definite maintenance problems. All unit paved surfaces have numerous joints between the pavers; and even with a perfect installation, these joints can hinder snow removal. Concrete paving block with a heavy duty base is often used in areas where vehicular traffic is expected or for commercial and public use areas. If installed on a proper base, brick can be used in these circumstances. To create an antique appearance, particularly with concrete paving block, pavers are tumbled in large drums to break off corners and sharp edges. This look gives the appearance of paving that is aged or has been in place for many years. Permeable unit pavers are standard units that have either truncated corners or wider spacers to create a wide but stable joint between units.

Figure 24-2 Interlocking concrete paving block is an excellent choice for both pedestrian and vehicular traffic.

Compared to traditional unit pavers, permeable pavers significantly increase the infiltration of water through the surface of the paving.

Typically used in turf locations where compaction from foot or vehicle traffic is a problem, open-cell pavers can be constructed of precast concrete or plastic rings attached to a mesh. Resilient pavers are manufactured from recycled materials, and the installation techniques are similar to those for precast concrete pavers. Resilient pavers have applications where softer surfacing is required, such as on playgrounds. Although priced higher than other unit paving choices, resilient pavers can be used to provide a surface with a "softer" feel. This type of pavement would be appropriate for certain

Figure 24-3 Brick paving provides rich colors and textures.

walkways and play courts (see Chapter 32, "Resilient Playground Surfaces").

Stone

Patios of limestone, bluestone, sandstone, granite, cantera, or slate are an aesthetically pleasing paved surface (Figure 24-4). The intricacy of shape, form, and pattern suggests a high level of craftsmanship. Concurrent with increased aesthetics for stone paving are higher costs and higher skill requirements for installation. Material availability has an impact on price, with lower costs in areas where stone is commercially quarried and available. To reduce the high cost of natural stone, designers are also relying on recycled stone and manufactured substitutes that

Figure 24-4 Dry-laid stone paving provides texture and a natural feel.

provide the appearance of stone. Some of these products include manufactured bluestone, recycled cobbles, recycled granite, and other stone reclaimed from construction and building demolitions.

Balancing the high costs just mentioned are moderate levels of strength and concerns about safety, particularly for stone paving in public areas. Maintenance and safety issues are similar to those for unit pavers. Stone paving has joints that can be irregular, creating safety hazards for pedestrians and making snow removal difficult. Any base failure or water below the paving can force the stone out of position, amplifying the problems. Only under certain circumstances (some granite units and cut stone placed on permanent base) is stone paving recommended for vehicular traffic or paving in commercial projects and public areas.

Although the material for stepping stones can be selected from any paving choice, **flagstone** is used most often for informal walkway applications. Stepping stones placed on earthen or thin, granular bases or on mortar puddles (a 1 inch thick layer of mortar) are inexpensive; however, these are suitable only for private uses.

Recycled Concrete Paving

Concrete that has been broken into random-sized chunks and removed from a site can be reused as a dry-laid paving surface (Figure 24-5). For concrete to be recycled, it must be broken into pieces that are the correct size. Pieces less than 8 inches across in the smallest dimension will be difficult to place and to walk on, whereas pieces larger than 2 feet in the largest dimension will require at least two people to lift them. The larger pieces pose the greatest challenge to accurately set and adjust. If recycled concrete has steel reinforcement, that reinforcement will need to be trimmed flush with the paver's edge and the irregular edges will need to be smoothed with a sledgehammer. In preparation for recycling, trim pieces so that they are the correct size and have edges split as close to vertical as possible.

Figure 24-5 Recycled concrete may be reused as a dry-laid paving surface.

Figure 24-6 Mortared stone provides a rich, stable stone paving.

Mortared Paving

Mortared paving has a cement/sand mixture, called mortar, that spaces and supports the paving materials (Figure 24-6). Mortar in the joints between materials provides even spacing and prevents water penetration. Paving materials that can be installed as a mortared surface include tile, brick, and stone, particularly random-shaped stone. Mortared paving can be durable if properly installed and maintained. If allowed to penetrate the joints of the surface, water will eventually damage the paved surface. This problem is far more damaging in areas of the country that experience freezing temperatures. Aesthetics of mortared surfaces are good, but installation is difficult and costly when compared to other paved surfaces. With proper maintenance, a mortared surface has a strength rating in the fair range. Surfaces that are improperly installed or poorly maintained or that use improper base materials may suffer from durability problems. A maintained surface is typically safe, but surfaces that are not maintained can cause those who walk on them to trip.

Granular Paving

Typically found in drives, walkways, trails, and, occasionally, outdoor living areas (Figure 24-7), granular paving includes such materials as crushed stone, crushed brick, pea gravel, and other permanent materials available as small pieces. In certain applications, soil and finely ground aggregate are bound using soil stabilizers to create paved surfaces. A variation of the soil stabilizers are epoxy resins that are blended with a variety of aggregate types and then installed using hot-mix asphalt equipment to form pathways and parking areas. Depending on the geographic region, granular materials sold as decomposed granite (or D.G.) fines, blue fines, gold fines, ¼ minus, granite sand, and similar headings that include pieces of crushed stone ⅜-inch in size or smaller can be used for granular paving surfaces. For decorative areas, a wide selection of pebbles and smaller stone up to ½-inch can be placed to create a flexible yet attractive surface.

Figure 24-7 Granular paving provides functional walkways.

Selection of such materials requires a careful review of use and placement. Thin applications of granular paving make the installation less durable. Although they provide consistent texture and color for aesthetic applications, granulars do not suggest a high level of craftsmanship. Installation is easy and costs are typically low, and these are reasons why granular materials are often used in residential settings. Granulars with permanent edgings such as stone, brick, or concrete balance cost and aesthetics for walkways and outdoor living areas. Safety problems such as washouts, poor traction, and sharp edges exist for some materials. Maintenance is moderate to high for granulars, with the constant refurbishing of surface materials, edging upkeep, leveling, and cleanup after materials that track inside. Durability of fine granular surfaces can be improved by adding soil stabilizers. Granulars are typically not suitable in areas where erosion and public safety are concerns.

To improve permeability of water without compromising the ability to support heavy traffic, a wide range of cellular (or plastic grid) paving options have been created. Typical application of cellular paving would be service access points, emergency access, and overflow parking areas. Although it requires base preparation similar to other paving options, cellular paving places a layer of plastic rings or grids over the base and fills the voids with granular materials or turf. These plastic cells provide adequate strength to support vehicles while allowing surface runoff to filter through the paving surface.

Asphalt

While usually installed by specialty contractors, hot mix **asphalt** paving is used for roadways, drives, walks, and trails in the landscape. Versatile installation also makes asphalt useful as a base material for unit pavers. Composed of bituminous materials mixed with aggregate and sand, asphalt is heated to high temperatures to improve its workability and bonding. Installed while hot, using special spreading and compaction equipment, asphalt provides a functional wearing surface for foot and vehicular traffic. When properly installed over a stable base, asphalt can be relatively free from maintenance. Because of the limited aesthetics of the surface, asphalt is seldom used when a high level of craftsmanship is desired. Cost for asphalt depends on labor and material prices. Installation requires the use of highly specialized equipment and experienced crews. A variation of asphalt, cold mix has a similar composition but is used for patching potholes in paved surfaces. Because of the specialized equipment and installation procedures required, asphalt installation is not covered in this text.

ACCESS TO SITE AND DELIVERY OF MATERIALS

Once the project has begun, workers will need access to the site, and materials must be delivered to the site. Ideally, this access route will not cross over the prepared base of paving surface. Plan a route that provides access to the site by equipment as large as a concrete truck and as small as wheelbarrows and foot traffic. Unit pavers and granular paving material typically require delivery by large vehicles, flatbed trucks with loading cranes and, dump trucks. Skid-steer loaders and other moving equipment must have a route and room to operate as they deliver the materials or move those materials from stockpiles.

Labor and time can be saved if installation is planned for effective delivery, pick up, and removal of pavers and granular materials. "Effective" here means that the delivery, pick up, and removal of pavers and granular materials will not disturb completed installations, will not unduly delay the installation process, and can be completed without repeatedly returning for partial loads. For example, to speed the selection process when laying stone, contractors can designate a staging area where they can lay out several pieces of stone. Also, having a stockpile of granular material delivered to the site will save labor and time to have extra material picked up and removed. Locating an area to stockpile additional granular material may also benefit the client who could use the material for future refurbishing.

On sites where access is difficult, it may be more cost-effective to have the concrete pumped to the delivery location. A pumping rig is positioned on the site where delivery equipment can access it. Concrete is then pumped through ground or overhead tubes to where it is needed. When pumping concrete a large, contained basin is required for washing out the pump when the pour is completed. The pump and lines hold a significant amount of unused concrete that must be held until it hardens, and then disposed. This adds costs for pumping but saves in labor and allows concrete to be placed in locations that could otherwise not be paved.

PROJECT LAYOUT

Measure and place project location stakes and stringlines to guide the initial excavation. Painting or "chalking" (pouring a line of base path chalk) the limits is often easier than fighting with strings. Mark and excavate an area that goes 1–2 feet beyond the actual paved area to create an apron that can be used for construction and later used to gradually match the new paving to the existing grade.

Once paving has begun, you can achieve the highest quality and efficiency by moving through the project without pause. This requires that materials be delivered and prepared for installation. Any equipment that will be necessary for site preparation or cutting should be present at the proper time.

STRIPPING SOD

Remove sod from the entire construction area and recycle it to bare areas of the yard or compost the sod. Once you strip the sod, remark the project edges and identify project elevations, typically with grade stakes.

MATCHING EXISTING CONCRETE AND ASPHALT SLABS

When new paving abuts old cast-in-place concrete slabs or asphalt paving, it is beneficial to prepare a straight edge against which new paving is placed. To prepare the edge of existing pavement, mark and cut a straight line using a cutoff saw or mobile concrete saw. A dry diamond or carborundum blade is required to cut most paving materials. The cut should be vertical and through the pavement. Chip away rough edges with a chisel. Excavate old pavement and prepare the edge for new pavement. Concrete paving may also require joining old paving to new paving (see Chapter 25). If asphalt is cut, you may apply a spray tack coat to improve adhesion of new pavement.

EXCAVATING

Using the most efficient means available, dig out excess soil until you achieve a uniform depth over the entire paved area (Figure 24-8). For paving with an edging, the base excavation should extend 1 foot beyond the finished edge to support the edging. Check the depth and cross-slope, often by running a string between grade stakes and measuring down with a tape measure. To avoid a less stable fill area, avoid over-excavation. Stockpile the excess topsoil for use in backfilling edges (Figure 24-9).

Actual depth of the excavation depends on which surface material is used, the subgrade soil conditions, and the weight of the traffic on the surface. Table 24-1 suggests appropriate base depths based on the type of paving material and the type of traffic on the surface. To determine excavation depth, add the paver dimension, the thickness of any sand or mortar setting bed, and the thickness of the base. If the paving material is designed to be seated, or vibrated into the **setting bed,** as is the case with some unit pavers, subtract the manufacturer's recommended seating dimension (typically ¼ inch) from the excavation depth. Verify base requirements with a design professional or manufacturer for the situation. Poor soils require additional depth or alternative base treatments as noted in Chapter 12 and the following paragraphs.

Table 24-1 General base thickness chart for various paving materials

Paving Type	Pedestrian Traffic	Occasional Vehicles	Auto Traffic	Heavy Traffic
4-inch concrete slab	3 inches	4 inches	6 inches	8 inches
Interlocking paving block with 1-inch sand setting bed	4 inches	8 inches	8 inches	16 inches
Clay paving brick with 1-inch sand setting bed	4 inches	8 inches	8 inches	Not recommended
2-inch unmortared stone with 1-inch sand setting bed	4 inches	Not recommended for this traffic type		
2-inch mortared stone with 1-inch mortar base	4 inches	Not recommended for this traffic type		
3-inches granular paving	3 inches	4 inches	Not recommended	

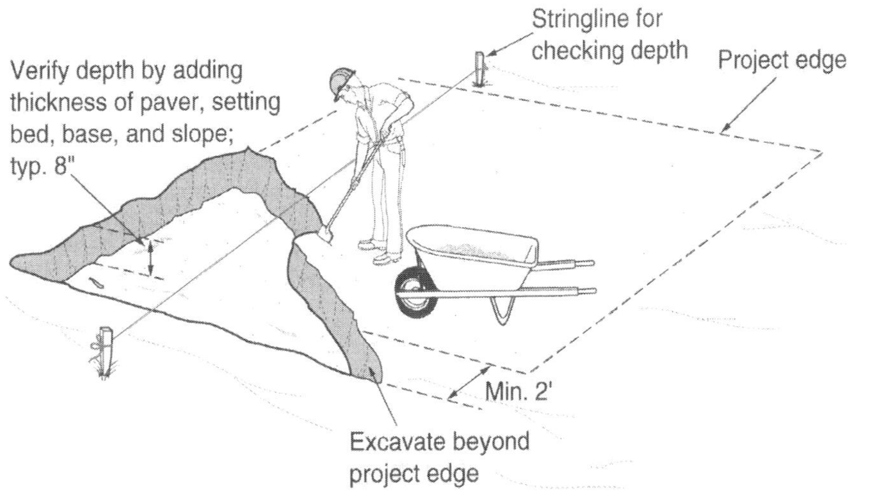

Figure 24-8 Excavating a site for paving.

© Delmar/Cengage Learning.

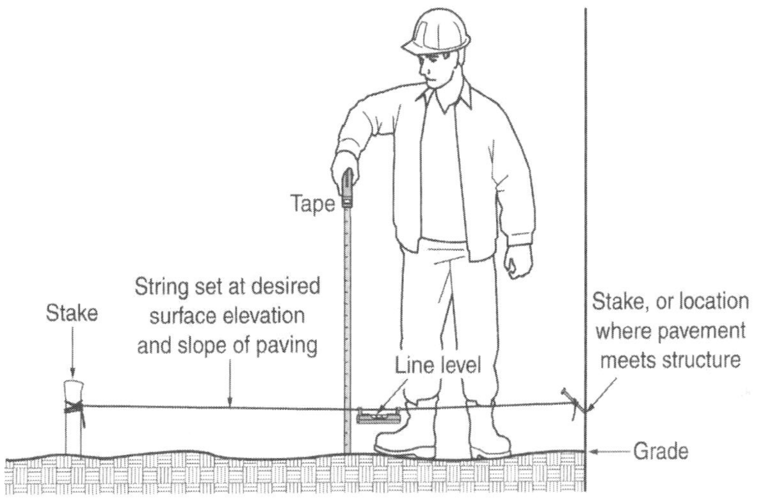

Figure 24-9 Checking the cross-slope and depth of pavement excavation.

© Delmar/Cengage Learning.

The depths are general recommendations from manufacturers. Verify actual base depths required for a project with an engineer.

Rough Grade Preparation

Because paving creates relatively flat surfaces with slight slopes introduced for drainage, creating the proper grade is important. Attempting to accommodate slopes that are too steep leads to difficult installation and surface slippage. On such slopes, you may have to install retaining walls to create a slope that is stable and flat enough to pave. On the other hand, slopes that are too flat result in future problems with water drainage. Grade also directs surface runoff away from structures. A slope of 2% (¼ inch fall for every 1 foot of horizontal distance) is recommended for most paving. Although flat cross-slopes (even sloping the entire surface one direction) are the easiest to construct and the best for drainage, you may have to occasionally introduce variable cross-slopes, or warping, in the pavement to accommodate drainage and to match existing elevations. Warping makes installation difficult, but warping is preferable to poor drainage.

Subsurface Utility Work

Paving is not easily changed; hence, other work that might affect an installation should be completed before paving begins. All underground utilities in the area should be in place, and trenches below the paving should be backfilled and compacted. Empty conduit can be placed if future utilities are anticipated. See Section 4 for a discussion of related utility work.

Subgrade Problems

The best subgrade is undisturbed, sandy-clay soil. Placing base on topsoil or unconsolidated soils can expose paving to subgrade movement. Therefore, remove unsuitable materials and backfilling with base material. Consult a soils engineer when there is uncertainty about the subgrade's condition.

Soil Problems. Occasionally, subgrade soil problems must be corrected. Identify problem soils by looking for areas that are wet, spongy, or sink under foot traffic. Also look for soils that have leaf and twig debris or a foul smell. If these signs are present, excavate these soils and replace them with base material. If the depth exceeds 1 foot, special subgrade restoration will need to be designed by the soils engineer.

Drainage Problems. If water stands in an area or seeps into the area excavated for the base from any direction, chances are the site has subgrade drainage problems. Sloping the subgrade the same direction as the surface assists in removing water. During dry seasons, there may be no indication of water; however, mucky, gray soils that smell like sewage indicate drainage problems. Water that percolates through the paving surface is usually minimal and is expected to be absorbed into subgrade soils. If you suspect subsurface drainage problems, consult a soils engineer. One solution is to install subgrade drainage tile in the wet area. Place a 4-inch perforated plastic drain tile wrapped in a geotextile sock in 1-foot deep trenches spaced 5 feet apart (Figure 24-10). Run the trenches the length of the paved area from the high side to the low side. Connect each tile to a collector tile at the paved area's low end and outlet this tile to a drain, storm sewer, or swale. Backfill and compact each trench with washed stone.

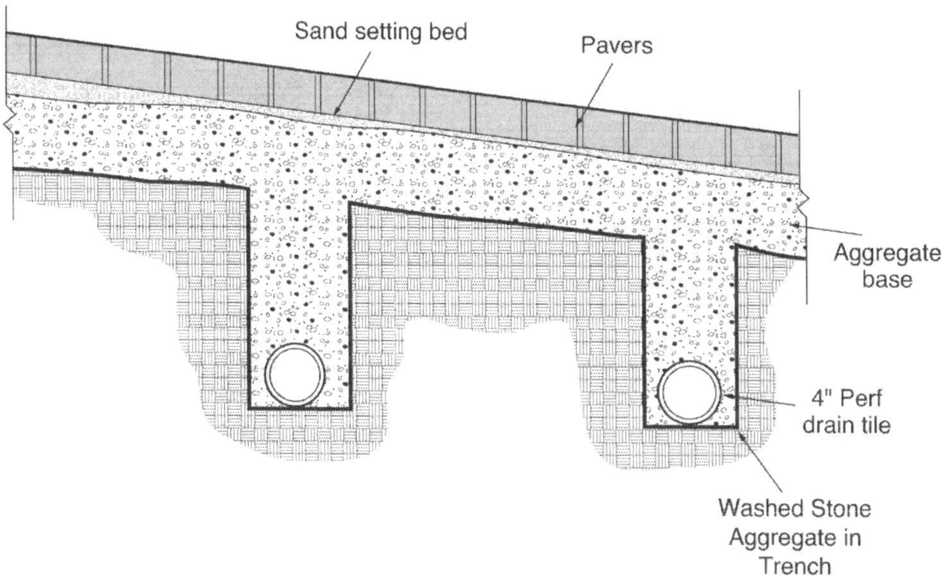

Figure 24-10 Cross section of tile placement to drain paved area base.

Grade Preparation and Subgrade/Base Compaction

Undisturbed earth is preferable for subgrade. If a paving installation is constructed in an area where the subgrade has been disturbed, proper compaction is necessary. If required to create a flat surface for paving, walls should be constructed in advance and the backfill compacted to meet base specifications. Also, all heavy traffic (deliveries of building materials, etc.) through the area should have ceased, or alternative routes should be established to protect the paving from traffic for which it was not intended.

Compacting subgrade in most small landscape operations is typically done using a vibratory plate compactor. Alternatives to a plate compactor include a rammer or vibratory roller. For best compaction results, select a plate compactor that has a compactive force of 5,000 pounds at 75–90 cycles per second. A vibratory plate compactor operates similarly to a self-propelled lawn mower. Start the engine and steer using the handles. To work tight corners, lift the handles vertically and twist the plate compactor to change direction. If the plate compactor has multiple operation settings, use the high-force/low-frequency setting for subgrade and base compaction. Always run the plate compactor at full throttle. Utility trenches under paved areas should be compacted in layers, or lifts, of 6 inches as the trench is backfilled. Small areas that cannot be accessed by a plate compactor should be hand-tamped.

To verify that the paving's foundation is stable, testing the compaction of subgrade and base is highly recommended. Engineers use measuring standards for determining if a material has been compacted to its maximum density, and the most commonly used standard is modified Proctor density. Projects performed under contract may require lab testing of soil and base samples to verify proper compaction. For projects without construction documents, obtaining Proctor test results may be cost-prohibitive. However, contractors can perform an informal test of base firmness. They can observe if heavy equipment operated over the surface leaves any rutting or depressions, which indicate incomplete or improper compaction, or an unstable subgrade.

INSTALLING GEOTEXTILE

Unit pavement, dry-laid stone, and granular paving projects may be designed for placement of a geotextile below the base to assist in maintaining separation between the base and subgrade soils. Select appropriate geotextiles with thermal spunbond or woven construction. Do not use weed barrier or geogrid to substitute for geotextiles. Place the geotextile on the subgrade and extend the material up the sides of the excavation and any structures around the entire perimeter of the project. To keep it out of the way during construction, staple the geotextile to a structure and then trim the excess after placing the pavement. If the area requires more than one piece of geotextile, overlap the joints by at least 18 inches.

INSTALLING BASE MATERIAL

Choice of base material varies from one geographic region to another; however, in most areas, a base of granular crushed stone ranging in size from dust to pieces that pass a ¾-inch sieve is preferred. This material is termed ABC (aggregate base course). A more formal description is National Stone Association Class 2 aggregate. When compacted, this blend usually provides adequate support for residential paving projects. Base material should have enough moisture that a handful of it holds together when squeezed. Dry material requires wetting during installation to compact properly.

Spread base material in 2-inch lifts over the paving area and level the lift with a rake or **screed** (Figures 24-11 and 24-12). Remove all clumps of soil or other debris and compact with a plate compactor. Make two compaction passes with the plate compactor at different angles. You obtain the best compaction results by working from the outside edge to the center, from a lower side to a higher side, or by working up and down slopes.

Check the elevation of the base after you install each lift. The slope should not have

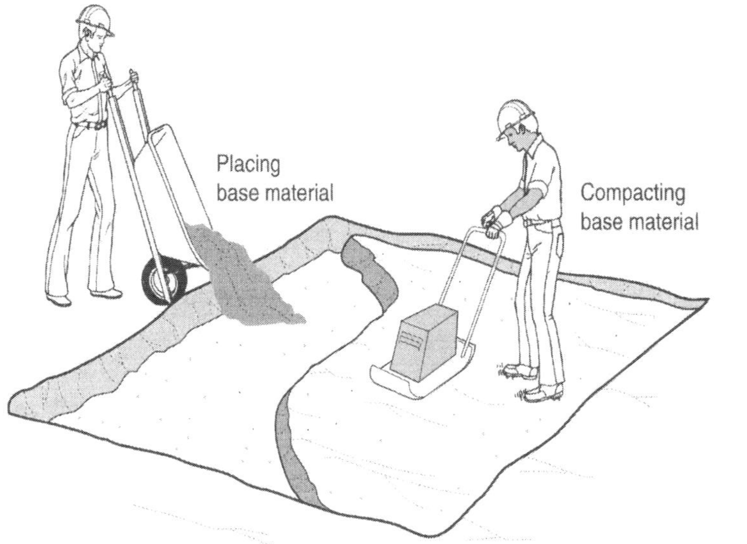

Figure 24-11 Placement and compaction of granular base.

deviations of more than ⅜ inch from desired grade and should reflect the slope desired for the surface. To level the base for an evenly sloped area, first check along a structure or existing edge for proper elevation. From that edge, check the sides of the base installation for proper grade. Between the sides, use a stringline or straight board to check for high or low spots across the center. You can also check the base by rolling a pipe over the surface and looking for bumps or depressions. Mark any unleveled areas with paint. Add a thin layer of base if low, or scratch out excess base with a rake if high. Recompact and verify for proper base grade. Repeat the process until you complete the base. Most unit pavers, dry-laid stone, and granular pavers will require that some material be placed along the edge to hold the pavement in place. This edge restraint can also serve as a decorative treatment for concrete and mortared paving material.

INSTALLING EDGE RESTRAINTS FOR PAVED SURFACES

Depending on the choice of paving, some edging materials should be placed after the base has been installed and before the setting bed is installed.

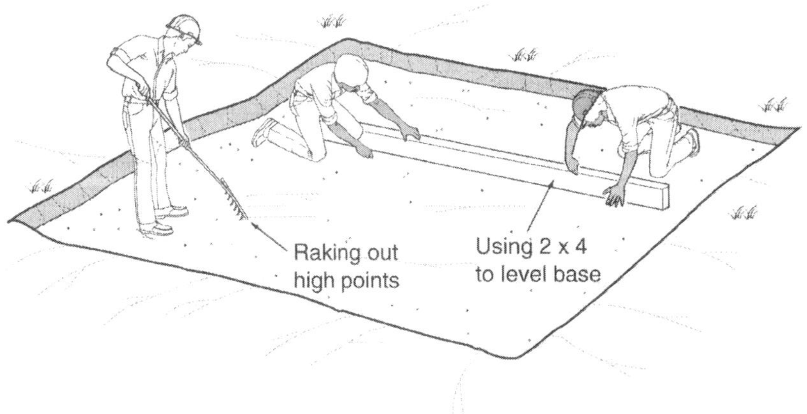

Figure 24-12 Leveling the base.

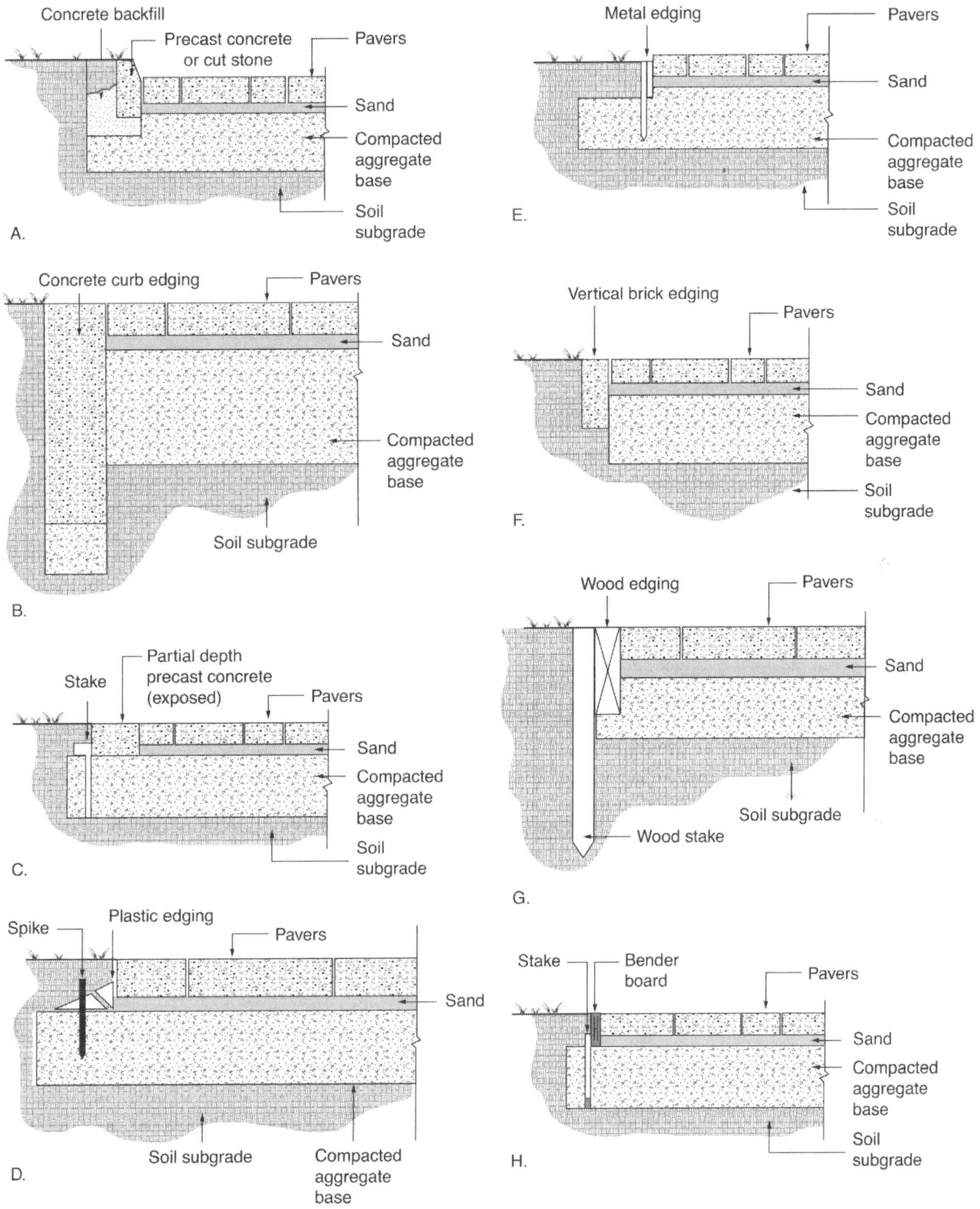

Figure 24-13 Pavement edge restraints.

Many edgings require special construction techniques and will seriously disrupt the pavers that have been installed. Other edgings work better when installed after the majority of the pavement has been placed. These edgings work best when installed before the partial pavers have been cut and installed. The common types of edgings in landscape pavement and their installation techniques are identified in the following paragraphs (Figure 24-13).

Stone (Pre or Postpaving Placement)

Wall stone makes an acceptable edging for dry-laid stone and clay brick. If used elsewhere in the project, the stone carries the design into the paved areas. Unless buried at least 8 inches, stone edging is not recommended for surfaces where the pavers must be seated. To install stone, select a heavy wall stone material, typically 4–8-inches wide. Longer stones make a more stable installation, with shorter stones used to turn corners. Excavate a trench around the area to be paved, and set the stone level with the desired finish grade for the patio. If desired, a strip of landscape fabric can be placed under the stone to reduce weed growth between blocks. After placing the stone, backfill and compact around the outside edge and build paving layers up on the inside (Figure 24-13A). For added stability, the edging stones can be set in a mortar bed with mortar backup on the outside edge.

Concrete Curbing (Prepaving Installation)

Concrete curbing makes a durable and long-lasting edging for a paved area. To install curbing, begin by excavating a trench along the perimeter where the curb is to be placed. Make sure the depth is correct for the thickness of the curbing selected. If the trench is too deep, fill with a granular backfill. Construct forms (see Chapter 25, Concrete Paving) with the top of the forms set at the finish elevation of the paved area. Fill with concrete and finish (Figure 24-13B).

Precast Concrete (Prepaving Installation)

Precast concrete edging units can be used to secure most unit pavements. Install prior to installation of the setting bed and paving but after the base has been installed. Mark the alignment of the edging and set the blocks in place directly on the prepared base. If openings for spikes are available, secure into the base using 10-inch spikes. Fill any voids between paver and edging with base material. Backfill and compact the area outside the paved area prior to placing the pavers (Figure 24-13C).

Composite Materials and Bender Board (Prepaving Installation)

Several composite materials can be used as edge restraints in applications that are straight or have large radius curves. Having a limitation to bend, many composite materials will not bend at all or, if shaped into radii tighter than 20 feet, will break. If a wood look is desired but the installation is designed with curves and radii, **bender board** may be an appropriate edge restraint. Manufactured of thin overlapping strips of lumber, bender board allows installation in radii as small as 5 feet.

To install composites or bender board, excavate a 6-inch wide trench slightly deeper than the edge restraint width along the entire alignment of the pavement edge. After excavating the trench, remark the exact pavement edge using marking paint. Install treated 12-inch long 1 × 2 stakes every 18 inches along the alignment of the edge restraint. Drive the top of the stakes at least 1 inch below the top of the desired elevation of the pavement surface. Beginning at one end, hold the restraint to the stakes and drive galvanized 10d nails through the edger into the stake. You can substitute 2-inch, rust-resistant screws for nails to minimize disturbance of the stake. If necessary, adjust the elevation of the stake before fastening. Trim the edge restraint to the proper length before installing the final section. When sections require joining, drive stakes at each end of abutting pieces of restraint. Some composites are manufactured with interlocking joints. Fill pavement base against the inside of the restraint and place pavement. When you have installed the pavement, fill and compact the outside of the edge restraint before seating pavers (Figure 24-13H).

Plastic (Pre- or Postpaving Installation)

The current standard for concrete paving block is the use of flexible plastic **edge restraint** specifically designed for this application. This edging is notched so that it can be bent to very tight radii, is installed with metal stakes or spikes, and is not visible after installation. Install this edging either before placing the setting bed or after completing installation of full pavers and before cutting and placing edge pavers.

Prepaving installation requires marking the alignment of the pavement edge. Place the edging firmly on the base and secure using stakes or 10-inch spikes. Trim edging to fit. Joints should be as tight as possible, with gaps covered with geotextile to prevent setting bed sand from seeping. Use this edging as a screeding guide for setting bed placement.

Postpaving placement should begin by using a steel trowel to cut a vertical edge down from the pavers, through the setting bed sand, to the base. Scrape away this sand. Beginning at a structure or a corner, take a length of the edging and, with minimal disturbance to the paved surface, tuck the notched side of the edging under the setting bed. Placing the edging directly under the setting bed and on top of the base will assure that enough of the paver is covered to hold it in place. Slowly work the edging under and tightly against the pavers along the length of the side (Figure 24-14). If necessary, tap edging lightly with a hammer to force it under the pavers. Verify that at least half the length and thickness of each paver is covered with edging, and then trim off extra edge restraint. Place and drive metal edging stakes or 10- inch spikes through the openings and into the pavement base at 1-foot increments along the edge. Driving the stake or spike at a slight angle toward the pavement base will draw the edging in tighter against the pavement. Fill any voids between the edging and paver with base material. Backfill and compact outside the edging before seating pavers (Figure 24-13D).

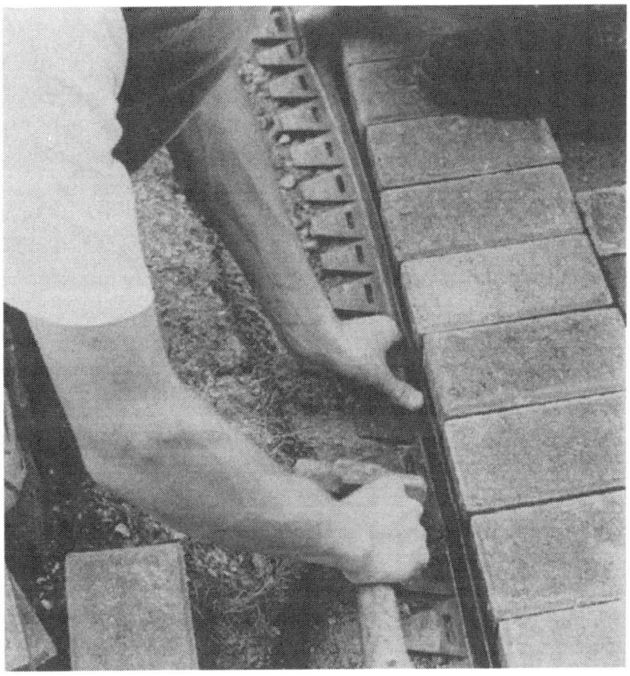

Figure 24-14 Installation of plastic edging after placement of pavers.

Metal (Postpaving Installation)

Metal landscape edging can be used to hold the pavers in place. Install metal edging after all pavers are cut and placed. Measure and precut pieces of edging for each side of the paved area so that the entire perimeter is covered. Using a steel trowel, cut the setting bed sand away in a vertical edging along the pavers to the base. Starting at a corner, hold the metal edging 1 inch below the top of, and against, the sides of the pavers. Through the notches in the edging, drive edging stakes into the base at 1-foot increments along the edge. Backfill outside the edging and compact before seating pavers (Figure 24-13E).

Vertical Bricks (Postpaving Installation)

This method provides limited stability and works best with brick pavement and pavements that are not seated. Vertical brick edging should be installed after all bricks have been placed, including half and partial brick. To install vertical brick edging, carefully excavate a 9-inch deep trench along the entire perimeter of the paved area. The trench must form a vertical edge going straight down along the outside of the pavement. Place a small amount of granular material in the trench and place brick vertically against the pavement. By adding or removing granular material, adjust the height of the edging so that it is flush with the paved surface. Backfill outside the edging and compact immediately after placement. Using a small amount of mortar instead of soil for backfill will make the installation more stable. When the mortar hardens, cover it with soil (Figure 24-13F).

Wood (Pre- or Postpaving Installation)

Although a wood edging provides restraint, it warps, decays, and heaves and, hence, should be considered only a short-term option. Cutting and filling of partial pavers should be completed after this edging is installed. To install wood edging, select a decay-resistant, dimensioned lumber and cut it to length for each side of the paved area. Larger-dimensioned lumber, such as 4 × 4 or 6 × 6, reduces problems with warping, but you may also use a 2 × 6 for short-term installations.

Re-treat cut ends with a wood preservative. Excavate a vertical trench 6 inches deep along the outside edge of the paved surface. Place the wood edging in the trench tightly against the pavers. Drive treated 2 × 2 stakes every 2 feet along the outside of the edging. Fasten stakes to the edging using galvanized nails or 2½-inch, rust-resistant screws. Backfill outside the edging and compact (Figure 24-13G).

CHAPTER 25

Pedestrian Concrete Paving

OBJECTIVES

By reading and practicing the techniques described in this chapter, the reader should be able to successfully complete the following activities:

- Form a concrete pour.
- Form concrete stairs.
- Install joints in a concrete pour.
- Pour a concrete slab and stairs.
- Finish a concrete slab and stairs.

Concrete can be placed in any shape or form, can be colored or stamped to look like another material, is cost-effective, and is durable as a paving surface. For these many reasons, concrete is a staple in the world of landscaping. Countering the versatility of concrete is the challenge of installing it. Although competing paving materials also have their challenges, the preliminary work required to ensure a successful concrete pour is unmatched by that of other paving types. This chapter describes the forming, pouring, and finishing of a typical concrete installation. Included in this chapter are instructions for forming both flatwork and stairs, along with information about typical finishes available for concrete.

RELATED INFORMATION

Information in this chapter is supplemented by instruction provided elsewhere in this text and in other sources. Before undertaking the activities described in this chapter, read the related information in these sources:

- Safety in the Workplace, Chapter 7
- Basic Construction Techniques and Small Equipment Operation, Chapter 8
- Materials and Site Preparation for Paving, Chapter 24
- NCDOT Standard Specifications for Roads and Structures

PLANNING THE PROJECT

Preparation of base for concrete projects should be completed according to the instructions provided in Chapter 24.

Concrete Finishes

Several choices are available for concrete finish textures, and their procedures and timing differ depending on the choice. The following list explains common choices for finishes. Instructions for creating each finish are listed in the "Surface Texturing and Finishing" section of this chapter.

- **Float** Finish. Using the float as a finish produces a slightly rough surface that provides adequate traction. The float finish can be applied parallel to edges of the slab or joints or applied in an arcing swirl texture.
- Broom Finish. A stiff-bristled shop broom texture provides an excellent nonslip surface. When combined with the bordered segment approach described for a float finish, the broom finish creates an attractive appearance (Figure 25-1).
- Colored, Impressioned Finish. Concrete can be colored and stamped with special forms to create a surface that looks like stone, granite, or brick. Color can be added to the concrete while it is mixed or sprinkled dry on fresh concrete and troweled into the surface. Expert concrete finishers can also add color as a mortared topcoat over a slab.

Figure 25-1 Broom finish for concrete walkway.

- Seeded Exposed Aggregate. Exposed aggregate surfacing can be installed by sprinkling pea gravel or other fancy stone on a smoothed, wet concrete surface and using a trowel to embed stone in the top of the slab (Figure 25-2). After the concrete begins to dry, it is "scrubbed" with a hose and broom to remove the top film of concrete to "expose" the aggregate that was embedded earlier. One recurring maintenance problem with an exposed aggregate surface is that moisture can work under the aggregate and break it from the surface.
- Integral Exposed Aggregate. A variation on the previously described aggregate surface is an integral exposed aggregate. The problem of surface deterioration is minimized by mixing the special aggregate right into the concrete at the plant. Instead of being a weak addition to the surface, the aggregate is mixed completely into the full slab. The finished product of this surfacing is obtained by scrubbing the slab before it sets or sandblasting the slab after it dries.
- Rock Salt. This pockmarked surface is created by sprinkling rock salt on a finished surface and rinsing it after the curing process begins. This finish provides a rustic texture that looks interesting with colored concrete. Rock salt finish is not recommended in areas where the surface can be damaged from water that freezes in the indentations (Figure 25-3).
- Acid Etch. This slightly roughened surface is created by acid eating away the smooth trowel finish on a slab. Although a good surface for traction, acid tech requires treatment of the entire surface because the acid is difficult to spot apply.
- Cobbled Concrete (Traffic Medians). To warn drivers of improper entry, large rounded stone can be imbedded into concrete to create a rough cobbled surface (Figure 25-4). This finish would not be appropriate for pedestrian walkways.

Planning Concrete Delivery and Pouring

Concrete pours require extensive route planning. When preparing for a pour, consider how the

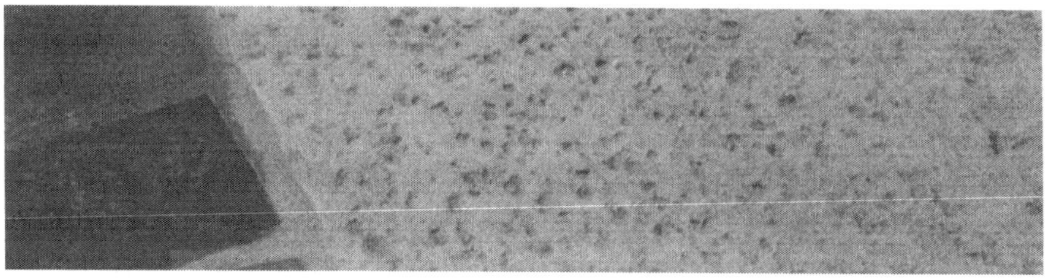

Figure 25-2 Seeded exposed aggregate concrete finish.

Figure 25-3 Rock salt concrete finish.

mixer will gain entry to the site, where the pour should begin and end, and how access will be gained to finish the surface.

CAUTION

It is imperative that the route for the mixer will not cause it to contact overhead utility lines or damage underground installations or valuable plant material.

If the mixer can access the entire pour, then the need to transport concrete by wheelbarrow is eliminated. At times, it may be beneficial to leave a section of forms out and have the mixer drive across the base to access a remote corner. The many extensions that a mixer carries and the experience of a driver will save a great deal of labor. If route problems are too difficult to overcome, consider pumping the concrete. If access or pumping is not possible, use wheelbarrows. A wheelbarrow can carry 2–3 CF of concrete at a time to the necessary locations. Plan the pour so that an open area at the end of the pour allows screeding beyond the forms. Allow open areas along both sides of a pour to provide space for floating, finishing, and edging. Working against a wall and in corners creates problems finishing the slab from the edge. Verify that the **forms** and base are completely prepared before the concrete arrives.

Figure 25-4 Cobbled concrete surface for traffic medians.

It is best to order the concrete ahead of time. Even in small communities, concrete suppliers may need a day or two lead time to reserve concrete. Do not expect concrete suppliers to give priority to small orders, especially if you call them at the last minute. Well in advance of the pour, inform the concrete supplier of any special colors, aggregates, fibermesh, or other additives that need to be in the concrete mix. Suppliers may not stock some of these items and may have to order them, adding more time for delivery.

If available, the details and specifications for concrete mixes should be obtained from the landscape architect or engineer for a project. For most landscaping pours, a common mix is 4,000

PSI (sometimes termed *7 bag mix*) concrete with a 3-inch **slump,** which is a measure of the amount of water in concrete. Water directly affects the strength of concrete—the more water in the mixture, the weaker the slab. Table 25-1 shows the relationship between water/cement ratios and strength for concrete. When placing your order, specify a drier concrete than actually desired. You can add water at the site before placement. Check the consistency when the mixer arrives to see if more water is needed (consistency checks are described in "Placement of Concrete" later in this chapter).

Occasionally, concrete must be mixed in small batches by hand. This operation requires a mixing tub or wheelbarrow that will accommodate approximately 3 CF of material. Mix 1 part cement (one-half bag, approximately 47 pounds), 2 parts sand, and 3 parts aggregate together with approximately 3–4 gallons of water. Work the materials back and forth with a mortar hoe or shovel until thoroughly mixed. A chopping motion works well when attempting to incorporate moisture into dry materials. If additional water is necessary, add it in small amounts and remix until the concrete is of proper consistency.

Table 25-1 Water/cement ratio effect on compressive strength of concrete

	Water/Cement Ratio by Weight			
	0.4	**0.5**	**0.6**	**0.7**
Days after pour	Compressive Strength in PSI (pounds per square inch)			
28	5,800	4,700	3,700	3,000
7	4,000	3,100	2,400	1,700
2,500	1,900	1,500	1,000	
1	1,000	700	480	250

Notes:

1. Compressive strengths shown are ±200 pounds per square inch (PSI).
2. Data shown is for air-entrained Type 1 Portland cement with moist curing at 70° F.
3. Flexural strength is approximately 79% of compressive strength.
4. Ratio example: 0.4 indicates approximately 1 pound of water (approximately 1 pint) for every 2.5 pounds of cement in a concrete mixture. This ratio will vary with cement and aggregate type.

Source: Adapted from *Design and Control of Concrete Mixtures,* 12th ed., Portland Cement Association.

FORM CONSTRUCTION FOR SLAB POURS

Concrete pours depend on reliable forms. Properly installed forms should be anchored to withstand the force of several dozen pounds of wet material being dumped into them at high rates of speed. Stable enough to maintain the proper grade at the perimeter of the project, forms must also be strong enough to withstand the **screeding** and finishing work that will be performed upon them.

Selection of materials for forms depends on the thickness and shape of the pour, with 2 × 4s providing the most common method of pouring a 4-inch thick, straight-edged slab (a 2 × 4 produces a slab that is 3½ inches thick). Thicker pours may require dimensioned lumber that is wider (2 × 6s or 2 × 8s) or rental of metal forms. Curved sections of a pour can be constructed with forms of ¼-inch masonite siding cut into strips that match the slab's thickness. Additional materials that can be used to form curved sections include ⅜-inch plywood cut into strips the same width as the pours thickness and bender board edge restraint. Easiest forming is accomplished with metal forming stakes (Figure 25-5). The stakes are approximately ½-inch round metal with holes along the entire length of the stake. Wood stakes should be 2 × 2 or 1 × 4 material and 8 inches longer than the slab is thick (e.g., 12-inch stakes for a 4-inch slab). Because their double heads make them easy to remove, **form nails** are the best choice for nailing dimensioned lumber forms; however, using deck screws to connect forms reduces the disruption of forms as a result of hammering.

Figure 25-5 Metal stakes for concrete forming.

Begin form installation by selecting a starting point at the project's highest corner or next to a structure. Set form material on edge along the outside of the project edge (Figure 25-6). Forming should match any existing pavement grades that abut the new slab (Figure 25-7). At the high end of the form, drive one of the stakes along the outside edge of the form material. Metal stakes should be driven below the top of the form, whereas wood stakes can be left above the form and trimmed later. Drive a form nail through the stake and into the form material, holding the top of the form at the desired elevation for the top of the slab. Placing the head of a sledgehammer on the inside of the form opposite the nail will make driving the nails easier. Repeat this process at the other end of the form, and then adjust the elevation by tapping the stakes down or prying the form up. Adjust until the entire form follows the required grade along the projects outside edge. Add additional stakes along the form every 2 feet, driving and nailing carefully so that you do not disturb the elevation. Once you have the form in place, move to the next form and repeat the process. Be sure the forms butt together tightly. Add an extra 1 × 4 stake behind the joint for stability. Forms work best if the sections are at least 2-feet long, but use whatever length is required to make a continuous connection. Continue forming around the entire project.

Figure 25-6 Installing and leveling forms for a concrete pour.

Curved forms should be set up in a similar manner. Nail from the inside of the form into the stake because the nail will project into the concrete if nailed from the stake side (Figure 25-8). If using masonite forms, use nursery nails to fasten forms to the stake. Stake curved forms every 1 foot for additional support. In some installations, it may be easier to complete all the straight forms before preparing the curved sections. Because curved forms are a challenge to maintain in correct alignment and elevation during installation, reinforce them at several locations along the form.

At locations where posts or other improvements will penetrate the surface of the concrete pour, an opening, or boxout, must be formed. A boxout will frame this opening and provide identification of an area where concrete should not be placed (Figure 25-9). Frame the opening with form material that matches the slab thickness. Position the box in the correct location and drive stakes into the base on the inside of the boxout. You can determine the correct elevation of the boxout forms by using a string level resting on side forms. Place the string level on the side forms passing over the boxout. Adjust the boxout until the correct elevation is obtained and fasten it to the stakes.

Figure 25-7 Installing form flush with top of adjacent slab.

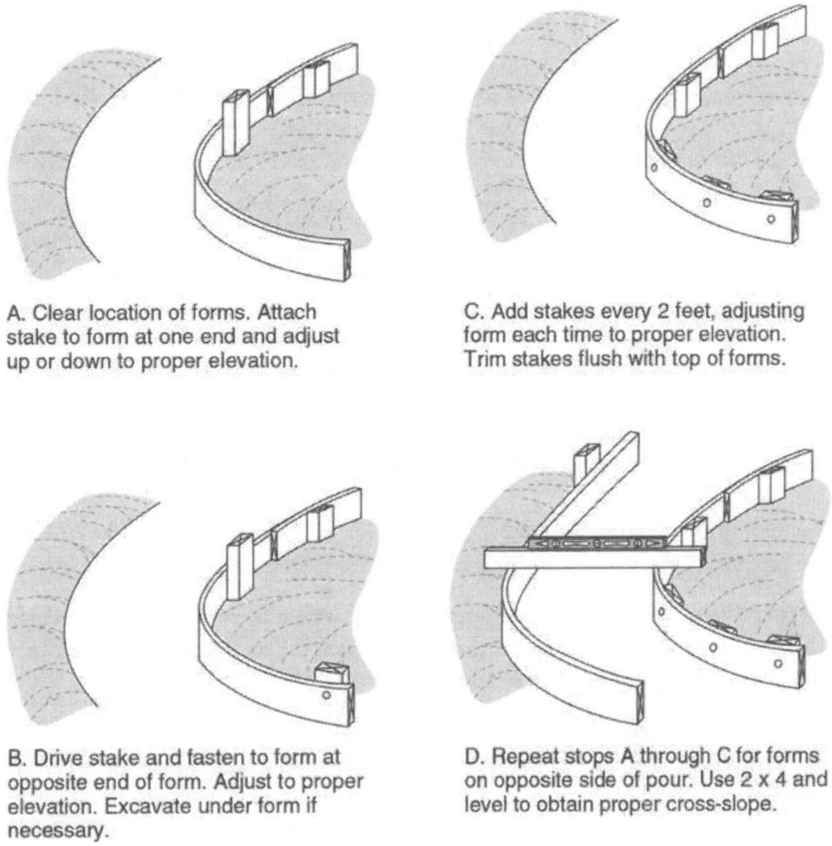

Figure 25-8 Curved form installation.

© Delmar/Cengage Learning.

Forming Curbs

When used as edge restraint for paving or as edging for planting beds, **curbs** are formed independently before installation of the project. To install curb forming, cut ½-inch plywood in strips the same width as the curb's thickness.

At the back of the curb, drive 2 × 2 stakes every 18 inches along the alignment of the pour. These stakes should extend at least 8 inches into the ground and 8 inches above the top of the proposed curb. Hold the plywood forms against the stakes, adjust the forms to the correct height, and fasten them to the stakes using deck screws or form nails installed from the inside of the form through the stake. Place two fasteners at each stake, one at the top and one at the bottom of the form. Repeat the process for staking and placing the form along the front side of the curb. Locate the stakes for the front forms directly across from the stakes for the back side. It will be easier to

Figure 25-9 Box out to identify area where concrete should not be poured.

© Delmar/Cengage Learning.

fasten this side from the outside, through the stake and into the form.

To maintain spacing of the forms, fasten a 1 × 2 spreader between each pair of front and back stakes 6 inches above the top of the forms (Figure 25-10). This will reduce the chances of the forms being pushed apart when the pour begins. Spacers may also be placed inside the forms to hold them in position during the pour. These spacers can be metal flanges or blocks of 2 × 4 cut to the exact width of the pour. Because these interior spacers will remain in the pour, verify that the location does not impact the pours aesthetics or structure. If any wiring or irrigation lines need to pass through the curb, cut a piece of 1-inch diameter (or whatever size is needed to accommodate the passing material) Schedule 40 pipe to the exact width of the curb. Position the pipe where the passage is to be located. Drive a nail through the form into the center of the pipe from both the outside of the front and back form to hold it in position.

You can make the forms more stable by driving #4 rebar behind the forms between each pair of stakes. If you need to provide additional stability at the top of the form to obtain a straight edge on the pour, fasten a 2 × 4 set on edge along the form's top and bottom outside edge before it is placed. This will require that the trench for the pour be widened and the stakes placed back 3½ inches from the front and back of the curb (Figure 25-11).

Figure 25-10 Forms for pouring curb.

© Delmar/Cengage Learning.

Using Wood Headers

Instead of constructing forms that are removed following a pour, contractors can construct forms that remain and serve as expansion joints and decorative edging to the concrete surface (Figure 25-12). These permanent forms, called **headers,** must be constructed with a decay-resistant lumber. Kiln-dried redwood, dried-treated lumber (wet-treated lumber may shrink), and composite materials are available choices. Although wood headers offer aesthetic advantages, many older installations have maintenance problems as the wood decomposes.

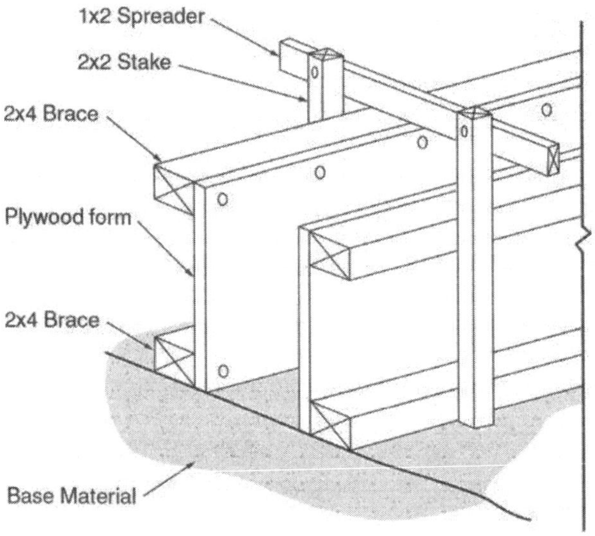

Figure 25-11 Forming for concrete curb.

© Delmar/Cengage Learning.

Construct wood header forms in the same manner as that used for the previously described temporary forms. In each location where a contraction joint or header is planned, cut forming material, set it on edge, place it flush with the top of the forms, and connect. Every foot along both sides of the header, drive galvanized 16d nails halfway into the header. These nails will project into the concrete and, when the concrete sets, will anchor the header to the slab. When all forming is complete, place wide masking tape over the tops of all headers to protect the lumber from scuffing during concrete placement and finishing. Remove the tape when the pour is complete.

Checking Forms

After forming is complete, check the grade around the perimeter to be certain the elevations are correct. Cross-slopes can be checked by placing a 2 × 4 on edge from the form on one side to the form on the other. A level placed on top should show a slight drop between the sides. Backfill to the top of the outside of the forms and add base material to just below the bottom on the inside. Fill any gaps or openings of ½ inch or less with an expanding spray foam insulation from an aerosol can. Spray the foam in the opening and let the foam expand and harden. Trim any excess to match the form's surface. To keep them from interfering with screeding and finishing, the tops of any stakes that stick above the forms should be cut with a saw.

Figure 25-12 Wood header between paved slabs.

Leveling Base

Make a **base screed** by cutting a 2 × 4 (or the dimension of lumber selected for forms) 10 inches shorter than the width between the forms. To serve as a handle, at each end of this screed nail a 1 × 4 laid flat, on top, that extends 8 inches beyond the end of the screed. Set the flat handles of this screed on top of the forms and, using a sawing motion, move it from one end of the pour to the other to check the depth of the formed area. Add additional base material and screed inside the forms to ensure a uniform slab thickness (Figure 25-13). Sprinkle a fine granular base material (stone screenings that pass a ⅜-inch sieve) into the areas that look low, and rake material away from any area that appears high. This screed should move easily from one end to the

Figure 25-13 Screeding 3/8s minus granular base to a consistent depth. Base will be compacted after screeding.

other with the compacted base just below the bottom of the screed. Compact the base using a vibratory plate compactor.

FORM CONSTRUCTION FOR STAIR POURS

One of the most difficult forming and pouring jobs is the placement of stairs in landscapes. Not only must the setup hold concrete horizontally between forms, but it must also hold concrete vertically. This situation is often compounded by the existence of walls, structures, or other landscape elements that do not provide an open work area. Because of this difficulty in preparation for a pour, forming and pouring stairs are often left for specialty contractors. Whether performed by the landscape contractor or a specialty contractor, form construction for three types of stair pours are: (1) independent forming, or pours that allow forming the stairs before other improvements are installed; (2) suspended forming, or pours that require forming after improvements such as wall structures are installed and that require hanging forms between the improvements; and (3) a method in which forms are wedged into place.

ADA Stair and Ramp Requirements

A designer will integrate requirements of the Americans with Disabilities Act (ADA) into many projects. When forming and pouring concrete stairs and ramps, contractors will be impacted by these ADA requirements. Among the work impacted is forming the face of the risers, finishing the nosing on stairs, and providing safety markings at the top of each riser or ramp (Figure 25-14).

For example, a designer may require stairs with no open risers, a rounded nosing of ½ inch and the outer edge of the tread with a special marking to satisfy ADA recommendations (Figure 25-15). The landscape contractor will need to be aware of the special requirements when preparing and finishing walks in public areas.

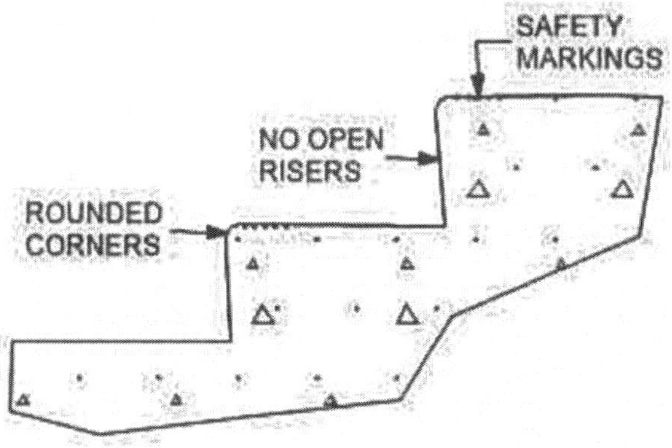

Figure 25-14 ADA finishing requirements for poured concrete stairs.

Independent Forming of Stair Pours

Pouring stairs before any of the surrounding landscape improvements have been installed often provides the opportunity to independently form a set of stairs. This allows contractors to form all parts of the stair, including sides and risers. Be certain the location and elevation of stairs match other improvements before forming. Independent pouring can be completed in four steps, as illustrated in Figure 25-16.

Figure 25-15 Tool used for creating safety markings at the top of a poured concrete ramp.

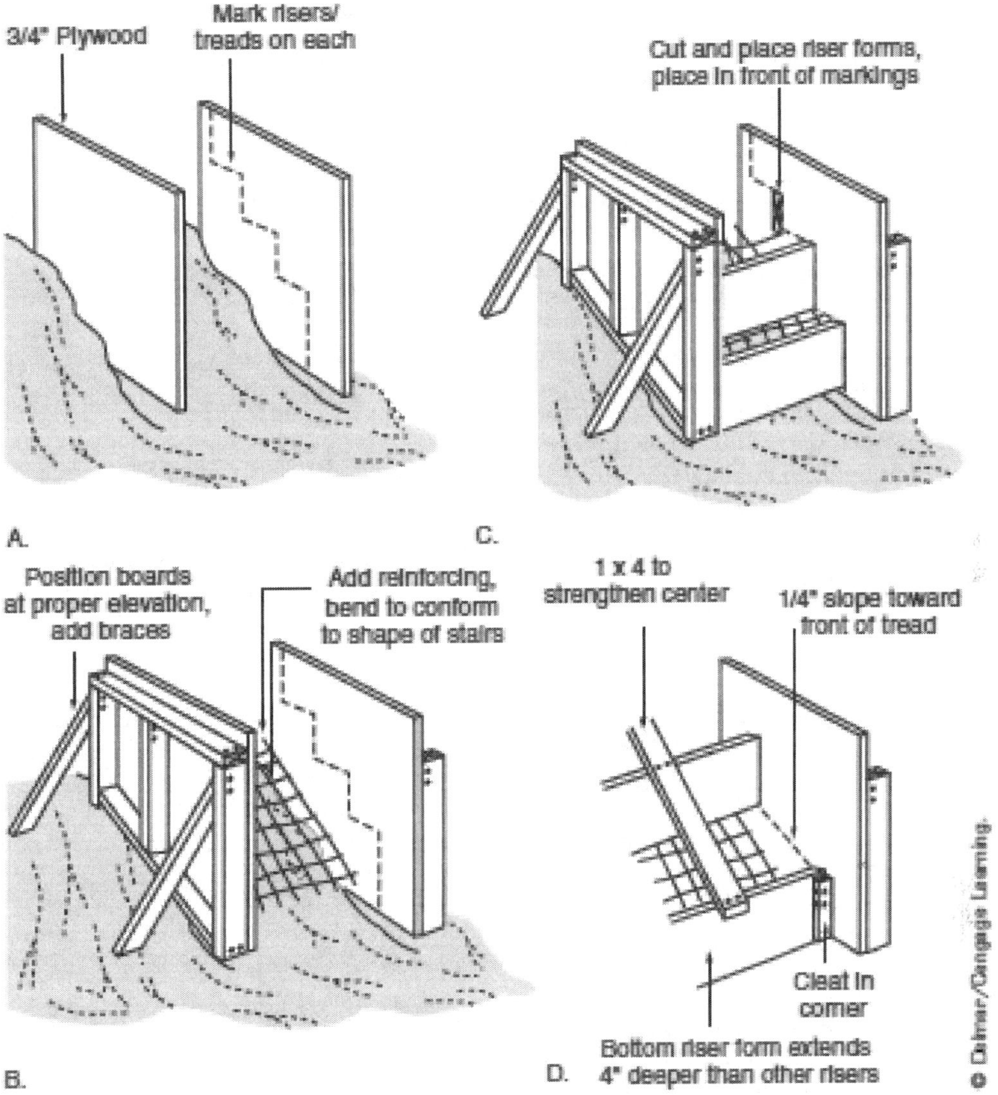

Figure 25-16 Independent forming of concrete stairs. A. Marking side forms. B. Securing side forms and installing reinforcement. C. Installing riser forms. D. Bracing the forms.

Begin the form construction by preparing forms for the sides of the pour. Use a ¾-inch plywood for side forms. Mark the alignment of risers and treads for one side of the entire stair run on the lumber. Repeat this marking for the other side of the stairs. Side forms do not need to be cut.

Excavate the pour site and place one side form, verifying that the treads are at the correct location and level. Drive 2 × 4 stakes behind the form, and anchor them in a manner similar to that used in anchoring forms for flat work. Repeat this process with forms on the opposite side of the pour, verifying that this side is positioned at the same level as the first side. Some contractors install riser forms first and then use the riser to set the second side form. Prior to constructing and installing riser forms, place any reinforcing along the ground in the pour area. All reinforcement must be held above the ground to assure that it is embedded inside the pour. If using **welded wire mesh** (WWM), bend the mesh to conform closely to the stair contour. Place dobies or metal chairs to hold the WWM above the subgrade, thus assuring that the mesh is embedded in the concrete. An alternative to WWM is fibermesh, which is added to concrete for stair pours.

Using 2-inch dimensioned lumber that is wider than the calculated riser height, measure and cut risers to match the width of the stair opening. Any gap larger than 1/16-inch at either end will allow concrete to seep through when pouring. If the stairs are not a constant width, mark and measure each stair in its location to verify the correct length. After trimming the length, cut the lumber the long dimension (rip cut) to the correct height for the riser. Rip cutting at a 45° bevel will provide room at the bottom of the riser form for finishing the tread with a trowel (Figure 25-17). The riser for the bottom stair should be 4 inches deeper than the others to provide the depth necessary for paving that will abut the stairs. The bottom riser form does not need the bevel cut Beginning with the bottom riser, nail the riser form in position using form nails driven through the outside of the side forms. Check for level side to side across the top of the riser form and plumb down the front; then secure using deck screws placed from the outside of the side forms into the end of the riser form. Repeat this process for each of the risers. Before completing connections for each subsequent riser, check for a slight fall between the bottom of the upper riser form to the top of the lower riser form. Properly calculated and constructed stairs should have a tread that tilts ¼ inch per foot toward the front of the stair to prevent standing water. Fasten 2 × 4 bracing to the outside of the form for additional strength.

To brace the form, add cleats in the corner formed by the back of the riser form and the side form. Forms wider than 3 feet may require additional bracing to prevent bowing after concrete placement. Near the center of the stairs, screw a 1 × 4 to the tops of all the riser forms.

Suspended Forming of Stair Pours

Occasionally, landscape contractors construct forms for poured concrete stairs that must fit between existing walls and structures. Use of walls or structures as the "sides" to the forms saves a step in construction, but it also eliminates the support for the riser forms. To accommodate

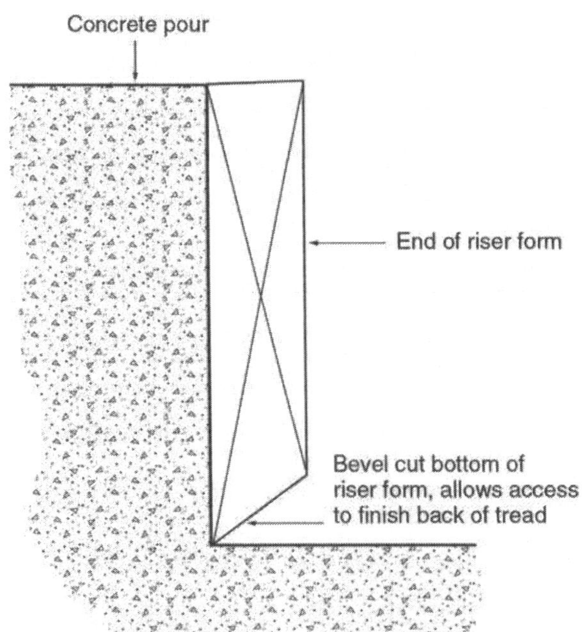

Figure 25-17 Bevel cutting the bottom of riser forms.

this lack of support, cut and hang, or suspend, the riser forms from beams that run over the top of the pour. This type of pour should be completed before any paving is done above or below the stairs to allow anchoring support beams.

Before constructing this type of form, place any required expansion material against structural objects against which the stairs will make contact. Concrete stairs expand and contract, creating pressure against a structure foundation. If expansion joint material is not installed, damage to the structure may occur. Also suspend any reinforcing above the ground in the pour area. If using WWM, bend the mesh to conform closely to the stair contour. An alternative to WWM is fibermesh for stair pours.

Installing an anchor that connects the stairs and a building foundation or concrete wall may also be required. Foundations and concrete walls have surfaces that allow stairs to rise or settle over time. To anchor the stair to the sides, drill 1/2-inch diameter holes 2 inches into the wall. Cut 6-inch long pieces of ½ inch (#4) steel reinforcing rods and drive them into the holes. Leave the 4-inch stub projecting into the stair pour area. Place one anchor per riser.

Constructing suspended forms begins by marking the riser and tread locations on the sides of the pour. Select a piece of 2-inch dimensioned lumber that is wider than the riser's height. Measure the length for the first riser and cut the lumber to the correct length. Rip cut the lumber to the riser height using the 45° angle described in "Independent Forming of Stair Pours." Repeat for each riser. The riser for the bottom stair should be 4 inches deeper than the others and does not need the bevel cut.

Beams mounted on stakes running from the top to the bottom of the pour will be used for support of the riser forms. Support beams must be spaced close enough and braced well enough to hold the weight of the riser forms, the concrete, and the workers who will lean on them when finishing. Place a beam 1 foot in from each side of the stairs, with an additional beam in the center, and one for every 3 feet of width for the stairs. At the top and bottom of the stair location, and in alignment with each of the beam locations, drive 4-foot long 2 × 4 stakes with sharpened points 18 inches into the ground. Between the pair of stakes at each side of the pour, attach a 2 × 4 that sets just above the height of the planned risers. If a stair run has more than five risers, these beams should be constructed of 2 × 6s. Once installed, the stakes may need to be braced to prevent movement. The two outside beams will be used to initially hang the riser forms, with the center beams added after you secure and level the riser forms (Figure 25-18).

Beginning with the bottom riser, attach 18-inch long 2 × 4 extensions on edge to the back of the riser form at locations under where the beams will pass. Using the riser markings on the side walls as guidelines, place the precut riser form in the correct position under the support beams and tack the 2 × 4 extensions onto the beam. Adjust the riser form to level along its length and plumb down the face; then securely connect the riser form extensions to the beam at both ends. To further brace the riser form, connect angled braces from the beam to the base of the riser form. This will prevent the concrete from pushing out at the bottom of the riser. Repeat this process for each riser form to the top of the stairs. Before completing connections for each riser, check for a ¼ inch per foot downward slope between the bottom of the upper riser form and the top of the lower riser form.

When you secure the risers to the beams at each edge of the stairs, you may install center beams and riser connections. Use caution not to disturb the level previously established for the risers. Additional bracing may be added to secure the forms, but leave access to the inside of the forms for placing and finishing the concrete. Placement of concrete by hand reduces the chance of form failure. Figure 25-19 shows a suspended form in place for a pour. In this diagram, the verticals supporting the riser forms also serve as a brace for the next higher riser form. A 2 × 8 has also been used to hold the center of the riser forms in place during the pour.

Wedge Forming

When a stair pour is located between two existing flat, solid, well-anchored objects such as building walls, stairs may be formed by wedging a riser

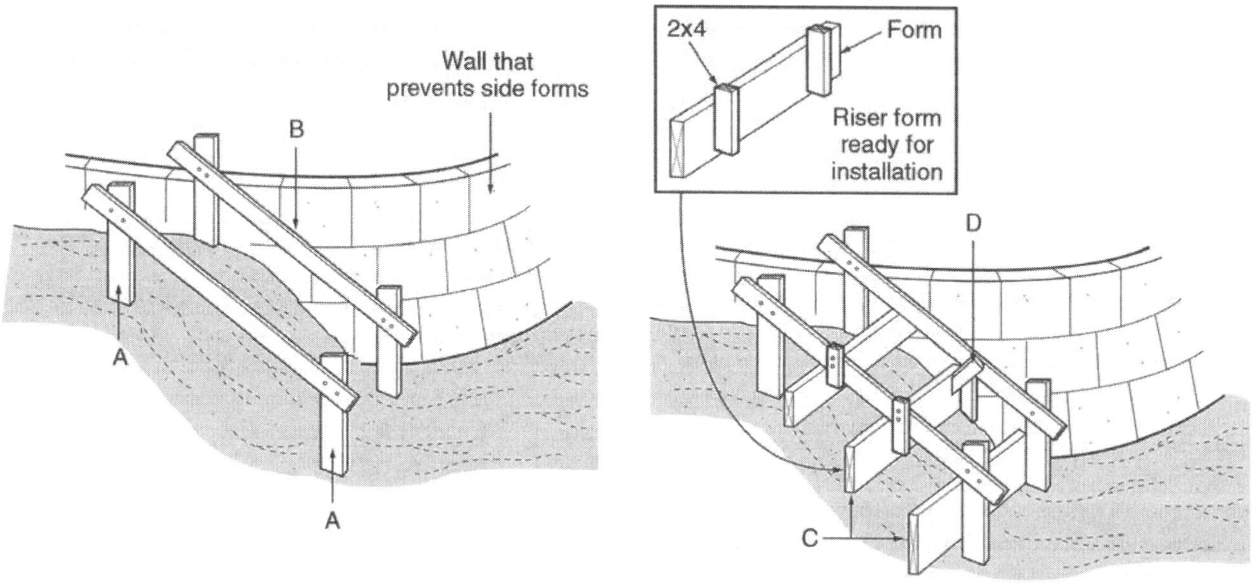

Figure 25-18 Suspended form construction. A. Stake installation at top and bottom. B. Support beam installation. C. Riser form attachment. D. Bracing riser form.

Figure 25-19 Suspended forming for pouring a concrete stair. Riser forms are supported by verticals along the side. The centers of the riser are held in place with a 2 × 8.

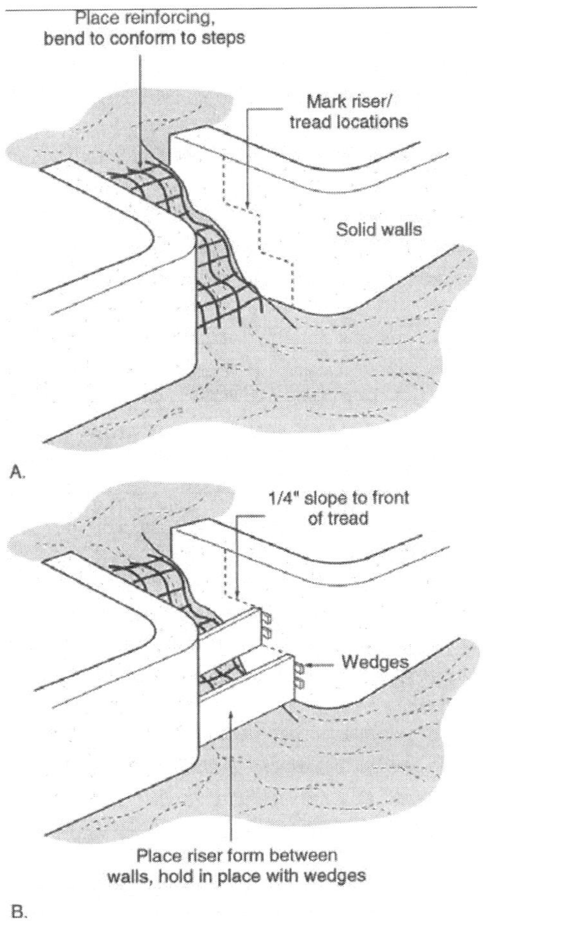

Figure 25-20 Wedge forming stair risers. A. Marking riser/tread locations and placing reinforcement. B. Installing and securing riser forms.

form between the two objects (Figure 25-20). Although this method saves time-consuming construction of form supports, wedging also has the risk of form failure if the riser form cannot be tightly wedged between walls.

Place any reinforcing material and expansion joint material before installing the form. On the surfaces at each side of the stairs, mark the location for the stair treads and risers. Measure the length between the marks for the first riser form. Cut a piece of 2-inch dimensioned lumber ⅛ inch shorter than this measurement. Rip cut the length of the lumber to match the riser's height. Rip with a beveled bottom similar to the riser forms for independent and suspended pours.

Position the riser form and drive a shim between the form and wall to wedge the form tightly into position. If necessary, adjust the location using a hammer. Fill gaps of ¼ inch or less with expanding foam insulation or caulking. Let the foam expand and harden; then trim away any excess. Repeat for each riser. When pouring concrete, carefully hand shovel concrete into the stair behind the wedge forms to reduce the chance of form failure.

JOINTING AND REINFORCING

After finishing the forming, prepare any joints and reinforcing that can be done before pouring. This work includes installation of any **expansion joints** next to fixed objects, preparation of **construction joints,** and installation of wire mesh for reinforcement. **Contraction,** or **control, jointing** is performed after the pour is complete and is covered later in this chapter.

Using Reinforcement

Reinforcement material is a subject of much discussion in concrete circles. Some say wire mesh does little to help strengthen concrete, especially if it is improperly installed. Others still insist on the value of WWM to reduce the effects of contractive cracking and to strengthen the slab. Welded wire mesh is a 10-gauge wire that is welded in 6-inch squares. If using WWM, roll it out across the entire area of the pour and flatten it (Figure 25-21). Overlapping the joints slightly provides seamless reinforcement. Hold the mesh back a few inches from the edges in case it moves when the pour begins. Use a fencing tool to cut WWM when required.

> **CAUTION**
>
> WWM is typically supplied in rolls that must be unrolled and flattened before they can be used. When unrolling WWM, hold the end in place to prevent recoiling and injury. WWM must be suspended above the subgrade to assure it is embedded within the concrete pour.

Cut holes around objects that are in the middle of the slab. Keeping the mesh flat requires significant bending and shaping, but this is

Figure 25-21 Welded wire mesh reinforcing cut and placed before pour.

necessary because bows will cause the WWM to protrude above the slab.

Fibermesh is an alternative to WWM that requires no preparation, but using fibermesh can be a problem in the finishing stage. Fibermesh, which is tiny strands of fiberglass, is added to the concrete while it is being mixed. The strands bond to the concrete and form an integral reinforcement. Finishing is slower because the strands of fiberglass drag on the equipment. The finished look of the slab with fibermesh can have a "fuzzy" appearance until the strands wear. The fine fiberglass strands of this reinforcement appear to add a great deal of strength to the slab and may serve as an adequate strength replacement for WWM.

Another reinforcing material is deformed steel reinforcing rod, also termed **rebar,** a rigid bar used to strengthen concrete in pours. The surface of rebar has tiny ridges, or deformations, that keys with the concrete hardened around them. Cut rebar using a hacksaw, heavy-duty bolt cutter, or cutting torch. Rebar can be placed in a grid network inside thick slabs or placed along the edge of a slab to add strength. Rebar is purchased in lengths and is specified by fractional diameter. This diameter is typically stated in eighths—for example, a #3 rebar is ⅜-inch in diameter. Diameters are available up to 2 inches, but most landscape work requires #3 or #4 rebar.

When rebar is to be positioned inside the concrete slab, it needs to be supported in place during the pour. Two materials, chairs and dobies, are available to hold the rebar slightly above the base during the pour. Chairs are short metal baskets with indentations that hold the rebar above the base surface. Place chairs directly on the base, and place the rebar in the indentation. Wrap wire ties around the chair and rebar to anchor the rebar during the pour.

Dobies are short, precast concrete blocks with wire ties protruding from the top. Set the dobies directly on the base with the rebar positioned on top. Twist the wire tie around the rebar to hold it in position during the pour (Figure 25-22).

Installing Construction Joints and Anchoring Adjacent Pours

If plans are to complete the pour in more than one session, a construction joint, or a clean vertical

Figure 25-22 Dobies hold rebar in place during concrete pours.

Figure 25-23 Construction joint set at a breaking point in pour.

© Delmar/Cengage Learning.

joint from which future work can be started, will need to be formed (Figure 25-23). This joint is created by installing a 2 × 4 form staked into place where the pour stopped. If using wood joints in the pour, you can use any of the wood headers as a construction joint for the project. Planning the location of construction joints will be important if the joint pattern is part of a decorative pattern of surface joints.

When pouring slabs at different times, one of several joining methods should be used to hold both slabs in the same position. An existing concrete slab may be undercut to help join slabs. Under excavate the existing slab 4 inches deeper and back 4 inches from the edge. When pouring the new slab, be certain to tamp concrete into this void. Another method for joining slabs is to drill ½-inch diameter holes 4 inches into the edge of first slab and insert ½- inch (#4) rebar into the holes. The rebar should extend into the new slab area 12 inches (Figure 25-24). Space these rebar connectors every 2 feet along the length of a slab's edge. A third way to joint slabs is to use a keyway joint. A **keyway** is a metal channel that is nailed to the pour side of the board forming the construction joint (Figure 25-25). Keyway channels form an indentation into the slab, creating a lip into which concrete from the next pour will flow and interlock the slabs.

Attempting to join two, 4-inch slabs with rebar or a keyway joint results in only 1–1½ inches of concrete above the rebar/keyway that is weak and prone to cracking. If the keyway or rebar joining is desired, the slab should be thickened to 8 inches at construction joints to provide more concrete above and below the rebar/keyway. To thicken a slab at a joint or edge of a pavement pour, excavate the base to 8 inches deep in an area 8 inches back from the slab edge or joint location. This extra depth should extend across the entire width of the slab, or along the entire edge where the thickened slab is desired. The transition from the thickened base to the normal base should be tapered at a 45° angle from the lower depth to the normal depth (Figure 25-25).

Installing Expansion Joints

Expansion joints absorb the expansion of concrete when temperatures warm the material. **Expansion joint material** should be placed between a slab/stair and any permanent object in or adjacent to a pour. This list typically includes buildings, curbs, deck posts, light posts, hydrants, foundations, and any other object that can be moved as the slab expands.

Figure 25-24 Rebar placement along edge of pour to anchor new slab to existing concrete.

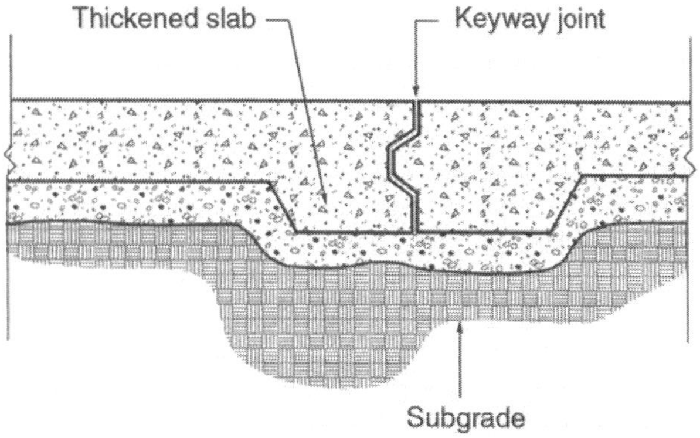

Figure 25-25 Keyway joints and thickened slabs.

Materials used for expansion joints include a premanufactured, ½-inch thick plastic that comes precut in 4-inch and 6-inch widths in varying length rolls, or a ½-inch thick by 4-inch wide asphalt-impregnated fiberboard that comes in 8-foot lengths. The plastic material is very flexible and fits most installations, whereas the fiberboard is rigid and works best in straight installations. In certain applications, expansion joint material must be installed as the paving is poured.

This expansion joint leaves a gap in the continuous run of concrete. The placement of an expansion joint in the pour requires that the joint material be supported while the pour is executed. To join the slabs, thicken the pour to a minimum of 8 inches for 1 foot on either side of the pour. Based on the design or situation, expansion joints may not require and reinforcing to join one side of the slab to the other. If an anchor between slabs is specified, cut and place a piece of expansion joint material the full thickness and width of the slab. Bore ½-inch holes 4 inches down from the top edge and at every foot along the length of the material. Place the expansion joint material in the center of the thickened portion of the slab at the correct location for the expansion joint. Cut 1-foot lengths of deformed #4 rebar and center them in every bored hole in the expansion joint material. Position the expansion joint upright and support the rebar on both sides of the expansion joint using chairs or dobies. When pouring the slab, hand shovel concrete on either side of the joint to hold it in position. Verify that the expansion joint has not moved and is not covered by concrete while the pour is being placed and finished. Verify the rebar is not protruding through the slab surface. If rebar extends above the surface, push it back into the slab with a shovel. After the slab has cured, a sealant may be applied over the expansion joint (Figure 25-26).

To attach expansion joint material to structures, mark the top of the slab with a chalk line and use concrete nails to fasten the joint material along that line. If the object does not accept nails, try wrapping the joint material around the object and taping it in place, or attach it using a construction adhesive.

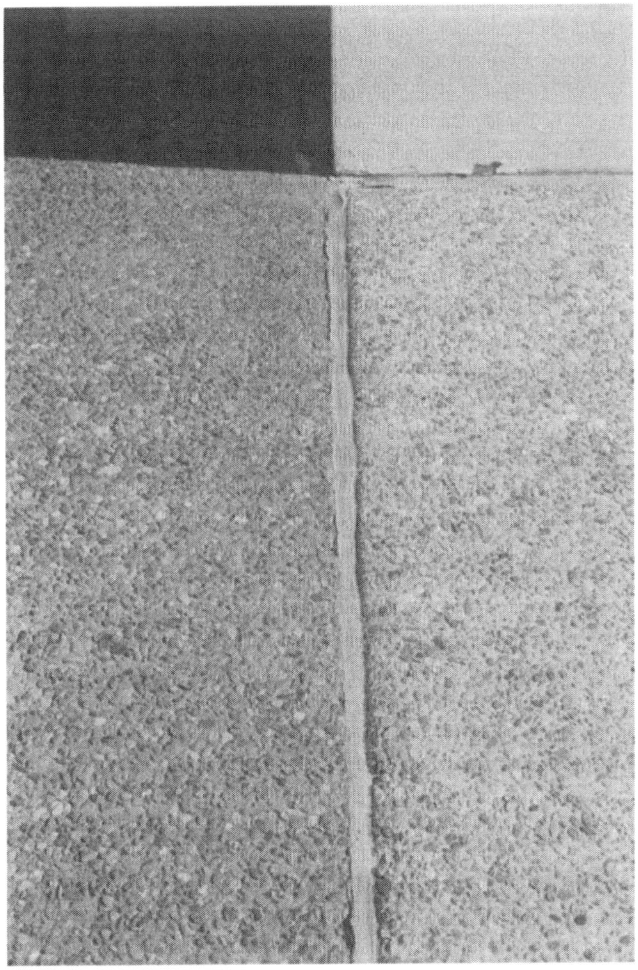

Figure 25-26 A sealed expansion joint between two exposed aggregate concrete slabs. If the joint is manufactured from asphalt impregnated material, no sealant is required.

WEATHER CONDITIONS AND PAVING

Weather conditions such as rainfall, snowfall and temperature can impact a concrete pour by effecting the quality of the finished slab. If rain is imminent or forecast before it is anticipated that the concrete will be cured, postpone the pour until the weather is suitable. Snowfall adds a double challenge to a concrete pour, with both the excess moisture from the snow and the reduced temperature. Temperature can also impact the speed and quality of the curing process. Do not pour concrete if the subgrade or base course, or any of the aggregate particles are frozen. Do not pour if air temperatures, away from artificial heat or in the shade, drop below 35 degrees F. Stop work until the air temperature is 35 degrees F. and rising. Do not pour if the air temperature in the shade is 90 degrees F and rising or if the concrete temperature is greater than 95 degrees F[3].

If the concrete is already poured and the temperature drops below 35 degrees F, insulate the concrete to prevent cooling at a rate greater than 5 degrees F. per hour until cured. If anticipated temperatures are above 90 degrees F., cover, keep top wet and protect the concrete to assure proper curing. If rain occurs after concrete is poured, cover and protect the unhardened surface.[3]

PREPARATION BEFORE POURING

Between the forming and the pouring, a few steps may be required to assure the success of the project. Although minor in scope, these steps cannot easily be completed when concrete is flowing into the forms.

Temporary Screeding Rails

Screeding of concrete is an important step in the pouring process. Screeding uses a long, straight piece of lumber or metal to smooth the rough concrete into a surface that can be finished. Occasionally, pours may have slabs that are wider than available screeds or no forms on one side, such as next to a building. If this is the case, consider a temporary screeding rail as a solution. A temporary screeding rail is a rigid metal conduit placed parallel to forms and supported on short stakes. This rail supports the screed and is slid to a new position as the screeding progresses. As you move the screed, shovel concrete into the void left by the rail and smooth the concrete by following the steps of the concrete finishing process. Leave the stakes that supported the

[3]NCDOT 2012 Standard Specifications, Section 7, 2012.

screed in the slab. Failing to slide the pipe every 2 feet or so will make reaching the void more difficult. At the end of the pour, remove the rail.

Stakes that support the temporary screeding rails are made of 1 × 4s, driven into the base to within 2 inches of the finish grade. Two nails spaced the width of the conduit are driven into the top of the 1 × 4. Leave only 1 inch of the length of the nails sticking up so they will not project above the concrete surface when finished (Figure 25-27). Adjust stake height to place the top of the temporary screed rail at the desired height (Figure 25-28). A typical screed rail is a 2-inch diameter, galvanized, Schedule 40 electrical conduit. An alternative is to set up temporary wood forms that are removed and to fill the void after screeding.

Form Break Compound

Spray the inside of the forms with a form break compound or light kerosene. These chemicals reduce the bonding of concrete to the forms, making removal of forms an easier chore and causing less damage to the concrete.

Figure 25-27 Support stakes for temporary screeding bars. These stakes will be buried in the slab. Verify that nails do not project above screed bars.

Figure 25-28 Temporary screeding rails used for screeding wide pours. The top of the rail should be set at the desired thickness of the slab.

Final Check

Go through the checklist again before the concrete arrives. Included in the checklist are some last-minute steps to prepare for the pour:

- On hot days, sprinkle the base with a light shower of water before pouring to slow the curing process.
- Make sure all necessary tools are easily accessible.
- Prepare ahead of time for bad weather. Have a cover ready for the surface.
- Make sure any routes for access are free of debris to avoid accidents.
- Have preselected locations for excess concrete and mixer cleanout.

PLACEMENT OF CONCRETE

Begin the pour by checking the slump of the concrete. Correctly checking the slump requires filling a 12 tapered cone and tamping the concrete inside. Invert the cone on a solid surface, remove the cone, and measure the amount the concrete "slumps" below the top of the cone. A 3-inch slump is standard for slabs. If you cannot make a formal slump check, you can use other methods to determine concrete preparation. In a visual check, concrete with proper consistency should look like a thick stew. If the concrete fails to move down a wetted chute, it is probably too dry; if it pushes water out along the sides of the chute, it is probably too wet.

Another check is to chop through a pile of concrete and see if ridges remain. If ridges crumble, the concrete is too dry; if ridges slump, the concrete is too wet. It is better to add water to concrete that is too dry than to have concrete that is too wet. If the concrete pour is on a slope, a low slump will be necessary to keep it in place when working from the top of the slope to the bottom.

CAUTION

Concrete contains caustic materials that can cause burns after prolonged contact with the skin. Avoid contact between bare skin and wet concrete, and wash thoroughly after working with concrete.

Placing and Screeding

Once you have prepared the concrete for pouring, position workers to make the task efficient. Placing one worker in rubber boots in the middle of the pour to push concrete and to help pull the screed with a rake is an effective use of labor. Position two workers on either side of the pour, one to operate the end of the screed and the other to shovel concrete to the locations required.

When the concrete has reached the proper consistency, place it in piles, working the chute from one side of the forms to the other. Using rakes and shovels, spread the concrete in front of the screed. If using WWM, use the rake to hook the mesh and pull up gently to seat it in the center of the slab. If the WWM rises above the surface during the pour and cannot be forced back down, lift the mesh up and cut out the offending section with a fencing tool, bending the edges back down into the slab.

When approximately 2 linear feet of the pour has been leveled with rakes and shovels, begin screeding. Using a 2 × 4 that is cut 2 feet longer than the width of the pour, rest the screed on the forms. With a side-to-side sawing motion, gradually pull the screed forward until the concrete is leveled and the aggregate is pushed down into slab (Figure 25-29). Be certain to keep the screed resting on the forms to ensure the proper thickness of the slab. If the screed is difficult to move, try dragging the screed forward 1–2 feet without the sawing motion to rough level the concrete; then go back and rescreed using the sawing motion. Tilting the top of the screed forward can also make the screeding process easier. It is typically easier to pull, rather than to push, the screed. If large pours are planned, the work may benefit from renting a power screed. The power screed is a flat, horizontal plate mounted on a framework. A motor vibrates the screed, and workers push the machine forward across the forms.

Figure 25-29 Placing and screeding concrete.

In corners or areas where both ends of the screed cannot rest on a form or temporary screeding rail, you can use a technique termed **wet screeding.** Perform wet screeding by resting one end of the screed on a form, holding the unsupported end of the screed at the approximate finish elevation, and performing the sawing action of screeding. Although this technique is not recommended for large areas, small spaces or short runs can be successfully leveled using the previously screeded area as a guide for the elevation of the area being wet screeded.

If low spots or honeycombing voids appear after screeding, workers with shovels should sprinkle concrete on the spot and repeat the screeding. Screeding should be completed in as few passes as possible. When finished, the surface should be level, have no holes, and should resemble a sheet of rough-sawn plywood.

Bull Floating

Almost immediately after the screed passes, workers can begin floating the surface with the **bull float,** a wide, flat metal blade with a long handle that is pushed and pulled over the surface several times. This process further smoothes the surface and embeds the aggregate in the slab; it may not be practical in tight areas or on small pours. Most bull float handles are adjustable, allowing a person of any height to operate it on any reasonable width of slab. Because the float handle is long, watch out for power lines and windows behind and above its path.

Figure 25-30 Bull floating a concrete slab.

CAUTION

Review the area before bull floating. If the handle comes into contact with power lines, a worker could be electrocuted. Also, if it strikes them, the handle can cause damage to structures and injury to people.

The long-handled bull float is set on the near side of the slab and slowly pushed across the slab, keeping the leading edge of the float off the concrete by holding the handle low. When the float reaches the other side, lift the handle up and slowly pull back along the same path, keeping the leading edge high by holding the handle high (Figure 25-30). If the float sinks into the concrete surface, remove the float and wait a few minutes before continuing. If the float digs into the concrete, you are holding the front edge too low. Using a repetitive jerking motion may help the float move easier on the first pass. Float the surface as many times as necessary to create a smooth, glasslike surface without holes or voids; then pick up the float, move it down one width, and continue. Between sections where you move the float, tiny ridges will exist but can be troweled out later. If the float becomes coated with chunks of concrete or debris, stop and rinse the surface.

Darby Floating

A **darby float** may be used in areas that are too tight to reach with a bull float. The darby is a narrow, 4-foot long float made of wood or metal, with handles on top. Operate the darby by lifting the leading edge when moving the float across the surface. Make several arcing passes with the darby, exerting slight pressure on the trailing edge. This pressure will bring moisture and the fine particles of concrete to the surface to fill any small voids or holes.

Floating and Troweling

Floating and troweling is the laborious step of working the surface with flat-bladed tools that push the aggregate farther down into the pour and cause water and fine particles to move up to the surface. Two troweling steps are recommended for concrete slabs: (1) floating, performed with a wood or metal float, and (2) steel troweling, performed with thin steel trowels. Exterior slabs may need only the first step, as is the case when planning a rough, broom texture for the surface; but smoother surfaces and interior slabs may require both steps to prepare the surface properly for finishing. Floating and troweling works best starting at the point where the pour began and working in the same direction that the pour progressed. This finishes the surface in approximately the same order in which it will harden. Watch for portions of the pour that are in direct sunlight or in areas where the concrete may harden more quickly. These areas may need to be floated or troweled sooner.

Floating can be done with wood or **magnesium floats,** also known as *mag floats.* Begin once the surface has begun to lose the wet sheen left from bull floating. Test the surface before finishing. If the tool sinks easily into the surface when pushed straight down, wait a bit longer. Working quickly, move the float in a sweeping, arcing motion across the concrete surface to remove any ridges, holes, or other irregularities. Pushing down hard with the back edge of the float while holding the leading edge above the surface makes floating easier and more productive (Figure 25-31). Floating is done while the concrete is just beginning to dry, so the majority of this step is completed with the worker standing to the edge of the slab. Reach as far inward as possible; then move to the other side of the slab or use kneeboards as described in the next paragraph.

If the slab is too wide to reach from outside the pour, use a pair of 24-inch × 24-inch sheets of ½-inch plywood, termed **kneeboards,** to reach the center. Gently position the first kneeboard and step onto it; then place the second kneeboard within a step from the first. If the board sinks completely into the surface from your weight, delay until the concrete hardens a bit more. If the board does not sink at all, move quickly.

Kneeboards should be spaced close enough to step from the first board to the second. If unable

Figure 25-31 Floating a concrete slab from the edge.

to reach the center of the pour, then reach back and pick up the first kneeboard and move it closer to the center. Repeat this process as many times as necessary. When you are positioned, float/trowel the area around and up to the kneeboard. Step back to the kneeboard closer to the edge (Figure 25-32). Peel up the vacated board and reverse the placement process used to get to the center. Weight on the board will cause it to stick to the concrete surface, requiring it to be "peeled" from the concrete.

Once you remove the board, float/trowel out any indentation. It is important that the kneeboard leave no indentation of the surface of the concrete, so if necessary trowel out any irregularities in the surface caused by the kneeboard. If the concrete is hardening quickly,

Figure 25-32 Using kneeboards to reach center of a concrete slab for floating. Concrete must begin to set before boards can be placed on the slab.

you may need to make several passes over the surface while exerting pressure on the float to bring moisture back up to the surface. Extra concrete may be placed by the shovelful to fill low areas or to repair serious damage. Properly floated/troweled surfaces appear smooth and wet and will have no holes, ridges, or irregularities. The surface should look prepared enough that it could be left in that condition if no other finishing were to take place.

If a smooth surface is planned or if the surface is still rough after floating, you need to perform steel troweling. Begin troweling after the sheen has disappeared from the surface, and use the same process outlined in the floating description. When done properly, steel troweling creates a very smooth surface that is slick in exterior applications. Consider renting a power trowel to save a lot of labor on surfaces that are intended to be smooth. The power trowel is a large piece of walk-behind equipment that uses a motor to drive a fan of trowels.

Used primarily for interior slab finishing, the power trowel has limited applications in exterior use.

SURFACE TEXTURING AND FINISHING

When the concrete has begun to set, you can begin surfacing and texturing. Instructions for obtaining the finishes described in the chapter introduction are described here. Proper timing of each operation is also identified.

- Float Finish. Floating for a finish should be done after the surface has begun to harden; the intention here is different than that of the first floating operation. Use a back-and-forth motion that eliminates a pattern and provides uniform results. You may need to apply extra pressure on the float to get a rough surface. Jointing the slab into squares, rectangles, or other geometric segments creates an interesting surface out of what could otherwise be a very dull finish. Using the edger around each segment creates a border that highlights the finish inside. To obtain a swirl float finish, press hard to work a large quantity of soft material to the surface. Work the surface in horizontal rows of arcing swirls that slightly overlap each preceding row. Along the slab edges, float a single. horizontal swath. On the next horizontal row, begin applying arcing half-circle swirls evenly across the row (Figure 25-33). Overlap the horizontal swath of the slab edge with the swirls. In the next horizontal row, continue the swirls, slightly overlapping the previous row and offsetting by one-half pattern. Continue this pattern across the entire surface to be finished.

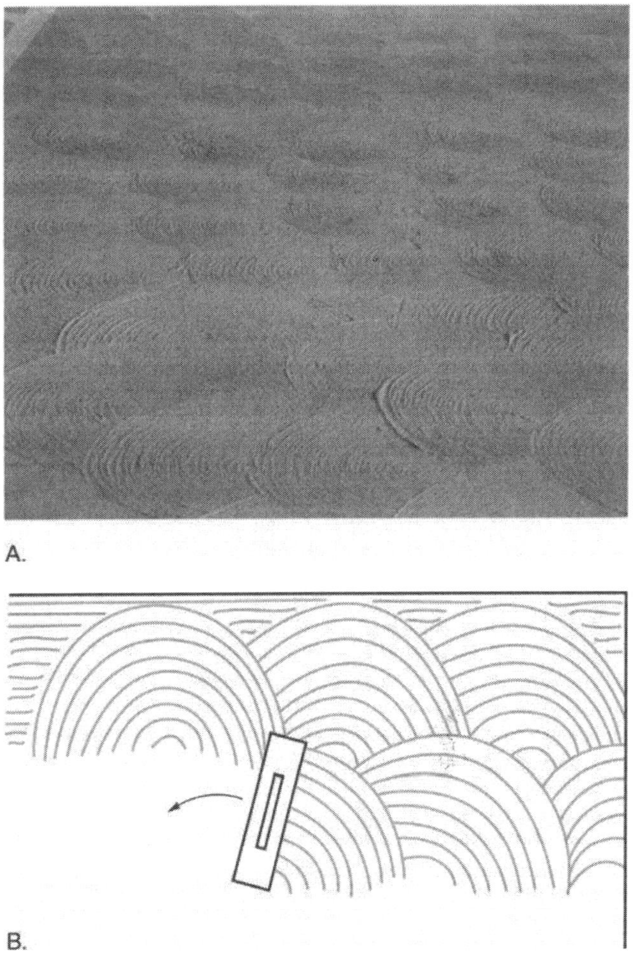

Figure 25-33 Swirl finish on concrete slab. A. Finish. B. Technique.

- Broom Finish. Brooming should be done when the surface is firm to the touch but not dry. The broom will create a ridged pattern that should be perpendicular to the direction of traffic but parallel to the direction of drainage off the slab. Extend the broom to the far edge of the slab or to a location where a joint will be placed, set the broom down lightly, and pull with a single, smooth motion to the near edge of the slab (Figure 25-34). Repeat this motion the full length of the slab, using a slight overlap from one pull to the next. If the broom becomes plugged with wet concrete or begins to drop small "kernels" of concrete, set the broom head on end to the side of the slab and tap it a few times to dislodge the debris. You can use small hand brooms to surface tight areas.
- Colored, Impressioned Finish. (Using some versions of this process may be

Figure 25-34 Broom finishing a concrete slab.

restricted to contractors who hold licenses from manufacturers.) This process involves two steps: (1) coloring the concrete and (2) impressioning, or stamping; the surface. The first step is accomplished by adding a powdered color to the concrete while it is mixed or by sprinkling powder on the wet, screeded surface and floating it into the concrete. Manufacturer's instructions recommend the best method for adding color. The powder must be mixed thoroughly and evenly into the surface of the concrete. Finishing proceeds in the same manner as that for plain concrete until after troweling. When the sheen from troweling has disappeared, stamps are carefully placed on the slab surface and are either pounded down with a rubber mallet or forced down by the weight of a person standing on them. If the stamps sink into the surface, postpone the operation until the concrete has hardened a bit more. When one area has been successfully impressioned, pull up the stamp and place it on the slab adjacent to the first area stamped. Repeat this process until you have impressioned the entire surface. Small areas and irregular spaces will not allow stamping. However, you can hand finish these areas by pushing the blade of a brick set into the wet concrete. When hand finishing areas, follow the same pattern made by the stamp. Work quickly with the stamping operation; otherwise, the concrete could harden before you complete the impressioning work. This type of surface is not edged or jointed as described for float and broom finishes.

- Seeded Exposed Aggregate. Broadcast the special aggregate over the surface after bull floating and, using a trowel, embed it into the top of the slab. Float the surface just until the aggregate disappears. Floating too long will bury the aggregate too deep. After the concrete begins to harden enough to support a person's weight—in approximately 2 hours—lightly "scrub" with a hose and broom to remove the top film of concrete and "expose" the embedded aggregate. If the scrubbing operation gouges the surface and dislodges aggregate, stop immediately and repair the holes; then wait for the slab to harden further. Six to seven days later, wash the surface with a mixture of 9 parts water and 1 part muriatic acid or trisodium phosphate (TSP).
- Integral Exposed Aggregate. Pouring and finishing proceeds in the same manner as that for plain concrete until just before the slab is nearly hardened. When the slab supports a person's weight—in approximately 2 hours—begin a light "scrubbing" of the surface with water and a broom. Scrub only enough to wash the

top film of concrete off the surface and expose the aggregate near the surface. An alternative to scrubbing the surface is to lightly sandblast the concrete 2–3 days after the pour to expose the aggregate. Because you can easily gouge the surface or dislodge the aggregate, work carefully when exposing the aggregate and when jointing and edging this type of surface.

- Exposed Aggregate Using Retardants. Pour and finish in the same manner as plain concrete, then spread surface retardant over the surface of the poor. This retardant prevents the surface from hardening as quickly as the concrete below the aggregate. After the concrete is set up, wash the top to expose the aggregate.
- Rock Salt. To create rock salt texturing, first finish the surface with the desired texture. Colored or plain concrete with a float or broom finish is the best surface. Before the concrete hardens, or when your thumb leaves about a ¼-inch deep impression, sprinkle ¼–⅜-inch grains of rock salt over the finished surface in the desired pattern. A random pattern, with some heavy concentrations interspersed among lightly textured areas, provides an attractive surface. Trowel or roll the salt into the surface so only the tops of the grains are visible (Figure 25-35). You can use a special salt roller to provide the correct pressure for embedding the salt crystals. Use caution not to leave marks when rolling or finishing, and do not embed the salt crystals too deep into the concrete. Cover and cure the concrete for 2–5 days. Uncover the slab and rinse it, brushing the remaining salt from the surface.
- Acid Etch. Complete the pour and allow the surface to cure for 2 weeks or longer. Mix 9 parts water with 1 part muriatic acid and apply evenly over the surface. Let the water/acid mix work at the surface until the desired texture is achieved. At

Figure 25-35 Using a mag float to embed rock salt crystals for a rock salt finish.

that point, rinse the surface thoroughly, scrubbing with a broom to remove material.

- Cobbled Concrete. After completing the floating and while the concrete is still workable, embed 4–6-inch rounded stone into the soft concrete surface. Stone, or cobbles, can be placed closely or in any pattern that the designer or contractor selects.

> **CAUTION**
>
> Muriatic acid and trisodium phosphate (TSP) can cause severe burns. Follow manufacturer's instructions for mixing and applying these chemicals. Wear protective clothing, avoid contact with skin, and do not inhale the fumes.

> **CAUTION**
>
> When mixing acid and water, always add the acid to the water. Never add water to acid. Adding water to acid will cause the mixture to spray and splatter, creating the potential for burns. Always wear protective clothing, gloves, and eyewear when mixing chemicals.

Contraction Jointing

Before the concrete has lost all workability, you should complete the edging and contraction joints. Although these two operations use similar tools and methods, the purpose for each method is quite different. Edging rounds and smoothes the slab's edge corners to reduce chipping of the edge and to help separate the slab from the forms. Edging also provides an aesthetic function by providing a contrasting surface texture when compared to the finish of the slab's interior. Jointing controls cracking as the slab dries and the concrete contracts. Contraction shows up as cracks in the slab's surface; and to control where cracking will occur, contraction (or control) joints are placed in the slab's surface. Without these joints, cracking would occur at random weak points in the slab, and seldom in aesthetically pleasing patterns. Depending on the weather, contraction jointing may be done with a jointing tool while the slab is still wet, or the jointing can be done one day after the pour with a saw. If the weather is hot or the pour is in direct sunlight, jointing with a tool may need to be done shortly after the finishing is completed. Commercial installers typically use saws, but the equipment and blades are expensive. Similar to edging, jointing also provides a contrasting surface texture and helps define squares or other geometric forms created in the slab.

Planning joint locations requires the application of the mathematical formula presented in Appendix D. When spacing the joints, you want to avoid joints that create acute angles. Acute angles are weak points where the slab will crack without a joint. Space joints wider to avoid an acute angle. Consult an engineer or design professional with questions regarding joint placement.

Jointing with a hand tool requires a guide to keep the joint straight across the slab. This is usually provided by laying a piece of dimensioned lumber on the forms from one side to the other, parallel to where the joint is desired (Figure 25-36). A 2 × 8 should be adequate for this. Gently lay the 2 × 8 in place and step halfway across the slab. Begin at the center and press the **jointer** into the concrete. Work the jointer forward and backward, always holding the tool tight against the 2 × 8. You obtain the best results by lifting the leading edge of the tool while pressing down on its back edge. If the slab is drying quickly, the jointer may work up pieces of aggregate. Use the flat part of the tool to push them back into the slab, and then work back and forth over the aggregate with the jointer's back

Figure 25-36 Jointing a concrete slab using a jointing tool run alongside a 2 × 4 guide.

edge until smooth. Going back and forth several times over the surface will usually work up enough moisture to rework the surface. Continue the jointing until you reach the slab's edge.

Move to the other side of the slab and repeat this process from where the previous joint began. Carefully lift the guide board and move it to the next joint location. If necessary, retouch the surface texture when you remove the board. Installing joints down the center of a long slab with a jointing tool is a difficult process. You must set the guide in the correct location and access it using kneeboards. When completed, jointing provides a ⅜-inch deep joint; this is the weak area in which contraction cracking will occur.

You can complete jointing after the concrete has dried. You will need a cutoff saw or walk-behind concrete saw equipped with a carborundum or concrete blade. After the concrete has hardened enough to walk on (no later than the next day depending on the weather), use a chalk line to snap the location of all joints. Start the saw and slowly run the blade along each mark. Use caution to make the cuts only one quarter the depth of the slab (for a 4 inch slab the cut should be 1 inch deep) and straight. Using a 2 × 4 guide may help you keep the sawed joints straight.

CAUTION

When cutting concrete, always wear long-legged pants, hard hat, ear protection, safety glasses, dust mask, and gloves to protect yourself from the dust, noise, and debris.

Edging

Edging should be done following the completion of surface texturing (colored, impressioned concrete is not edged) and may require additional work with the tools because the slab may be nearly dry (Figure 25-37). Dip the edging tool in a bucket of water to make working the surface easier. Use the **edger** in the same manner as the jointer, pushing the edger along the form with the leading edge lifted and putting downward pressure on the trailing edge. Work around all edges that need to be finished. If it is difficult working corners, start the edger in the corner and work outward; then work back toward the corner to cover any marks left in the surface.

COMPLETING THE POUR

The final steps to a successful concrete pour involve protecting the concrete from curing too rapidly and removing the formwork placed to contain the pour.

Curing

Curing is the process of slowing the drying of concrete after it is poured. Following the pouring of concrete, maintaining moisture and temperature in a pour allows the concrete to dry slowly, thus increasing the strength, reducing the

Figure 25-37 Edging a concrete slab.

permeability and reducing the problems associated with cracking. A pour that dries too quickly is unlikely to reach maximum strength and can suffer from surface and internal cracking. Every concrete project cures, but proper curing by maintaining moisture levels and keeping the temperatures in a moderate range extends the life of the concrete. Some pours may cure properly without intervention, but to assure a successful cure, the following are some methods to enhance the process.

Covering with polyethylene or burlap. Covering your pour will be most effective when cold or hot temperatures are expected, or if strength and durability are critical factors. Many smaller residential pours are not covered unless these conditions area expected. After you complete all finishing operations and surface water has disappeared, cover the work with a plastic sheet, wet burlap or spray on a **curing** compound. Covering retains heat and moisture as the slab cures, improving the slab's strength and reducing surface cracking by slowing the drying process. The cover should be a polyethylene film with overlapped and taped joints, and should lie flat on the surface to avoid discoloring. Black polyethylene can be used when cold temperatures are expected. A cover also provides some protection from rain and sunlight and identifies the project site as a construction zone.

If burlap is chosen to cover the surface, thoroughly wet the burlap and apply in a manner that does not damage the finish. Burlap must be kept wet throughout the curing process.

Leave the cover in place a minimum of 24 hours. The curing period is 3 days for standard concrete mixes, and up to 7 days for pozzolan mixes. If the temperature drops below 40 degrees F the curing period will be extended. Coverage for 3–7 days is ideal. Remove the covering, either burlap or polyethylene, when moisture no longer condenses on the underside of the plastic[3].

Curing Compounds. Curing compounds are one method often used in North Carolina. If using a membrane curing compound, apply at a minimum rate of .0067 gal/sf. Apply evenly without puddling or ponding on the surface using mechanical spray equipment. Spray should be applied within 30 minutes of concrete placement and after the surface dries. Protect the membrane from damage and cover any disruptions with polyethylene or burlap3.

Protecting the Pour.

If you have concerns about traffic or animals passing over a new slab, erect a temporary fence around the project to further protect the work.

Removing Forms

Approximately 2–4 days after the pour is completed, you can remove the forms. Uncover the slab and use a claw hammer to remove the form nails from the stakes. Using a careful, prying motion with a shovel or pry bar, gently work the stakes up and away from the forms. When you have removed all stakes, gently work the shovel or pry bar between the slab and the forms and pry outward. Use great care during this step so that the edges of the slab do not chip. A finished slab will still be "green" (the color is actually a dark gray that will dry to a light gray over a few weeks), but it is ready for backfilling the edges. Keep foot traffic off the slab for 2–3 days, and keep any vehicle traffic off the slab for 1–2 weeks.

STAINING CONCRETE

You can add color and interest to new or existing concrete using exterior concrete stains and paints. To revive or renovate older concrete surfaces without having to replace them, use a colored stain to provide almost immediate change. On new concrete installations, use staining to obtain desired design effects. Painting, although not as versatile as staining, is often used to surface athletic facilities such as tennis and basketball courts. Note that colors applied to the surface, whether stain or paint, will eventually wear. A more permanent solution to concrete coloring is to use integral dyes that are mixed into the concrete at the concrete plant.

General Information

Several variations of stains and paints are available for exterior use, with most falling into one of two categories: (1) acid-based stains that etch the surface and allow metallic salts to bond color to the concrete and (2) water-based acrylic stains that either penetrate the surface to color the concrete or bond a color to the existing surface. Both types of stain produce permanent opaque coloration, with acid-based stains providing a range of earth tones and waterbased acrylics providing a wide range of colors. When choosing stain to alter a concrete surface, please note that stains are not intended to hide imperfections in a surface such as cracks, spalling, or patches. Stains will, in many cases, highlight these imperfections. Note that the information provided by most stain manufacturers are only guidelines, and the only way to preview the end result is to test an area. Many factors will alter the actual color and finish, including the age of the concrete, the amount of cement in the mix, the finish of the surface, and the type of aggregate used.

CAUTION

Stain should be handled and applied with care. Follow manufacturer's recommendations for safety when using coloring products. Protect valuable surfaces and elements adjacent to the area being treated from damage as a result of runoff and overspray.

Concrete Preparation

The beginning step in preparing concrete for staining is to verify if the concrete can be successfully stained. Sealers previously applied to older concrete surfaces will prevent the stain from penetrating the concrete. To test for sealers, sprinkle water on the surface and verify that the water does not stand on the surface but penetrates the concrete. New concrete surfaces must cure the proper amount of time to achieve the correct pH and moisture levels. At a minimum, new surfaces should set for 14–28 days before staining, and some stain manufacturers recommend a curing period of up to 60 days. To test for pH, apply a paper test strip to the surface. A desirable pH is between 9 and 10. To test for moisture content, tape a 1-foot square sheet of plastic over the concrete's surface for 24 hours and see if moisture accumulates on the underside of the plastic. If so, wait until no moisture is evaporating out of the slab. Some manufacturers recommend immediate staining of the concrete; so, verify the requirements of the product you are using.

Depending on the type of stain and the age of the concrete, further surface preparation may be required. New concrete should be ready to stain unless a smooth finish was applied. If the surface is smooth, etch the concrete with a mixture of 1 part muriatic acid and 20 parts water. An alternative would be a stronger mix of citric acid with water.

Sprinkle this mixture over the surface with a plastic sprayer or watering can and allow 1 hour for the etching to work. Follow with a thorough rinse with clean water. If staining existing concrete, you will need to clean and perhaps etch the surface. To prevent irregular staining, remove all foreign material from the surface.

Cleaning methods include scrubbing, sanding, and grinding. Scrubbing is for mildly dirty surfaces and should be accomplished by mixing an organic degreaser with water and vigorously scrubbing the surface with a nylon bristle brush. Power washing is an alternative that can speed the scrubbing process. For surfaces with paint or heavy staining, clean by sanding or grinding. Sand using a floor buffer with #80 grit sandpaper, or grind using a floor grinder with a fine grit diamond pad. For both sanding and grinding, attempt to maintain an even surface finish without patterns that will cause irregular staining. Areas that are heavily sanded/ground will absorb more stain and appear darker than lightly sanded/ground surfaces. Final preparation would include masking any areas not to be stained. Use a heavy-duty paint masking tape to protect these surfaces.

Stain Application

To apply stain, first mist the prepared surface lightly with water. Using a plastic sprayer, apply stain with a circular pattern nozzle in an even pattern. Overlap small areas to maintain a consistent appearance. To create a more consistent pattern, follow the spraying with a circular brushing with a medium-bristle brush. Avoid excessive overlap or brushstrokes when applying the stain. You can also use a medium-bristle paintbrush or roller to apply stain. For acid-based stains, a "fizzing" of the surface indicates that the stain is properly reacting with the concrete. Remove any residue and excess stain by mopping the pools or lightly rinsing the surface.

Leave the stain on the surface for approximately 4 hours (unless manufacturer's recommendations are different). If possible, avoid walking on the surface until it is dry. The surface must be dry before you apply additional coats of stain or sealer. For acid-based stains, rinse the surface with a mixture of clean water and 2 tablespoons of baking soda to neutralize the acid.

Sealant Application

When the stained surface has dried, you can apply sealer. Apply a light coat of sealer using a brush or roller; avoid leaving brush marks. Allow the sealer to dry and apply a second coat. To achieve the desired effects, you may have to apply additional coats. Most sealers are acrylic urethane, polyurethane, or epoxy products, with the choice determined by the manufacturer's recommendation.

PAINTING CONCRETE

Concrete stains create an opaque coloration of the surface, whereas paints provide solid color for outdoor surfaces. Painting, rather than staining, concrete has advantages; namely, painting can hide patchwork and patterns can be stenciled onto the surface. Typically epoxy-based, paint for concrete can be tinted a wide range of colors, and silica sand can be added to create a slip-resistant surface.

Concrete Preparation

Before you can paint concrete, its surface must be dry and free of any residue. Prepare the surface by power washing with water and a mild detergent. After cleaning the surface, patch broken areas and fill cracks. Select nonshrink material that will bond well with the surrounding concrete. When the surface is dry, etch the concrete with a mixture of 1 part muriatic acid with 20 parts water. Sprinkle this mixture over the surface using a plastic sprayer or watering can and allow 1 hour for the etching to work. Follow with a thorough rinse, using one gallon of clean water mixed with 2 tablespoons of baking soda to neutralize the acid.

Paint Application

When the surface is clean and dry, apply paint using a brush or roller.

INSTALLING POROUS CONCRETE

Porous concrete, offered by the concrete industry under names such as Pervious® or Permeable® concrete, is a Portland cement concrete that allows water to percolate through the finished surface. Although similar to concrete in structural characteristics, porous concrete differs in composition and installation procedures.

Porous concrete is installed using many of the basic techniques described in this chapter, with a few significant exceptions. The initial difference is in form preparation, where an additional ½-inch shim is required on top of the forms to keep the screeded surface high enough for compaction to the desired finish elevation. A second difference is that the material is placed, screeded, compacted, cured, and jointed. To reduce filling the voids in the material, the steps of bull floating, wood floating, and steel troweling are not used for porous surfaces. Because this is a specialized finishing, the installer should have or should develop skills in working with porous concrete before attempting a contracted installation.

Ordering Material

Porous concrete is formulated differently from typical nonporous concrete. To obtain the open voids in the material, the percentage of fine aggregates is greatly reduced. This reduction in fine particles, typically to around 3 CF per CY of concrete, prevents the filling of all pore space between the aggregate. One manufacturer recommends smooth ⅜-inch aggregate to create a mix with approximately 15% voids. To ensure that the concrete maintains workability and stability, it should be mixed with a slump of 1½–3 inches. A water-to-cement ratio of 0.30 is typically recommended. A hydration stabilizer is often added to slow curing.[1]

Installing Porous Concrete

For a porous surface, the subgrade can be either a lightly compacted subgrade for erosion control installations or a layer of granular base for surfaces that will support traffic. If the surface supports only light traffic, the success in percolating water into the subgrade can be improved by using an 8–36-inch base of clean angular crushed stone of 1–2½-inch diameter.

Placing a nonwoven filter fabric below and along the sides of the washed angular base creates a holding basin similar to a french drain below the pavement. This allows water to slowly percolate into the subgrade (Figure 25-38).

Form preparation follows the steps outlined for concrete, with the addition of a ½-inch shim on top of all forms to increase the pour depth. This additional depth will be required to accommodate compaction during finishing. Ground surfaces may require additional thickness to accommodate the grinding dimension. Jointing concrete mix is placed using wheelbarrows or a ready-mix chute directly on the base. Using shovels and rakes, distribute the concrete as evenly as possible between the forms in front of the screed. The low slump of the concrete makes with neighboring slabs should be accomplished using fiberglass-reinforced plastic rods. Porous it more difficult to evenly distribute the concrete. Screeding with a single pass from an adjustable mechanical vibrating screed is recommended. Following screeding, remove the shims on top of the forms to allow finishing.

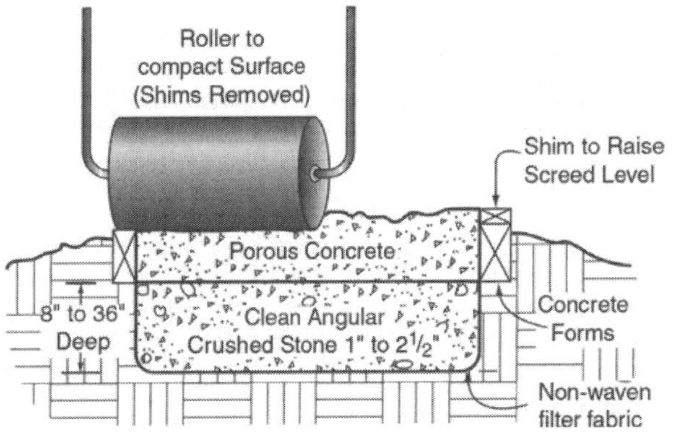

Figure 25-38 Cross section of a porous concrete installation.

[1]U.S. Concrete, Previous Concrete Sample Specification, February 2003, 3–7.

Accomplish the finishing of the porous surface by using a 10–15-inch diameter steel drum roller that you will pass over the surface only enough to compress the slab to the finish elevation. No work with bull floats or trowels is required. To avoid sealing the pores in the concrete, excessive working of the surface is discouraged.[2] Correct low spots in the surface by sprinkling loose concrete into the spot and hand-tamping.

Contraction joints can be installed either before curing, using a ridged drum "pizza" roller that you pull from one side to the other, or following curing, by sawing or grinding to achieve uniformity. Curing of the surface is critical and begins by misting the surface to prevent drying after compaction. Then cover the surface with heavy (6 mil) plastic sheeting for 7–10 days.

[2]Ibid.

CHAPTER 26

UNIT PAVERS

OBJECTIVES

By reading and practicing the techniques described in this chapter, the reader should be able to successfully complete the following activities:

- Install unit pavers in a recognizable pattern.
- Prepare the site for installation of unit pavers.
- Lay unit pavers.
- Finish a unit paver installation.

Including manufactured paving material that is laid by hand, unit paving provides opportunities for color, texture, and pattern unique to the landscape industry. This chapter covers the installation basics used for unit paving materials such as brick, interlocking concrete pavers, asphalt block, and adobe. Included in the information are descriptions of paving patterns and specific installation techniques. Open-cell paving installation is described at the end of the chapter.

RELATED INFORMATION

Information in this chapter is supplemented by instruction provided elsewhere in this text and in other sources. Before undertaking the activities described in this chapter, read the related information in these sources:

- Safety in the Workplace, Chapter 7
- Basic Construction Techniques and Small Equipment Operation, Chapter 8
- Construction Layout, Chapter 9
- Materials and Site Preparation for Paving, Chapter 24
- Site Furniture, Signage, and Prefabricated Playground Equipment, Chapter 32
- Interlocking Concrete Paving Institute (ICPI) Standards
- Brick Industry Association (BIA) Standards

PLANNING THE PROJECT

Construction of unit paver surfaces can be a time-consuming project. To avoid problems, plan the installation before beginning any work. Following are some considerations for planning a unit paver installation.

Paving Patterns

Examples of common paving patterns are identified in Figure 26-1. Because of the special shapes in which they are manufactured, certain paving materials may allow only one pattern. Use caution when purchasing brick pavers. If the units are not modular (length twice as long as width), patterns such as herringbone and basket weave will not work. Placement order for each pavement pattern is shown in accompanying figures. Paving brick should be solid and without any cores or surface openings.

- Running Bond. Running bond is a pattern in which pavers are placed in staggered, horizontal rows. Pavers are placed end to end in one row; and in the next row, they are set end to end but are offset by one-half paver. Pavers that work in this pattern include most interlocking concrete pavers, all brick, and any paver that is not modular. Old roadway bricks can often be used only in this pattern (Figure 26-2).
- Stacked Bond (also called Jack-on-Jack). Stacked bond is a pattern in which pavers are placed side by side in even horizontal and vertical rows. Pavers that work in this pattern include many interlocking concrete

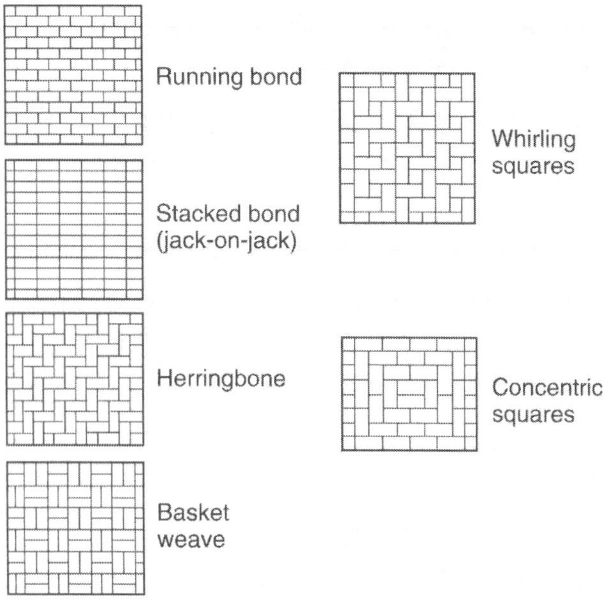

Figure 26-1 Common unit paving patterns.

pavers (all sizes), most brick, adobe, and any modular paver (Figure 26-3).

- Herringbone. Herringbone is a pattern that places horizontal and vertical blocks in a diagonal pattern across the paved area. The finished pattern leaves a zigzag, or

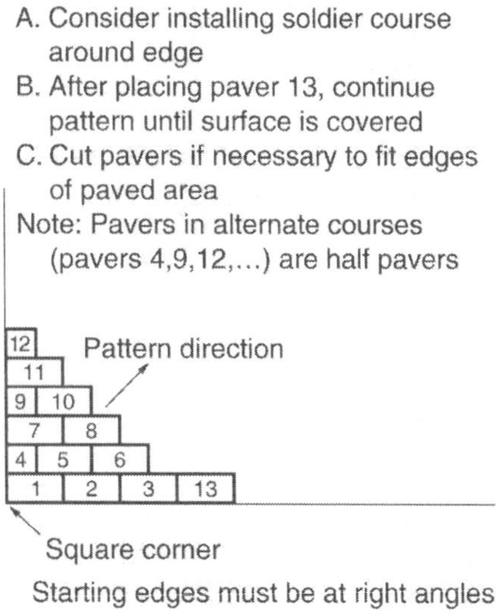

Figure 26-2 Running bond pattern installation.

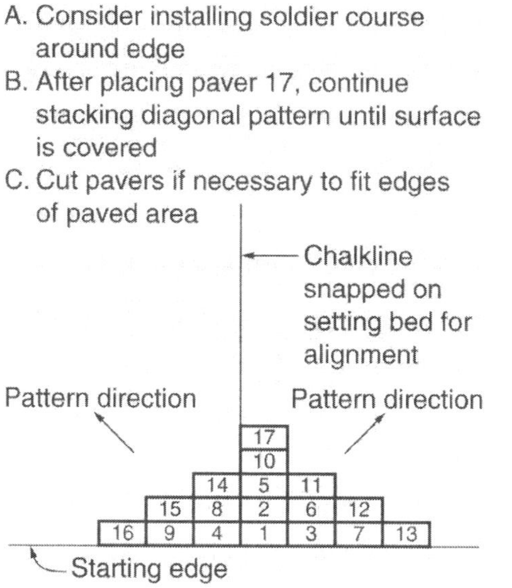

Figure 26-3 Stacked bond pattern installation.

herringbone, appearance. Halves are required for starting this pattern. Any modular paver can be used in this pattern (Figure 26-4).

- Basket Weave. Basket weave places two pavers vertically, and then two pavers horizontally. This alternating pattern is

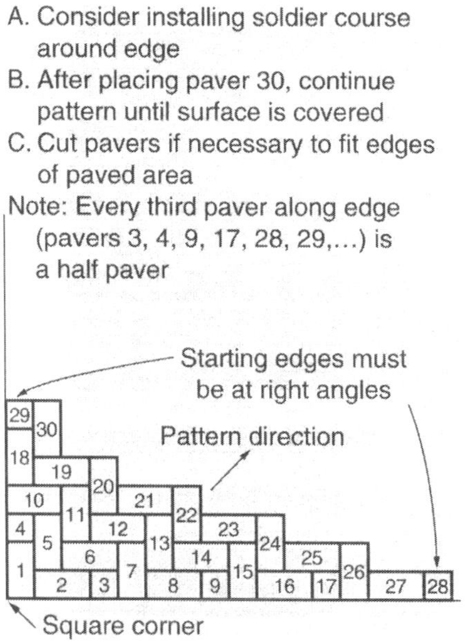

Figure 26-4 Herringbone pattern installation.

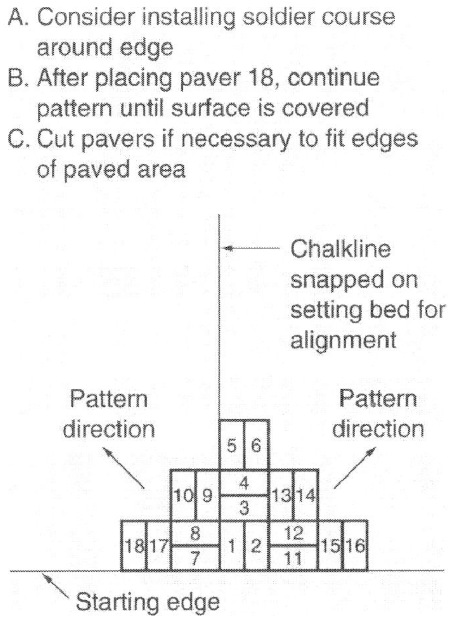

Figure 26-5 Basket weave pattern installation.

repeated across the entire paved area. Any modular paver can be used in this pattern (Figure 26-5).

- Whirling Squares. Whirling squares place four pavers in a square pattern around a half-brick center. This pattern can be offset to create an even more interesting pattern. Halves are required for this pattern. Any modular paver can be used in this pattern (Figure 26-6).
- Modified Basket Weave. Variations of the basket weave are possible. A common variation includes placing an extra vertical between the vertical and horizontal pairs in every other row. Any modular paver can be used in this pattern (Figure 26-7).

Brick and Interlocking Concrete Paver Specifications

When selecting brick and interlocking concrete pavers for a project, be aware that these products may differ slightly from similar building products on the market, particularly in strength, dimension and color. Clay paving brick are made to different tolerances as specified by ASTM C 902-93 and

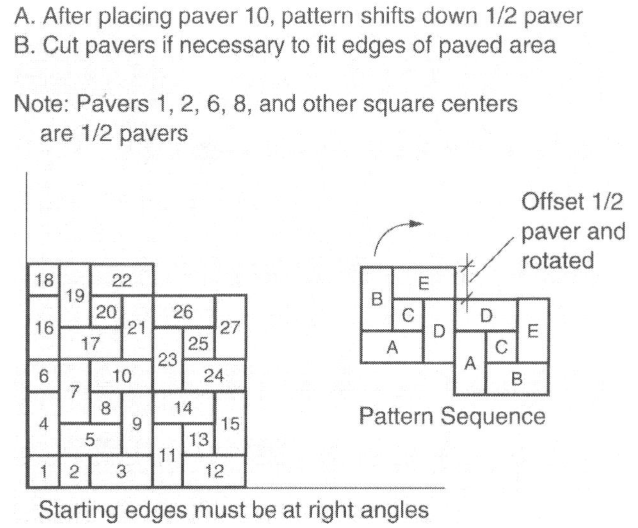

Figure 26-6 Whirling squares pattern installation.

BIA Technical Note on Brick Construction 14A. This specification identifies the manufacturing controls, dimensional tolerances, and related characteristics of clay paving brick. Concrete Interlocking Pavers are made as specified by ASTM C 936, which addresses similar

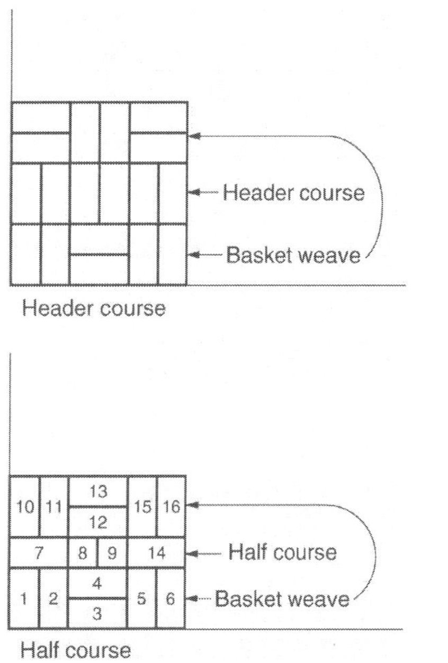

Figure 26-7 Basket weave pattern variations.

considerations as the clay paving brick specification. When purchasing materials, assure that the products you are buying meet or exceed these standard specifications.

Concrete Interlocking Pavers

Interlocking concrete pavers are also available in a variety of shapes that create patterns when installed in stacked or running bond. Some common shapes of interlocking pavers include (Figure 26-8):

- Rectangle. Modular rectangular paver.
- Double Score Rectangle. Modular rectangular paver with a score line in the center to create an impression of two halves.
- Octagonal. Paver with an octagonal body and interlocking tab.
- Dentated. Paver with an interlocking angled edge.
- Cobble. Combination of modular rectangular and square stones.
- H Block, I Paver, or Dogbone. Paver with an interlocking H shape.
- Permeable Pavers. Block with truncated corners or wider side spacers.
- Porous Pavers. Precast blocks with porous surfaces to allow drainage through the material.
- Circle Pavers. Wedge-shaped stones to form various radii circles.
- Euro-Cobble®. Combination of modular rectangular stones. Also named Villa®.
- Balboa Pavers®. Arced edges that interlock in patterns of four stones.
- Bishop's Hat®. A combination of triangular stones with small square center blocks.
- Custom Pavers. Molded stones in the shapes of animals and custom designed shapes.

®Pavestone Manufacturers and ®Gecktostone.

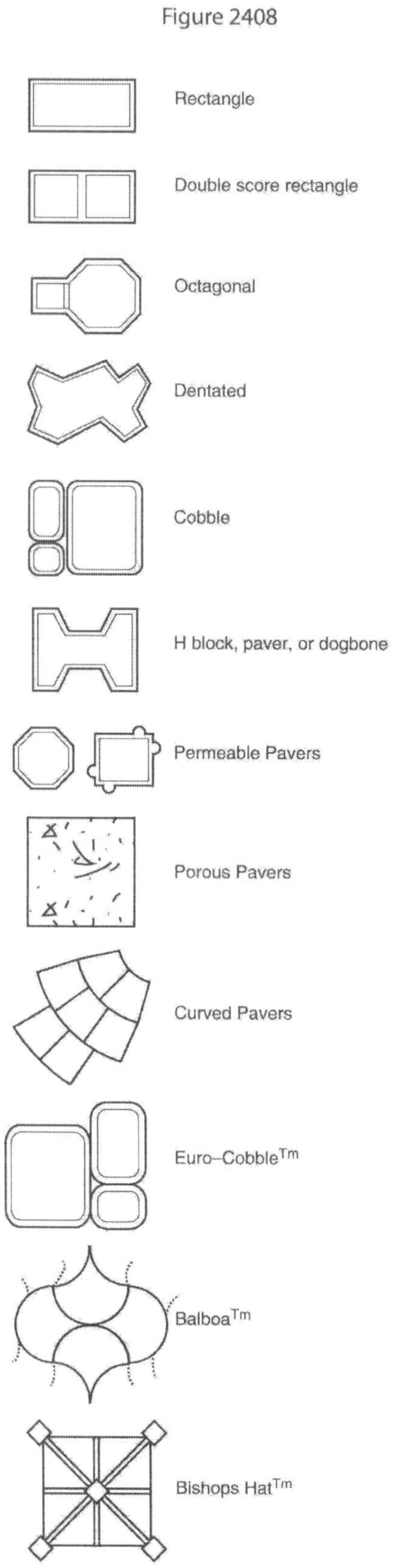

Figure 26-8 Interlocking concrete paver shapes.

Permeable Pavers

When excess surface drainage from a paved area becomes a concern, the design professional may choose to use permeable interlocking pavers. Permeable pavers, which are suited for most low traffic and pedestrian paved areas, are interlocking pavers with joints filled with small stone. Water flows through the joints and into an open graded base and is collected in the voids between the base stone. From there the water can be allowed to percolate into the subgrade or collected and directed into a drainage system. This system significantly reduces the runoff from a paved area while also providing a level of filtration for pollutants that are picked up from the paving. Installation of permeable pavers will require special base preparation before the setting of pavers.

BASE MATERIAL

Base preparation for most unit paving installations is similar to the process described in Chapter 24. However, for some pavement types, there are alternatives for using an aggregate base with a setting bed. Installation over a previously paved surface, or pavement that must carry heavy traffic loads, may require an alternative to a crushed stone pavement base. Regardless of material, the base under the entire paved area should be consistent. Differential settlement can occur in areas where the unit pavers move from one type of base onto another.

Valleys and ridges typically develop over time where base materials change. In all base materials, the top of the base surface must be constructed with a maximum of plus or minus 3/8 inch over 10 feet. In addition, base material should be compacted to a minimum of 98% standard proctor density. Some alternative treatments are:

- Concrete or Asphalt Base. Placement of brick or concrete pavers on a sand setting bed over concrete or asphalt is possible if the base is level and has no cracks or serious surface disruptions. If the proposed base surface has broken joints or other disruptions, paving is not recommended. The installation may suffer long-term deterioration if placed on a base that does not drain properly. Geotextile should be placed over concrete or asphalt bases to prevent sand from settling into cracks in the pavement and joints. If pavers are placed on an impervious base that has no drainage, holes should be drilled at the low edges of the subpaving to allow moisture that has passed through the pavers to drain through the base. The holes should then be filled with clean open graded washed stone and covered with geotextile.
- Mortar Base. For some applications, brick or stone paving is placed on a mortar base. See Chapter 26 to review the situations and methods for this type of paving.
- Permeable Paver Base. When permeable pavers are chosen for surface material, the subcourses will change from compacted stone with a sand setting bed to open graded washed stone. For permeable pavers that allow full exfiltration of water into the subgrade one example would be: a minimum 6 inch thick number 2 stone subbase course is placed on the subgrade. A geotextile may be used if specified. On the number 2 stone a 4 inch thick layer of open graded number 57 stone is placed. The bedding course is a 1 ½ inch to 2 inch layer of number 8 aggregate. A number 8 aggregate is used to fill the joints between the pavers. Variations include limiting the exfiltration by installing geotextiles or impermeable membranes on the subgrade, the placing drainage tile through the subbase course to collect water and direct it away from the site.

EDGE RESTRAINTS FOR PAVED SURFACES

All unit pavers require some sort of edge restraint to prevent the outer courses from wandering. The methods and timing of the placement vary, depending on the design of the project, but several choices are described in Chapter 24.

ADHERING PAVERS TO STEPS

When pavers are to be placed on step treads or edges of stoops, pavers must be set in a thin bed of mortar or an adhesive must be applied to bond the paver to the material below. Mortared installations should be completed according to the manufacturer's instructions. Pavers bonded to stairs should be cut with joints of 1/16 inch or less. Use a one-part urethane or similar type of adhesive to bond the pavers to the outer edge of the stoops.

PLACEMENT OF SETTING BED

A thin layer of material on which the pavers will be set should be placed over the compacted base. The setting bed should be screeded to an approximately 1-inch thickness (ASTM C 33) across the compacted base. Because the pavers are resting directly on this material, the setting bed must be sloped in the proper direction and be set at the proper elevation. Clean, coarse, concrete sand with crushed/angular and not rounded particles is the preferred material for a setting bed. Stone dust, fines, limestone screenings, and other materials provide inconsistent compaction after pavers are set. Setting bed sand should contain enough moisture that it forms a ball when squeezed in the palm of the hand. Sand that is too dry will need to be wetted slightly prior to screeding.

Precise screeding of the setting bed can be accomplished using a board notched to fit adjacent pavement or preplaced edge restraint. If using a paved edge for screeding, be certain the base screed is notched to accommodate the thickness of the paver minus ¼ inch (Figure 26-9). Screeding can also be accomplished by working off 1-inch diameter screed rails that are set directly on the base. Screed only the area of the setting bed that will be paved immediately. Screed perpendicular to the rails when possible. To match existing grades, small sections may need to be screeded in areas where the pavement cross-slopes, or warps. Screed the setting bed and lift out the temporary screed rails, filling the voids left by the rails with additional sand and smoothing with a steel trowel.

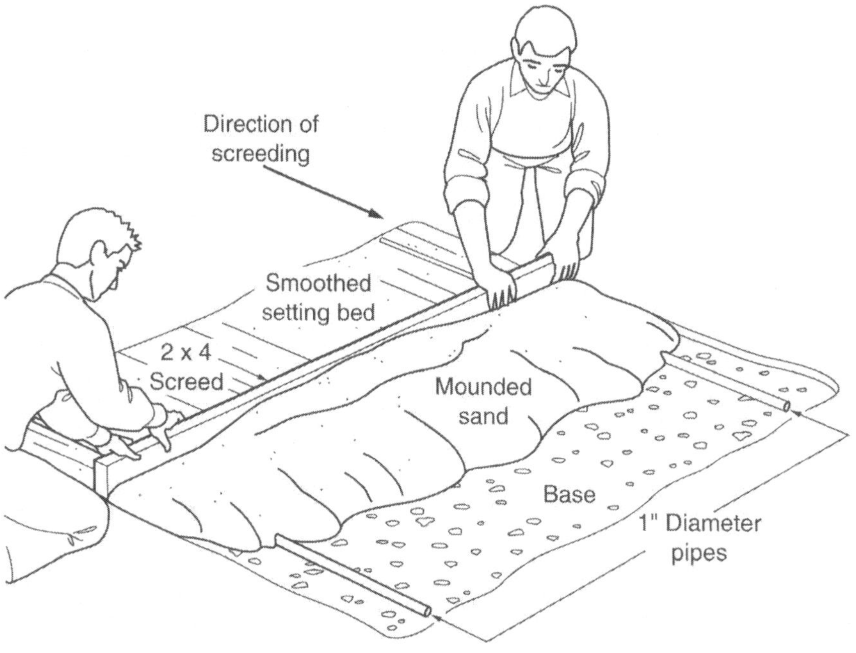

Figure 26-9 Screeding setting bed for unit pavers. The 2 × 4 slides across the 1-inch diameter pipe leaving a smooth surface.

Figure 26-10 Soldier course at edge of pavement.

Headers

Similar to those discussed in Chapter 25 for concrete paving, headers can separate brick paved surfaces into smaller paved areas. Typically, decay-resistant wood headers are installed prior to the placement and screeding of the setting bed. The headers are then used as a screed support for leveling the bedding sand.

UNIT PAVER PLACEMENT

Placing unit pavers requires craftsmanship that is created through planning, patience, and creativity in completing an installation. Unlike bulk paving materials that are placed and finished, the placement of each paving unit must be considered.

Patterns and Edge Course

Before beginning a project, lay a test area large enough to see how the pavers will fit together. For each of the patterns, place a soldier course of full pavers around the entire perimeter (Figure 26-10). This course eliminates placement of cut and partial pavers adjacent to the edge restraint; it also reduces breakage and movement problems.

Beginning Placement

Choosing a beginning line for laying pavers will be based on what the finished product is to look like. With the potential variability of shapes to be paved, select a beginning location that will allow the desired pattern to be obtained with minimal cutting of pavers.

One method commonly used for paver placement is the T method, which begins paver placement in a line perpendicular to one of the project's straight edges. The straight edge often used for alignment is a structure or existing paved surface that the paved area abuts. For patios with sight lines through the doors and into the paved surface, consider centering the T layout on the

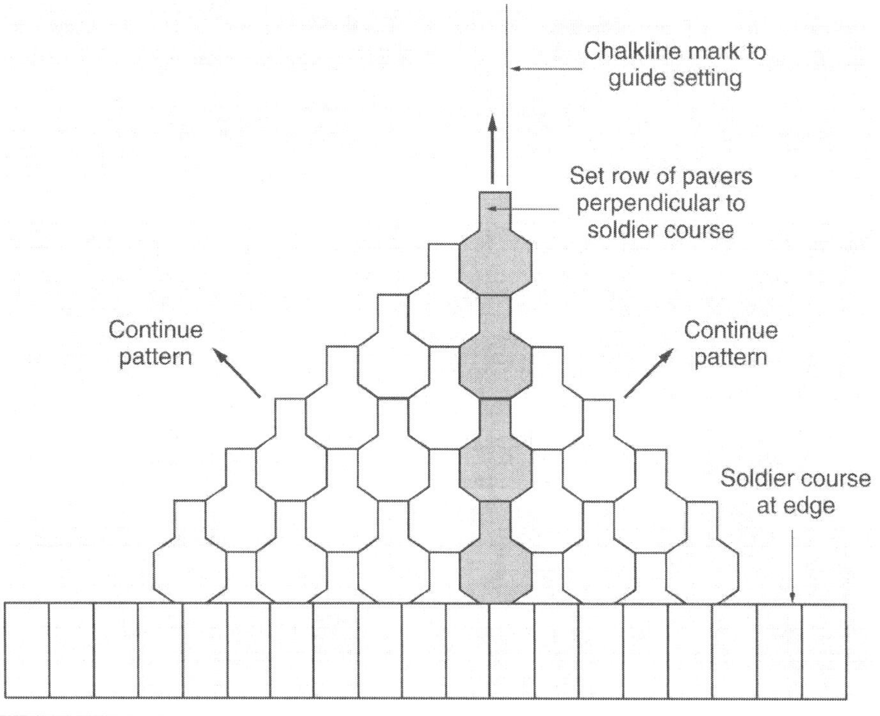

Figure 26-11 T pattern for placement of unit pavers.

door to ensure a full pattern in front of the door. Near the center of this straight edge, lay out a line at a 90° angle to the straight edge that runs through the center of the paved area. Snapping a chalk line on the screeded bedding sand along this alignment will help maintain the pattern. Extend the pattern along this line for four or five courses, and then fill the area between the straight and perpendicular lines (Figure 26-11). This method works well for rectangular-shaped areas where minor variations from perfect horizontal and vertical lines will be noticed. Most patterns can be laid with this method.

Another method for placement is to begin at a structure or wall and work out one row at a time. This method works well for curved walkways and irregular shaped areas where minor variations from perfect vertical and horizontal alignment will not be noticed. This method is also easier for placing herringbone patterns. Without a structure or paved area against which to align paver placement, snap a chalk line across the screeded bedding sand for alignment.

When using the herringbone pattern for placement, you may find that beginning in the corner of a project, rather than using the T or horizontal method, to be more beneficial. With a corner beginning point, you can more easily place this complex pattern and continue the placement in one direction across the project. Problems will be encountered with either method if the paved area is between walls that are not at right angles. If you encounter this situation, expect to do a great deal of cutting along one or both walls.

To speed the work, stack several piles of pavers near where you will begin placing them. Become familiar with the paving units. Note that interlocking concrete paving block and precast pavers have a top side with a beveled edge. Other pavers may have patterns or textures on the upper side. Pavers placed upside-down will need to be removed and reinstalled with the wearing surface facing up. When paving large areas, you may need several pallets of material. To avoid problems with minor color variations between pallets, select pavers randomly from each of the pallets provided.

Figure 26-12 Beginning placement of interlocking concrete pavers.

Laying Pavers

Begin laying pavers according to one of the placement methods and patterns previously described. When placing the pavers, set them straight down onto the setting bed. Avoid dropping, angling, or twisting the paver. Allow the paver's weight to set it onto the sand bed. The paver should be placed with joints of approximately 1/16 inch (Figure 26-12) to a maximum of 3/16 inch. Some paver varieties have spacers cast into the sides of the paver; these spacers hold the pavers the correct distance apart. Set clay brick and other pavers with sides and ends touching.

If a paver pushes too far down into the setting bed, it may leave a small ridge of sand around the bottom edge. This ridge will prevent tight placement of the next pavers. Lift the paver out and lightly smooth the setting bed with a steel trowel. Use caution not to compact or vary the surface level when resmoothing the setting bed. Finished surfaces with unit pavers should have a variation of no more that plus or minus 3/8 inch over 10'.

Check paver alignment often as you lay the pavers. Verify that the joints are straight and that the pattern is correct. The joints (bond lines) of the paving should not vary more than plus or minus ½ inch over 50'. Place a stringline along the pavers' joint lines and check paver alignment every 10 courses. Adjust pavers using a pry bar. Avoid stepping near or adjusting pavers within 1 foot of an unrestrained edge. Continue laying pavers up to the edge restraint that is in place or to the edge marking. If you cannot complete laying pavers in a single session, temporarily restrain them with a piece of edging. Before continuing paving operations, remove the edging and repair the surface.

CUTTING AND FINISHING EDGES

Few unit paving jobs can be completed without cutting and placing partial pavers. Planning and selecting simple pavement patterns may reduce the number of cuts that have to be made; but anytime you encounter an irregular shape or structure, you can expect to do some cutting. To improve aesthetics and to avoid breakage and movement of pavers, place full pavers in areas where visibility and traffic is high. If the paving is to be utilized by vehicle traffic, no less than 1/3 of a full paver should be installed. Marking and cutting paving materials is described in Chapter 8. As an alternative to cutting half or partial pavers while installing the pattern, place all full pavers first; then mark, cut, and place partial pavers to complete the surface.

This will concentrate cutting into a single activity. Use caution not to alter the pattern when placing all full pavers.

Placing Cut Pavers

Placing cut pavers into position may require tapping the paver with a rubber mallet or shifting the pavers with a mason's trowel. Pavers should fit precisely into the opening (Figure 26-13). If the fit is too snug, trim a bit more off the paver. If

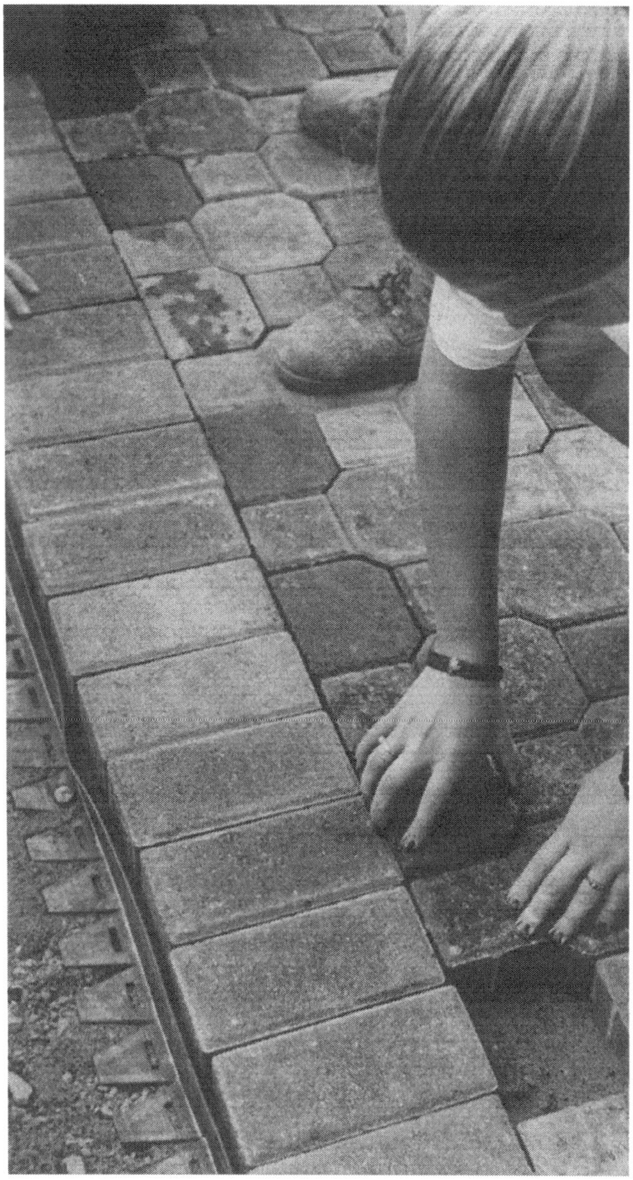

Figure 26-13 Setting cut pavers.

the paver can be removed without contacting any adjacent pavers, the cut was too extreme and should be redone using a new paver.

SEATING AND FINISHING THE SURFACE

After you have placed all pavers and edging, apply the final steps to a paved surface. This process may vary, depending on manufacturer's requirements, but most processes require the pavers to be "set" into the setting bed and to sweep sand on the surface.

Seating Pavers

Concrete paving blocks require a mechanical seating of the paving units (Figure 26-14) using a centrifugal plate vibrator with a minimum compaction force of 4000 to 5000 pounds. The seating of pavers vibrates them into the setting bed and forces the setting bed sand up into the joints between pavers. When seating clay brick pavers, use a plate compactor with a rubber mat on the plate to avoid chipping the units. Sweep all debris from the paved surface. Make two passes in this initial seating operation.

Place the plate compactor on the on one edge of the surface, start the equipment, and compact the perimeter of the surface. Compact in overlapping rows until the entire surface has

Figure 26-14 Seating pavers using a plate compactor.

been compacted, then repeat the operation in the opposite direction. Operate the plate compactor at least 6 feet away from unrestrained edges. This mechanical seating will push blocks down into the sand, leveling course as much as ¼ inch. When working against existing paving or a preset edging, run the plate compactor on both surfaces at the same time. Placing the plate compactor only on the new pavers may cause them to settle below the existing surface. Examine the surface for any damaged paving units. Use a paving puller or two screwdrivers to lift damaged units out of the surface. Replace damaged or broken units with new pavers.

Sweeping Joints

Filling the joints between the pavers helps create interlock and contributes to the waterproofing and stabilization of the surface. This is accomplished by shoveling dry, coarse sand onto the surface of the pavers and sweeping it into the joints. To prevent the loss of joint sand from erosive elements a polymeric sand can be used. Polymeric sands are a fine sand mixed with additives that, when mixed with water, bind the sand particles together. In either instance the surface should be clean before the addition of the stabilizing agent. Follow manufacturer's specifications when using these materials. Sweeping diagonally to the joints in two different directions is most effective in working the sand down (Figure 26-15).

Repeating Compacting and Sweeping Operations

Repeat the plate compaction and sweeping of joints until all joints are full.

SEALING UNIT PAVER SURFACES

Some unit paved surfaces can be sealed to protect them from stains and soiling. Pavement sealing is a specialized operation that involves washing the surface and applying formulated sealers. Contact paving manufacturers or distributors for their recommendations on sealing procedures for unit pavers.

Figure 26-15 Sweeping dry sand into paver joints.

CHAPTER 27

DRY-LAID STONE PAVING

OBJECTIVES

By reading and practicing the techniques described in this chapter, the reader should be able to successfully complete the following activities:

- Install dry-laid stone in a recognizable pattern.
- Prepare the site for installation of dry-laid stone paving.
- Lay dry-laid stone.
- Finish a dry-laid stone installation.
- Install a dry-laid recycled concrete paved surface.

Stone paving combines craftsmanship with technique in creating one of the most aesthetic paved surfaces. This chapter covers the techniques of dry-laid stone paving using limestone, slate, and other regionally available flagstone materials. Techniques for base preparation and laying also support the installation of modular paving materials such as granite and cut stone. In addition to dry-laid base materials, stone paving can be effectively laid in a mortar base.

Mortar base stone paving is covered in Chapter 28, whereas this chapter covers stone paving laid on a granular base. Also included at the end of this chapter are techniques for placing dry-laid stones informally as stepping stones.

RELATED INFORMATION

Information in this chapter is supplemented by instruction provided elsewhere in this text and in other sources. Before undertaking the activities described in this chapter, read the related information in these sources:

- Safety in the Workplace, Chapter 7
- Basic Construction Techniques and Small Equipment Operation, Chapter 8
- Construction Layout, Chapter 9
- Materials and Site Preparation for Paving, Chapter 24

PAVING PATTERNS

Selecting a pattern for stone pavement is based on the type of stone chosen for the construction project. Pavement patterns are generally identified as either modular patterns, for stone that is cut into square and/or rectangular shapes, or random patterns, for stone that is left in natural, uncut shapes. Examples of common paving patterns and the stone that works best in those patterns are listed below (Figure 27-1). Placement order for each pavement pattern is shown in accompanying figures.

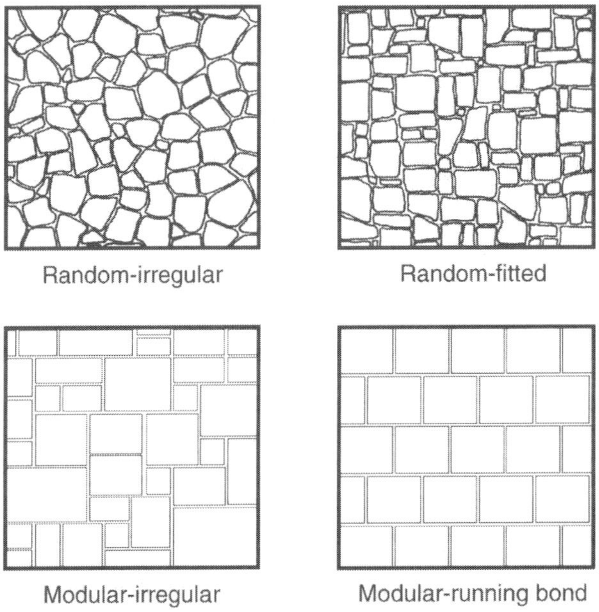

Figure 27-1 Common stone paving patterns.

- Random-Irregular. Pattern using irregular sized stone. Stone should be placed with small and large pieces evenly intermixed (Figure 27-2). This pattern requires an artistic eye to develop an attractive pattern throughout the installation. Intermix large pieces, rather than concentrating them in one area of the installation. Use the smaller pieces to create patterns that fan out from each side of the installation.
- Random-Fitted. Pattern using irregular-sized stone to create horizontal and vertical joints. Although stone sizes are intermixed, joint arrangement is maintained (Figure 27-3).
- Modular-Irregular. Pattern using stone of varying sizes with straight-cut edges. Widths are typically in multiples of 2, 3, or 4 inches so stone can be fit with horizontal and vertical joints (Figure 27-4). The intermixing of stone sizes and colors creates the richness of this pattern. Large stones should be interspersed throughout the design and placed with only minimal overlap with each other. When laid as separators between the largest pieces, the smaller pieces of stone appear like veins running from end to end and side to side in an installation.

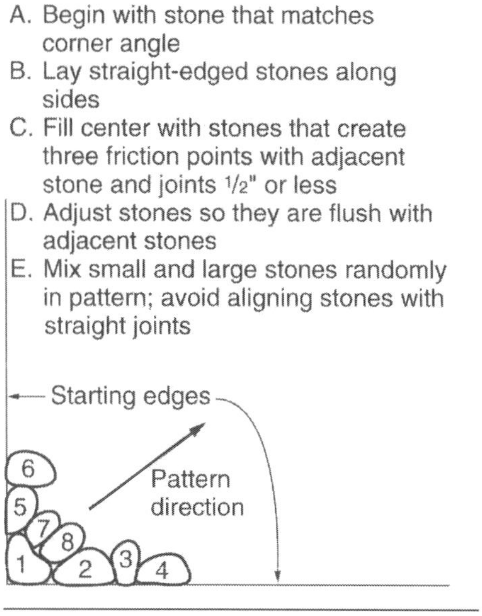

Figure 27-2 Random-irregular paving patterns.

- Modular-Running Bond. Pattern using stone of same size with straight-cut edges. Stone is placed in staggered pattern similar to that found in brick installations (Figure 27-5).

CHOOSING BASE MATERIAL

Base preparation for most dry-laid stone paving installations is similar to the process described in Chapter 24. Alternatives to a granular base with setting bed are:

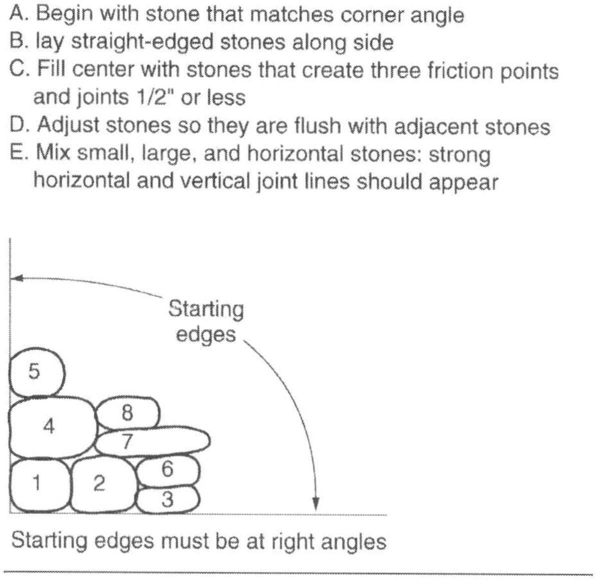

Figure 27-3 Random-fitted pattern installation.

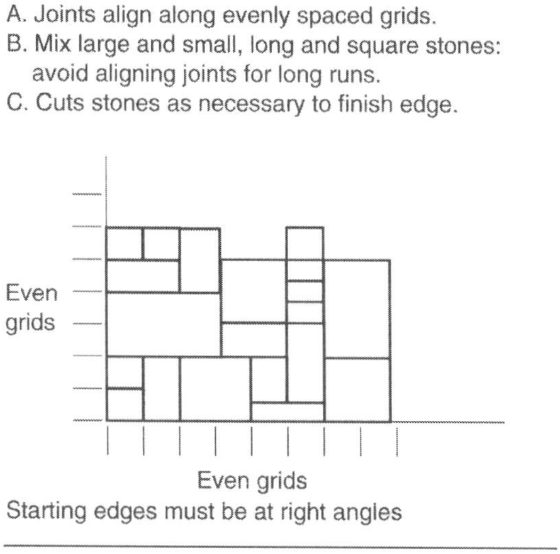

Figure 27-4 Modular-irregular pattern installation.

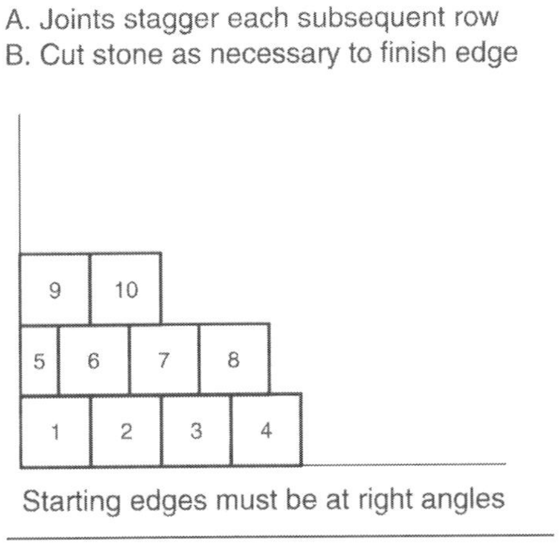

Figure 27-5 Modular-running bond pattern installation.

- Undisturbed Soil. There is always a temptation to place stone directly on a soil base. This can be done if the base is undisturbed and the expectations for a long-term, level surface are not high. The amount of work in preparation and placement is somewhat less than that for a proper base preparation, but the time and labor required for longterm maintenance offset the short-term time savings. It is not recommended in any area where public safety or heavy traffic will be an issue.
- Mortar Base. In addition to being dry-laid, flagstone may be set on a bed of mortar. See Chapter 28 to review the situations and methods for mortared stone paving.
- Concrete or Asphalt. Concrete or asphalt will substitute for granular base material if the surface is level and stable. Surfaces with deep depressions or ridges should be removed and replaced with a new granular base. If paving over an existing slab, place a setting bed of 2 inches to accommodate base variations.

INSTALLING EDGE RESTRAINT

If the project requires a permanent edge restraint such as a concrete curb, walk, or cut stone, install this edge before placing and screeding the setting bed (Figure 27-6). This minimizes disturbance of the paving after it has been placed

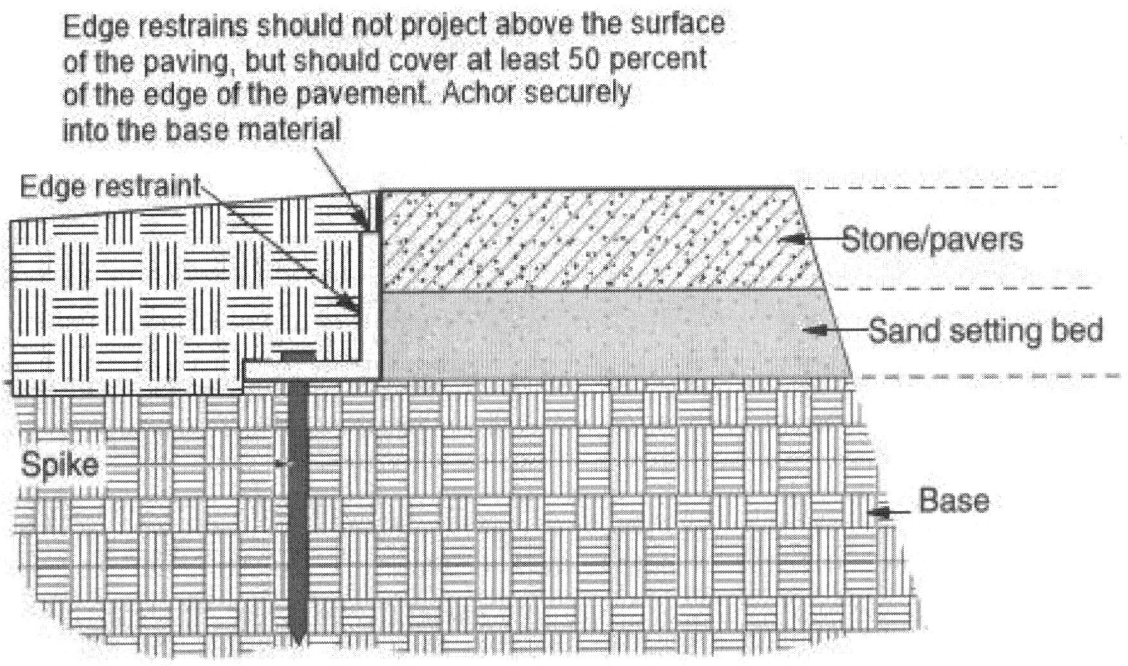

Figure 27-6 Edge restraint for stone paving.

and ensures that the finish grade of the stone matches the edging material. Edge restraints are described in Chapter 24.

PLACING THE SETTING BED

Because it often varies in thickness, stone requires a thin setting bed of fine granular material to maintain a level surface. Depending on the region, concrete sand or stone dust makes a good setting bed. Each is placed over the base and screeded smooth. Setting beds should not be less than 1 inch or more than 2 inches in thickness. Maintaining the 1-inch course provides the most stability for an installation. Because the stones are resting directly on this material, the setting bed must be sloped in the proper direction and be set at the exact elevation below the finish grade required. The proper elevation for the top of a setting bed is the finish elevation minus the average thickness of the stone.

Screed the setting bed using preinstalled edge restraint or temporary screeding rails. If using a paved edge for screeding, be certain the base screed is adjusted to accommodate the thickness of the stone. In installations where it is only important to maintain a positive slope, screed from stringlines stretched between grade stakes. This will create a surface with some minor variations, but this method is a much faster way to prepare for paving.

You may screed small amounts of the setting bed as the work progresses, or you may screed the entire area before laying any stone. If an edger has not been preplaced, use a stringline or paint line to mark the edge of the paved area. If the surface of the setting bed has dried out before you begin laying stone, wet the surface with a light mist from a hose attachment. Do not soak the surface, and do not disturb the setting bed during the wetting process.

PLACING STONE

Laying stone requires a great deal of placement and rearrangement of materials, particularly when you use random patterns. Lay a test pattern large enough to see how the stone fits together. One technique that helps with stone selection is to lean several stones against a fence or railing (assuming it will support the weight) so you can observe their shape, color, and other characteristics. Regardless of the pattern selected for the body of the paved surface, full stone with square edges should be placed around the entire perimeter. This placement reduces stability problems when small stone is placed adjacent to the edge. When transporting stone to the placement area, use available tools to make lifting and transporting easier. For example, if you place heavy stone in a wheelbarrow or on a two-wheeled cart (Figure 27-7), you can easily move it.

Beginning Placement

The objective of laying stone is to maintain a tight and uniform pattern across the paved area. Stone should have joints of less than ½ inch, and

Figure 27-7 Transporting heavy stone using a two-wheeled cart.

Figure 27-8 Proper placement of dry-laid stone. Note that surfaces are flush with surrounding stone and each stone makes contact with adjacent material. Joints are ½ inch or less.

adjacent stones should touch. Stone that is placed in random patterns is best laid in a fan shape. Begin in one corner of the paved area and work along the edges; then fill the space between (Figure 27-8). Use a structure or corner as the straight edge(s) against which the first fan of stone is aligned. You may move outer edges slightly, or you can trim the stones to create a tight fit. Some trimming and fitting of the stone is always necessary to insure regular jointing.

Another method for placement is to begin at a structure or wall and work out one row at a time. Select pieces with straight edges to use in placement next to structures or other restraints. This method works well for irregular-shaped areas where minor variations from perfect vertical and horizontal alignment will not be noticed. Snapping a chalk line on the setting bed will aid in maintaining alignment for patterns with straight joints.

Stone Laying

Begin laying stone according to one of the placement methods previously described. Have a mag float handy to smooth out any variations in the setting bed. Tapping the stone with a rubber mallet will also help fit it into tight locations. Before placing a stone, examine the edges for bevel. Bevels should be placed down when setting stone, reducing open joints in the surface (Figure 27-9). When placing the stone, set it straight down onto the setting bed and twist it slightly to seat. Modular stone must fit tightly against any adjacent stones already in place.

Irregular-shaped stone should make contact with adjacent stones at a minimum of three points to provide stability. Random patterns should have minimal joints. Although some joint space is expected, any stone that has fewer than three contact points or joints over ½ inch should be set aside or trimmed to fit, or a new stone should be placed (Figure 27-10). A flush surface must be maintained, requiring that stone height be adjusted as necessary by adding or removing setting bed material below the stone. Adjust the height and position of small stone by lifting and adding or removing setting bed material. Larger

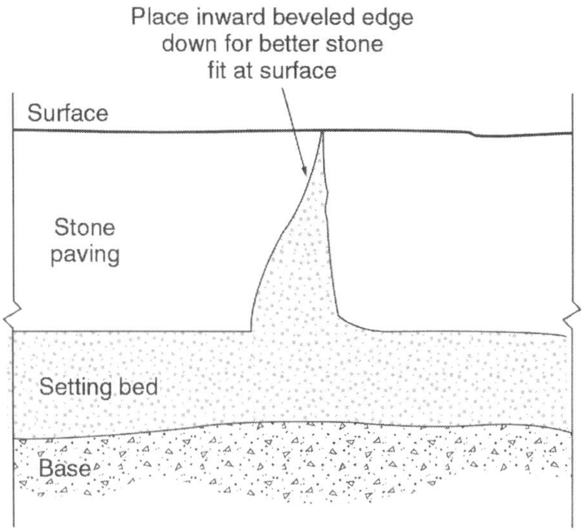

Figure 27-9 Proper orientation of stone with beveled edge.

stone may require the use of a lever or tool to perform the lifting and movement. You can use a pry bar to temporarily lift a stone for adjustment (Figure 27-11).

Check pattern alignment often as you continue laying stone. For modular stone, verify that the alignment is straight and that the pattern is correct. Make corrections by relaying stone or by gently tapping the sides with the rubber mallet. Continue laying stone up to the edger that is in place or to the stringline or paint marker at the edge. You can cut modular stone to complete edges, whereas you should fit and/or trim random stone to fill all voids up to the edging.

CUTTING AND FINISHING EDGES

Planning and selecting certain pavement patterns may reduce the number of cuts you have to make; but anytime an irregular-shaped stone or structure is involved, you can expect a certain amount of cutting. To the greatest extent possible, avoid the use of small stone pieces along the pavement edges. Methods for marking and cutting stone for the project are described in Chapter 8.

FINISHING THE SURFACE

Following placement of all stone and edgers, apply the finishing steps to a paved surface. This process varies, depending on the type of stone,

Figure 27-10 Placement of dry-laid stone in pattern.

Figure 27-11 Adjusting the position of a stone using a pry bar as a lever.

but most processes require that material be swept into the joints of the surface.

Filling joints between the stones helps hold them in position. To fill the joints, shovel concrete sand onto the surface of the pavers and sweep it into the joints. Sweeping in several different directions is most effective in working the sand into joints. Sand can be mixed at the rate of 2 parts sand to 1 part Type N mortar mix to create a weak mortar for flagstone paving.

Sweep the mixture into joints and lightly wash the surface with water. This mix hardens after the surface is washed and performs the role of a spacing material. Expect this weak mortar joint treatment to crack soon after placement because it is not a full-strength mortar placed on a stable base. Repeat the sweeping operation twice more within a week on all types of surfaces.

USING RECYCLED CONCRETE AS DRY-LAID PAVING SURFACE

Preparation and setting of **recycled concrete** follow the same steps as setting dry-laid stone, with only minor adjustments in the process. Prepare the base as you would for dry-laid stone. Edge restraint can be installed if desired. When placing recycled concrete, select and place pieces so that they fit aesthetically and structurally according to the same rules as dry-laid stone. Pieces should have joints of no more than 1 inch and should contact adjacent pieces in no less than three places. The surface should be flush with adjacent pieces.

Complicating the setting of recycled concrete are irregularities on the lower surface if the concrete was poured on an uneven base. To counter this problem, place a 1-inch setting bed of crushed fines or sand on top of your prepared base to provide a material that can be adjusted to match the profile of the lower surface. Round the sharp edges on concrete pieces by striking them lightly with a brick hammer. Several attempts at lifting and resetting may be necessary to level set recycled concrete (Figure 27-12). To speed the process, set the material on the base and slightly twist it; then tilt it up. Look for the impressions on the setting bed that indicate high points to be lowered. If you are setting large pieces of concrete (minimum dimensions of 18 inches), an exception to the 1-inch joint and adjacent stone contact requirements is possible. Properly set large pieces of concrete are unlikely to shift; so,

Figure 27-12 Level setting recycled concrete.

you can set them with joints up to 2 inches wide. Fill these joints with granular material or pea gravel, rather than sand.

Joints for recycled concrete are finished in a manner similar to dry-laid stone. If no edge restraint is placed, the material swept into joints should be larger than sand to reduce joint erosion. The surface of recycled concrete may also benefit from a light sandblasting to clean the material and to remove irregular textures.

SETTING STEPPING STONES

For informal paths, paving materials can be placed directly on an earth surface. Place stepping stones in locations where the path is desired. Arrange as necessary to accommodate a comfortable stepping pattern.

For a more stable installation, place the paving material and mark the material location by sprinkling base path chalk, floor, or lime around the edge of the paving material (Figure 27-13 A & B). Lift the paving material and excavate a shallow, level area at the location of the markings. The excavation should not be deeper than the thickness of the paving material and should extend slightly outside the markings (Figure 27-13 C & D). Replace the paving material and check for stability. If paving material rocks, lift and place a small amount of sand in low areas. Twist back into the excavation and recheck for level. Backfill around the material with soil to complete the installation. For additional stability, the stones can be laid on a 1 inch mortar bed.

An alternative method for setting stepping stones can be used in areas where the pavement can be flooded. This method requires a subgrade that will allow water to eventually drain away from the project. Excavate a 2-inch deep base below the stone. Place a 3-inch deep layer of fine sand over the entire area to be paved. Place the stone on the base and flood the area with water. While the sand is saturated, twist the stone down into the base until set at the proper elevation. Continue saturating the base and setting the stone until you have set all paving. Let the area dry and fill in joints with sand.

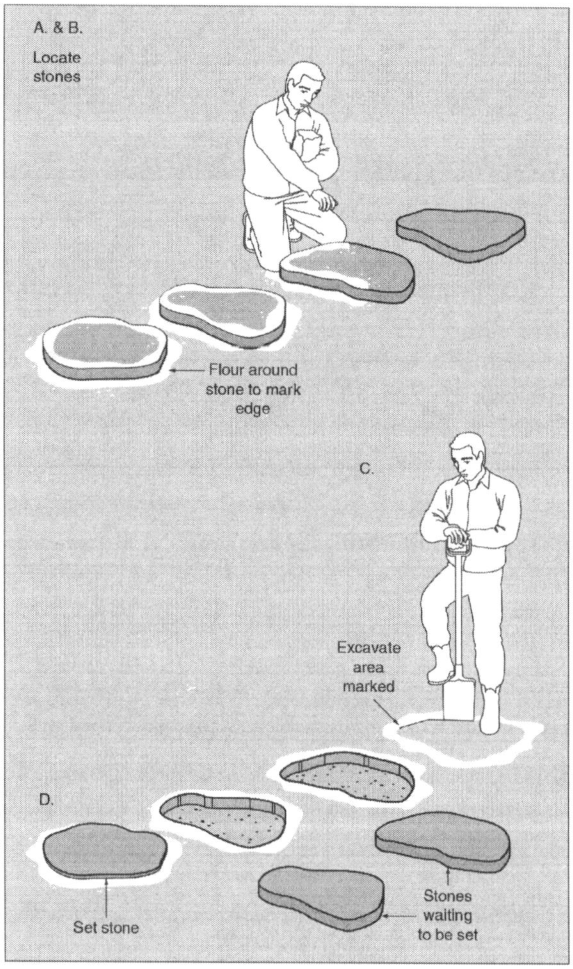

Figure 27-13 Installing stepping stones.

CHAPTER 28

MORTARED PAVING

OBJECTIVES

By reading and practicing the techniques described in this chapter, the reader should be able to successfully complete the following activities:

- Prepare the base for a mortared paved surface.
- Prepare mortar.
- Install paving on a mortar base.
- Finish a mortared paved surface.

Mortared paving is a surface in which bricks, stone, tile, or other paving materials are set in a bed of **mortar** with mortar-filled joints. When improperly installed, mortared paving will have durability problems in areas of the country where temperatures fluctuate above and below freezing. With proper installation, however, applications are appropriate in many situations. Choice of materials for mortared pavement is almost as great as the choice for dry-laid and unit pavements. Stone pavement, brick, and tile are common choices. This chapter provides the basic techniques required to set appropriate pavement types in a mortar base. Included are instructions on base and mortar preparation and on placement of paving material and finishing its surface.

RELATED INFORMATION

Information in this chapter is supplemented by instruction provided elsewhere in this text and in other sources. Before undertaking the activities described in this chapter, read the related information in these sources:

- Safety in the Workplace, Chapter 7
- Basic Construction Techniques and Small Equipment Operation, Chapter 8
- Materials and Site Preparation for Paving, Chapter 24
- Pedestrian Concrete Paving, Chapter 25

PLANNING THE PROJECT

Preparation for a mortared paving project requires examining the work situation and making choices regarding base, base preparation, paving pattern, and when half brick may be required. Complete the project planning by considering each of these situations before beginning installation.

Base Material

Base preparation for mortared pavement typically requires a solid base on which to place a mortar setting bed. This base is typically a concrete slab because of concrete's rigid nature. In some random stone applications, a compacted base similar to that described in Chapter 24 is prepared, and mortar is applied to that base. The possibilities of cracks developing in that type of surface are high, particularly in areas subject to freezing and thawing.

Base Preparation

If a concrete base is being used, prepare the surface in the manner described in Chapter 25, stopping after the screeding operation. The surface needs to be level and slightly rough so that the mortar will adhere to the base. When pouring a base for a slab or stairs that will have a mortared surface, verify that the elevation is lowered to leave an allowance for the mortar bed thickness and pavement material thickness. See Chapter 24 if a compacted granular base is selected.

Paving Patterns

The pavement patterns available for unit pavers can also be accomplished as a mortared pattern by spacing the pavers to create mortar joints. Examples of common paving patterns and the materials that work best in those patterns are located in Chapters 26 and 27.

Use of Half Brick

Stair locations may require application of half brick on mortar to maintain proper riser dimensions. Half bricks are paving bricks with full length and width dimensions but half the thickness. This narrow paver can set on a mortar bed with minimal increase in stair riser dimensions.

PREPARING FOR PAVING

Mortared paving requires preparation to avoid delays and problems when the actual paving begins. Practicing the patterns before performing an on-the-job installation speeds the work. Working small areas limits the amount of mortar that must be mixed. Observing weather conditions is also important. Unlike how it affects other unit paved surfaces, rain destroys an incomplete mortared project if the mortar has not set. By establishing a staging area close to the project, you can more conveniently mix mortar and prepare paving materials to speed the construction process (Figure 28-1).

Figure 28-1 Preparing for placement of mortared limestone.

Test patterns by laying a test area large enough to see how the paving material fits together. On small projects and stairs, lay out the entire paved area and precut the material. This test layout will save time during placement of pavement and will avoid placement of cut materials in locations that are unstable or highly visible. When placing unit pavers such as brick in mortar, place a soldier course of full pavers around the edge of the project. The soldier course will reduce small pieces of paving material adjacent to the edge and will improve the surface's durability.

CUTTING PAVEMENT MATERIALS

Methods for marking and cutting paving materials are discussed in Chapter 7. Stone and unit pavers that are set on mortar should be cut using a hydraulic splitter or wet masonry saw. Cleaving with a set may slow the process and leave uneven edges. You may need to hand shape stone with a mason's hammer to improve fit of irregular-shaped pieces.

MIXING AND PLACING MORTAR

As the setting bed that holds the paving material at the proper elevation, mortar is also used between the paving materials to hold them in position and to help create a surface impermeable to water. Mortar types vary from project to project and may be custom mixed or purchased in premixed bags.

When purchasing premixed mortar, type M or spec mix is typically used for flat, exterior applications. Table 28-1 identifies common mortar types and suggested mix ratios. When custom mixing, use a ratio of 3 parts **Portland cement**, 1 part hydrated lime, and 9 parts sand.

Table 28-1 Mortar mixes.

United States-ASTM C270

Parts by Volume

Mortar Type	Portland Cement or Blended Cement	Masonry Cement Type M	Masonry Cement Type S	Masonry Cement Type N	Hydrabated Lime or Lime Putty	Aggregate*
	1	–	–	1	–	4½ to 6
M	–	1	–	–	–	2¼ to 3
	1	–	–	–	¼	$2^{13}/_{18}$ to 3¼
	½	–	–	1	–	$3^{3}/^{8}$ to 4½
S	–	–	1	–	–	2¼ to 3
	1	–	–	–	Over ¼ to ½	·•
	–	–	–	1	–	2¼ to 3
N	1	–	–	–	Over ½ to 1¼	•
	–	–	–	1	–	2¼ to 3
O	1	–	–	–	Over $^{1}/^{14}$ to 2½	•

Notes:

1. Under both ASTM C270, Standard Specification for Mortar for Unit Masonry, aggregate is measured in a damp, loose condition and 1 CF of masonry sand by damp, loose volume is considered equal to 80 lb. of dry sand (in SI units 1 CM of damp, loose sand is considered equal to 1,280 kg of dry sand).
2. Mortar should not contain more than one air-entraining material.

Courtesy Portland Cement Association.

Small mortar quantities can be mixed in a clean wheelbarrow, in a wood box, or even on a sheet of plywood; but large jobs may require rental of a portable mixer. Blend the dry ingredients and mound in a pile using a shovel or mortar hoe. Make a depression, similar to a volcano's crater, in the top of the pile. Slowly add water in the depression and mix, using a pushing and pulling motion at first, then a chopping motion while pulling the mortar forward and backward (Figure 28-2). Pick up shovels of the mortar and slap them down to break up clumps.

Mix the mortar in workable batches. When working with a small crew, mixing several small batches is better than mixing a large batch that may harden before it is used. Deliver the mortar to the work area on a rigid material. If you place 18 × 18-inch squares of ¾-inch plywood in convenient locations around the pavement surface, then you can use this plywood for storing delivered mortar. If mortar begins to harden before it can be used, temper, or rewet, it. Sprinkle a small amount of water over the mortar and remix with a trowel. Use a chopping motion, occasionally picking up small amounts of the mortar and slapping them back on the board.

Laying mortared pavement requires working from a kneeling position on the base. Begin work in a corner that will allow exit without walking over newly laid material. Lay the pavement working backward, away from the beginning point. Shovel or trowel the mortar onto the base in a layer over about 2 SF of a corner of the work

Figure 28-2 Mixing mortar with mortar hoe.

Figure 28-3 Mortar placement.

area (Figure 28-3). With a trowel or rake, spread the mortar in a rough layer over this area. This layer should be approximately ½-inch thick for brick and ¾–1-inch thick for stone.

PLACING PAVEMENT

Placement of paving material requires proper alignment and elevation for all materials. For materials that are placed in a modular pattern, use a stringline or snap a chalk line on the base to maintain alignment. Random patterns typically have enough flexibility that aides are not required to maintain the pattern.

If there is no structure or paved area to begin placement of pavement, lay a stringline across the area and begin the first row by placing stone lightly against the string. Setting a stringline slightly above the finish grade will help ensure the paving material follows the desired alignment and will assist in maintaining the proper elevation (Figure 28-4). You may encounter problems with modular patterns if the paved area covers a corner between walls that are not at right angles. If you encounter this situation, you may need to cut pavers along the wall.

Placement of pavement is similar for all materials. Placement requires that the paving units be set into the mortar bed and the joint filled separately. Before placing stone, examine the edges for bevel. Bevels should be placed down when setting stone, reducing the irregularity of the surface. Stone should be placed with joints of ½–1-inch. Tile and brick should have uniform edges and a typical joint spacing of ½ inch. Push stone or tile into the mortar bed with a twisting motion, and use the trowel's handle to tap the material into alignment. Check for level and

Figure 28-4 Placement of stone using stringline to maintain proper elevation.

Figure 28-5 Leveling individual stones when placed.

correct as necessary (Figure 28-5). You may need to remove material that is significantly out of level or at an incorrect elevation and add or remove mortar. Replace the material and recheck for level and elevation.

Check pattern alignment often as you lay the material. Verify that the alignment is straight and that the pattern is correct. To make corrections, relay the stone or gently tap it sideways with the trowel.

JOINTING AND FINISHING THE SURFACE

After you have set a few paving units, fill the joints. Pick up a small amount of mortar on a small trowel and, holding the trowel at an angle next to the joint, push the mortar into the joint using a pointing tool. Joints can also be filled using a mortar bag filled with mortar that is squeezed into joints for finishing. Fill the joint and scrape away the excess with the trowel. Using a jointer or small trowel, press down on the mortar that was placed in the joints between paving units. This pressure will smooth the joint surface, press the mortar into voids in the joint, and compact the mortar surface (Figure 28-6). Refill with mortar and smooth all voids between edges of stone. Joints that are flat or concave are the best for horizontal paving.

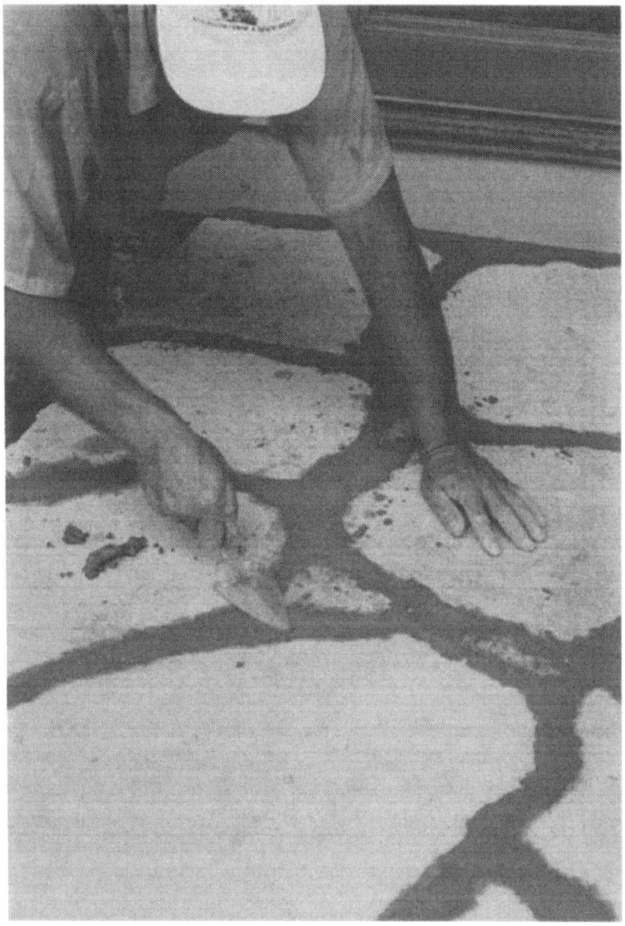

Figure 28-6 Finishing joints using a mortar trowel.

CLEANING SURFACES

After the mortar has hardened, clean the paved surface of any excess mortar and scrub it with a solution of 9 parts water and 1 part **muriatic acid** or **trisodium phosphate** (TSP). Rinse surfaces thoroughly. Remove difficult stains or deposits with a wire brush or trowel.

> **CAUTION**
>
> When cleaning pavement with acid and caustic cleaners, follow all safety precautions identified on the product label. Wear proper safety clothing. Contact and exposure to acids and caustic cleaners can cause personal injury and can harm plants.

> **CAUTION**
>
> When mixing acid and water, always add the acid to the water. Never add water to acid. Adding water to acid will cause the mixture to spray and splatter, creating the potential for burns. Always wear protective clothing, gloves, and eyewear when mixing chemicals.

CHAPTER 29

GRANULAR AND OPEN CELLULAR PAVING

OBJECTIVES

By reading and practicing the techniques described in this chapter, the reader should be able to successfully complete the following activities:

- Prepare a site for granular paving.
- Install granular paving.

Although granular paving materials are typically not considered a primary landscape paving surface, there are several applications for this type of surfacing in today's landscape. Loose, granular materials are found on private patios, historical paving surfaces, and playgrounds. Each of these paving surfaces must be installed to ensure its durability and compliance with safety and design goals. The following sections provide information specific to the applications of granular paving surfaces to the landscape.

RELATED INFORMATION

Information in this chapter is supplemented by instruction provided elsewhere in this text and in other sources. Before undertaking the activities described in this chapter, read the related information in these sources:

- Safety in the Workplace, Chapter 7
- Basic Construction Techniques and Small Equipment Operation, Chapter 8
- Materials and Site Preparation for Paving, Chapter 24
- Manufacturer's specifications.

INSTALLATION OF GRANULAR PAVING

As with all previous paving projects, advance planning improves the effectiveness and efficiency of the work operation.

Slope and Cross Grade

Due to the highly erodible nature of unstabilized granular paving, sites should be selected that have minimal slope or graded so that there is minimal slope. Erosion can occur on pathways with cross or longitudinal slopes that exceed 1%. The severity of erosion is based on the size of the granular material, the placement and the treatment of the stabilizer. Granular paving of any type should be installed without cross drainage and minimal slope.

Preparing the Base

Base preparation for most **granular paving** installations is similar to the process described in the section introduction. Because the wearing course is resting directly on it, the base course must be sloped in the proper direction and set at the exact elevation below the finish grade required.

Some alternative base treatments include:

- Undisturbed Soil. If the base is undisturbed and the expectations for a long-term level wearing surface are not high, granulars can be placed directly on a soil base. The amount of work in preparation and placement is somewhat less than that for a proper base preparation, but the instability of the surface and ongoing maintenance, especially refreshing of the surface, will offset the initial time savings. If using a very fine, granular wearing surface, the material could be "pumped" into the base by traffic. Pumping occurs in wet conditions when traffic pushes the granular material down and forces moisture and subsoil up. Eventually, the granular material will be completely embedded in the subsoil.

Granular materials work their way into a soil base much faster than they do into a prepared base, requiring refurbishing of the surface sooner than if a prepared base is installed. Placement directly over soil is not recommended in any area where public safety or heavy traffic will be an issue.

- Concrete or Asphalt. Granular paving should not be placed over existing concrete or asphalt bases. Granulars will not bond with a solid paving base and will erode or wear very quickly over such bases. Slipping of the granular material will compromise safety. The best solution is to remove existing pavement below where granulars are to be placed.

Using Landscape Fabric or Geotextile

If desired, landscape fabric or geotextile may be placed on top of the base material and under the granular paving. Installation of landscape fabric or geotextile reduces the loss of granular paving by separating the base from the granular material. Although the landscape fabric will initially reduce the growth of weeds, this benefit will lessen over time. Landscape fabric can create problems if areas of high wear expose the fabric. Once exposed, the fabric can create a tripping hazard and be pulled up, disrupting the surface of the paved area. If fabric is used, lay the fabric or geotextile flat over the entire base and fasten by driving sod staples through the fabric into the base. Trim the material at the edge restraint (Figure 29-1). Overlap any joints by 18 inches.

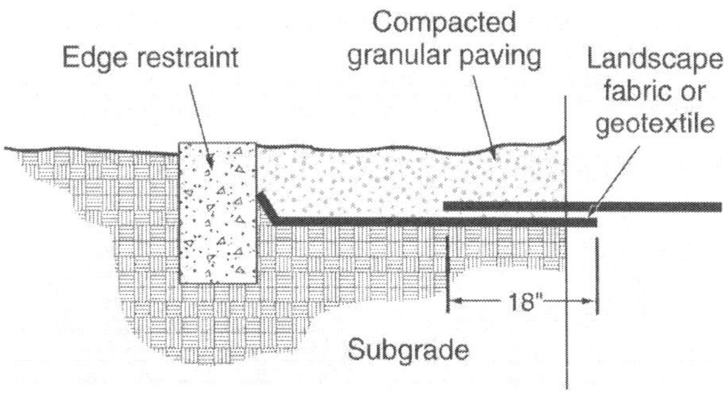

Figure 29-1 Proper placement of landscape fabric below granular paving.

Installing Edge Restraint

All granular paving installations require edge restraint to prevent migration and settling at the outer edge of the paved area. The methods used to edge vary, depending on the design of the project; however, some choices are described in Chapter 24. Do not select plastic landscape edge restraint for granular paving. Any edge restraint selected must cover the entire perimeter of the project to prevent granular paving from washing through open joints between edging pieces.

Preplacing Edge Restraint

Edge restraint material should be preplaced to provide a screeding guide for wearing course material. Install all edge restraint at the finish elevations desired around the entire area to be paved. Edge restraint may be temporarily left out of an area where access to the site is necessary and then placed as the paving reaches that segment of the project.

Adding Soil Stabilizers

Soil stabilizers can provide two benefits to fine-grained granular paving installations. First, they reduce the need for a geotextile fabric below the surfacing to protect the paving. Second, they bind the surface materials to reduce loss of pavement surface. To reduce soil working up into granular paving, use a urethane stabilizer. Pour the liquid over the subgrade to bind the soil and prevent dislocation. To reduce the erosion of fine or granulated particles such as ⅜s minus, fines, granite, or stone dust, blend liquid resins and emulsions into the surface course as it is installed. Mix dry products into the surface material before placement and wet them before compaction. Soil stabilizers provide few benefits for larger granular paving such as crushed brick or pea gravel. Epoxy resin soil stabilizers can also be blended with aggregate and placed using asphalt paving equipment for large installations.

Placing the Granular Wearing Course

Installation of a granular paving surface is similar to the placement of concrete. The depth of the wearing course will vary based on use and site conditions. A typical wearing course thickness would be 2 inches for pedestrian and bicycle traffic, but a thicker course may be warranted if heavier traffic is expected. Granulars are dry and can be moved with most common landscape equipment and tools. If the correct equipment is available, a small crew may place a great deal of this material in a short time.

Beginning Placement. Using the most efficient means available, deliver the granular material to the area to be paved. Provide an access point that will not disturb any of the preplaced edging. Begin placement at a point opposite the access point, and fill hard-to-reach corners first (Figure 29-2). Spread the granular material in a layer that is slightly thicker than the desired grade.

Figure 29-2 Placement of granular paving material.

Leveling the Wearing Course. To develop a level draining surface, screed or level the placed material. For large granular materials, leveling with a garden rake can usually produce a suitable wearing course (Figure 29-3). For fine materials, screeding will produce better results. To screed, select a long, straight 2 × 4 and nail pieces of lath to the bottom of the screed at locations where it will rest on edging. This will leave the screeded surface slightly higher than the surrounding paved areas to allow for compaction. Screed the paved area using the preplaced edging material as a screed support. To provide precise screeding of the open areas in the center, use temporary screed rails as described in Chapter 23. Dissimilar to the procedure for concrete applications, remove the stakes used to support the temporary screeding rails and repair the course around the disturbed area by raking material into the opening.

Finishing and Compacting the Surface

Following placement and screeding of all granular material, apply the finishing steps to a paved surface. This process varies, depending on the type of stone, but most processes require raking the material and compacting the surface.

Raking. Adjust the surface elevation of the granular material by lightly raking with a garden rake. Most granular materials require continual maintenance of this type to maintain worn areas. Loose granulars should be raked along the adjacent existing pavement to ensure that the two surfaces are flush.

Compacting. Large granular materials such as pebbles or loose stone will not require compaction. Compact fine granular materials with a vibratory plate compactor or sod roller to create a tight, drainable surface (Figure 29-4). The surface should be dry to prevent material sticking to the compaction equipment. Work from the low end to the high end, compacting and adjusting the level as required. If you encounter a high area, use the teeth of a garden rake to loosen the surface and the top of the rake to drag out material. Loosen low areas with a rake and sprinkle material over the depression. Recompact

Figure 29-3 Spreading large granular materials with a rake.

© Delmar/Cengage Learning.

Figure 29-4 Leveling and compacting paving installation.

© Delmar/Cengage Learning.

all adjusted areas. Most loose granular materials benefit from a light compacting; however, some materials may well up under the equipment and prevent even compaction. Hand tamp those materials that do not accept rolling.

Maintenance of the Surface. Granular surfaces will require maintenance beyond that of other types of paved surfaces. There can be a high amount of maintenance if the expectation of a clean, level surface is high. Traffic and seasonal activities will cause compaction, rutting and mounding of a loose granular surface, and normal wear over time can compact the surface material into the base or subgrade. Erosion can also create an irregular surface. Plan on additional time to restore, relevel and recompact the granular surfacing on any installation that receives average use. Annual refreshing of the surface is recommended.

INSTALLATION OF OPEN CELLULAR PAVEMENT

To reduce the problems associated with compaction of turf by pedestrian and vehicular traffic and to improve the permeability of paved

Figure 29-5 Precast concrete open cellular paving with grass growing in cells.

surfaces, a variety of cellular paving options are available to landscape contractors. Among the choices for cellular pavement are PVC rings attached to a fiber mesh, plastic grids with open structural networks, or precast unit pavers with an open-cell design (Figure 29-5). Each of these cellular pavers not only provides support for traffic, but also allows water to pass through the pavement into the subgrade, rather than running off the site. These types of pavement can be filled with granular paving materials, soil, or even with turf. Typical applications include service entries, emergency access points, and overflow parking areas. With proper installation, some cellular pavers can also be used in areas with light traffic. As with all manufactured systems, follow all manufacturer's specifications.

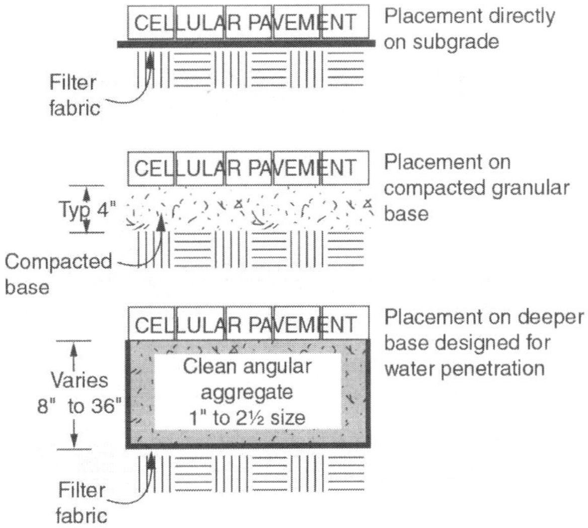

Figure 29-6 Base options for open cellular pavement.

Preparing the Base

Depending on the design and purpose for the paving, several options for base preparation are available for cellular pavement (Figure 29-6). For a simple installation, the pavers can be placed directly on a prepared subgrade. Excavate the area where the paving is to be placed to the paver's depth, correct any subgrade soil problems, level, and compact using a vibratory plate compactor. Lay a filter fabric, if desired, over the subgrade. A slightly more durable installation can be attained if you place 1–2 inches of granular base over the subgrade before leveling and compacting. If the paved area is to support vehicular traffic, install a compacted granular base as described in the section introduction.

If the installation is to retain runoff, a base of 8–36 inches of clean angular aggregate will be required based on the design for the pavement. Excavate the entire base area to the required depth and fill with aggregate. The fill should range in size from 1–2½ inches in diameter. Place a nonwoven filter fabric over the entire bottom and sides of the base area.

Placing Cellular Pavers

Begin placing cellular paving at the lowest end of the installation. Lay the pavers across the grade,

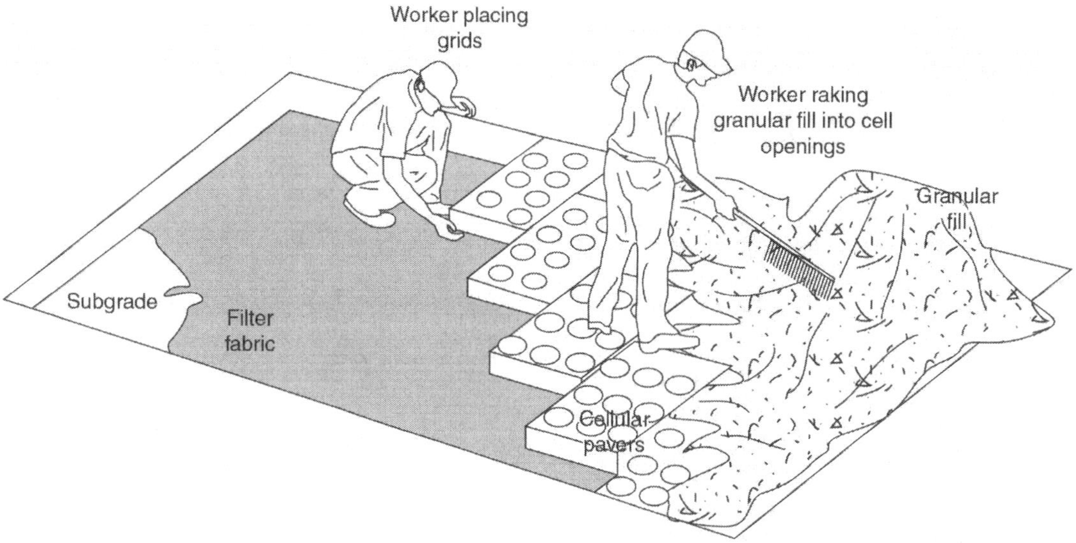

Figure 29-7 Placement of open cellular pavement units and filling with granular material.

interlocking the units if necessary. The pavers should be in firm contact with the base and set level and flush with adjacent pavers (Figure 29-7). Install cellular pavers level and flush with adjacent pavement, adjusting the base height if necessary. Cut around irrigation heads and vertical elements that project through the pavers. Make any cuts in the pavers using a reciprocating saw (for plastic products) or a wet masonry saw (for precast concrete products).

Finishing the Surface

Cellular paving can be filled with a variety of materials. Granular paving, pebbles, stabilized soil, or soil with seed can be used to complete the surface of the paved area. To use granulars, pebbles, or stabilized soil, place backfill over the entire area by hand or by using hand equipment. Once you place the backfill, rake the surface level and compact using a drum roller. Fill any low areas or voids. To create a surface with turf, backfill with 1 inch of coarse concrete sand, followed by topsoil, to within ½ inch of the top of the pavers and apply turf seed over the surface. Keep the area thoroughly watered until the first mowing; then scale back watering to a normal schedule.

SECTION 6

SUMMARY

Specialty paving of outdoor areas is a basic skill required of most landscape contractors. Section 6 covered the selection of materials and the preparation of base for most paving types. Specific instructions were provided for installation of pedestrian concrete paving, including the forming for flatwork and stairs, unit paving, dry-laid stone paving, mortared paving, and granular paving.

When choosing a paving material for a project, consider the durability, safety, maintenance, aesthetics, cost, permeability, sustainability, and installation characteristics of each material available. With the variety of paving materials to choose from, you can select at least one that meets the demands of the project. One of the more common paving materials for landscape projects is concrete. Whether left "plain" or treated with one of several surface textures and colors, concrete is a durable choice. Unit pavers are also widely used for landscape applications. Interlocking concrete paving block, asphalt pavers, brick, cut stone, adobe, and pavers from recycled materials create a look of craftsmanship. If site drainage is a concern, concrete unit pavers can be constructed with a base that reduces runoff. You can also obtain an aesthetically pleasing surface by using a variety of locally available stone paving materials. If placed in a bed of mortar with mortar joints, many of the unit materials and stone can be given added stability. Stone and other paving materials can be used for stepping stones. Granular paving is an inexpensive way to cover flat walkways and outdoor use areas, but can be high in maintenance activities. Compacted turf areas can be treated using open-cell pavers, which have openings filled with soil and seed or granular materials.

Preparing for paving requires a stable subgrade. In most situations, this will involve excavating to the proper depth and examining the subgrade for any moisture or soil problems. If you encounter any unstable areas or problems with drainage, address these problems before installing a paving base. Any compaction and/or utility work required below the paved area should also be completed before base installation proceeds. Undisturbed earth provides the most stable subgrade, and fill areas require special compaction techniques to avoid settling problems. Base material is then placed over the subgrade and compacted in preparation for the various types of paving. If edge restraint is required for a paving material, verify whether the restraint should be placed before or after paving installation.

Pedestrian concrete paving installation requires extensive preparation prior to the actual paving activities. You must prepare the forms, level the base material, install reinforcement, and plan joints before the concrete arrives. Form materials are typically dimensioned lumber for straight sections and flexible masonite for curved edges. Forms must be securely anchored with staking and backfill to prevent failure during the pour. Stairs can be formed in open areas by building forms for sides and risers; in enclosed areas, by suspending riser forms from beams running over the top of the stairs. For all forms, check their stability carefully before concrete arrives to reduce the chance for failure.

Concrete pours begin with the placement of concrete directly from the truck or transported by equipment to remote areas. The material is leveled initially using a hand or mechanical screed. Smoothing of the surface with a bull float and hand float follows. In locations where a very smooth surface is desired, an additional floating with a steel trowel follows. Each of these steps is intended to embed the aggregate into the slab and bring the fine materials to the surface. Before the slab hardens, special surface finishes are applied and the surface is edged and jointed. The new pour is sprayed with a curing compound, or covered for 3–7 days for curing. Forms are removed after 2–4 days. If control joints are to be cut with a saw, it is done at this time. Both new and existing concrete can be stained or painted to achieve various decorative effects.

Installation of unit pavers requires a setting bed over the base course. Composed of sand, this course is placed approximately 1-inch thick and screeded to obtain a level surface that mirrors the desired finish surface. One of the variety of patterns is selected for the project, and pavers are placed beginning with a *T* or horizontal pattern, working out from a wall or straight edge. Pavers are individually placed across the entire area to be paved and, if not already in place, edge restraint is installed. Working with unit pavers requires special edging to hold the pavers in place. Many choices are available, based on aesthetics and requirements of the paving installation. Unit pavers require cutting and placing of partial pavers to fill voids along edges and around corners. Pavers are seated into the setting bed using a plate compactor, and the joints are swept with dry sand to lock the pavers into place. If installing permeable pavers to reduce runoff, the base preparation is changed to a deep layer of open graded stone and fine stone is placed in the joints between pavers.

Dry-laid stone paving and recycled concrete are installed in a manner similar to that of unit pavers, with the exception that some stone choices have no formal pattern to guide placement. A setting bed is installed and screeded, and individual stones are placed beginning in a corner or along a straight edge. Random stone must be carefully selected for fit, whereas cut stone may be placed in patterns similar to those of unit pavers or in special patterns developed by the designer. After placement, edge restraint is placed and joints are swept with fine granular material. Stepping stones are marked and the base excavated and leveled. Steppers are then replaced and leveled. Although it requires little for a setting bed and no edge restraint, recycled concrete can be difficult to move and place because of its weight.

Stone and most unit pavers can be installed on a mortar bed with mortared joints if the design requires. For a more durable installation, a concrete base is recommended instead of a granular base. Patterns for installation are the same as those used with unit pavers and dry-laid stone, with the exception that allowance must be made for mortar joints between paving units. After the base has been installed, mortar is mixed and placed in a thick layer over the base. Paving materials are set in the mortar bed and adjusted to the correct elevation using a trowel. Placement continues with the installer backing across the base while laying pavement. Edges and corners require cutting of materials, but edge restraint is not required. When the setting bed has begun to harden, the joints are filled using a mason's bag or a trowel and pointing tool. Joints are smoothed with a joining tool. When all mortar is set, the surface can be cleaned with a weak acid mixture if necessary.

Granular pavement can be installed with or without base material. Consideration may be given to placing landscape fabric under the granular material to reduce weeds and prevent the paving material from being pumped into the base. Edge restraint is required and must be placed before granular material is installed. Place the paving material over the base, and screed or level with a rake to the appropriate depth across the entire paved area. Some materials require compacting the surface, whereas other materials are ready for use immediately after placement. Plan on increased maintenance, including refreshing and releveling the surface, if the desire is to have a clean, level surface for granular paving. To address concerns with routing excess water off sites via paving, materials that allow water to percolate into the ground have gained importance. These materials include a wide range of open cell pavements and products that reduce runoff by allowing infiltration of water through the paving surface.

Section 7

FREESTANDING WALLS

INTRODUCTION

This section describes the construction materials and installation techniques for a variety of freestanding walls. Chapter 30 discusses freestanding walls that are made of basic materials: those that are stacked dry, such as fieldstone; those that are mortared together, such as stone, brick, concrete block, and cast-in-place concrete; those with stucco or veneered finishes.

PRECONSTRUCTION CONSIDERATIONS

Before installing any freestanding wall, first locate the property lines. Do not rely on recollection or on the property owner's descriptions for boundary locations. You can more easily locate the property line than relocate the wall. Nor would the property owner wish to deed away the small strip of land the wall rests on after an error has been made. Property lines are based on legal descriptions, and a surveyor's expertise may be needed to locate the actual corners. Also, consider constructing the wall slightly inside the property lines to maintain a margin of error. Flagging the locations of all elements before surveying and ensuring that required footings are within the property boundary will allow adjustments to be made before posts are installed.

When constructing along property lines, the contractor must obtain permission from adjacent property owners for access to their land during construction. Minimal space is required to construct most projects, but even a small encroachment may create problems. Always leave adjacent property clean and in good condition.

SUSTAINABILITY SUGGESTION

- Make use of recycled and reused materials before purchasing newly manufactured products. Recycled concrete and recycled wood can create landscape features. These materials lend a natural look of antiquity without using toxic chemicals to treat them or importing other materials from great distances.

PRODUCTIVITY SUGGESTIONS

The following suggestions may provide general ideas from which project productivity can be improved:

- With masonry, lay out the base course to verify the number of units required for a wall. Begin work by building opposite corners and stretch mason's line between corners to maintain alignment and elevation.
- Construction of vertical walls require extensive knowledge of the materials and techniques of such construction. Vertical wall construction should not be attempted without prior experience. If unfamiliar with the construction techniques discussed herein, additional education including a possible internship are recommended.

CHAPTER 30

FREESTANDING WALLS

OBJECTIVES

By reading and practicing the techniques described in this chapter, the reader should be able to successfully complete the following activities:

- Plan the successful installation of a freestanding wall.
- Prepare the foundation for a freestanding wall.
- Build a dry-laid stone freestanding wall.
- Construct a freestanding wall of masonry units.
- Pour a cast-in-place freestanding wall.
- Apply a stucco or veneer surface to a freestanding wall.

When space separation is required but the design dictates a substantial look, a freestanding wall may be the best choice. The freestanding wall incorporates the benefits of a fence with the permanence of a landscape wall. Although it is expensive and time-consuming to construct, the freestanding wall adds a strong sense of permanence to a site.

Freestanding walls should not be confused with landscape retaining walls (see Section 5). Both retaining walls and freestanding walls require special construction techniques to maintain stability, but their construction is for very different reasons. Retaining walls endure pressure from the forces of soil and water behind the wall, whereas freestanding walls must overcome the force of wind to remain upright. Freestanding walls typically do not retain soil and do not require drainage accommodation. If these conditions exist on all or part of a wall, the design must be adjusted to address these forces.

This chapter provides construction details for installing several styles of freestanding walls. **Fieldstone,** or rubble, walls use stacked stone to recreate the look of antiquity and history in design. Masonry walls consist of manufactured materials mortared together to create visually pleasing barriers. Cast-in-place concrete provides a durable installation and, with additional work, can be an attractive space divider. Most stable freestanding wall materials can be coated with stucco or veneer to add color and texture to a plain installation. In addition, any wall construction can be used for installing piers or columns used to identify entries, to mount signs and lights, and, occasionally, to anchor posts in wood fence construction. Piers can also be constructed simply of rubble-filled cages when a quick temporary marker is required.

RELATED INFORMATION

Information in this chapter is supplemented by instruction provided elsewhere in this text and in other sources. Before undertaking the activities described in this chapter, read the related information in these sources:

- Construction Math, Chapter 5
- Safety in the Workplace, Chapter 7
- Basic Construction Techniques and Small Equipment Operation, Chapter 8
- Pedestrian Concrete Paving, Chapter 25
- Mortared Paving, Chapter 28

MATERIALS FOR FREESTANDING WALLS

Many material choices exist from which walls can be constructed. Included below are some of the common choices.

Dry-Laid Fieldstone (Rubble) Walls

Fieldstone, or rubble, is irregular-shaped round or rectangular stone that is weathered by natural forces. When used in rustic, rural settings, fieldstone walls are one of the most attractive landscape additions available. They are primarily used for boundary identification, with separation and enclosure being additional functions. A contractor must be a skilled craftsperson to place stones in a stable, yet appealing, pattern. Maintenance requires occasional reconstruction of wall segments.

Masonry Walls and Piers

Many common building materials (stone, fieldstone, brick, block, and adobe, for instance) can be attractively used in a masonry wall and piers (Figure 30-1). Although they are expensive and require a great deal of expertise to construct, masonry installations perform all functions required of fencing with a high level of aesthetics. Masonry walls and piers require little maintenance.

Cast-in-Place Concrete Walls

Durable walls can be constructed of concrete poured into vertical forms, referred to as **cast-in-place.** Finishes that can be applied to concrete walls include bush hammering, sandblasting, and **stucco** or **veneer.** Concrete walls can also be left unfinished or cast with special integral aggregates or decorative **form liners** (Figure 30-2).

Figure 30-1 Stone masonry wall.

© Delmar/Cengage Learning.

Figure 30-2 Cast-in-place concrete wall.

© Delmar/Cengage Learning.

Stucco and Veneer-Finished Walls

Specialized finishes of stucco and veneer can be applied over walls constructed of precast concrete or masonry to achieve a variety of visual effects. Stucco, a cement mixture spread in a single heavy layer or several thin layers over a prepared surface,

Figure 30-3 Stucco-finished wall.

can be colored or finished with a variety of surface textures (Figure 30-3). When selecting stucco products for exterior landscape applications, choose Portland cement stucco rather than EIFS (exterior insulation foam systems) products. EIFS is a waterproof acrylic product more suitable for building structural components, other than landscape posts and walls that require insulation.

Veneer is a layer of decorative surfacing material applied to a wall using mortar. Typical veneers include brick, stone, and a variety of cultured materials that resemble brick and stone.

Veneer layers can be the full thickness of the surfacing material or can be a thin layer of the material laminated to the wall surface.

Rubble Cage Piers

When a boundary marker or entry pier is required but there is no time to build a masonry or other form of pier, rubble stone can be placed loose inside a rounded cage constructed of heavy-gauge wire fencing. Although it requires little craftsmanship, the rubble cage does provide a quick and functional pier of natural materials.

PLANNING THE PROJECT

Beginning a masonry wall with a detailed design will reduce the number of field decisions and problems encountered during construction.

> **CAUTION**
>
> Freestanding walls over 6 feet in height in non-residential areas must be designed by a design professional. Check state and local codes and consult the local building administrator for guidance.

Masonry Patterns

Although fieldstone typically employs a random pattern, several common arrangements are possible for masonry walls. Figure 30-4 illustrates some of the patterns available to the mason.

Masonry Wall Thickness

Most masonry walls using concrete block and wall stone are constructed the thickness of a single material, or **wythe.** A single wythe of these materials often provides adequate strength and wind resistance to keep the wall upright. Brick is typically constructed using a double wythe to provide the necessary stability. These two wythes periodically have a unit running perpendicular between the two as a bridge, or reinforcement, that ties both wythes together. This bridging course, called a **header course,** is common in brick wall construction. A third choice for masonry installations is a veneered wall. A veneer is a single wythe of a concrete block, or other backing material, and a single wythe of brick or stone veneer. Veneer can be placed on one or both sides of the backing block.

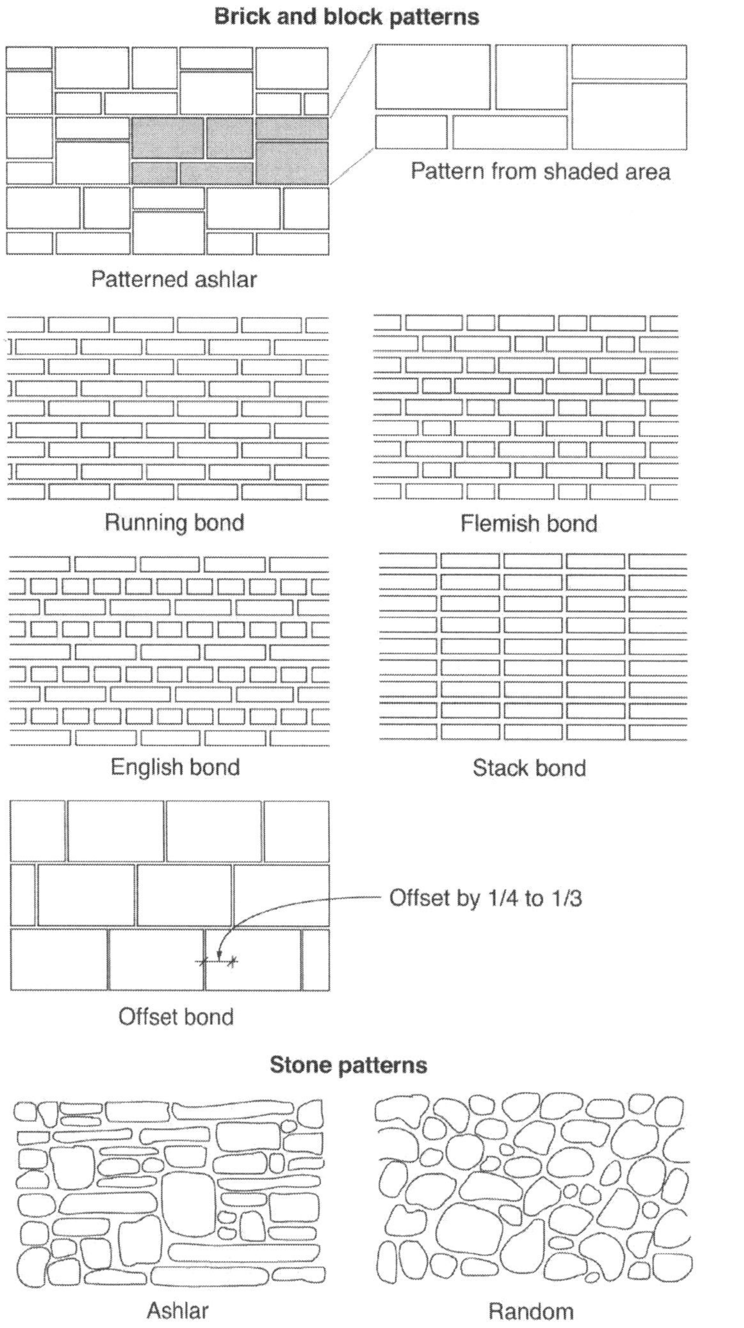

Figure 30-4 Masonry wall patterns.

Freestanding Wall Shape and Wind Resistance

Because they are impermeable to wind, freestanding walls are subjected to extreme wind load. Strong winds can blow with enough force to topple a tall wall if precautions are not taken to counter these forces. The most common countermeasure is to avoid long, straight sections of wall. With corners or piers added to its structure, a freestanding wall gains significant wind resistance. Adjusting the alignment of a wall by adding a few niches or corners may also prevent the wall from toppling. Although it provides some wind resistance, a serpentine alignment increases the construction difficulty.

DRY-LAID FIELDSTONE (RUBBLE) WALLS

Properly installed dry-laid fieldstone walls represent the best of the landscape contracting palate. Both science and art come together in the preparation and construction of this landscape classic. When planning the dry-laid rubble wall, utilize a minimum wall thickness of 16 inches, with wider thicknesses permitted. The maximum wall height of an unreinforced rubble wall should be no more than four times the walls thickness, with a maximum height of five feet. Reinforcement will improve the stability of a wall of any height.

Preparing the Base

Lay out the wall using a stringline (or hose/rope for curved walls) along the alignment. Grade preparation for fieldstone walls requires installation of a stable granular base. Excavate a base trench 6 inches deep and 12 inches wider than the wall width along the entire wall alignment. Fill the base trench with granular base material and compact.

As an alternative to a granular base, select large stones and bury them for a base. Place these stones in an excavated trench below grade and lay them with the flattest sides oriented upward.

Placing Stone

Sort stone for use in appropriate courses, reserving the largest flat stones for a wall cap. Stone walls are assembled by hand, laying one course at a time along the length of the wall. Sides may be vertical for walls 4 feet tall and less and have a batter of 1 inch per foot for taller walls. This batter will require widening the base so the wall face can taper back on both sides. The minimum width for a stone wall over 2 feet tall is two wythes. Walls may benefit from slightly battering, or angling, the bottom stones of each wythe slightly inward at the base (Figure 30-5). Rounded stone may require a pyramidal cross-sectional form for the wall. In walls with wide bases, use the most attractive stone for the outer wythes and fill the center with rubble and less workable pieces (Figure 30-6).

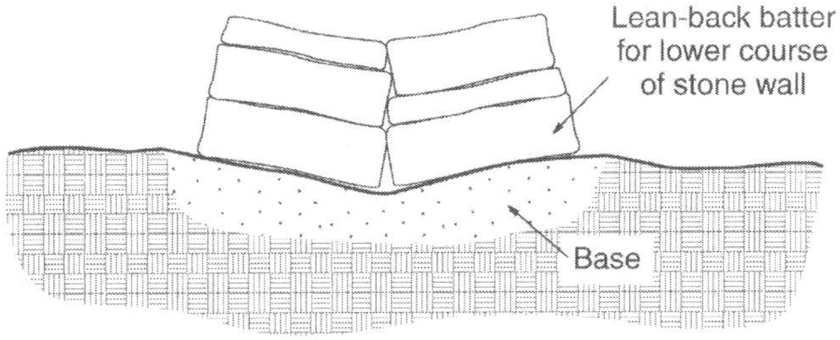

Figure 30-5 Lean-back batter aids the stability of stone walls.

Working with stone requires patience and a visualization of how each piece will fit with other pieces (Figure 30-7). Find a nice flat surface to face outward along the wall face. If a stone does not fit with those below, try shaping the surface using a stone hammer. Use small flat pieces to shim under those stones that do not fit perfectly. To enhance the wall's artistic nature, review the techniques for stone placement outlined for dry-laid stone retaining walls in Chapter 21 (see, in particular, Figure 21-7). You can use the same techniques to enhance freestanding walls.

The most attractive placement of the stone is in horizontal courses that are of uniform thickness along most of the wall's length. Courses should be primarily composed of stone that is of a similar thickness; but of interest, you can create short segments by stacking several thin stones. The regularity for the wall can be varied occasionally by placing a taller/larger stone that

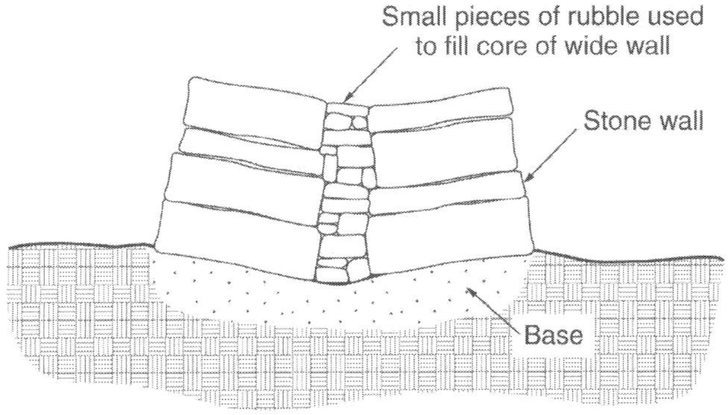

Figure 30-6 Small pieces of rubble can be placed in the center of a wide stone wall.

Figure 30-7 Rubble wall stone placement.

interrupts the course(s) above. Every 5 feet (more or less) in every other course, place a stone perpendicular to the wall face to tie the courses together (Figure 30-8).

Stepping the courses when the grade rises or falls is preferable to following the grade along the wall alignment. Begin placement at the lowest point of the wall and build courses up to a point where the wall steps. Raise the base and continue with the next course on top of the previous wall courses and the new base. Avoid placing stone in locations that create vertical joints extending between two or more courses. Stone in an upper course should bridge two or more stones from the course below, and the ends should be at least 4 inches from a vertical joint in the lower course if possible.

Curved walls with tapered edges can be constructed by selecting and placing stone. If the curve is concave, place the narrower end to the outside of the wall; if convex, place the narrower end to the inside of the wall.

When building corners, be certain to interlock the courses as you place them. The last stone for the course entering the corner from one direction should be a longer stone that stretches from the corner deep into the wall well down the other direction. The next course should alternate that arrangement. Complete the wall by installing the reserved capstones. These stones should be large enough to cover all wythes and provide a slight overhang. You may have to perform some shaping to obtain a good fit for the caps.

For even more stability in the dry-laid fieldstone walls, particularly when the wall height exceeds 3 feet, is to place a poured concrete footing under the wall. Further strengthening is achieved when J bolts are inserted into the footing and allowed to project into the center of the wall. A network of horizontal and vertical rebar can be wired together to strengthen the installation. Adding a mortar backing or mortar fill for interior courses will improve stability. When stacking, add a thick course of mortar along the interior of the wythes to stabilize the stone and reduce shifting. Mortar backing can perform the same task, but may make the back side of the wall less attractive. Apply a thick course of mortar to the back of the wall and work it 1 to 2 inches into the joints between the stone. Excess can be scraped of and wire brushed when dried.

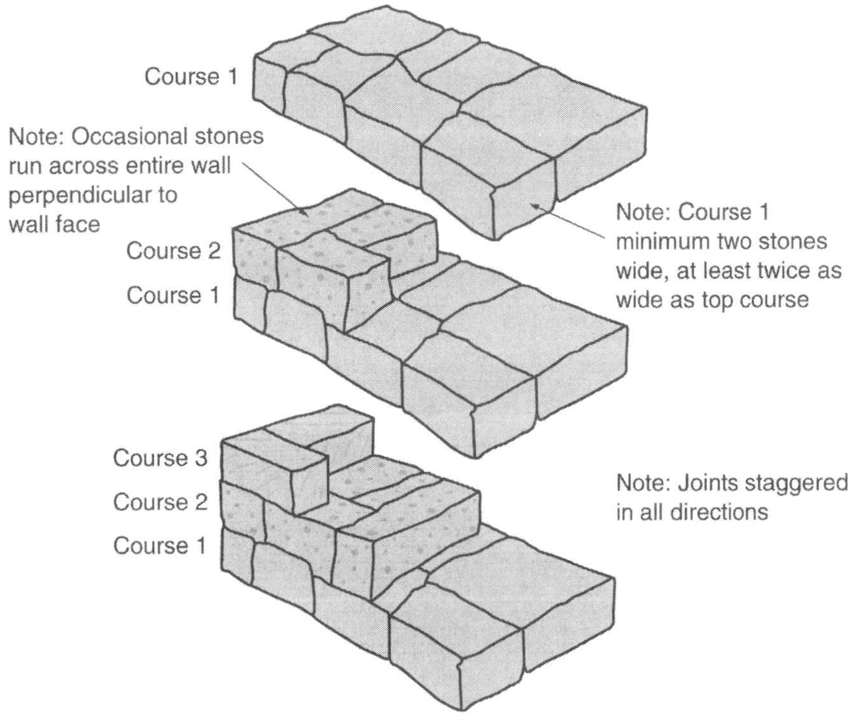

Figure 30-8 Dry-laid stone wall layout of base course and subsequent courses.

CONSTRUCTING FOOTINGS FOR MASONRY AND CAST IN PLACE CONCRETE WALLS.

Footings for masonry and cast-in-place concrete walls are constructed as reinforced slabs with the top of the footing 1 foot below grade and 1 foot wider than the wall's width. Even wider or deeper footings may be required for walls that are taller or on less stable soil (Revisit Chapter 25 for information on forming and pouring the concrete slab that serves as the footing.) A design professional should determine the actual width and thickness of the footing. Under the entire footing location, place a minimum of 4 inches of granular base material. Form the footing using 2 × dimensioned lumber (Figure 30-9). Stake the outside of the pour every 18 inches using 2 × 2 stakes or rebar. Within the footing, place two #4 rebars running the entire length of the footing. Every 2 feet, place a #4 rebar perpendicular to the lengthwise reinforcing. Tie these crosspieces to the lengthwise reinforcing. Use dobies or chairs to support this network of rebar (see Chapter 25).

Brace the pour from the forms on one side to forms on the other side for added stability. For cast in place concrete walls that are over 4 feet in height, or any wall with a heavy horizontal load from wind or backfill, center a metal keyway or a 2 × 4 on the underside of these cross braces before installing them. Coat the keyway or 2 × 4 with kerosene or form break compound. This will form a key or channel, in which the base of the wall will be anchored. At every 2 feet along the length of this footing, place **J bolts or L shaped #4 rebar** that protrudes 6 to 18 inches above the top of the footing. This projection length will increase the stability of the wall over a shorter height. To determine the minimum safe height a design professional should be consulted. These bolts also assist in anchoring the wall to the footing. Any conduit for electrical lighting or signage should be

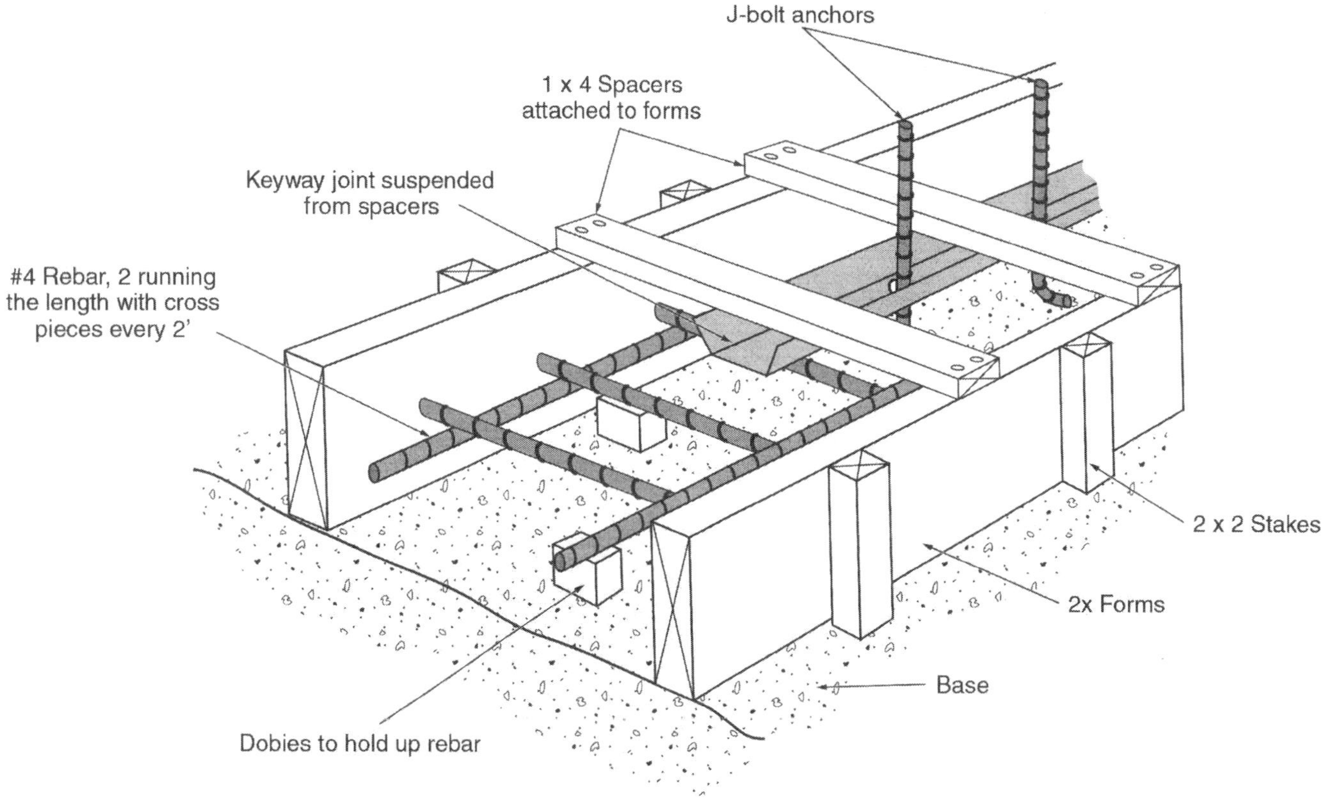

Figure 30-9 Footing for cast-in-place concrete wall.

placed into the footing before pouring. Stub the conduit through the pour and up through the footing near the center of the proposed wall location. Cover the end of the conduit with duct tape.

Pour the footing, making sure that concrete is tamped under and around the keyway (if used) and that the J bolts or rebar protrude directly up from the footing. Finishing the surface of the footing with a rough trowel or broom finish can improve the adherence of the wall mortar to the footing. Cover the pour for curing. After the concrete has cured for a minimum of 2 days, remove the forms and carefully remove the keyway (if used). If you used a 2 × 4 for the keyway, cut and remove it from the pour. Snap a chalk line on the form at the location for the front and back of the wall.

MASONRY (STONE, BLOCK, AND BRICK) WALLS AND PIERS

Combining the beauty of unit materials with mortar creates a wall that provides durability and presentable aesthetics throughout its life. Stone and brick masonry walls are prized for their attractiveness, whereas block walls provide a less-expensive alternative with several surface treatment options.

> **CAUTION**
>
> Free standing masonry walls may require a design by a licensed professional. Check local codes to verify the height which a wall can be built without a professional design.

Constructing Footings

Construct footings as described in the section previously.

Performing Layout and Preparing Materials

Prepare the footing to accept the mortar by scrubbing off all debris with water and a broom. When dry, use a chalk line to mark two straight lines 4 inches in front of the face of the proposed wall. These guidelines will serve as reference marks for alignment of the first course of the wall. When constructing walls using brick or concrete block, carefully measure the wall dimensions and mark beginning and ending positions on the footing. Lay out the brick or block without mortar (a process called **chasing a bond**) to verify dimensions before you start mortaring. Because brick and concrete block cannot be cut like stone to aesthetically fit small voids, your measurements must be precise.

Prepare materials to be used before beginning the wall construction. Clean off any old mortar and discard broken or damaged items. When using brick, be certain that halves are available before you begin laying them. And when using stone, lay out a variety of stone to speed the construction of a stone wall. Dip the stone in water for a short time before installation; this prevents the stone from drawing moisture too quickly from the mortar. If the stone draws too much water from it, the mortar will dry more quickly, potentially reducing its strength.

Mixing and Placing Mortar

After you have prepared all materials, you can begin mixing the mortar. Typical mortar types for exterior wall applications are S and N. Instructions for selecting mortar are explained in Table 28-1. Refer also to mortar mixing for paving in Chapter 28.

Applying the mortar to the masonry units will take some practice. Use a pointed mason's **trowel** to apply mortar. When placing mortar on the base or the top of a masonry unit, pick up a trowel full of mortar and apply the mortar to the material with a light slapping motion. At first, you may find mortar application difficult; but with practice, you will learn how to place mortar exactly where it should be placed. When applying mortar to the sides of a masonry unit, a slapping motion prevents mortar from sliding off when the unit is held upright. Apply mortar generously to fill the joints since any extra will be squeezed out when you place the unit.

When placing concrete blocks, be aware that they have a top and a bottom. The top of the block has a wider edge than does the bottom; this wider edge holds mortar. Bricks or stones have no top or bottom; however, bricks may have a front and a back.

Placing the Base Course

Using the reference marks as guidelines, place generous beads of mortar along the front and back locations of the wall unit. This bead should be thick enough that when the block is set excess mortar squeezes out from under the block and there are no voids in the joints. Set the first unit on these beads and check for the proper height and for level in both directions. Use the handle of the trowel to tap the unit into proper alignment and level. If the wall is constructed with a double row of wall units, both units must be level between front and back.

When you have properly aligned the unit, use the trowel to vertically slice the excess mortar away from the unit. Slide the excess mortar away from the wall and do not reuse it. Mortar that has come in contact with the ground will pick up soil and other debris that will weaken the mortar if it is remixed.

If installing concrete block or brick, use a stringline to maintain alignment and level for each unit. Place and level the blocks at both ends of the wall and install stringline hooked to each block using a line block, a small wood clip that holds mason's twine in place. This stringline should just touch the top front corner of both end blocks. As the wall grows in height, move the stringline up one course at a time. With brick construction, build a small section of the wall four to five courses high at each end of the wall. You can then stretch the stringline between these end sections while you lay the center part of the wall. You must individually align and level irregular stone units.

Continue laying the wall block by placing two more beads of mortar on the base for the second unit. The second unit should be **buttered** with mortar at the end that abuts the previously placed unit. If mortar fails to stick to the block when buttering, try applying the mortar using a slapping motion with a trowel full of mortar aimed at the block end. Place the unit and use the trowel handle to adjust alignment against the stringline and to achieve proper spacing. Joints between units should be approximately 3/8 inch. With each unit placed, verify for level with the previous unit and check level front to back. Scrape away excess mortar.

Continue placing beads of mortar and units along the entire length of the base course (Figure 30-10). If you started laying from both ends, you will need to place a unit between the two end units. Butter this closure unit on both ends and carefully slide it between the units already in place.

Placing Subsequent Courses

Place subsequent courses following the design pattern required. Do not align joints vertically in a masonry wall unless this alignment is specified in the design. Most patterns begin the second course using a manufactured half block or brick. Special end and corner blocks are available for concrete block products. For double-wythe brick walls, you can place a brick perpendicular to the wall direction to create the half required to offset the pattern. For stone walls, you can cut the stone or select a shorter piece to offset the joint pattern.

Install subsequent courses by first applying a layer of mortar to the top of the previous course and placing a block on it. Check for joint spacing, alignment, and level in both directions. Setting blocks on both corners first will allow you to move the stringline up one course. Continue laying block in subsequent courses in the same manner as the base course (Figure 30-11).

Horizontal reinforcing should be installed every other course for concrete block. The standard horizontal reinforcing is a narrow steel ladder with angled crosspieces that is buried in the mortar placed on top of the units (Figure 30-12). No. 3 or 4 rebar is used for vertical reinforcement for tall walls. Every 32 inches, place a vertical bar into a core of the block or opening between wythes. **Grout** around the reinforcement to hold it in place. Double wythe brick walls will require vertical rebar installed

Figure 30-10 First course laying and leveling.

© Delmar/Cengage Learning.

Figure 30-11 Masonry courses showing stringline used to keep blocks aligned.

© Delmar/Cengage Learning.

Figure 30-12 Horizontal steel reinforcement embedded in mortar.

every 2 feet horizontally in the grout cavity between the wythes, and horizontal reinforcing every 3rd course that is placed in the mortar between the bricks and tied to the vertical rebar. See manufacturers specifications for any horizontal reinforcing for single wythe brick walls. Unless the courses are laid with straight, horizontal joints, reinforcement in wall stone applications is impractical.

If the wall or pier has a mechanical fixture such as a light base, signage anchor, or gate hardware, lay the wall up to the point where the fixture is to be located. Complete any connections to the previously placed conduit that are required, and place the fixture in the next course. Placement may require cutting or piecing a partial unit to make room for the fixture. Fill around the fixture with mortar and continue adding courses. Small additions such as gate hardware or anchors for signs may be embedded in the mortar between courses. Verify the dimensions and locations for all such installations before work progresses and mortar hardens. If the wall or pier has a veneer finish, place small, galvanized strips of corrugated metal, called **veneer ties**, every other course. Bend these ties into the joints of the veneer to anchor the two wall wythes together.

Another method to integrate wythes of different block or brick sizes or materials is to place horizontal anchors between the wythes. The anchors are placed every 3 feet horizontally and every 18 inches vertically. Stagger the placement so that all anchors do not align vertically. Anchors can take a variety of forms and shapes, but most are galvanized metal have a projecting plate or wires that are set into to mortar of courses for each side of the wall. The particular type selected for a wall will depend on the style and size of brick/block.

Allowing for Utility Runs

If the wall requires the installation of lighting that is integral in the wall, a conduit may have to be placed through the wall's center. This utility run is typically created by using two narrower block wythes, rather than one wide wythe, then placing conduit in the space between the wythes. When you encounter a light fixture, remove a block or trim the front of a block to place the fixture housing. Installation of the wiring can then be done by the licensed electrician.

Striking Joints

Joint finishing, or **striking,** is generally performed by running a special tool over the mortar in the joint to smooth and compress the mortar (Figure 30-13). Striking provides a more attractive finish for the mortar and makes the mortar joint waterproof. Several patterns are available, with the most common being a concave pattern. Other choices include a squared, or raked, joint, a rustic joint, an angled joint that is inset at the top and flush with the unit at the bottom, and a V joint (Figure 30-14). Each of these patterns requires a special jointing tool.

Scraping the mortar away from the surface of the wall by striking downward with a trowel creates flush joints. Running a rounded jointing tool over the joint with a firm and steady pressure creates concave joints. The tool should rest evenly on the units on both sides as you strike the joint. Squared or raked, angled, and V joints are created with special jointing tools. Joints should be struck to an even depth along all joints. Hold the jointing tool with your finger running along the units to maintain a consistent strike. Allowing mortar to ooze from between the units creates the rustic joint. Selection of joint style will be based in part on the area's weather and the type of finish to be placed on the wall. Squared and raked joints will hold water and ice in cold-weather climates, creating potential problems from expansion. Because they will leave small gaps between the joints and the units, flush joints are appropriate only for walls that will be veneered or receive stucco.

Figure 30-13 Striking joints on a masonry pier.

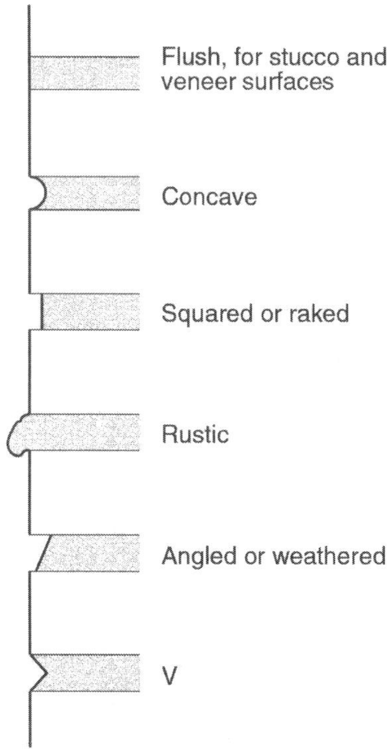

Figure 30-14 Joint patterns.

Begin striking joints at the bottom course with the horizontal joints; then strike the vertical joints. Continue up the wall in this order until you reach the newly laid block. Timing of the striking operation is important. When the mortar begins to lose its sheen, it is time to strike the joints. Striking too soon will push mortar out of the joint; waiting too long will allow the mortar to harden. Laying block at a slow pace may require laying one course and stopping to strike joints. Because you do not remove the excess mortar to achieve the rustic joint, this joint requires no striking.

Grouting Cores

Walls with concrete block, double-wythe brick, or double-wythe veneer block will have an open cavity in their centers. This cavity needs to be filled to maintain structural strength and to reduce moisture infiltration inside the wall. Wait until the mortar has set for 24 hours before filling the cavity with grout. Grout is a light mortar mix with double the sand content of typical mortar. Mix and place the grout in a bucket; then pour it into the cavity until filled.

Failure to properly and completely grout the interior of the wall can allow moisture to accumulate inside the wall, which may eventually lead to efflorescence on the surface of the wall. Efflorescence is the residue of naturally occurring salts that are dissolved inside the wall, move through the wall and eventually are deposited on the outside of the wall when the moisture evaporates. Efflorescence leaves an unattractive whitish powder or film on the outside of the wall that can be difficult to remove.

While there is no total solution to controlling the problem, steps can be taken to reduce this issue with masonry units. In addition to grouting, additional steps can be taken to reduce efflorescence. Reducing the amount of materials that contain soluble alkali sulfates is an initial step. This would include wall units and mortar that contains Sodium and Potassium sulfates. Various admixtures for use with mortar also make claims to reduce the problem. Preventing water from entering into the wall during construction is a second step. Cover work that is in progress to reduce unnecessary introduction of water. Grouting the core, capping the top of the wall and following quality construction practices will also aid in reduction of efflorescence.

Capping

When building walls with cavities in the center, the top of the wall must be capped to prevent moisture from entering the wall. Both brick and concrete block have special capstones manufactured for this purpose. Veneer block walls may require cutting and placing a row of block perpendicular to the wall direction as a cap. Some designs select a cap unit that overhangs the wall faces slightly. Finish grouting the wall to the top of the cavity and lay beads of mortar on the top course. Set the cap course in a manner similar to laying any course, checking to maintain alignment and level both directions (Figure 30-15). If any type of structure support or fencing is to be attached to the top of the wall, insert supports or J bolts into the soft mortar between capstones and retouch the mortar. Scrape away excess mortar and strike the joints.

Figure 30-15 Capping a masonry pier.

Cleaning the Surface

When all mortar has hardened, clean the surface of the wall. Large pieces of mortar can be removed by rubbing a hammer over the surface. If mortar or grout has run down the wall and stained the surface, you will need to scrub it with a mixture of 9 parts water with 1 part muriatic acid. Use caution for personal health and the health of surrounding plant material when cleaning with these materials.

CAUTION

When cleaning pavement using acid and caustic cleaners, follow all safety precautions identified on the label. Wear proper safety clothing. Contact with and exposure to acids and caustic cleaners can cause personal injury and can harm plants.

CAUTION

When mixing acid and water, always add the acid to the water and never add water to acid. Adding water to acid will cause the mixture to spray and splatter, creating the potential for burns. Always wear protective clothing, gloves, and eyewear when mixing chemicals.

CAST-IN-PLACE CONCRETE WALLS

Cast-in-place freestanding walls introduce a number of possibilities to the landscape. Although they are not commonly used in residential settings, the variations of finishes available and their durability make such walls a viable option in many landscapes. They do, however, have limitations. Contractors must dedicate extensive time to construct them and must brace forms to reduce the risk of form failure. Also, pouring a footing separate from the vertical wall requires additional time in construction. Because cast-in-place freestanding walls are difficult to construct, only experienced concrete contractors should undertake their construction. Note that the construction of cast-in-place freestanding concrete walls will be quite different from a structural standpoint than a cast-in-place retaining wall. An experienced contractor should engineer and construct any cast-in-place wall of any height used to retain soil.

Constructing Footings for cast-in-place Concrete Walls

See the section before masonry walls on how to construct concrete footings for cast-in-place concrete walls.

Forming and Pouring Concrete Walls

Assembling and installing the form for one side, installing the interior reinforcing, and then forming and installing the other side are the steps to forming the wall. Common materials for forming include rented metal forms, ¾-inch plywood, or 1 × dimensioned lumber. Install rental forms according to instructions provided by the manufacturer or rental company.

When using plywood or dimensioned lumber, construct the form flat on the ground next to the footing. Build a framework of 2 × 4 lumber with verticals spaced every 1 foot between a base plate and a top plate. Apply plywood to one side of this framework and trim to match the outside edge of the framework. This framework should run the entire length of the wall, but you may build it in sections that a small crew can lift into. If the wall is to have special finishes, such as board forming or form liners, these need to be installed before placing the form in position. Attach these decorative forms to the inside of the form framework.

After the form is complete, tip the framework onto the footing and temporarily brace it into position. Drive 2-foot long 2 × 4 stakes securely into the ground at 2-foot intervals along the entire length of the footing. Correctly position the base of the form on the proper chalk line on the footing. With the form in position, temporarily anchor the base plate of the forms to the footing using concrete nails or a **power driver** sunk into "green" concrete. Have an assistant stabilize the form until it is braced. Brace the top of wall using 2 × 4s or larger lumber fastened to the form framework verticals and angled outward to the stakes along the footing. The level of bracing will increase significantly as the height of the pour increases. Tall walls will require additional bracing from 2 x 6 lumber. Add a second brace at the bottom of the form verticals running out to the stake (Figure 30-16). If you built the framework in sections, lift and place each section; then fasten to the previous section using lag screws or carriage bolts.

When one side of the forming is complete and braced, you can place the interior reinforcement. Cut enough #4 rebars to place one vertically every 2 linear feet along the

Figure 30-16 Form framework for a cast in-place concrete wall.

length of the wall. These rebars should be 4 inches shorter than the wall's height and will serve as vertical reinforcement. At each location where a J bolt protrudes from the footing, tie one of these vertical rebar to the J bolt. Beginning 1 foot above the footing, attach horizontal #4 rebar to each vertical rebar. Continue the horizontal rebar along the entire length of the wall.

Install horizontal rebar at 1-foot intervals to the top of the wall. If any conduit is to be placed into the wall for utility connections, place the conduit before you install the other side of the forming. Anchor conduit to the reinforcing and connect it to junction boxes fastened to the inside of the forms (Figure 30-17).

After reinforcing is complete, assemble the forms for the opposite side in the same manner as the first side. To enclose the ends of the pour, first rip cut a length of 2 × lumber to the wall's width. Then trim the board's length to match the height of the wall. Position the piece of 2 × lumber vertically between the wall forms. Fasten the 2 × into the correct position by inserting several deck screws or 16d nails through both side forms and into the 2 ×. When you have correctly positioned and braced all forms, add additional bracing across the tops of the forms. Tall walls may require form ties be installed halfway up the wall along the entire length to securely hold the forms together. Drill through both forms, insert the tie completely through the form, and secure the tie on the outside to hold the forms. Several manufacturers have form ties in lengths and materials that work with different types of forming. When you have completed the forming, spray the inside of the forms with form break compound or light kerosene.

To hold the reinforcing in the center of the wall during the pour, insert 14-gauge wire ties through the forms and tie them to the rebar. Drill ⅛-inch diameter holes through both sides of the forms. The holes should be directly across from each other every 2 feet along the length of the wall and 1 foot down from the top of the wall. Insert the end of a 14-gauge wire through the hole on one side. Reach into the form and pull the length of the wire into the form, leaving the end protruding through the form. Wrap the wire

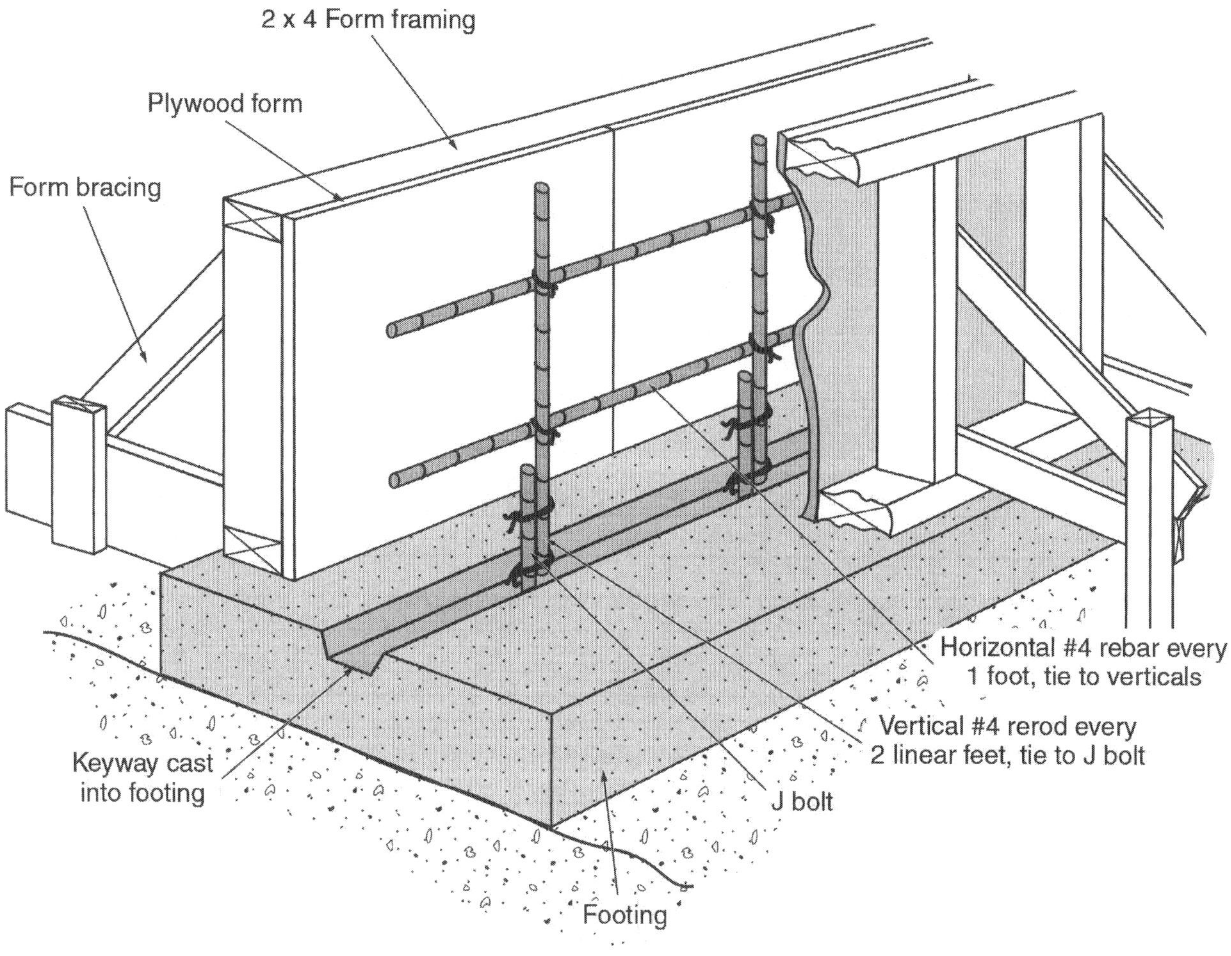

Figure 30-17 Reinforcing cast-in-place concrete wall.

around the rebar reinforcing and push the end out the opposite hole so that at least 8 inches protrude out the other side of the form (Figure 30-18). Pull on the wire from one side of the form until the rebar is positioned in the middle of the forms. When the rebar is positioned correctly, wrap the tie wire around a 16d nail outside forms on both sides. Add any additional bracing necessary to secure the forms. Using heavy stakes, anchor all bracing securely to the ground.

Pouring the Wall

Any special aggregate should be mixed into the concrete before placement. Pour the concrete slowly into the wall cavity, evenly raising the level across the wall. Pour the entire wall in a single continuous pour, unless specific control joints are planned. To aid in the placement of **concrete pumping** service that can drop material down into the form cavity, rather than lifting concrete to the top of the forms. As the concrete is poured, constantly check the forms for leaks and bulges and immediately repair any problem areas. Tap the sides of the walls with rubber mallets as the pour progresses to reduce **honey-combing** of the walls. When the concrete reaches to top of the forms, remove the top cross bracing so the top of the wall can be finished. After the concrete has cured for 2 days, carefully remove the bracing and forms. Snap or cut the ties to remove the forms.

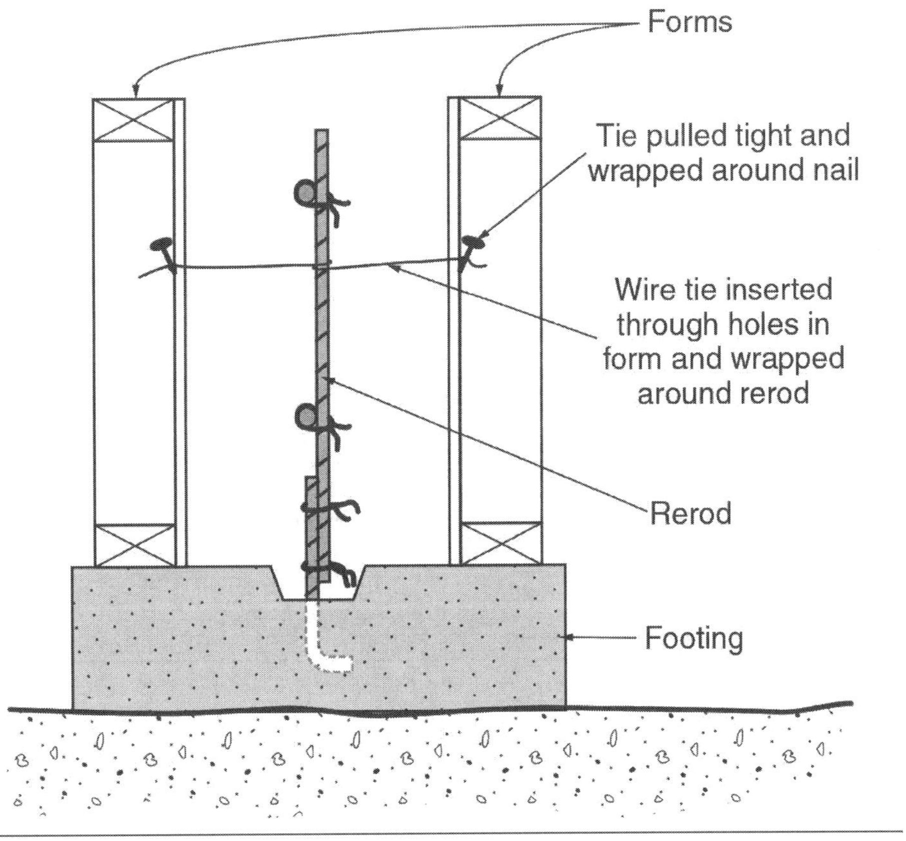

Figure 30-18 Supporting reinforcing in the center of forms using wire ties.

Finishing Concrete Wall Surfaces

Many walls are left as plain concrete without any further treatment. However, if a special finish is desired, the surface can be treated by sandblasting, **bush hammering,** or surfacing with stucco, veneer, or paint. Sandblasting creates a slightly rough texture by shooting sand at high pressure against the concrete. Wait 2 weeks before sandblasting. Control the texture of the finish by the speed with which the sandblasting tool is worked across the wall. Specialized aggregate placed in the concrete will typically require sandblasting to expose it on the surface. Bush hammering roughens the surface and is accomplished using a pneumatic or electric-powered drill. Insert a toothed head into the drill chuck, and lightly hammer the entire surface to create a rough, grooved surface (Figure 30-19). Wait a minimum of 4 weeks before applying a bush-hammered surface to a new wall.

Stucco or veneer surfaces can also be applied to concrete walls. See the following sections for preparation and installation of these specialized surfaces. Although not common in exterior situations, certain Portland cement paints, acrylic latex paints, and rubber-based paints can be applied. Successful applications of each of these paints rely on a clean surface.

STUCCO WALLS

Adding color and texture to the idea of landscape walls can be accomplished by using stucco. A versatile material that can be applied over most base wall materials, stucco can be tinted or blended to achieve a variety of surface colors and textures.

Single-Coat Stuccos

A fiberglass-reinforced stucco product may be applied in a single coat of ⅜ inch thickness over

Figure 30-19 Concrete finished by bush hammering.

cast-in-place concrete and masonry walls. This product is installed without joints or backing mesh. To install this product, construct a framework without joints or mesh, clean the wall surface as described in the following section, and apply the material using a trowel in a swirl texture. Allow the surface to dry for 48 hours before applying any special finishes.

Preparing Framework for Multi-Coat Stuccos

Stucco application can be made to a variety of wall types, including wood frame, masonry, and cast-in-place concrete. With the exception of wood frame, walls can be constructed using the instructions in the preceding sections combined with the additional preparation and finishing described here. Stone walls, both dry-laid and mortared, and any wall material that is not stabilized against shifting and movement are not acceptable frameworks for stucco surfacing.

Applying Stucco

Stucco can be applied to a variety of backing materials. For exterior work application to masonry and cast-in-place provides the most durable wall surfaces, but on occasion the landscape contractor may be required to build a decay resistant wood framework on which stucco is applied.

Masonry. Clean, rough-textured masonry surfaces can accept stucco without additional preparation. When constructing new masonry walls intended for stucco surfacing flush strike joints in the masonry. Sandblast or wash surfaces that are not clean at high pressure. Dirty surfaces can also be prepared for stucco application by rinsing them with trisodium phosphate (**TSP**) mixed according to the manufacturer's directions. Mix the solution, apply it to the wall, and scrub the wall with a wire brush. Let the surface dry before working it. Wear proper protective clothing and follow all safety precautions when cleaning surfaces. Avoid contact between the cleaning solutions and metal.

Cast-in-Place Concrete. In many cases, stucco can be applied directly to concrete walls. If smooth, oily, or coated with any type of lubricant, including form break, the surface must be cleaned before stucco can be applied. Clean the surface using TSP as explained previously in preparing mortared walls. Apply a dash bond, or adhesive, to concrete to improve keying between the wall and the stucco. Dash bonds are liquid mixtures of 1 part cement with 1½ parts sand that are applied with a brush or trowel.

Some concrete bonding adhesives are designed to assist in mortar bonding, and special acrylic modified bonding adhesives can be used when your total surface thickness is less than 1 inch. When using bonding adhesive, apply a layer approximately 1/16 inch thick with a roller in the area you plan to stucco immediately. Apply the base stucco coat when the glue is tacky. If cleaning is ineffective, apply self-furring galvanized steel diamond mesh lath to masonry walls mechanically using galvanized waffle head screws or concrete nails.

Wood Backed Walls. Stucco application to walls with wood frameworks requires the construction of a concrete footing to minimize wall movement and subsequent cracking. Install the footing using the instructions provided in the pedestrian concrete paving Chapter (Chapter 25), adding anchors to support the wall framework. Construct a heavy framework of 2 × dimensioned, decay-resistant lumber. An alternative to a concrete footing is to install posts in a manner similar to a wood panel fence, with a framework constructed between the posts. This method has the potential for increased cracking as a result of variable settlement of the posts.

Over either type of framework, apply ¾-inch plywood sheathing that has been dried under cover for 60 days to minimize shrinking. Fasten sheathing to the framework using rust-resistant wafer head screws or nails. Using rust-resistant screws, rather than nails to fasten components, particularly the application of sheathing, will provide additional protection against the framework shifting and cracking the stucco finish.

Galvanized flashing, called a **weep screed,** is fastened along the bottom of the entire installation, and metal flashing is installed at any location where the stucco abuts an unfinished surface to direct water away from adjacent wood components. A waterproof membrane of building paper is stapled to the sheathing to prevent water from reaching the wood structure. Building paper waterproofing should cover the flashing along the bottom and side installations and be placed under the flashing at the top of the installation. Begin installation at the bottom of the wall, and overlap the lower piece 4 inches with the upper piece. Staple building paper waterproofing to the sheathing.

Galvanized wire mesh of 18- or 20-gauge with a 1-inch hex pattern (also called *hex metal*, *hex mesh*, *poultry netting*, or *chicken wire*) or self-furring lath of galvanized steel diamond mesh is fastened to the framework over the waterproofing membrane to improve the keying of the stucco (Figure 30-20). Cut the mesh or lath with tin snips at expansion and control joint locations. Cover all surfaces to be finished with this mesh or lath.

Installing Expansion and Control Joints

If the wall exceeds 15 feet in length, a vertical control joint should be installed through the stucco veneer to accommodate any expansion or contraction of the surface. Control joints are also recommended for every 144 SF of large wall surfaces, or approximately 12-foot × 12- foot square. Preformed rust-resistant metal joints are available that can be nailed or screwed to the framework. Cut any hex mesh or metal lath with tin snips along the location where a joint is placed. Take care that no stucco material fills the joint when you perform the surfacing.

Applying the Base Coat

The base coat for stucco, also called **scratch coat,** can vary in thickness from ¾ inch if placed over metal lath to ½ inch if placed directly on a wall surface. Thicknesses in this range are applied in either 2 or 3 coats. To mix the stucco base coat, blend 2 parts clean moist sand with 1

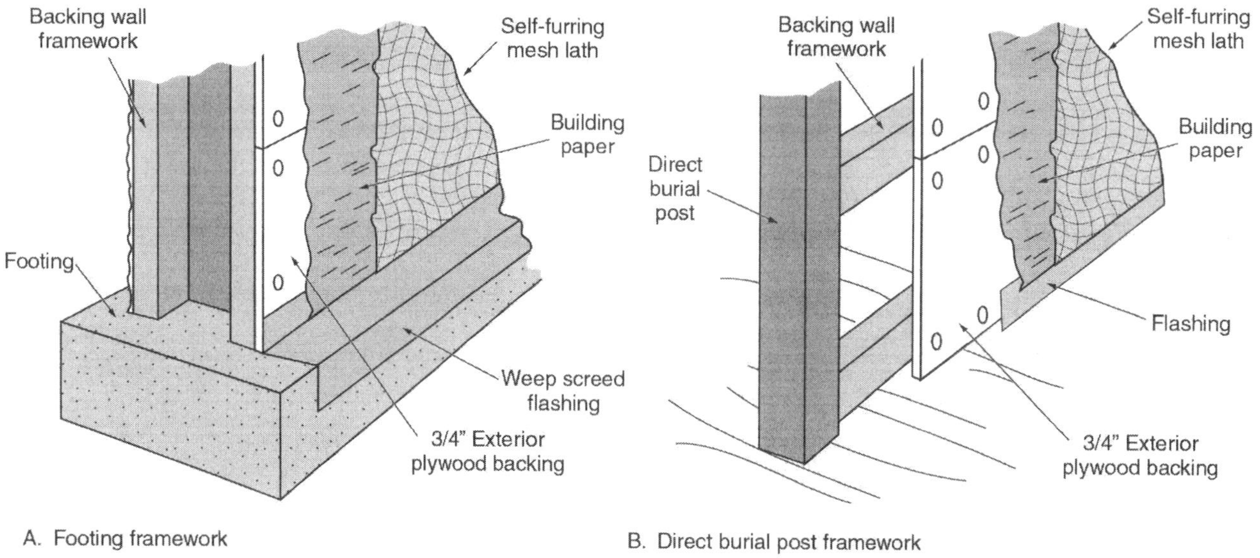

Figure 30-20 Stucco wall construction.

part Portland cement. Add water and mix, adding additional water as needed to obtain a thick consistency. When selecting sand, keep in mind that the size of the sand will affect the surface texture.

Before applying the stucco to concrete or masonry wall frameworks, slightly moisten the surface with a light mist to improve the curing. Apply the stucco using a drywall trowel or spray equipment. Begin at the top of the wall and work toward the bottom, applying a ½ to ¾-inch thick coat. The coat should be of uniform thickness and without ridges or low points. Before the stucco dries, use a scratcher or notched trowel to "scratch," or deform, the surface. This process improves the **keying,** or interlocking, with the next coat. Do not gouge ridges thicker than ¼ the thickness of the stucco layer (Figure 30-21).

Let this base coat dry for 48 hours before applying additional coats. If using three coats, apply ¼-inch thick second coat in the same manner without the scratching. Let the second coat dry for 48 hours before finishing. To ensure an even surface for the first or second coat, check the depth and adjust it by running a vertical screed board over the surface. This process, called **rodding,** will knock down areas that are thicker than desired and locate low spots in the surface.

Finishing Wall Surfaces

The final layer for a stucco application is called the **finish coat.** This coat may be prepared using the same formula as the base coat if a gray finish is desired or if the surface is to be painted. If light color stucco is to be applied, add 1 part lime to the sand and cement mixture. Many stucco walls are intended to be earthy or bright colors; and to obtain this finish, a pigment is added to the mix. Prepigmented dry stuccos can be purchased, or the pigment can be added with the water used to hydrate the mix. Many of these pigments are mineral-based, including iron oxides that provide a rich range of earthy colors. Special aggregates and sands can also be used in this surface coat to obtain the desired finish.

Mix the finish coat and apply it using the same top-to-bottom technique as the base coat. Apply a finish coat of ¼ to ⅜-inch thickness. If a special texture is desired, apply it before the coat sets. Choices of surface textures include the sand float texture, which is obtained by floating the surface with a concrete float; California texture, which is obtained by applying the finish coat with thick ridges that are knocked down using a steel trowel or concrete float; and the Spanish texture, which is a coarser version of the California. Dabbing with a damp sponge can also finish

Figure 30-21 "Scratching" the first coat of stucco to improve keying of the second coat.

surfaces. Almost any variation of surface texture can be obtained by practicing with the available tools and methods (Figure 30-22).

If the surface is to be painted or stained, let the finish coat dry for 48 hours prior to applying any coloring. Because stucco allows water vapor to penetrate through the surface, only use paint with 100% latex formulated for stucco or masonry-penetrating stains manufactured with silane or siloxane. Avoid use of silicon or paraffin-based surface coatings, except for the portions of your surface below grade. That area will require sealing to reduce wicking of water and the possibility of efflorescence, the white film that is left on the wall surface when salts are washed out of the stucco.

INSTALLATION OF VENEER FINISHES

Veneer surfaces are used when an attractive finish is desired over a load-bearing backing wall. Stone, brick, and other masonry materials can be applied as a full wythe, or thickness, veneer or a cultured or cut product can be applied as a thin surface veneer. Although the appearance of each application method is similar, the installation differs in preparation and execution. The backing wall may be concrete or masonry prepared to accept veneers.

Full-Thickness Veneers

Veneers allow the contractor to create a wall that provides the appearance of brick or stone, without constructing the entire wall from the more expensive materials. In addition, veneers often are applied to a wall that is more structurally suited to the situation. This section covers veneers that are the full thickness of the material rather than a thin slice of the material.

Ledger. Preparing a wall for a full thickness veneer requires the installation of a ledger on which the veneer can be set. This ledger must be

Figure 30-22 Stucco finishes. A. Float finish created by running a damp wood float over the finish coat. B. A broom finish roughens the finish coat by pulling a hand broom lightly over the surface. C. The California finish is created by applying ridges of stucco to the finish coat, then knocking them down using a trowel. The resulting ridges create an irregular texture.

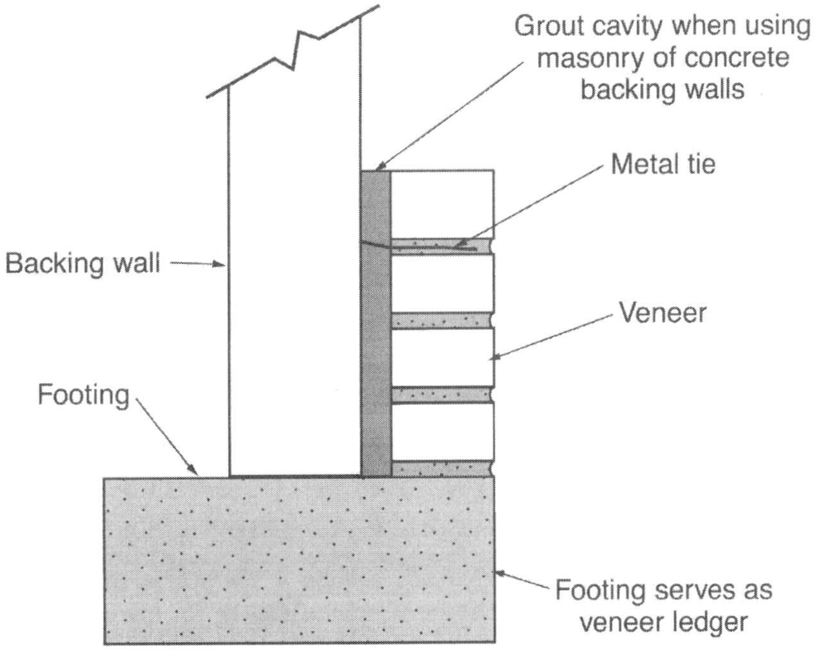

Figure 30-23 Veneer application.

as thick as the veneer plus 1 inch. Although it is possible to construct a ledger after the backing wall, most are built as part of the original wall construction. A spread footing may be used as a ledger, or a notch formed into concrete walls can also be used for this purpose. With wood walls, widening the concrete footing, rather than the wood frame, is the better practice (Figure 30-23). It is also possible to build a ledger from masonry blocks.

Cleaning. For veneers to be applied to masonry or concrete surfaces, the surface must be free of oil, paint, dirt, and other surface irregularities. To clean the surface, you may sandblast, spray with high-pressure water, or scrub with a TSP mixture and wire brush. Follow all safety precautions when cleaning surfaces.

Waterproofing and Flashing for Wood Backed Walls. While there are more permanent backings for veneer surfaces (concrete and masonry), the application of veneers over wood backing may occasionally be used. Veneers set in front of wood-backing walls require a sheet of waterproof sheeting be applied over the wood surface. Building paper or a similar heavy, weather-resistant barrier will work. Lap any joints 4 inches and seal with roofing tar. Metal Z flashing should be applied over the ledger and under the waterproof barrier. When setting the base course of the veneer, insert ¼-inch hollow tubes through the bottom bed of mortar every 16 inches to serve as weepholes for moisture that may pass through the veneer.

Ties. For veneers to be anchored to the backing wall, metal ties are fastened to the backing wall vertically every 16 inches and horizontally every 32 inches. These ties are then placed into the mortar joints of the veneer. Ties are galvanized, corrugated, light-gauge metal strips 1 inch wide and approximately 4 inches long. Fasten to wood walls using 8d nails or to concrete or masonry walls using concrete nails. You can also place ties in the joints of a masonry backing wall as it is constructed.

Mixing Mortar. Mix mortar using the formula of 1 part Portland cement, 1 part hydrated lime, and 5 parts fine sand. Type N mortar may be substituted for the cement and lime mixture and blended 1 part mortar with 3 parts fine sand. Mix to a thick consistency that is firm and moist.

Include any desired color additives as you mix the mortar.

Laying Veneer. Veneers are installed using the techniques explained in the masonry wall construction section. Begin by chasing a bond to ensure that the desired units will fit the space to be veneered. Cut any partial units that will be required. Lay a bed of mortar on the ledger and place the first course. For bricks and other veneers that are uniform in size and shape, build the corners/ends and lay the courses using the completed corners/ends as a guide. If laying stone or irregular-shaped units, lay each course individually. Maintain the 1-inch space between the veneer and the backing wall; and when encountering the ties, bend them into the joints between courses. Check the installation periodically to verify that the units are installed in the desired pattern and with uniform joints. Strike the joints when the mortar has dried to the touch (Figure 30-24).

Figure 30-24 Cultured stone veneer mortared to a concrete block wall.

Grouting. When applying veneer over concrete and masonry backing walls, grout the 1-inch cavity between the veneer and the backing wall. With wood-backing walls, the cavity is left ungrouted. Mix and install grout at the beginning of each day for the veneer set the previous day. Use a grout mixture of 1 part Portland cement and 3 parts sand. Blend to a flowable mixture and pour into the cavity.

Capping. If the top course of the veneer does not end under a ledge, eave, or other protected covering, you must place a cap over the veneer and the grout cavity. After grouting to the top is completed, lay a bed of mortar across the top course. Set veneer units that abut the backing wall and cover the wythe of the veneer, plus extend beyond the front of the veneer approximately 1 inch. You can purchase special veneer capping material to complete this course, or you may cut masonry units to create capping material with the correct dimensions. Fill and strike the joints between the capping material.

Cleaning the Surface. If any loose mortar is present, wait 1 week and clean with a wire brush and a TSP mixture. Follow all safety procedures when cleaning surfaces.

CAGED RUBBLE PIERS

To obtain a quick boundary or entry marker, consider the construction of a caged rubble pier. Although simple to build, caged rubble piers have limited durability as a result of the forces of weather and gravity.

Begin installation of caged rubble piers by selecting a heavy-gauge wire fencing the same width as the desired height of your pier. Trim the fence to the correct length, determined by multiplying the diameter of your pier by pi (3.14). Bend the fencing into a circle and create a cage by tying the ends together using 14-gauge or larger

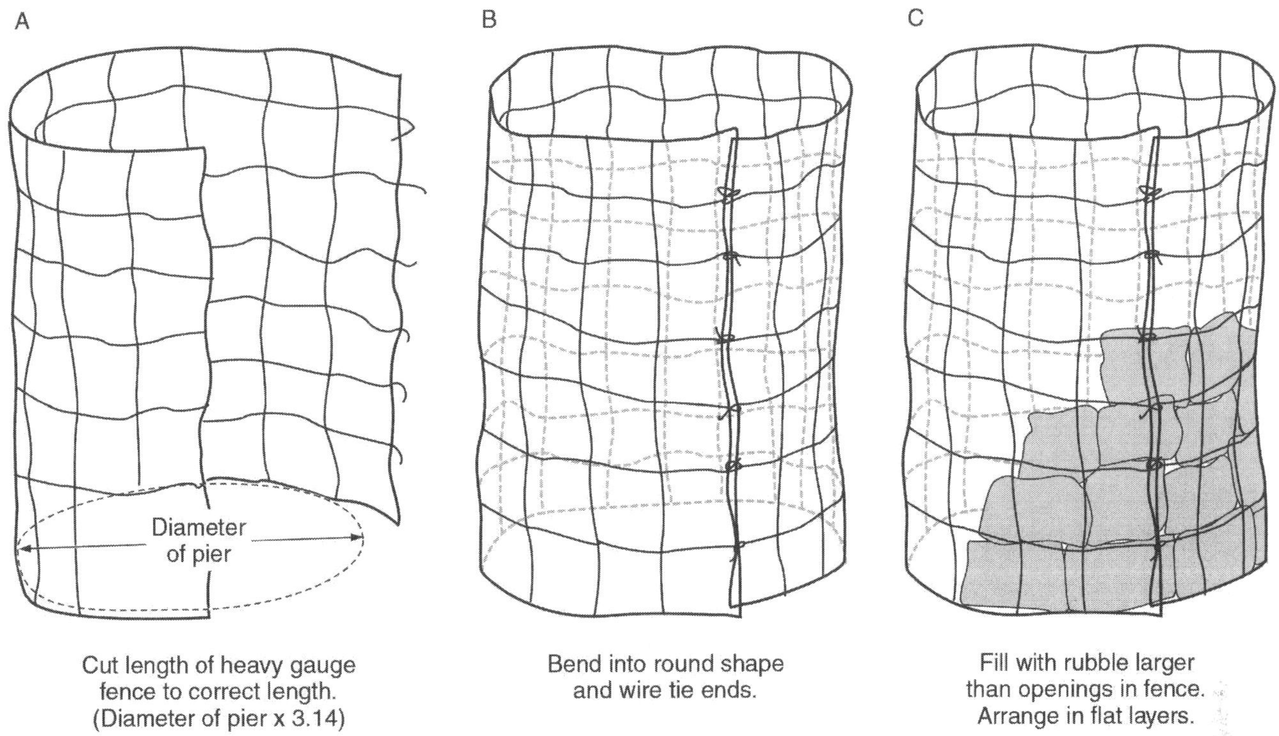

Figure 30-25 Rubble filled wire cage piers.

wire (Figure 30-25). Secure these ends at several locations. When connected, position the cage where the pier is to be located. Fill the cage with rubble that has at least one dimension (length, height, or width) larger than the openings in the cage. Rubble can be flat or rounded, or a mix of unused stone. To achieve additional stability, bury the cage 6 inches before adding rubble.

Some piers of this construction can be used as supports for rail fence material. To install fence rails, first place the cages so that the rail will fit between a pair of cages. Remember to include length for the portion of the rail that fits into the pier. Fill both cages to the level where the rail is to be positioned. Insert the rail through an opening in the wire. If necessary, use a fencing tool to cut a larger opening for the rail to fit, and then insert the rail. If using several piers, fill them all and then insert the rails at one level before moving to the next higher rail. Continue placing rubble to the level of the next rail. Repeat the fitting until you have installed all rails.

SECTION 7

SUMMARY

When a separation or definition of space is necessary, a freestanding wall is often sought as the solution. Section 8 explained the installation of such separators. Included in the section was information pertaining to the selection of materials and site preparation that described the specific installation techniques for dry-laid fieldstone walls, and masonry walls. Preparation for all of these requires a consideration of alignment, slopes, surface appearance, maintenance, and access to the construction site.

Dry-laid fieldstone (rubble) walls are constructed by placing stones of irregular shape along the proposed alignment of the wall. Stone may be placed at its natural angle of repose, or it can be laid to maintain sides that are vertical.

Masonry walls and piers require a footing on which to place masonry units. Alignment is checked, mortar is mixed, and units along the base course are placed, carefully leveled, and plumbed. Each of the following courses is carefully placed on top of the previous course, with the height and spacing maintained throughout the construction. Reinforcement is placed in the mortar joints, and joints are struck as the project goes up. When the wall is complete, the center cavity of the wall is filled with grout and the wall is capped.

Cast-in-place concrete walls as described in this section are not designed to be used as retaining walls. Concrete walls require the pouring of a footing separate from the wall. Inserted in the footing are ties that anchor the wall to the footing. The wall is formed and cast separately. Stucco walls are a surfacing that can be applied to masonry or concrete walls, and in some situations wood backed walls. Stucco is typically applied in one or more coats over a prepared surface. Finishes for stucco can provide rich color and textures to an otherwise bland wall. Veneers also provide a decorative surface of brick, stone, or other wall material over a structural background. Built on a ledge or adhered to the wall surface, veneers enhance the appearance of a plain wall.

SECTION 8

SITE AMENITIES

INTRODUCTION

Sound, aesthetic design depends on the creative arrangement of major landscape elements such as walls, structures, paving, plantings, and lawns. However, in many designs, the site amenities provide the "flair" and extra interest. These amenities, which include everything from decorative pools to flagpoles, can enhance and enrich the overall design scheme, often making a qualitative difference in a project (Figure S8-1).

Amenities that landscape contractors typically install are discussed in this section. Each of the three chapters covers a different type of amenity: water features; premanufactured **site furniture** and play equipment; and edgings, planters, and plant protection. The first chapter on water features explains the installation of static decorative pools created from flexible pool **liners,** cascades, waterfalls and fountains. The chapter on site furniture details the anchoring and assembly of benches, trash receptacles, signage, bike racks, play equipment, and other exterior furnishings. Safe surfacing for play equipment is also covered in the play equipment chapter. Patio amenities such as outdoor kitchens and firepits. Finally, the process of edging installation for several different materials, including natural edges, plastic and metal edgings, brick, stone, precast, and concrete curbing, is explained. Also presented in the final chapter is the installation method for premanufactured landscape elements such as planters, **tree guards,** and **tree grates.**

If the scale of the project is very large, landscape contractors may have a small role in completing amenity installation. As project size increases, so does the chance that a specialized subcontractor may have to finish the work. When responsibility does fall to landscape contractors, they must pay careful attention to the plans and specifications of the job. Many times the designer or property owner has selected a particular amenity for its type, style, or detail; and should landscape contractors substitute the wrong model number, they will have to correct that error, a costly correction. Private clients use amenities to enhance a landscape, but the cost of designer benches, decorative pools, and similar details can be very high. To provide this extra level of detail to a residential setting, landscape contractors can rely on the wide range of premanufactured amenities available through distributors.

SUSTAINABILITY SUGGESTIONS

- Make use of recycled and reused materials before purchasing newly manufactured products.
- Reduce energy consumption by selecting local amenities, rather than importing materials from great distances.
- Select amenities made of biocomposite materials, rather than from virgin resources.

CHAPTER 31

WATER FEATURES

OBJECTIVES

By reading and practicing the techniques described in this chapter, the reader should be able to successfully complete the following activities:

- Build a cast-in-place decorative pool.
- Install a rigid liner decorative pool.
- Install a flexible liner decorative pool.
- Add a fountain to a decorative garden pool.
- Construct a water cascade.
- Install a decorative fountain.

Whether a design relies on the reflections of a static decorative pool or on the dynamic sound and motion of a waterfall, a well-planned addition of water can be more provocative than any other design element on a site. New construction materials have made the introduction of water into the landscape a feasible undertaking. Traditionally, landscapes have relied on construction using concrete-lined decorative pools with underground plumbing. Although this construction technique has not disappeared, the advent of pool liners, small pumps, and plastic tubing has made the addition of water features more affordable and has brought the world of water into the residential domain.

Although today's technology allows for water features to be easily implemented in landscapes, their high-maintenance character has changed very little. In all climates, the decorative pool owner must make a commitment to regulate water quality; and in some climates, the pool may require periodic draining if the feature is to stay attractive and functional.

RELATED INFORMATION

Information in this chapter is supplemented by instruction provided elsewhere in this text and in other sources. Before undertaking the activities described in this chapter, read the related information in these sources:

- Construction Math, Chapter 5
- Safety in the Workplace, Chapter 7
- Basic Construction Techniques and Small Equipment Operation, Chapter 8
- DC Site Lighting and Related Electrical Work, Chapter 17
- Pedestrian Concrete Paving, Chapter 25
- Freestanding Walls, Chapter 30
- Pertinent codes and ordinances.

TYPES OF WATER FEATURES

Decorative pools and water features can take many forms in the landscape. At first, understand the difference between swimming decorative pools and decorative pools. Building codes separate the two types of water elements, with swimming pools being intended for occupancy and requiring the services of design professionals and contractors licensed for their construction. Decorative water features are intended for viewing and are the subject of this chapter of the text. The components of water features can be combined and shaped to follow any design concept desired. Following are the components whose installation is described in this chapter:

Decorative pools and Water Features

Standing and moving water is used in many forms in the landscape to attract attention, to provide sensory experiences, or to support aquatic wildlife. Whether moving or static, water features can be generally categorized into the following groups:

Static Decorative Pools. Static decorative pools are water reservoirs without any moving water. Static decorative pools can be constructed of concrete, which is common for larger or commercial applications, or with vinyl pool liners. Pool size, form, and depth vary based on design.

Cascades. Water that gently flows on the surface from a higher elevation to a lower elevation is termed a **cascade**. A shallow channel, often lined with stone or gravel, contains the water as it flows between elevations. Cascades can be constructed on steep or gradual slopes and with either a concrete or vinyl channel. A water source, either a pump outlet or a decorative pool, and an ending decorative pool and drain are required to make the cascade function properly. Water is often circulated from a lower pool to the top of the cascade to produce the water movement visible in the cascade.

Waterfalls. Water that drops from a higher elevation into a lower reservoir is a waterfall. Depending on the effect the designer attempts to achieve, the drop can be a constructed as a quiet, simple, short drop; a loud, dramatic, tall drop; or a combination of both (Figure 31-1). Waterfalls require a water source at the top and a reservoir at the bottom to collect outflow.

Figure 31-1 Waterfall.

In-Pool Fountains. Fountains are powerful pumps with special orifices that project water upward out of a reservoir. Depending on the size of the pump and type of orifice, water may project several feet into the air or simply bubble to the surface. Different types of fountains can be combined for special effects. Fountains can be designed and incorporated into walls, decorative pools, and rock formations.

Decorative Fountains. With the advancement in manufacturing of materials such as precast concrete decorative and metalworking, decorative fountains can now be used as an accent anywhere in the garden. Built separately from any pool or dynamic water feature, these decorative elements come in a variety of shapes, materials, and finishes that allow water to be used as an accent for almost any landscape theme. Decorative fountains typically require a reservoir basin for water recirculation and one or more higher level decorative pools and/or water outlets to feed the fountain.

PLANNING THE PROJECT

The need for planning the construction and the placement of site amenities exceed most aspects of landscape construction. In addition to the complex nature of the construction, many amenities require work by others including utility connections, paving and foundations, and plantings as part of the installation. Details of amenity planning are described below.

Timing of Water Feature Placement

Water feature construction must occur in several phases. During utility construction (see Section 4), consideration should be given to drainage, water source, and electrical source issues. Multilevel water features may also require landscape walls. Placement of liners, edging, pumps, and other necessary elements typically occurs between finish grading and planting operations.

Design of Water Features

The design of the water feature must address several issues that will affect construction. The purpose of the water feature will determine the shape, depth, and equipment choices. Clients may desire flat sheets of water for reflection, pond gardens with plants, or ponds for fish. Reflection decorative pools may require dark surfacing on the pool to enhance the water's reflectivity, whereas aeration and filtration systems should cause minimal disturbance in the water surface. Pond gardens will require varying depth levels to accommodate the various types of plants necessary to maintain an attractive and balanced garden. If the pond is to house fish, depth and filtration will be critical issues to maintain pond quality. Each of these water features will require special filtration and aeration to reduce problems with algae and unwanted aquatic plant life. With this range of choices, professional design assistance is recommended for any water feature, simple or complex.

Pumping Equipment. Pumps perform essential functions of circulating water for decorative pools, ponds, waterfalls, cascades, and other water features. Typical pumps for water features are electrical submersible pumps using magnetic drives sealed in waterproof plastic housings. Most pumps are rated by the amount of water they pump per hour, or gallons per hour (GPH), with some rated by the number of gallons they pump per minute (GPM). A general rule for selecting equipment is to install a size that will pump half the pond volume every hour (e.g., a 1000-gallon pond should have a minimum of a 500-GPH pump). The pump may need to be larger if water filtering equipment is connected to the pump or if water features require water to be pumped out of or above the surface level of the feature. In many instances, the best approach is to use two pumps. One pump can be dedicated to water circulation and a second dedicated to filtering and/or waterfalls or cascades. Pumps should be UL rated for underwater use and connected to a circuit that is GFCI protected.

Filtration and Aeration. Water within a pond or pool will require various types of filtration to maintain water quality and clarity. Solid wastes in water features are typically removed by mechanical or sand filters. With these filters, the water is pumped through the filter; and the larger particles are trapped in the filtering medium. Skimmers can also be placed in a pond or pool installation to assist in trapping solids. Skimmers are an intake placed at the edge of the pond into which water flows by gravity. Solids are trapped in the skimmer filter, and the water is recirculated to the pool. A type of filter commonly used in ponds that house fish are biofilters. To break down wastes that fish produce, particularly nitrogen wastes, bacteria must be present. Biofilters house a media with extensive surface areas on which these beneficial bacteria grow. In some pond installations, stones or rocks are placed in the bottom of the pond to support plant growth and to create surface for bacteria growth.

The bacteria that filter water require oxygen to survive. To improve its oxygen content, water must be aerated. Aeration can be accomplished through recirculation, often using bubbler fountains. A general rule for good pond aeration is to recirculate the entire volume of the pond every 2 hours. In addition to encouraging bacterial growth, filtration is often used to reduce algae growth in water features. Ultraviolet (UV) clarifiers remove suspended algae from the water and improve water clarity, particularly for reflecting pool installations. As with pumps, all electrical equipment should be rated for submersible use and connected to a GFCI circuit.

Plants for Garden Ponds. Plants are often a key aesthetic part of a water feature as well as a water purifier. Ponds and decorative pools that are properly constructed can support a variety of aquatic plant life that enhance the beauty of the feature, oxygenate the water, and reduce algal growth. Types of pond plants include those that oxygenate the water, marsh plants, lilies, floating plants, and marginal plants. Selection and planting requirements for each are as listed below.

Oxygenating Plants. Plants that grow in water both oxygenate the water and maintain its quality. Oxygenating plants will be placed at various depths, depending on the species, with a minimum water depth of approximately 1 foot to a maximum of around 3 feet.

Marsh Plants. This class of plants typically are set on ledges at depths varying from 1–1½ feet.

Lilies. A wide range of lily species are available for aquatic plantings. Most lilies grow in water up to depths of 5 feet. Line the bottom of a one or two gallon nursery container with shade cloth or newspaper. Plant the lily tuber in the pot at a slight angle. Fill the top with small lightweight stone and set the pot in the pond. Do not overplant with lilies, as they can spread and overgrow in pond settings.

Floating Plants. As the name suggests, floaters are not planted but instead placed on the surface of the pond. The parrot's feather should have a small weight (a sinker or a large hardware nut) attached to the root mass with a rubber band.

Marginal Plants. Marginal plants are placed around the perimeter of the water body in areas that are either covered with shallow water or on land but in soils that are occasionally or constantly saturated. The placement will depend on the species. Plants can be installed in the ground or placed in containers that are set on a shallow shelf or ringed with stone.

A general rule of thumb for plant selection is that 25–50% of the water surface should be covered by plants. Plant material can be planted in stone and rock placed at the bottom of the pond, placed in special baskets with an aquatic compost, or left in the original plant container and covered with sand and small-diameter stone or lava rock. Covering the root-ball with stone will reduce the opportunities for fish to disturb the soil and make pond water murky. When planting in containers, most designers recommend using a planting medium with low nitrogen and phosphorus content to reduce algae problems.

Laying Out Water Features

Pool locations can be located by painting the perimeter of the installation prior to excavation (Figure 31-2). Stakes within the reservoir area can mark proposed finish grades and guide filling and excavation procedures. Dynamic water features often involve decorative pools on multiple levels with connecting features such as cascades and waterfalls. Each of these features should have location and grade verified prior to construction (Figure 31-3). Electrical and recirculation piping routes should also be identified before beginning construction. Preliminary layouts may reveal minor adjustments necessary to improve the feature's performance.

Figure 31-2 Layout of a multilevel water feature to be constructed with flexible pool liners. White lines indicate the approximate outside edge of each pool. Overlap area is where the waterfall will be placed.

Testing Water Feature Operation

Unlike for most landscape features, the visual appearance of a water feature is not the final test of a proper installation. Testing of the various components as they are completed is important to avoid disruption of features for repairs later in the project. Test the utility connections when they are installed. As you install component features, test the liners for leaks, the pumps and tubing for proper operation, and waterfalls and cascades for flow before moving to the next stage.

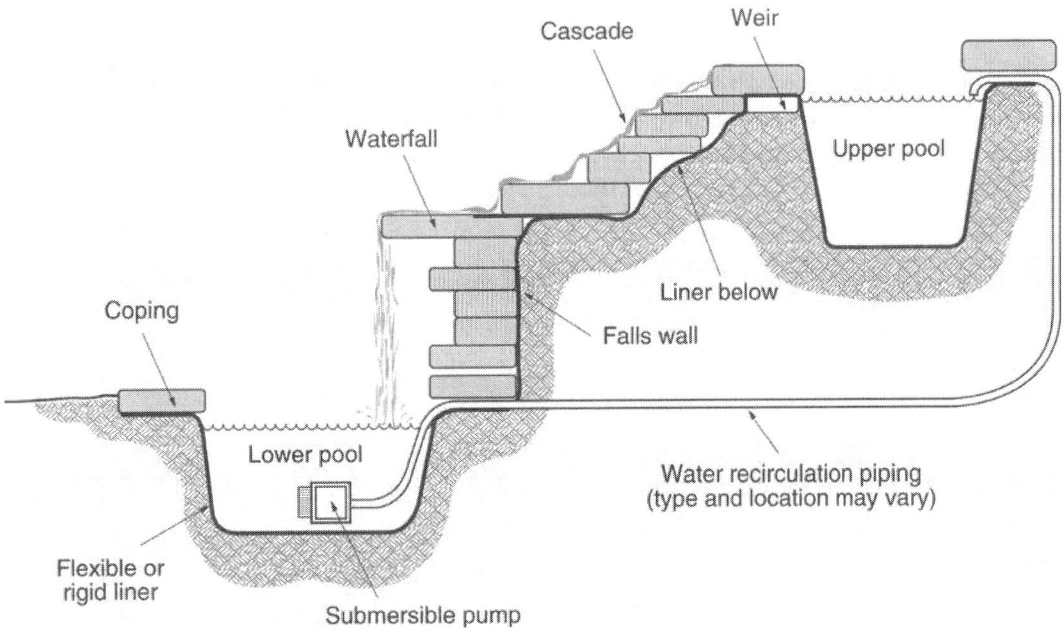

Figure 31-3 Cross section of water feature showing components.

Testing waterfall and cascade operation is critical. Few adjustments can be made after the landscape treatments are completed. Fill all reservoirs and turn on the pump or water supply. Verify that the basins are maintaining the proper water elevation. If necessary, make adjustments in pump and weir opening size to correct flow problems in these two areas.

Cascades can be tested by filling all reservoirs and operating the pump. Water should flow evenly from top to bottom down the center of the channel. If the liner pieces are not properly placed, the flow of water may miss the decorative liner completely. For a flexible liner, adjust the pieces by twisting them so the water flows down the center. For a concrete liner, add small pieces of stone, or perhaps even mortar, to divert the water back to the center. Position the stone placed over the liner so that water flows over, and not under or around, the pieces.

Locating Bridges

Bridge location should be based on the bridge function, aesthetics, and water conditions of the feature. If the bridge is crossing a body of moving water, care should be given to the position of the footing. Consult a design professional if you have doubt about the stability of the footing position or about potential bridge failure.

SITE PREPARATION FOR WATER FEATURES

Depending on the size and type of water feature, preparing the site may require several activities ranging from utility connections to grading and drainage to foundation preparation.

Site Conditions

Grade preparation is essential before decorative pools and channels can be excavated. Because decorative pools require level surfaces, it is easier to grade a level, compacted area prior to digging the reservoir area. Similarly, cascades and waterfalls need varying degrees of grade change, meaning the subgrade for each must be prepared before construction begins.

Hours of hand excavation can be saved if the locations of features are marked before filling operations are undertaken. Because settlement will disrupt the level conditions required to make the features work properly, it is also important to maintain proper compaction in areas under and around water features.

Electrical Source

Electrical circuits that supply power to exterior fixtures should be ground fault circuit interrupt (GCFI) circuits. If the feature is to be serviced by running a power cord to an exterior receptacle, the landscape contractor's primary concern will be ensuring a nearby receptacle exists and locating a concealed route from the pump to the receptacle.

A large feature will usually have a dedicated circuit(s). Burial of the electrical source should be accomplished before excavation of the feature. Conduit is required for high-voltage circuits, and the conduit may be placed now and the wire pulled in at a later time. Stake the electrical service point for the feature and excavate an 18-inch deep trench between the two points. In the trench, place a 2-inch or larger Schedule 40 PVC conduit with radius ends that bring the conduit to the surface. Cover the ends with duct tape. A licensed electrician should perform electrical wiring.

Water Source

Water may be provided periodically through a hose connected to an external **hose bibb** or through a separate line dedicated to the water feature. Water provided through a hose requires minimal preconstruction preparation and is usually an acceptable way to supply water for a small residential setting. Larger decorative pools and commercial applications have a much higher demand for water, and frequent filling with a hose will prove to be a nuisance. In these cases, provide a separate underground supply line to save time and maintenance over the long run. As with the electrical source, final, above-grade connections of the water source can be completed after the water feature is installed.

If a separate water supply line is provided for an exterior feature, it should be either excavated below frost depth or sloped toward the source to allow for backdraining when necessary. The source of water will most likely be inside a nearby structure where a supply line is located. Inside the structure, provide a water shutoff and backdrain to allow the system to be shut down and drained to protect pipes from freezing. Consideration should also be given (and may be required in some locations) to installing a backflow preventer in the water line. This will prevent accidental contamination of potable water supplies from exterior sources.

The backflow preventer should be installed by a licensed plumber 2 feet higher than the high point of the water supply line. If the outflow end of the water supply never comes in contact with the water feature (air break), the backflow preventer may not be necessary. Verify water source requirements with a professional engineer or building official before beginning installations.

Drainage of Decorative decorative pools

At some point, the water feature will need to be drained. Emptying the pool can be accomplished using a portable submersible pump. Pumping water out of the pool, rather than building a drain, provides fewer risks of leakage, and drain plugging, and may be a more cost-effective method if the pool is not drained frequently. Pumping, however, does require the rental of equipment and the constant monitoring of the pump and outlet to prevent backups and flooding.

> **CAUTION**
>
> When installing any electrical device in or near a pool, there is a danger of electrical shock or electrocution. Buy only devices approved for submersible use. Assemble, place, and connect such devices according to the manufacturer's instructions. Connect all exterior devices to GFCI circuits.

Installation of Subdrains

When positioned over soils with high water tables or poor internal drainage, subsurface water can lift and damage a rigid or flexible liner. A subdrain is necessary under the pool to remove subsurface water and to reduce the chance of such damage. Excavate the entire pool basin 4 inches deeper than required. Excavate a 6-inch deep × 6-inch wide trench along the center of the entire length of the pool basin's bottom. In this trench, install a 4-inch diameter socked, perforated drain tile. Continue the trench and tile to an outlet point. Cover the tile and entire bottom of the excavation with 4 inches of pea gravel before installing the liner or constructing the pool.

INSTALLATION OF FLEXIBLE AND RIGID LINERS FOR STATIC DECORATIVE POOLS

Liners allow a variety of shapes and configurations for decorative pools. Flexible liners are placed in shapes matching a custom design, whereas rigid liners are available in a variety of interesting shapes. Although not appropriate for all installations, liners allow for a variety of shapes and depths in pool construction.

Layout

Begin flexible pool installation by marking the proposed perimeter of the pool with paint. This marking provides a guideline for excavation of the reservoir. Rigid liners require transferring the exact pool perimeter dimensions to the location where the pool will be placed (Figure 31-4)

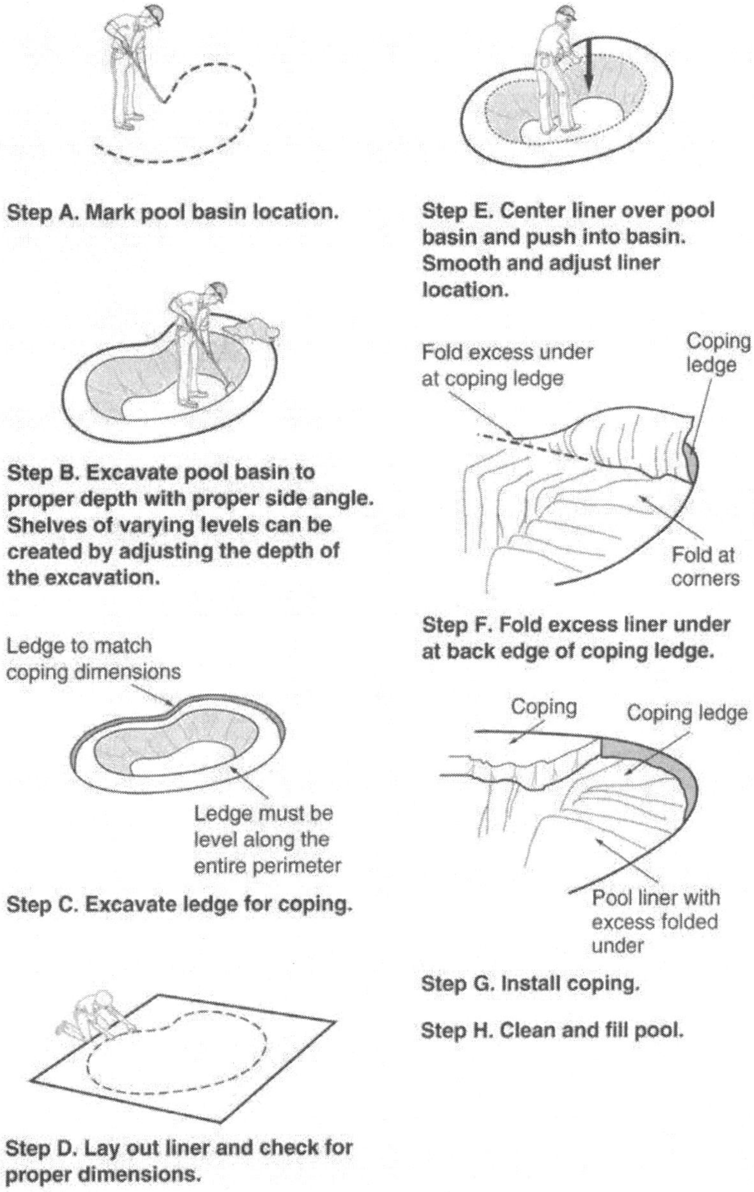

Figure 31-4 Installation steps for a flexible liner pool.

Excavation

Excavate the **reservoir basin** to the correct depth over the entire area. Very steep angles work best to create side walls; but in a sandy soil, the angle may have to be shallower to avoid sidewall collapse. The bottom of the flexible pool liner basin can be excavated to different levels if the design requires, but each terrace should be sloped slightly toward the low end of the basin (Figure 31-5). Bottom areas where fountains or pumps are planned should be excavated level to allow the pump to set flat. Remove all rocks and prune any roots protruding into the pond basin. You can make corrections to the base by adding sand.

Around the entire edge of the reservoir basin, excavate a level ledge for **coping material.** The depth of this ledge should be the same as the thickness of the coping material and the width of the ledge slightly narrower than the width of the coping material you have selected. If edge installation is unstable, excavate the ledge deeper and install precast concrete wall caps level around the entire pool perimeter. The depth of this ledge should be deep enough that when edge material is placed, it will match the finish grade of the material that is adjacent to the pool (walk, patio, lawn, etc.). *Verify that all points of this ledge are level.* Any low point in this ledge will create an unplanned drain where water will spill out of the pool. Correct low points by filling with fine granular material. You can vary the depth of the bottom excavation to create shelves on which plants, lighting, and fountains can be placed (Figure 31-6).

Protective Barrier (Liner Pad)

When excavation is complete, install a spunbond geotextile protective barrier (also called a *liner pad* in some publications). This barrier can be a heavy-gauge, nonwoven weed barrier. The barrier will need to be large enough to cover the entire basin. Place the barrier in the basin and form it to the shape of the sides and coping ledge. Trim the barrier at the back of the coping ledge.

Flexible Liner Placement

The pool liner must be sized to provide coverage of the reservoir. To calculate liner length, add the maximum length of the pool, plus twice the depth, plus 3 feet. To calculate liner width, add the maximum width of the pool, plus twice the depth,

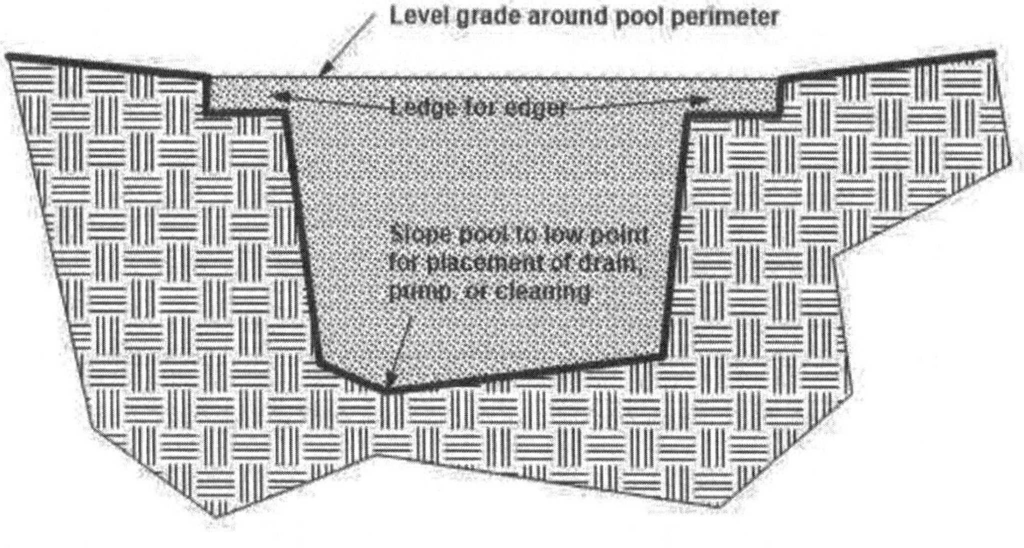

Figure 31-5 Flexible liner pool excavation.

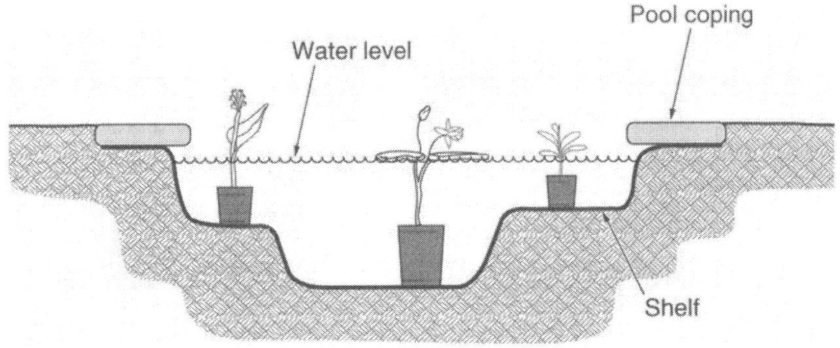

Figure 31-6 Varying pool depth to create shelves.

plus 3 feet. For large decorative pools, you can splice separate liners together using bonding material available from the manufacturer. Unfold the pool liner on a flat area. Pull the liner over the reservoir basin; step carefully inside the reservoir and gently work the liner down to the bottom of the basin (Figure 31-7). It is best if workers remove their shoes to reduce the risk of puncturing the liner. Be sure the liner sets as flush as possible on the bottom of the basin. After the workers have molded the liner to the basin shape, add a few inches of water to the pool to assist in forming the liner to the bottom of the excavation. Mold the liner over terraces, tucking and folding where necessary to accommodate grade changes. Use the same process to fold the liner up the vertical sides and over the coping ledge created at the top of the pool. Fold and tuck the liner if required to adapt to corners. Wipe the liner clean before climbing out.

Verify again that the coping edge is level around the entire perimeter. Adjust if necessary. Fold any excess liner back under the pool at the coping ledge. This will provide additional liner in the event adjustments are necessary. Using a sharp utility knife, trim and remove extreme excesses (exceeding 2 feet) that disrupt the even placement of coping. Check to make sure the liner is snug against the sides and bottom of the basin. Use caution not to puncture the liner; even small holes create serious leaks. If you damage a liner, take it to a tire shop for repair.

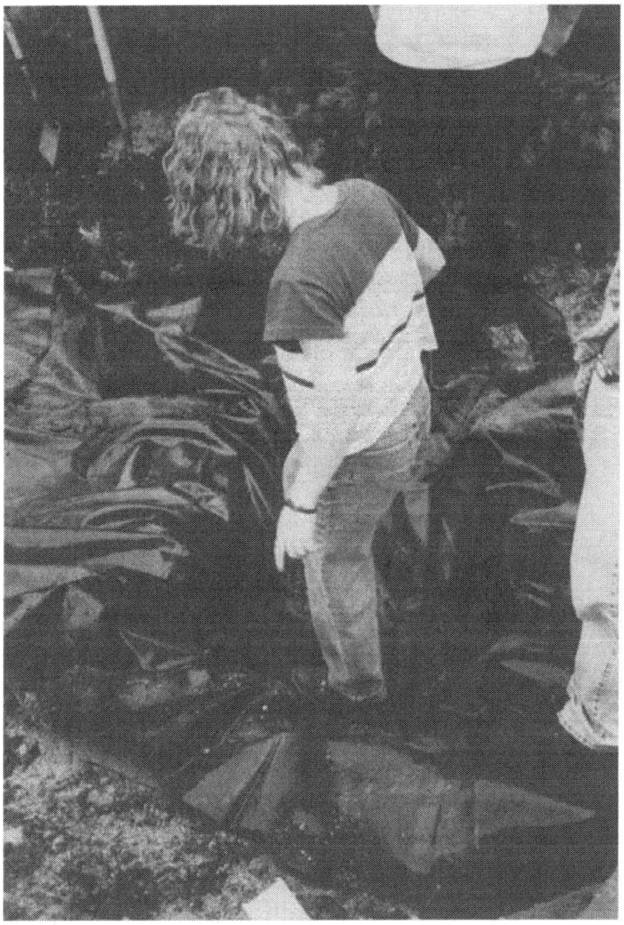

Figure 31-7 Installation of liner in flexible liner pool.

Rigid Liner Placement

Follow similar steps for installing a rigid pool liner. Mark the location based on the actual shape of the pool. Excavate the pool to the proper depth, leaving ledges in the subgrade where there are ledges in the pool. Excavate a level ledge for the coping around the top edge of the pool

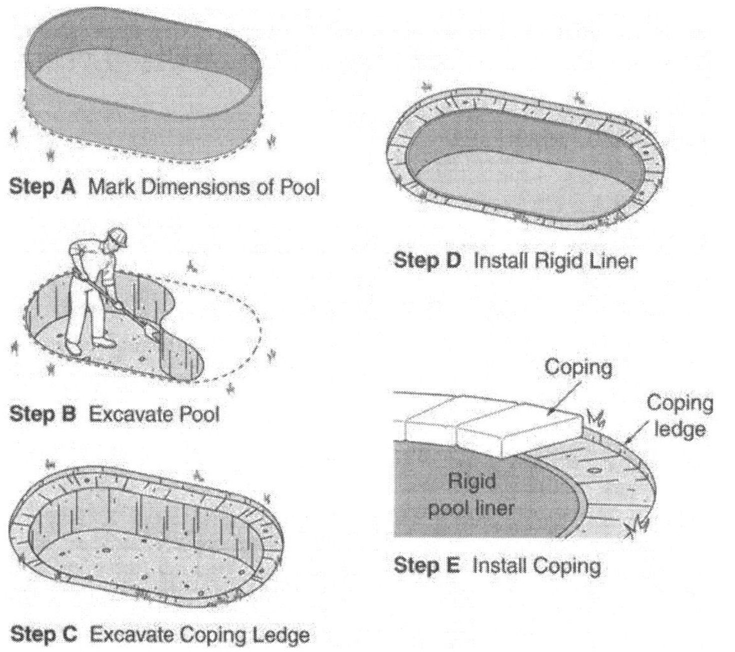

Figure 31-8 Installation steps for a rigid liner pool.

(Figure 31-8). After you have completed the excavation, carefully place the rigid liner into the basin and test it for snug fit. If the liner sides bow, or if the liner does not sit level or completely in the excavation, remove the liner and adjust the excavation. If the liner sets too low in the excavation, adjust the bottom elevation using sand or pea gravel. When you have correctly positioned the liner, use sand to backfill any visible voids between the liner and the excavation.

Edge Treatment

Once you have stabilized the flexible or rigid liner, you can place the coping material. Select and place coping pieces so that they fit together tightly with no liner visible between pieces. Place the coping pieces so that they overhang the edge of the pool approximately 2 inches to hide the top edge of the liner (Figure 31-9). Clean inside of the pool with water and sponge. Fill the pool to within 2 inches of the bottom of the coping.

Lighting

Lighting can be added to a pool by purchasing a submersible waterproof lighting kit. Most pool lighting is used to provide a low level of light that highlights the surface or plant material growing in a pool. Lighting that is installed on a switched circuit can be controlled from a remote location.

Assemble the kit according to the manufacturer's instructions and place it on a level portion of the pool's base. If a higher elevation is required, paint a concrete block black and set the block on a level location on the bottom of the pool. Place the light on top of the block.

Run the cord for the light along the bottom and up the side of the pool. Place the cord under the coping at the top edge of the pool and route the cord to a GFCI circuit. Hide the cord in conduit or under plant material.

Filters and Aerators

Biofilters and UV filters are often designed with submersible housings and connected to pumps that force water through the filter. If pressurized in this manner, the filter can be placed at any water level. An ideal location is to place the filter directly in front of the pump assembly. Passive filters that use gravity and natural circulation to filter the pump must be placed at the highest discharge point for water entering the pool or

Figure 31-9 Edging a flexible liner pool.

pond. Skimmers are placed with the inflow elevation at the desired water elevation of the pool or pond. For best performance, skimmers should be positioned opposite any water discharge into the feature such as a waterfall, cascade, or recirculation tube. Special aeration equipment must be mounted slightly below the water surface level with the discharge orifice projecting above the surface level. To obtain the proper elevation for setting aerators, you may need to excavate a shelf or stack stone or heavy blocks on the pool's floor. On large water features with multiple aerators, space the equipment equally around the feature.

INSTALLATION OF FOUNTAINS

Fountain installation can be accomplished using a stationary pump or a floating fountain. Most fountain installations are placed within a pool or pond and use water from the basin of the pool for spray. Fountains that do not have decorative pools typically include some method for water recirculation or water supply. A licensed electrician should complete electrical connections.

Stationary Pump Fountains

Select a location in the pool basin that places the fountain on a level surface at the correct depth. If necessary, place a support block (concrete block painted black) in the pool to raise the fountain pump. Lower the pump into the basin and secure it in place. Bring the electrical connection out through a preplaced conduit in a concrete pool or between coping pieces for a liner pool. Complete the electrical connection by plugging into a GCFI electrical receptacle or connecting to a GCFI switched circuit. Fill the basin with water and test the fountain for proper operation (Figure 31-10).

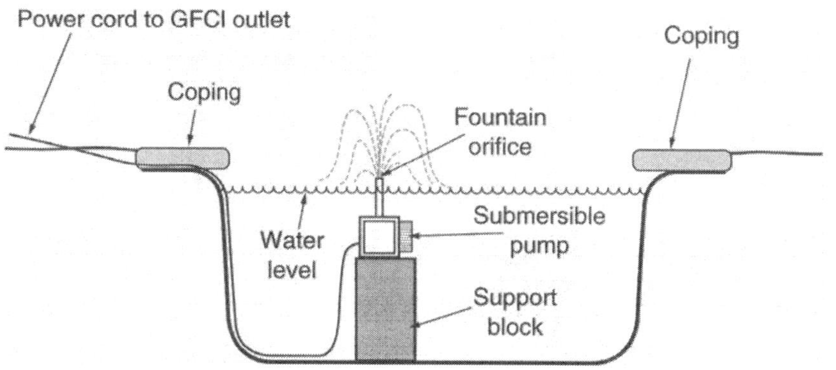

Figure 31-10 Installation of a pool fountain.

Floating Fountains

Floating fountains require that the pool be filled before placement. Fountains that float in a pool are anchored to the sides or bottoms using cables/ropes or a weighted anchor. A maintenance rope is also run to the side and placed where it can be used to pull the fountain in for repairs. To anchor the fountain, fasten the anchor to the fountain using stainless steel cable or polypropylene rope. Load the fountain and anchor into a boat (or alternatively, wade into a shallow pond) and position the fountain in the desired location. Lower the anchor into the pond and verify that it is securely resting on the bottom. For ponds that have fluctuating water levels, manufacturers typically recommend mooring the fountain to the side of the pond. Use stainless steel cable or polypropylene rope fastened to a duckbill® anchor placed just below the waterline at the shore. Attach electrical cables to the fountain with waterproof connections and float them out with the maintenance cable. After you have completed the anchoring and electrical connections, test the fountain.

INSTALLATION OF WATERFALLS AND CASCADES

The creation of waterfalls and cascades requires installation of basic elements that, when assembled properly, can create a dramatic landscape feature.

Lower Basin

The first element to consider for waterfall or cascade construction is the basin that will collect water at the bottom of the falls. The basin may be constructed using the flexible or rigid liner pool techniques described earlier in this chapter, but the pool must be constructed with part of the basin positioned directly under the location where the falls will deliver the water. The projected fall of water should land in this lower basin far enough from the edge to allow water displaced by splashing to remain in the pool. If you use a flexible liner for the lower basin, build the vertical sides of the pool basin in this area with concrete blocks under the liner to provide stability (Figure 31-11). This wall can also provide support for the falls and any basin used above to supply the falls. The lower basin contains the pump that recirculates water to the top to supply the falls.

Water Supply/Upper Basin

The second consideration for a waterfall or cascade is the water source at the top of the falls. The falls can be supplied by water flowing out of an upper reservoir basin or directly from a water supply line recirculating water from a pump in the lower basin. Because an opening is needed to allow water to exit the pool, rigid vinyl liners cannot be easily used for upper basins unless they are molded to accommodate water falls.

When an upper basin is constructed for a waterfall, the edge should be placed as close as possible to the lower basin. Flexible liner basins will rely on the retaining wall to support the portion of the upper basin that will supply the falls (Figure 31-11).

Figure 31-11 Construction of a wall between flexible liner decorative pools set at different levels. The upper pool is adjacent to the lower pool with a waterfall planned between the two.

Weir and Pump

Decorative pools require the construction of a weir at the location where water is to drain from the pool to supply the falls or cascade. A **weir** is an opening in the edge of the basin with dimensions that allow only a calculated amount of water to pass (Figure 31-12). The depth and width of this opening should be taken from plans or calculated by a design professional because the size of the opening will control the amount of water that supplies the falls. In the absence of precise weir calculations, construct an oversized weir because the flow through the weir can be restricted but not easily increased. The weir needs to be placed lower than the perimeter level of the pool to allow water to exit the pool. Construct the opening in a flexible liner pool by over excavating the earthen dam to the dimensions desired.

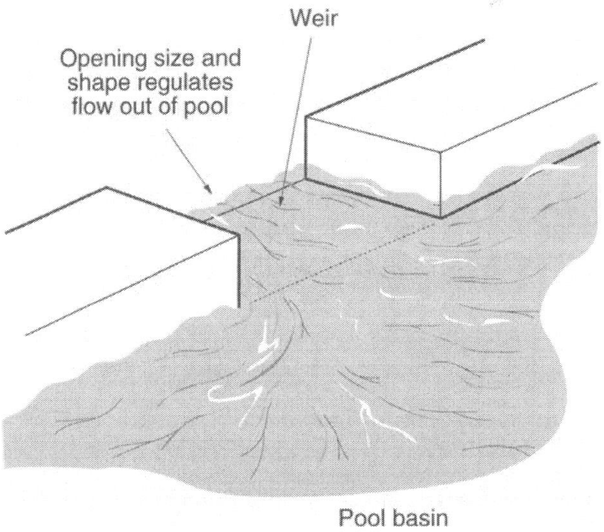

Figure 31-12 Weir diagram.

The amount of water that flows through a waterfall or cascade is not a chance occurrence.

Control of the water amount is primarily the weir's function. Another factor that controls the water flow is the capacity of the recirculating pump. Both of these factors work together to provide either a light or a heavy flow of water through the falls channel. If the water flow from the falls does not meet design expectations, consider installing a higher volume capacity pump or using more than one pump. Flows over a waterfall can be concentrated by narrowing the weir. If the lower basin is running dry and the upper basin is running over, the weir is undersized and needs to be enlarged or the volume of water being pumped needs to be reduced.

Recirculation Piping

Installation of waterfalls and cascades requires piping for recirculation of water between basins. Rigid piping is required in higher volume operations, whereas flexible tubing can be used for pumps with a capacity of less than 10 GPM. This piping should be placed between supply and use locations while the basins are being constructed. With flexible liner decorative pools, the piping runs over the edge of the pool hidden between coping pieces. Piping between decorative pools can be hidden by plants. To hide the installation of flexible tubing and reduce kinking of the tube, place a 3-inch diameter, nonperforated drain tile along the route of the recirculation tubing and slightly underground and pull the tubing through it.

Projection Channel

Rigid wall decorative pools may have water spill directly from a weir into the lower basin, but many water features have a projection channel that carries the water from the supply out over the lower basin (Figure 31-13). This projection ensures that the water will fall into the lower basin and will not miss the pool. The projection channel can be custom-cast out of concrete or can be constructed from pieces of flat stone.

Large volumes of water require special construction to ensure the water does not flow off the sides of the projection channel. Supporting the channel also requires some form of structure under the channel and anchoring. The greater the amount of projection for the channel, the more

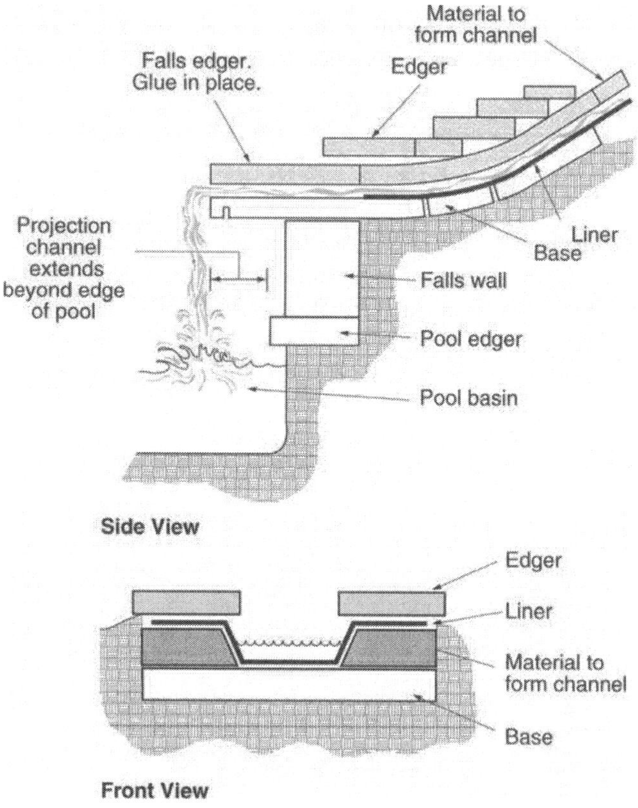

Figure 31-13 Projection channel construction for waterfall.

difficult it will be to anchor. If possible, the channel should be tilted forward slightly to help the water project farther out into the lower basin and slightly concave on the surface.

If water is clinging to the end of the projection channel, either tilt the channel farther forward or cut a **reglet** (Figure 31-14), or a shallow cut across the underside of the channel. Reglets break the surface tension between water and the projection channel, allowing water to fall, rather than to adhere, to the surface. Cut a reglet with a wet masonry saw; the reglet should be approximately ¼ inch deep and run the full width of the channel.

Multiple Falls

Installations that call for multiple falls can be constructed using multiple basins and projection channels, or they can be constructed as a series of falls where the projection channel is the supply for the next falls (Figure 31-15). Either

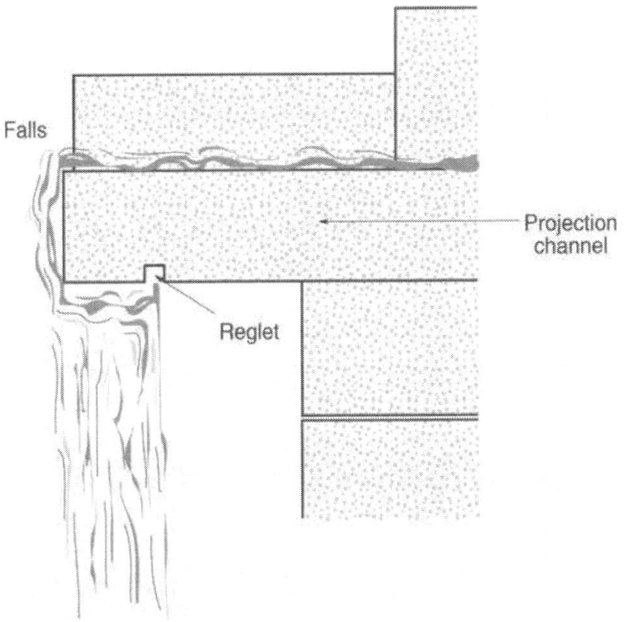

Figure 31-14 Location of reglet, used to break surface tension of water.

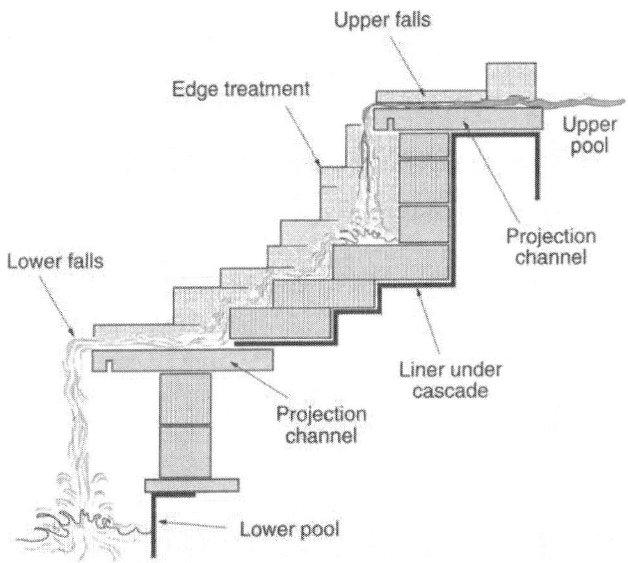

Figure 31-15 Falls channel construction for multiple falls.

arrangement requires careful positioning of channels to ensure that the water falls on its target.

Cascade Channel

The channel for the cascade is a wide, shallow, U-shaped channel that runs from the top weir to the lower weir. The cross section of the channel should be approximately twice the cross section of the upper weir to accommodate the water flow and decorative lining material placed in the channel. The channel may follow any alignment desired, as long as the proper cross section and downward slope are maintained.

Excavate the entire route of the channel. Maintaining a consistent slope provides an even flow of water from top to bottom. Varying the slope provides a more interesting water flow but requires that the channel be widened to accommodate heavier flow in areas. Edges of the channel need to be elevated high enough that water stays in the channel (Figure 31-16).

Waterproofing the channel can be accomplished by cutting a linear strip of pool liner material and placing it in the excavated channel. If splices need to be made or corners must be turned, overlap two pieces of liner approximately 1 foot, placing the higher section on top of the lower section. When the waterproof lining is completed, decorative material such as rock or stone is placed in the channel to hide the waterproofing. Rock is placed along the entire length of the channel, spread from side to side to obtain complete coverage of the liner. Stone must be placed in the channel beginning at the bottom. Each succeeding piece of stone should overlap the previous piece and should have a slight forward slope.

An alternative to flexible liners for a cascade channel is pouring a concrete channel. Dimensional requirements for the cross section remain the same as those for the liner channel. Before the concrete has hardened, the decorative pieces should be placed. For rock, pour them into the channel and seat them into the concrete using a trowel. Wash lightly after the concrete has hardened slightly. To place stone, begin at the bottom of the cascade and push the decorative liner pieces into the concrete, forming the base of the channel. Continue placing the stone tilted slightly forward and toward the center of the channel until you reach the top weir.

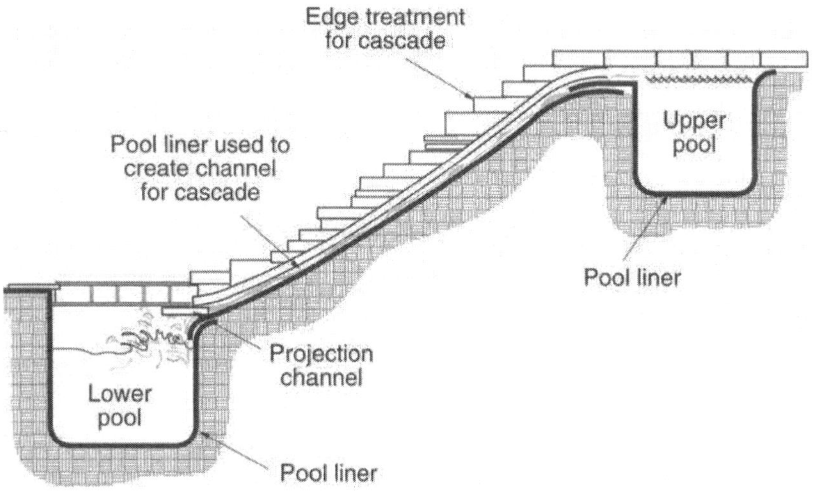

Figure 31-16 Falls channel construction for a cascade.

Edge Treatment

Complete the installation by treating the edges of decorative pools and adding edging material or plants. In falls and cascade channels, stacking stone pieces two to three high in some locations can create the illusion of water flow that has cut through several layers of stone (Figure 31-17).

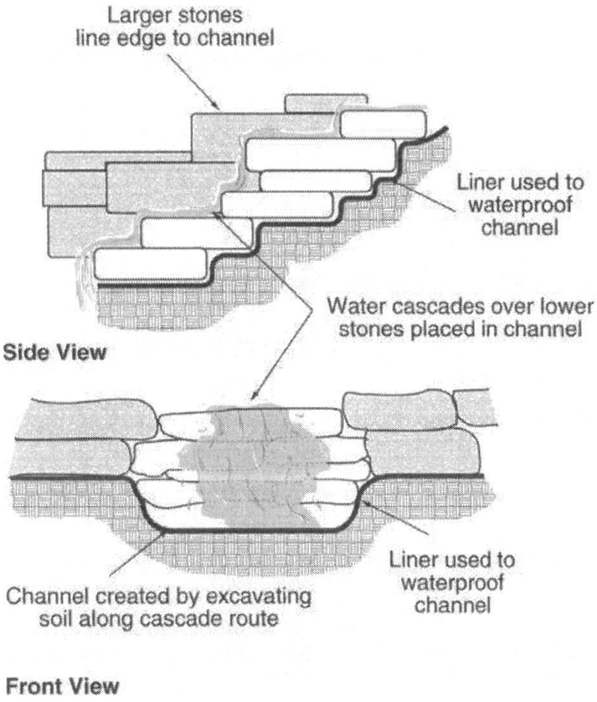

Figure 31-17 Cascade edge treatment.

Careful placement of plant material can hide wiring, tubing, and other rough edges of the falls installation.

INSTALLATION OF DECORATIVE FOUNTAINS

When designing a decorative fountain, an almost infinite number of possible forms and styles are available. Precast concrete, metal, and stone have been used to create standing and wall fountains, and creative garden designers are turning urns and old pottery into focal water features. Fortunately, the installation requirements are very similar for almost all styles available. Most fountains are constructed using a reservoir basin at the lowest point to collect the water and house a recirculation pump. Above that level is typically a water outlet where the water for the fountain is discharged. Between those points is a tube that carries water from the pump to the outlet and, depending on the design, one or more intermediate basins or surfaces over which the water cascades into the reservoir (Figure 31-18). To make the fountain function, water must be added by a water supply, possibly even a hose or bucket, and electricity is necessary to operate the submersible pump.

Before extensive preparation is undertaken, review the type of fountain to be installed. Certain fountains require preparation similar to

Figure 31-18 A decorative fountain with multiple cascade basins.

installation of water features, whereas other fountains are kits that require only a stable foundation (or placement method), an electrical outlet, and a hose/bucket to supply water. Review fountain directions, if provided, to verify what steps need to be undertaken to create a successful installation.

Foundation/Mounting

A key to any water feature is to keep it upright, and this requires stable installation on a footing or wall. If the fountain is wall mounted, first verify with an engineer that the mounting wall is strong enough to hold the fountain's weight and that plumbing and electricity necessary can be brought to the site without significant remodeling. Wall-mounted fountains typically come with a bracket that is secured to the wall studs with lag screws or into masonry or concrete with expanding screws. The fountain is then "hung," or mounted, to the bracket for support. It is not uncommon to have multiple mounting brackets for a single fountain. When installing the bracket, verify that it is level in order for the fountain to function properly. Depending on how the water is recirculated and how the power is supplied, you may need to drill holes in the wall before mounting the fountain.

For standing fountains, a stable footing should be constructed to support the fountain. Lightweight fountains may be able to stand on concrete blocks or bricks on stable soil, but fountains over 50 pounds should have a concrete footing poured to support the fountain and keep it level. Using the instructions for pouring concrete in Chapters 25, form and pour a footing that matches or slightly exceeds the dimensions of the fountain base. Place conduit for water supply, drain, and electrical connections through the center of the footing. Verify that the footing is level and if any anchor bolts are required before completing the forming and pouring the concrete.

> **CAUTION**
>
> A properly licensed contractor should complete all utility connections.

Utility Connections

Utility connections will vary, depending on whether the fountain is preplumbed, wall mounted, or standing. Preplumbed fountains need only the electricity connected (often by plugging the fountain cord into a GFCI outlet) and water placed in the fountain. If the fountain is not preplumbed, utility connections will differ. If wall mounted and separate plumbing is required, the holes for utility connections should have been created prior to mounting. Behind the wall, connect the electricity to a GFCI outlet or circuit, connect the fountain to a water supply (if a separate supply is required), and route the recirculation tubing from the pump in the

Figure 31-19 Utility stubouts for a decorative fountain. Electrical and plumbing run through the hole in the center of the base. Other stubouts are for lights and irrigation for the planter.

reservoir basin to the supply at the top of the fountain. In rare cases, the fountain may also require a separate drain be connected to a sanitary sewer system. Standing fountains require that the reservoir basin or any support pedestal be set and plumbing connections run inside the fountain. Access is typically gained to utility connections before upper basins are set or through a handhold in the fountain's base (Figure 31-19).

When making utility connections, verify that all electrical outlets are connected to a GFCI circuit. A separate switched circuit for fountains and any associated lighting makes operation and maintenance easier. Water supplies that are connected to potable water should have a separate backflow prevention and shutoff valve installed. All pumps used should be rated for submersible use. For maintenance and to accommodate issues with freezing temperatures, a method to drain water from the fountain should also be installed. In small fountains, this can be accomplished using a drain plug at the low point of the fountain or a hand pump and hose; but in large fountain installations, a drain should be plumbed to a nearby sanitary sewer or other appropriate disposal point. You may be able to route fountain drains to gray water systems or to cisterns for irrigation.

Basin Placement

Once utilities are connected, finish placing any upper basins or water outlets for the fountain. Wall-mounted fountains typically come as a single piece, but certain models may require a backing plate and upper water outlet be installed over a basin. Fasten these components as directed by the manufacturer. Standing fountain components are typically stacked, with each subsequent basin or element fitted into the one directly below. Before placing the water outlet, finalize any connections of recirculation tubes to the fixtures supplying the outlet.

Testing

When you have made all connections, fill and test the fountain to verify proper operation. Any necessary adjustments in level will be apparent through uneven flow through the components of the fountain. Use plastic or metal shims placed under the reservoir basin to make any adjustments in standing fountain. Wall-mounted fountains may require repositioning of the bracket(s) to obtain even flow. Once you have verified proper operation, install aesthetic treatments to hide utility sources, footings, and other functional parts of the fountain.

CHAPTER 32

SITE FURNITURE, SIGNAGE, PREFABRICATED PLAYGROUND EQUIPMENT, OUTDOOR KITCHENS, AND PATIO AMENITIES

OBJECTIVES

By reading and practicing the techniques described in this chapter, the reader should be able to successfully complete the following activities:

- Assemble site amenities.
- Anchor site amenities.

Adding furniture and site amenities to a landscape design often provides a finished touch difficult to obtain through use of other landscape elements. The aesthetic effects of pavement, walls, lawn, and plant material are enhanced by the thoughtful placement of seating and lighting. The use of the site is improved when trash and bikes are contained and proper signage is provided. Play equipment adds energy to parks, schools, and playgrounds. Although typically reserved for the commercial landscape, use of such design tools has expanded into the home landscape with the advent of residential grades of amenities.

Much of the furniture for a site is purchased from custom manufacturers, and landscape contractors can install it. Although there are similarities among installation methods, be certain to review the instructions provided by the manufacturer carefully to ensure that neither you nor the property owner void warranties or guarantees. See resources in Appendix F.

RELATED INFORMATION

Information in this chapter is supplemented by instruction provided elsewhere in this text and in other sources. Before undertaking the activities described in this chapter, read the related information in these sources:

- Construction Math, Chapter 5
- Safety in the Workplace, Chapter 7
- Basic Construction Techniques and Small Equipment Operation, Chapter 8
- Pedestrian Concrete Paving, Chapter 25
- Freestanding Walls, Section 7
- Applicable building codes and ordinances

TYPES OF SITE AMENITIES

Property owners and landscape contractors have a variety of amenities from which to choose to enhance the site. Not only do these amenities enhance the site's appearance, but they also increase the site's functionality and usefulness.

- Benches. Site seating is available in a variety of shapes, materials, and finishes. Styles most often found include contour and historic benches. Seating is manufactured in wood, metal, stone, fiberglass, recycled plastics, and precast concrete. Most seating anchors directly to concrete slabs, with some seating requiring footings or posts that are direct buried in the ground.
- Park Tables and Grills. Heavy-duty picnic tables and charcoal grills are designed for use in park and recreation areas. Most tables are manufactured of metal and/or wood and grills are welded steel. Direct burial and concrete slab mounting are the most common installation options for these amenities.
- Outdoor Firepits and Fireplaces. For decoration and for warming during the cold seasons, cauldrons where a fire burns real or artificial logs create a cozy setting in residential and commercial settings. Outdoor firepits and fireplaces can be as simple as a level surface where wood is burned or as

complex as gas-fired, auto-starting porcelain logs set into a fireproof hearth.

- Outdoor Kitchens. The concept of outdoor grilling has advanced to the point where entire meal preparation and service are now possible in an outdoor kitchen. Equipped with grills, refrigerators, sinks, and storage, an outdoor kitchen gives cooks an escape from the summer heat and allows them to enjoy modern conveniences in the exterior environment.
- Trash Receptacles. Trash receptacles are decorative enclosures into which garbage containers are placed. Materials used to construct the receptacles include wood, metal, precast concrete, or fiberglass. Most are manufactured to be anchored to a concrete slab, but some are mounted on a post that is buried in the ground or anchored to a footing. Shapes of receptacles can vary, but most are typically round or square.
- Signage. Identification of businesses and traffic routes or just a display of general information can be conveyed in the landscape with signage. Many types of signage are available, with ground-mounted, also called *monument,* and post-mounted signage being the most common. Many signs also require placement of electrical lines to illuminate the sign for night viewing.
- Bike Racks. Many designs are available for securing bikes. Most are manufactured from metal and anchored to a concrete slab or are directly buried (Figure 32-1).
- Bollards. **Bollards** are short posts used to identify the perimeter of a plaza or circulation route (Figure 32-2). Often used to separate pedestrian and vehicular traffic, bollards can be manufactured of wood, metal, stone, or other materials and may have lighting incorporated. Installation can be direct burial or concrete slab mounted.

Figure 32-1 Bike rack anchored in a concrete slab.

Some bollards are designed to be removed for access and emergencies, hence requiring a footing installation.

- Flagpoles. Flagpoles are available in various heights, operation mechanisms, and materials. Although flagpoles are usually metal, some are made of precast concrete and wood. Flagpoles require direct burial or anchoring to a footing buried to frost depth or deeper.
- Light Standards. The posts on which pedestrian lights are mounted are called **standards.** Styles include contemporary, historic, western, or architectural. Materials typically include metal, wood, or precast concrete. Most light standards require a footing that is buried to frost depth or deeper.

Figure 32-2 Bollards used to separate vehicular and pedestrian traffic.

- Prefabricated Play Equipment. Similar to other amenities, play equipment has a wide variety of choices available. Most pieces are manufactured with a framework of wood or metal posts that are directly buried or mounted on a footing. Engineered equipment for play activities is then attached to the framework. Platforms, slides, climbers, and many other pieces of play equipment are available to the client. Custom-built wood structures follow plans prepared by the design professional and typically use direct burial for post installation. To maintain a safe environment, the surfacing placed below the play structures must meet playground safety standards. To address this issue are several loose or rubberized surfaces that can be installed under play equipment.

PLANNING THE PROJECT

Planning for amenity installation can be characterized as organizing chaos. Differing pieces of equipment from a variety of manufacturers, each with unique requirements for preparation and installation, create a situation that requires extensive planning on the contractor's part.

Timing Placement of Site Furniture and Play Equipment

Footings and slabs on which the furniture is anchored can be efficiently constructed when concrete for paved areas and structures is poured. Because it is often shipped assembled and finished, site furniture should be protected until installation and until completion of major exterior construction projects. Furnishings that require assembly and/or finishing can be more conveniently prepared off-site and then installed near the end of the project.

Manufacturer's Specifications and Shop Drawings

Materials purchased from manufacturers typically include installation and finishing specifications and shop drawings for proper installation. Contractors should obtain these specifications and drawings before any planning and installation begins and should compare them to those the design professional has provided. If there are discrepancies in materials, finishes, construction, installation, or other aspects, bring these immediately to the designer's attention.

Layout of Site Furniture, Signage, and Play Equipment

Site furniture is typically located by staking the footings used to anchor the amenity. Locate either the edges or the center lines of mounting slabs. Measurements should carefully conform to drawings. Once you set a footing for an amenity, you cannot adjust it to match the dimensions of the fixture.

Because most pieces of play equipment have multiple posts, layout is a challenge. As for site furniture, obtain the working drawings from the manufacturer before proceeding. Layout using a grid with two baselines is a common method for identifying post locations. Verify that the two baselines are square to each other and check measurements for square often. Because any variation will twist the play equipment structure, proper level must also be maintained between footing locations. Use grade stakes for each post to show the elevation and location of each footing. Verify the level between points if an amenity has several supports that must be buried. A level stringline, set at the proper burial depth, can be moved between each support location to verify that all supports are buried to the proper depth. Control burial depth for individual supports by placing a mark indicating ground level on the side of each support.

ANCHORING SITE FURNITURE, SIGNAGE, AND PLAY EQUIPMENT

Site preparation for furniture, signage, and play equipment is primarily limited to the construction of footings. Three common methods of anchoring most site furniture and signage include (1) direct burial of amenity supports, such as legs or posts, that are connected to the furniture; (2) installation of a slab onto which the furniture is anchored; and (3) construction of a frost-depth footing onto which the furniture is anchored. Signage may also be anchored by attaching to an existing structure such as a building, fence, or pole. The following sections describe the construction common for each of these techniques.

Direct Burial

For a fixture that requires direct burial, begin by locating the burial points where each support must be sunk. Burial can be accomplished by either driving the support into the ground using a sledgehammer or post driver or excavating a hole and placing the support. The excavation technique is more beneficial when you must place multiple posts and need a small amount of flexibility while making the connections. When selecting the first method, wrap the top of the support with heavy rags or place a block of wood on top of the support to avoid contact damage when driving. Using a firm stroke, drive the support into the ground. Stop periodically to check for plumb, for correct spacing between supports, and for proper orientation. Continue driving until the support is at its proper depth.

If you select the excavation approach, bore a vertical hole that is only slightly larger in diameter than the support. When you have reached the proper depth, set the support and backfill. To maintain proper elevation of the support, place a mark on the post at the correct elevation. Fill the hole a few inches at a time and compact, rechecking to verify plumb, proper depth, and orientation. Slightly raise supports that are set too deep by gripping the post, lifting straight up, and then adding a small amount of granular material. Supports with flanges or anchors may require a twisting or rocking motion as you raise them. After adjusting the support, verify plumb and recompact the soil. If specified by the manufacturer, certain direct burial supports may require the hole be filled with concrete.

Slab Anchoring

If the furniture or monument signage is to be anchored on a slab, you must form and pour the slab (see Chapter 25 for instructions on pouring concrete) and set anchors at proper dimensions before the concrete hardens. Verify the surface material and/or finish of the slab before pouring. The finish surface under a bench may not be the same as the adjacent paved surface; and if a special finish or allowance for pavers is required, this foundation slab must conform. To properly locate anchors, use stringlines or directly measure the placement locations. Place anchors shortly after the slab has been finished by pushing the bolt/anchor stem into the wet concrete and lifting up or wiggling slightly to settle the concrete around the stem. If the anchor sinks into the concrete, wait 15 minutes and attempt to reset it. Do not wait too long to set the anchors, or they may not insert into the slab. Wait at least 48 hours before connecting the amenity (Figure 32-3). You can install bolts after the concrete slab is finished.

Figure 32-3 Anchoring of an amenity support post to paving using an anchor bolt placed through the paving.

Frost Footing

Some amenities require the stability afforded by a footing that extends below the frost line. The actual depth to avoid frost heaving varies based on geographic location. When a footing is required, excavate a vertical hole that is the diameter required by the manufacturer or by the drawings. Verify that the depth meets the specifications. Amenities that have several supports may require multiple excavations. These holes typically do not need to be joined by a continuous footing if each extends below frost depth. However, if one hole is not the proper depth, it will move up and down at a different rate than the others, causing damage to the amenity.

If steel reinforcement is required, cut rerod 8 inches longer than hole depth and secure by driving them into the soil in the bottom of the footing hole. Many footings can be poured without being formed by placing the concrete and finishing the top of the footing with a trowel. However, you may need to form the entire footing, or at least the top 6 inches of the footing, using a tubular paper form. These conditions include situations where the footing extends above the finish grade, where unstable soil conditions may collapse the hole, or where the hole was excavated in an irregular shape. To prevent them from frost heaving, footing holes should have vertical sides. Holes that have a wider diameter at the top are subject to frost pushing up on the footing, countering the advantage of having a footing below frost depth.

Finish the top of a footing with a wood float, doming the surface slightly so that water can drain away from the post. After the footing is

Figure 32-4 Anchoring of an amenity support on a footing poured separately from the concrete walkway.

poured, place anchors on the top of the footing by pushing the anchor stem into the concrete and lifting or wiggling slightly to settle concrete around the stem. Before the concrete hardens, verify the spacing between anchors for fixtures that have multiple supports (Figure 32-4).

Footings with Electrical Service

In some cases, before the concrete is poured, the footings or slab may require additional work. For example, if the amenity will have light fixtures or lighted signage, you will need to install electrical conduit through the form before the pour can take place. For slab pours, excavate the trench for conduit and place the conduit in the proper finish location. Cover both ends of the open conduit with duct tape. Backfill the trench with granular fill material and proceed with the pour.

To install a round lighting footing, use an auger to excavate a round hole of the diameter specified and to the required footing depth. Select a tubular paper form of the specified diameter for the footing and trim it to a length the same as the footing depth. Through the side of the form, cut a 2-inch round opening for electrical conduit. The location should match the depth and position where the conduit enters the footing. Cut and connect a conduit bend and a straight section. Place duct tape over the openings at both ends of the conduit. Place the conduit in the form, with the bend exiting the opening and the straight section extending above the top of the form. Use duct tape wrapped around the conduit at the top of the form and at the side opening to position the conduit inside the form. Excavate an extra channel along the side of the footing to accommodate the conduit extending out of the footing. Lower the form into the footing excavation and orient the stub of the conduit bend in the proper direction.

Keeping the form in a plumb position, backfill with soil around the form. If reinforcing is required, construct the framework and place it inside the form. Pour premixed concrete into each form. Before the concrete hardens, center the conduit and insert any anchor bolts required for anchoring the fixture. When the concrete has set, peel away the top of the paper form.

Anchoring Signage to Another Structure

If no separate support is planned for signage, you may use existing structures to anchor signs. Connect signage to wood structures with lag screws placed into support posts or studs, or anchor signage to masonry units with expanding masonry bolts. If signage is attached to metal objects such as a fence, a backing strap is required. Position the sign at the proper location and insert a galvanized bolt through a hole in the sign (or through the sign's mounting bracket), through the fence, and through a hole in the mounting strap. Secure and tighten the nut using a lock washer. Various forms of mounting straps

Figure 32-5 Attaching signage to decorative metal fencing.

(Figure 32-5) will accommodate fencing, light standards, and other types of metal landscape amenities.

INSTALLING SITE FURNITURE AND PLAY EQUIPMENT

Installation of most amenities requires placing and finishing the furniture piece. In some installations, welding or special finishing may be required; and for other installations, an electrician or other construction specialist may need to complete the work.

Placement and Adjustment

Depending on the manufacturer's instructions, preassembly of all or part of an amenity may be required before installation. Amenities assembled piece by piece can be put together beginning at the anchors/supports and working up. Assemble any portions that are required and position them over the anchors. Carefully set the fixture on the anchors/supports and install connection hardware. Secure the fixture and then begin the process of leveling and plumbing.

There are two key criteria for placement of an amenity: (1) it must be placed at the proper location and elevation (Figure 32-6) and (2) it must be placed level and plumb. To maintain these criteria, connect the fixture securely but not fully tightened (termed *finger tight*). Check for level on a horizontal surface and plumb on two adjacent vertical surfaces. Adjust level as necessary and complete the tightening of all fasteners. If you need to make adjustments for level, remove the amenity and place galvanized washers over the anchor bolt to adjust the amenity to the proper level.

Surfacing

Safe surfacing below play equipment is required to maintain a fall zone. Consult the guidelines

Figure 32-6 Layout of a custom-built play structure.

Figure 32-7 Prefabricated play structure with resilient surface below.

published by the Consumer Product Safety Commission, for recommended materials and depths. Standards for proper playground surfacing depth are typically described by ASTM F1292 (Standard Specification for Impact Attenuation of Surface Systems Under and Around Playground Equipment). If granular surfaces such as mulch, granulated rubber, sand, or gravel are being used, excavate to the proper depth and layer the material into the area with minimal compaction (Figure 32-7).

Resilient Surfacing. Of the many surfaces used to mitigate falls from play equipment, resilient surfaces not only offer protection, but also provide color and access. Resilient surfaces are typically rubber products blended with polymers to create a soft, yet durable surfacing. Grouped into two general categories based on how they are installed, resilient surfaces provide an alternative to granular materials and mulch for playgrounds that are used often. Basing their decision on the type of playground equipment and the heights from which children may fall, the designer and the manufacturer specify the thickness of the surface material. The design criteria will also specify whether to install the surface using individual tiles or by pouring a mixture over a base. For each method, the preparation of the site and base is similar.

Subsurface Preparation. For a resilient play surface to be effective, a solid base must be prepared to support the surfacing. Most manufacturers recommend concrete for the base, but application over asphalt can be specified in some projects. In some cases, compacted granular bases are also possible. For concrete, pour a slab that has a slight slope to allow good surface drainage. The concrete should have a heavy broom finish and be cured for 14–28 days prior to installation. Asphalt should also have a slight slope for good drainage and have a wearing course with small surface aggregate and a tight surface. A granular base should be a minimum of 4 inches of compacted stone, typically a fine granular base, with a minimum surface variation of ¼ inch. A slight slope for drainage is also necessary. Some manufacturer's specify an open French drain system when using a granular base. For granular bases, a filter fabric is required over the base. All base material should be clean and free of debris and serious surface variations. Any play equipment, site furniture, or other vertical elements within the play surface area should already be installed.

Installation of Tiled Products. Once the base has been prepared, installation of the resilient tiles can proceed. The installation will be generally the same for all products, with variations depending on whether the tiles are installed using adhesive or held in place using interlocking edges or pins. For either fastening method, lay the tiles out for 24 hours prior to installation so they can consistently adjust to the temperature. Tiles shrink and swell during temperature extremes, and all products should be at the same ambient temperature before installation. It is also helpful to plan and mark the installation prior to placing the tile. Because few sites have square corners and sides, identify a starting point where there is a right angle or use a center starting position with a horizontal and vertical layout line at right angles to keep the installation square. When marking the layout, be certain to leave space for containment around the perimeter if necessary (Figure 32-8).

Adhesive Installation. Before beginning installation, verify that the surface is clean and dry. Adhesive installation will not work over granular bases. When you have completed the layout, select a starting point along one of the straight edges. Typical adhesive for elastic tiles is polyurethane, but follow the manufacturer's recommendations for all adhesives. Apply glue for a small number of tiles using a ¼-inch square or V-notched trowel. Set the tiles along the guideline, using a mallet to carefully adjust the alignment. Most manufacturers recommend

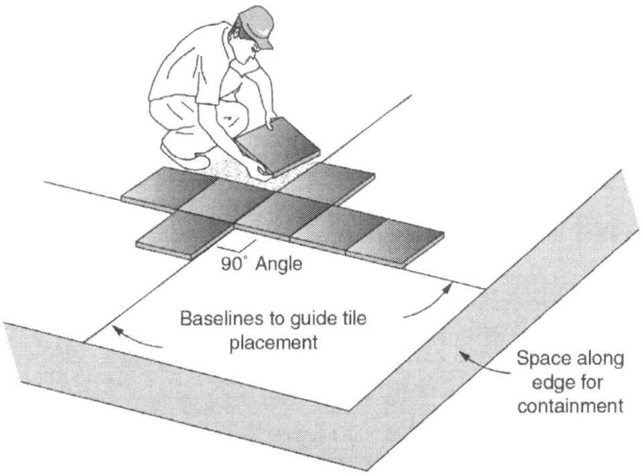

Figure 32-8 Guidelines used to lay out resilient paving tiles.

application of adhesive to the side of each tile where it abuts an adjacent tile. Use a caulking gun with a tube of adhesive for side application. When you encounter a vertical object, make a cardboard template of the cutout and trace the pattern onto a tile. Use a band saw or jigsaw with a coarse blade to make any cuts. Continue placing tile until you reach the boundary. Place any containment tiles or containment materials at the completion of the interior of the project.

Interlocking Installation. Before beginning installation, verify that the surface is clean and dry. Begin installation along one of the straight edges laid out in the previous step. Place the initial tile and interlock the second tile using the mechanism provided by the manufacturer. Some products will require the placement of several tiles before you insert a pin to hold the tiles in place. When you encounter a vertical object, make a cardboard template of the cutout and trace the pattern onto a tile. Use a band saw or jigsaw with a coarse blade to make any cuts. Continue placing tile until you reach the boundary. Place any containment tiles or containment materials at the completion of the interior of the project.

Installation of Poured Products. Resilient surfaces that are poured require similar base preparation as noted above. In many poured products, the edge treatment may differ from tiled installations. Typical poured edges include containment blocks or keyways to anchor the surface at the edges. In addition, resilient surfaces typically are poured in two stages, one pour for a base coat and a second pour for a wearing top coat. To pour a resilient surface, begin by masking any areas that are not to be primed or surfaced, including structures within the play area and elements outside the work area. Apply the manufacturer's recommended primer, typically with a large nap paint roller. Prime any vertical surface that will abut the resilient surface.

If mixing is required, mix enough material that you can use in a reasonable time period. Pour the mixture onto the primed base and spread it using a trowel or, if supplied or recommended by the manufacturer, a spreading squeegee. Spread the mixture evenly and smoothly to the depth required. Treat equipment with soapy water or mineral spirits to prevent the mixture from adhering to the trowels. Allow this base coat to dry completely before following with a surface coat. A second coat of primer may be required before you can apply the wearing coat. Mix, if necessary, and spread the wearing coat over the base coat to the depth required. In many applications, the wearing coat is applied ½ inch thick, but verify the depth with drawings and/or manufacturers specifications. Allow this coat to dry before walking on the surface.

Finishing

Site furniture can be shipped prefinished or unfinished, requiring various degrees of field finishing. Selection of finished or unfinished materials is based on cost, risk of damage during shipment or installation, and the contractor's ability to field finish the product. Prefinished materials should be covered or wrapped with a protective material until the construction project is complete. Finishing activities can range from priming and painting of a fixture to touching up minor surface damage caused by transportation and installation. Among the most common finish activities that landscape contractors complete are painting of light poles, staining or painting of benches, installing hardware, and installing liner cans for trash receptacles.

Contractors can perform finishing work after the fixture is placed. However, field finishing can be difficult because dust, inclement weather, or other construction activities can interrupt, delay, or even damage finishing work. The recommended process is to perform any painting or staining activities in an enclosed environment, carefully transport the items to the site for installation, and perform only touch-up finishing in the field if necessary. Finishing should be one of the last activities performed prior to the owner's final acceptance of the project.

INSTALLING OUTDOOR KITCHENS

Outdoor living continues to expand beyond relaxation and recreation. Since the advent of the outdoor grill, the concept of cooking outdoors to avoid summer heat has expanded with the outdoor kitchen. Once reserved to regions with mild climates and to the more affluent property owners, the outdoor kitchen continues to grow in popularity throughout the nation and across income groups. Construction of an outdoor kitchen can take many forms, from a makeshift setup of an ice cooler supplementing the grill, to a full-service kitchen with complete utility functions. To complete the high-end outdoor kitchen, skills from several chapters throughout this text, as well as specialty construction skills from several trades, will be required. Carpentry, foundation, utility, and finish work will all be necessary to complete the ultimate in outdoor living, the outdoor kitchen.

CAUTION

Verify with local building officials all codes and ordinances required to construct an outdoor kitchen. Obtain any permits before beginning work. Licensed plumbers and electricians should perform all utility installations and connections.

Figure 32-9 An outdoor kitchen with a stovetop, side burner, refrigerator, sink, and storage below. Firepit and lighted seat wall are in the foreground.

Planning

As with most other aspects of the landscape, the key to success in creating a functional outdoor kitchen is design and planning. Even more so than with a deck or patio, attention must be given to the components and the flow of activities to make an outdoor kitchen work. A design professional should design such a space to assure that all requirements of this specialized area are met. Among the many considerations are what appliances to put in the kitchen, how large the kitchen should be, what materials are needed, and, of course, what the climatic conditions are in the region.

A full range of appliances are available for use in many outdoor situations. Gas grills are the foundation of most designs, and many grills can be rolled into a compartment or set into a counter. To enhance grilling activities and to expand food production, side burners and food warmers are available as drop-in units that can be set into the counter. Stainless steel sinks and compact refrigerators are available for cleaning and storage, and a wide variety of prep stations, storage units, shelving, and trash compartments can be purchased as drop-in units set into prefabricated or custom-framed counters (Figure 32-9).

General sizes and specific dimensions will both be critical in outdoor kitchen design. Each appliance chosen will add to the counter space required. An outdoor space that is large enough to accommodate the required counter length, as well as provide dining and seating area and allow free traffic movement, will be necessary. On a detailed level, dimensions such as counter heights and clearance around cooking appliances will not change from interior spaces. Minimum counter heights of 32–36 inches and depths of 24 inches will be required not only to meet code, but also to make the space comfortable to use. Clearances around gas appliances and the provision of back splashes and vent hoods may also be necessary requirements.

Utility connections will also create planning challenges. Most outdoor kitchens use connections to interior household utilities, but the installation may not be as simple as running line indoors. A complete outdoor kitchen will require water (possibly hot and cold), gas, electricity (on a GFCI circuit), sanitary sewer, and possibly even communications (phone, internet, cable) connections. Routing and implementing utility connections should be verified early in the planning process, and a licensed professional should install all exterior stubouts.

Because they are exposed to the elements, the materials for outdoor construction must not only be attractive, but also be weatherproof and fireproof. Prefabricated components are available for outdoor kitchens, requiring the contractor to only assemble and level adjustable legs to complete setup. With the installation of a countertop and help from a specialized contractor to install and connect the appliances, an almost instant kitchen can be obtained. Custom construction can be framed with wood or metal, surfaced with stone, metal, or veneers, and finished with a variety of countertop materials. Because the construction is exterior, galvanized or rust-resistant metals or decay-resistant wood are recommended, and countertops of stone, stainless steel, or tile provide greater durability and more fire resistance than many typical interior materials. These materials also provide surfacing that can withstand the elements and cleanings to which outdoor kitchens are subject.

Among the other planning considerations for the outdoor kitchen are the access to the structure, protection of the work areas from the climate, and how the space will function during colder times of the year. Location near an access point to interior family space and/or kitchen increases the functionality of the outdoor kitchen. Adding an arbor or overhead screen also makes the space more usable with protection from the sun and rain, and adding a patio heater can extend the use of the space into the early spring and late fall months in most climates. Planning the installation so critical appliances like the refrigerator can be removed for the winter and water lines drained to avoid freezing allow even those who live in the coldest of climates to enjoy the outdoor kitchen space.

INSTALLING FIREPITS

Firepits formalize the romantic idea of the campfire into the landscape. Used in residential and commercial settings, firepits take the fire concept to a new level by introducing safety, convenience, and aesthetics. Firepits can be extensive custom additions or simple installations—e.g., a large metal cauldron with legs in which logs are loaded and a fire started. Many available premanufactured kits provide the necessary equipment required to enjoy the "modern campfire." Custom firepits are typically a decorative surround wall that creates an area inside which a fire can be safely managed (Figure 32-10). Custom-built firepits add features such as draining away water after a storm, fueling the fire using gas, and creating a surround that is durable and attractive.

CAUTION

Verify that local codes and ordinance allow open fires within your jurisdiction. Many locales have banned burning of wood as a result of air pollution issues, and many fire departments require screening over open fires to reduce the possibility of embers starting fires off-site. A licensed plumber should make all gas connections. A licensed electrician should make all electrical connections.

Planning

If the choices of what type of firepit to build or where to place it fall under the contractor's responsibilities, the safe construction begins with planning considerations. Based on what is legally allowed, a choice must be made regarding a firepit that burns wood and is ignited using a supplemental flame or a firepit that is equipped with gas burners and uses lava rock, porcelain

Figure 32-10 Firepit surround with coping and fireproof brick installed. Utility stub outs can be seen at the bottom.

Figure 32-11 Handhold in paving for utility valves and connections.

logs or other approved material as the heating medium. Placement will require identification of a level location that is free of any overhead and underground utilities, away from combustible materials such as structures and plant material, and provides a wide apron around the pit that accommodates seating and provides safe access.

Surround Construction

At the firepit site, remove turf under the pit and in the apron area; then using marking paint, mark the location of the surround wall. Excavate the surround area to the depth of the pit, plus base a minimum of 6 inches of material. If drainage below the pit is poor, a supplemental drainage system may be required to remove excess water. If the firepit will use gas for a fuel, the gas line should be stubbed under the base material near the inside edge of the surround wall location. A shutoff valve will be required near where the gas supply is located or where the line passes under the surround wall. Codes may require shutoffs in both locations. Any electronic ignition components should also be stubbed in using galvanized conduit. Installing a heavy-duty handhold over the service lines is a good place to locate valves and igniter switches (Figure 32-11). Place base material under the surround wall location and build the wall. Walls can be made of any fireproof material including stone, precast segmental wall stone, brick, or concrete. If an exterior or veneer is required, concrete or mortared materials provide the most stable backing.

After you have completed the wall, line the interior of the firepit using fire brick or a metal campfire ring (Figure 32-10). This lining will reduce long-term damage to the surround wall. Install any exterior veneer and surround wall cap required by the design. Place a layer of free-draining 1-inch drain rock in the base of the firepit to create a base for burners and/or fuel placed in the pit. Place a ring of expansion joint material around the outside of the firepit and install the apron material around the exterior. If the firepit uses wood lit by a supplemental flame, a purchased or custom-made metal screen may be installed over the firepit to contain embers.

Burner Installation

Please note that a licensed plumber should complete the following connections and testing. When building a firepit that uses gas-fired burners, the burner installation can be completed after the drain rock has been installed. Make the connections between the gas line stubbed into the pit and the igniter and burners. The igniters are a small valve that regulates the flow of gas and mix of air similar to those used in gas grills. The openings on the igniters and burners should be facing downward and supported approximately 3–4 inches above the drain rock with metal supports. Position the burners and, using a propane grill lighter, turn on the gas

Figure 32-12 Completed firepit. Lava rock and burners were installed in the bottom, with porcelain logs in the upper area of the surround.

and test the flame. Make any adjustments in the flame using the venturi valve on the igniter. After you have satisfactorily adjusted the flame, cover the igniters with wire mesh dome guards and place the lava rock or porcelain logs in the pit (Figure 32-12).

OUTOOR FIREPLACES

The addition of an outdoor fireplace can create a focal point for an outdoor living area that adds both aesthetics and function. Whether permanent or portable, the outdoor fireplace is an upscale version of the traditional campfire.

Planning the Project

Before considering the installation of an outdoor fireplace, review all applicable codes and ordinances that may impact the construction, including utility codes, structure and building codes and outdoor burning ordinances. Also, because of the complexity of the construction this phase of work is often subcontracted to specialty contractors and, in many cases, requires the assistance of a design professional.

An initial consideration for an outdoor fireplace is the placement. Such a feature should be located where it is accessible and convenient to use, yet placed away from flammable objects such as trees and shrubs and away from areas with strong winds or drafts. If the location is adjacent to or near another structure, proper separation must be provided to meet fire codes. Selection of a style of fireplace is also an early consideration. Fireplaces can be permanent installations, which require extensive site work and construction, or portable units that can be relocated around a site. While the portable unit offers convenience, the impact on the landscape is seldom as strong a visual anchor as the permanent installation. A third initial consideration is whether the fireplace will burn wood, use wood with a fire starting unit of gas flame, or utilize ceramic or artificial fuel with a gas flame. When a fire source is determined a decision will then be required as whether to build a custom constructed firebox and chimney, a prefabricated unit firebox/chimney unit or to use a prefabricated firebox insert.

Having the assistance of the design professional in making these choices will lead to a more satisfying decision that serves for many years.

Design considerations may include the addition of wood storage beside the firebox, placing a drain in the bottom of the firebox to accommodate rain water that might enter the fixture or providing an ash dump below the unit with a grate that allows ash to drop directly from the firebox. Each of these options will require additional steps in the following instructions.

Building the Fireplace Structure

Building the fireplace will require the installation of a solid foundation that can resist movement from frost and other environmental forces. Inspect the subgrade below the foundation to verify that it is stable and prepare a reinforced concrete slab on which to build. Consideration should be given to any utilities, such as a gas supply and electrical circuit, that might need conduit to be placed within a foundation and further consideration should be given to proving drainage from the bottom of the firebox. If a prefabricated firebox/chimney unit or firebox are used, install the foundation according to the manufacturer's specifications.

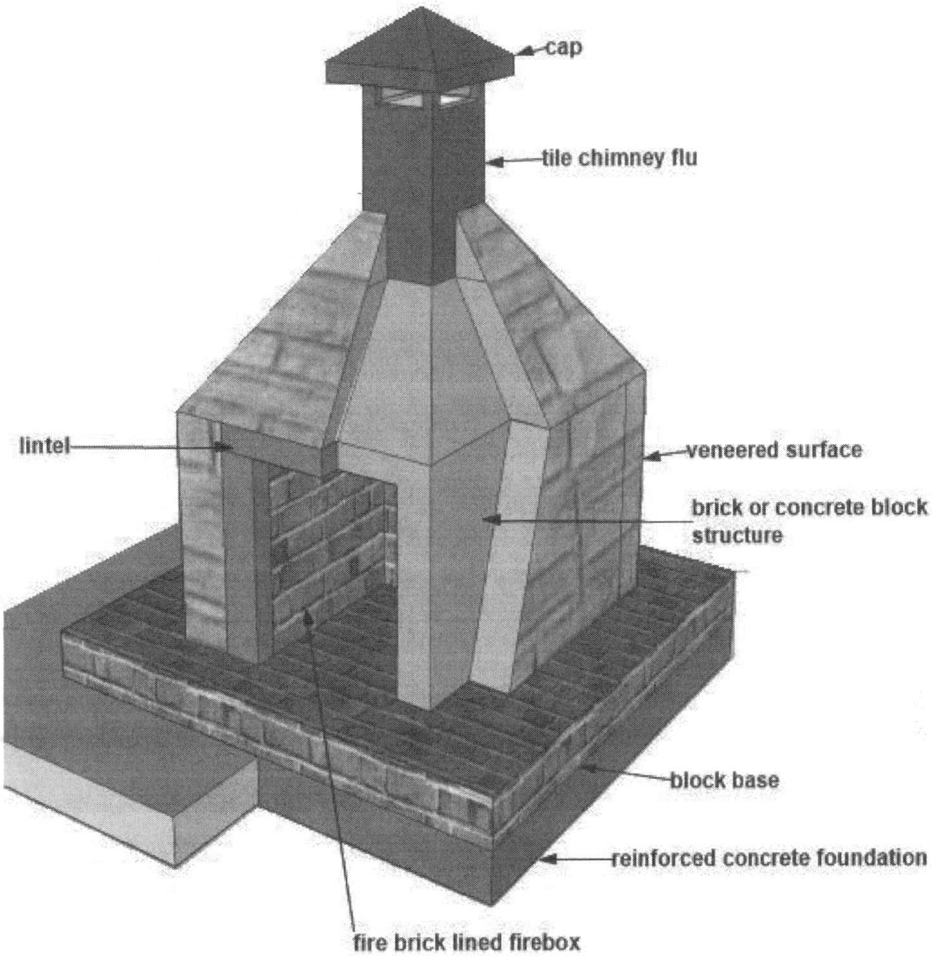

Figure 32-13 Custom outdoor fireplace construction.

On top of the foundation mortar a layer of solid block to the slab to level the surface. Varying methods are used to construct the firebox and enclosure. One method is to lay the sides of the firebox using fireproof block using refractory cement mortar, then encase the firebox sides and back with concrete block walls. Place concrete ties is the concrete block joints and let the mortar set between each step. Follow with the construction of the throat by mortaring offsetting (corbelling) block from the edges of the firebox to the chimney opening. (Figure 32-13) This step will bridge the difference in width between the firebox and the chimney. When the mortar has dried, mortar the flue into place (often a tile flu) and install concrete flu block around the clay tile flu. As with the firebox structure, install concrete ties in the block joints. When the construction is complete install the desired veneer over the entire fireplace, using a fireproof lintel to bridge the opening above the firebox.

Another construction method is to build the enclosure first and then line with fireproof brick or a prefabricated liner. If the entire installation is a custom fireplace, the structure that encompasses the firebox is built, then the flu for the chimney is attached on top of the firebox and the structure extending around the flu to the top of the fireplace (Figure 32-14). Prefabricated firebox/chimney units are placed on the foundation and the structure is added around the unit to the top of the fireplace. Prefabricated fireboxes can be placed before

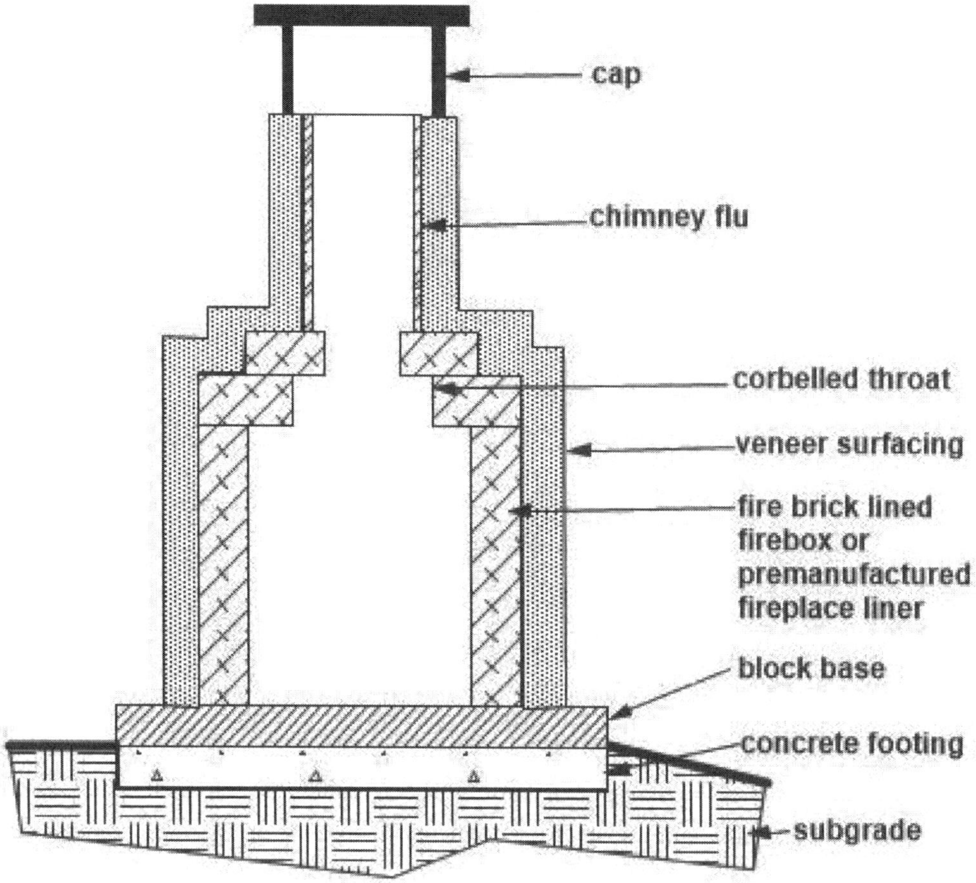

Figure 32-14 Outdoor fireplace cross-section

© Delmar/Cengage Learning.

structure construction or inserted after the structure has been erected. If a hearth and/or mantle are part of the design, the structure that supports these elements must be built along with the rest of the structure. Any utility routing and connection must be made while the structure is being erected. Final connections are completed during the finishing operation.

Finish Surfacing

Once the structure of the fireplace is complete, the surfacing of the feature is started. The custom firebox is lined with firebrick and the exterior of the fireplace is surfaced with a veneer of stucco, stone or brick. Capstones are often used to top off the chimney and any angular edges, as well as hearth or mantle corners. A chimney covering is anchored to the top and firebox coverings installed with the surfacing. If a hearth and/or mantle are included, install these special surfaces as required.

Connections and Testing

Installing any utility connections and controllers (such as pilot lights or thermostats) and, if utilized, artificial fuel, completes the construction. The systems installed should be thoroughly tested to ensure proper operation before considering the project complete.

CHAPTER 33

EDGING, PLANTERS, AND PLANT PROTECTION EQUIPMENT

OBJECTIVES

By reading and practicing the techniques described in this chapter, the reader should be able to successfully complete the following activities:

- Select a material for edging.
- Excavate a natural edge.
- Install plastic edging.
- Install metal edging.
- Install brick and stone edging.
- Install curbing.
- Install wood edging.
- Set planters.
- Install root barriers.

Defining, containing, and protecting plants require a variety of specialized construction materials and techniques. Edging is one of the more versatile materials available to the landscape designer. Edging can be used to define areas, hold pavement in place, and separate turf from planting beds. Edging materials require excavation of a trench, either by hand or by machine, and placement of material within the trench. Techniques are available for installing concrete edging using a special curbing machine.

Planters are valuable for providing proper planting environments in paved areas. Manufactured from wood, precast concrete, fiberglass, or composite materials, most planters require only placing and filling. Other installations may require that the planter be anchored to a paved surface. Tree grates allow air and moisture to reach tree roots in paved areas, whereas tree guards protect the trunk of the plant from damage. Tree grates and guards require preliminary work during the site paving stage and are placed and connected after planting is completed.

RELATED INFORMATION IN OTHER CHAPTERS

Information in this chapter is supplemented by instruction provided elsewhere in this text and in other sources. Before undertaking the activities described in this chapter, read the related information in these sources:

- Construction Math, Chapter 5
- Safety in the Workplace, Chapter 7
- Basic Construction Techniques and Small Equipment Operation, Chapter 8
- Pedestrian Concrete Paving, Chapter 25

PLANNING THE PROJECT

Planning the amenities associated with plant material typically occurs after the majority of the site construction has been completed, but ordering materials and preparation for items such as edger and tree grates will require action during earlier stages of construction.

Timing of Edging and Plant Protection Placement

Plant bed edging should be placed after the planting bed has been prepared but before the installation of weed barrier, plantings, and mulch. Installation of the edging prior to installing any weed barrier or mulch provides a depth guide for both. If the installation will not disrupt or damage the plant material, edging can be placed after planting.

Planters and plant protection devices should be installed as the project nears completion. Planters should be placed after all major site construction is completed but before planting operations begin. Although preliminary work for tree grates and guards is performed during the paving stages, finishing and placement should not occur until after all plant materials have been placed.

Layout of Edging

Painting is the easiest method to identify edging location (Figure 33-1), but a stringline may be used for straight applications. Experienced contractors may be able to locate edging as they excavate the trench, but errors require that disturbed areas be reseeded or resodded.

Figure 33-1 Layout of edging using marking paint.

Figure 33-2 Measuring for edging with measuring wheel.

Measurements for edging quantities can be performed by pacing or by using a measuring wheel (Figure 33-2).

INSTALLING LANDSCAPE EDGING

Although trench preparation requires consistency, it can be a laborious task. Preparation for landscape edging can be done by hand for small areas; but it is best done mechanically for large installations. To edge for landscape installations, follow the steps listed in the following sections:

Excavation of Edging Trench

Along the entire alignment, excavate a shallow, shaped trench that is approximately 1 inch deeper than the vertical dimension of the edging (Figure 33-3). The outside edge of the trench (side

Figure 33-3 Proper trench for edging showing vertical excavation on lawn side.

nearest the lawn or paving) should be excavated with a straight, vertical edge (Figure 33-4). This allows edgings to be positioned tightly against the adjacent material. The inside edge of the trench (side toward the planting bed) should be excavated at a 45° angle. For curbing and stone, brick, and precast edgings, the trench should be excavated with a flat bottom that is 2 inches wider than the width of the material. Depending on the type and what is placed on either side, the placement depth may vary. If the edging abuts a seeded area, the top should be flush with the finish grade. If the edging abuts a sodded area, the top should be placed 1 inch above the soil grade before sod is placed. Unless the manufacturer specifies otherwise, edging that abuts paved areas should be placed flush with the top of the paved surface.

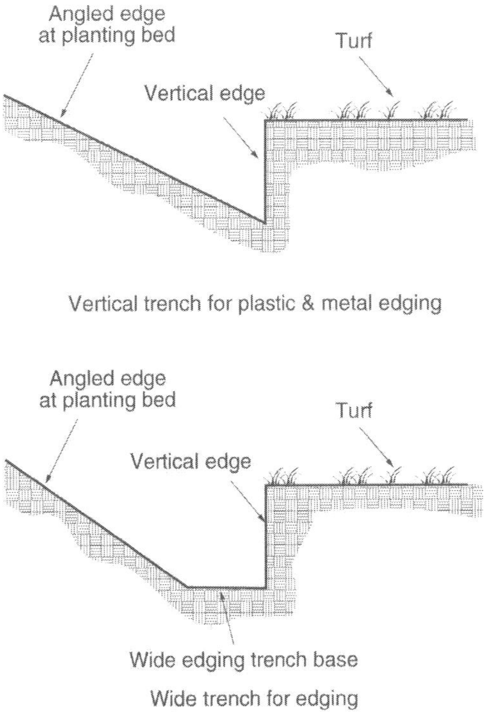

Figure 33-4 Cross section of edging trenches.

For large installations, rental of an edging machine is recommended. This piece of equipment cuts trenches with vertical and angled sides to the proper depth for plastic or metal edging (Figure 33-5). Additional blades are available that adapt the trench to wide materials or steeply angled trenches. The edging machine can be used to cut smooth radius corners and will save many hours of hand-digging. To operate the edging machine, mark the alignment of the edging and orient the machine with the rubber guard aimed toward the planting bed. Start the machine and gradually lower the cutting blade onto the alignment mark. Pull the edging machine slowly along the marking.

Edging Placement

Placement of specific edgings varies, depending on the material and type of installation. Installation techniques for many of the common edging materials are described in the following sections:

Natural Edges. A simple edge that conforms to any shape and requires little special preparation is the natural edge. Created by cutting a vertical

Figure 33-5 Excavation for edging using an edging machine.

trench with a shovel, natural edges join the planting bed with the lawn with no manufactured separator installed. Natural edges require periodic maintenance to keep the edge clean. Respading during the year is necessary as turf encroaches the planting bed.

Natural edges are created by using only the trench as a separation. Excavate the trench as instructed previously to a depth of 4 to 6 inches. Place the excavated material into the planting bed area. Continue this excavation along the entire length of the edging location. After the planting bed is tilled, fill the bed and trench with mulch.

Plastic Edging. One of the most commonly used edgings is the black plastic material manufactured in rolls and long strips. Flat and flexible, this edging can be bent to very tight radii, is installed with metal stakes, and has only the rounded bead on top visible after installation. The maintenance for plastic edging is high, as the edging is often worked up by frost and equipment and "shaved" by mowers.

Begin installation by placing a length of the edging flat against the vertical side of the trench. If the edging has a fold of plastic, or a V channel, place the fold to the planting bed side of the trench. Verify that the top of the edging, usually the rounded bead, is at the top of the trench and is set at the proper elevation. Place an edging stake in the V channel at the bottom of the edging. Holding the stake at a slight angle toward the turf area, drive the stake through the edging into the subgrade (Figure 33-6). Place edging stakes

Figure 33-6 Staking plastic edging by driving metal stakes through lip at bottom. Edging must be held flat against the edge of the trench with its top flush with finish grade.

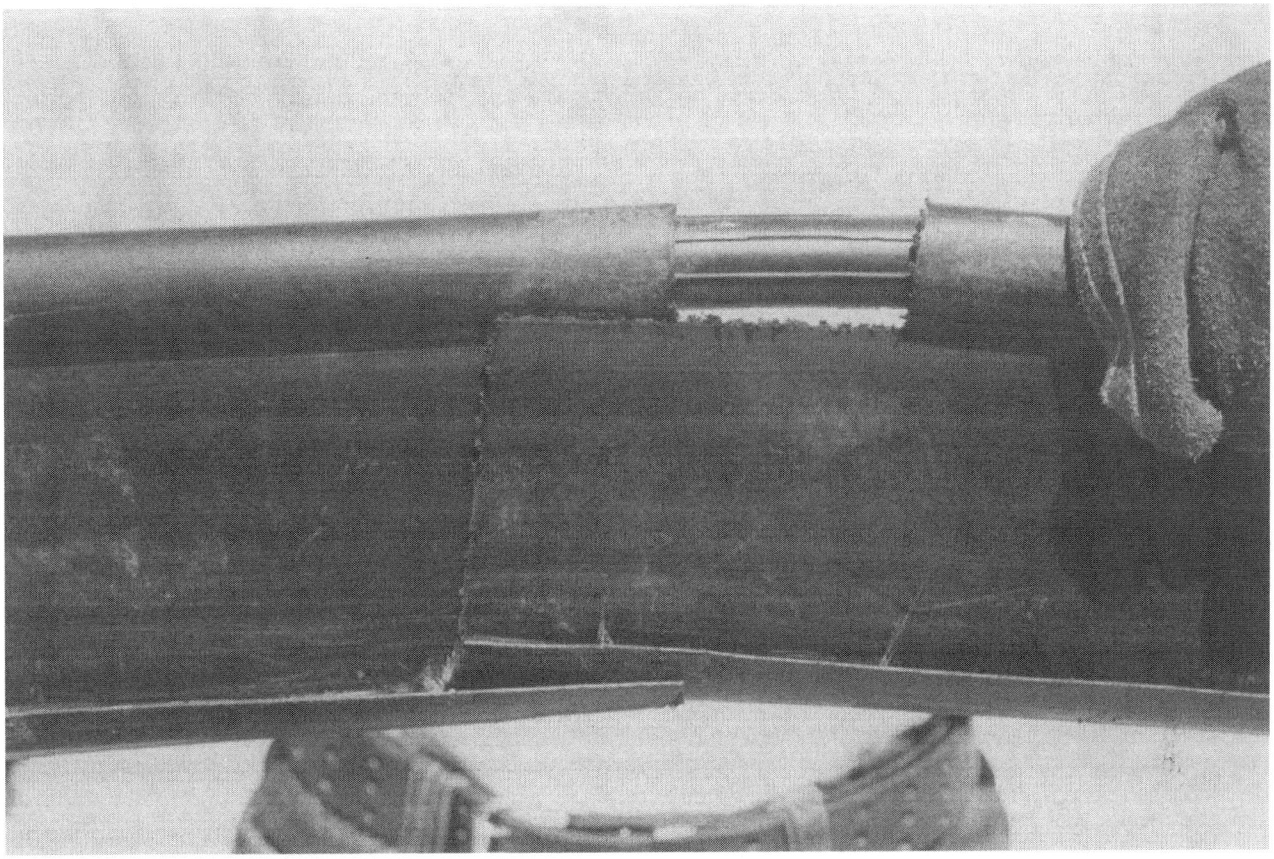

Figure 33-7 Joining pieces of plastic edging using tubing joiners supplied with edging kits. Notching the edging will improve connection.

every 2 feet along the length of the edging. Turn corners by bending the plastic edging around the corner. If the edging buckles when turning corners, cut 2-inch slits up from the bottom to **kerf** the edging.

Join pieces of edging by cutting 6 inches of the rounded bead off the top of one end of an edging piece. Verify that both pieces are facing the same direction. Push a joining tube halfway into the rounded bead of that piece of edging (Figure 33-7). Overlap the flat sections of edging and slide them together. Slide the remaining half of the joining tube into the rounded bead on the other piece of edging. Driving a nursery nail through the overlapped pieces will reduce the chances of unintentional separation. If smaller pieces of edging are required, measure and cut edging with a hacksaw or tin snips (Figure 33-8). Backfill and compact along the edge, leaving the grade on the planting bed side low enough to accommodate mulch.

Steel and Aluminum Edging. Steel or aluminum is a more permanent and higher priced choice for edging. Although not as flexible as plastic, metal edgings can still be used to wrap around corners or curves and is less likely to be worked up by frost or equipment.

Place a piece of metal edging in the trench flat against the vertical side and with the top at the desired finish elevation. Insert a stake through the slots in the edging and drive the stake straight down into the subgrade. Place stakes in every slot, typically every 2–3 feet. Turn corners by bending pieces at the proper location (Figure 33-9). Most aluminum and lightweight steel edgings bend

Figure 33-8 Cutting plastic edging using a hacksaw. Tin snips may also be used.

Figure 33-9 Turning corners with metal edging.

easily, but you may have to bend heavy steel edgings in a vise or cut them with a hacksaw halfway up from the bottom of the edging before they will bend. Measuring and bending before placement may make the process easier for heavy-duty edgings, but you must accurately measure the bends to achieve a proper fit.

Metal edgings typically have notches cut from each end of the pieces that interlock for joining. Some edgings are joined by hooking these notches together; others interlock using an edging stake (Figure 33-10). Make the connection with the pieces setting in the trench and continue staking. If smaller pieces of edging are required, measure and cut using a hacksaw (Figure 33-11). Backfill and compact along the edge, leaving the grade on the planting bed side low enough to accommodate mulch.

Figure 33-10 Joining pieces of metal edging using stakes provided by manufacturer.

Figure 33-11 Cutting metal edging using a hacksaw.

Vertical Brick Edging. Vertical bricks can be used for an edging for paved surfaces or planting areas. When stood on end, or edge, the bricks can introduce earthy textures and colors into the design, in addition to matching a paving material. Installation of brick edgings is more expensive and labor-intensive than installation of most edgings, but brick edgings are relatively maintenance-free when completed.

To install vertical brick edging, excavate the trench along the entire perimeter of the edged area the same depth as the long dimension of the bricks. The trench must form a vertical edge on the lawn side of the trench. Place a small amount of sand in the trench and place brick vertically against the sod edge. By adding or removing sand, adjust the height of the edging so that it is set at the desired elevation. Backfill and compact along the edge, leaving the planting bed side low enough to accommodate mulch. The installation will be more stable if you backfill with a small amount of mortar in place of soil. When the mortar hardens, cover it with soil. Turn corners by slightly flaring the brick, leaving small gaps between bricks at one end.

Flat Brick Edging. An alternative to the vertical brick edge is to place paving bricks flat, either edge to edge or end to end. This installation requires slightly less labor and material than installation of vertical brick edging.

Installation of a flat brick edging requires the excavation of a shallow trench the same depth as the brick thickness and 2 inches wider than the brick length. Flat brick edgings function nicely if the trench is angled up slightly on the planting bed side, leaving the bricks with a slight upward slant after installation. Place strips of landscape fabric in the trench before placing brick to reduce weed growth. Place the fabric flush with the outside edge of the trench and let it extend into the planting bed a few inches to overlap weed barrier placed in the bed. Place the bricks side by side, flat in the trench. Turn corners by fanning the brick around the corner, which will leave a small gap at the top or bottom between bricks. For a tighter fit around corners, diagonally trim every other brick with a wet masonry saw. If the trench is the proper depth, backfilling is usually not required. The installation will be more stable if you backfill with a small amount of mortar in place of soil.

Precast Block Edging. Manufactured concrete block can be used as an edging in almost any setting. Cast in a variety of colors and forms, these solid blocks are small enough to turn tight radii and are easy to work with. When properly installed, the precast units are low in maintenance.

Excavate a square or rectangular cross-section trench with a depth the same as the block height and 2 inches wider than the block width. Place strips of landscape fabric in the trench before placing blocks to reduce weed growth. Place the fabric flush with the lawn edge of the trench and let it extend into the planting bed a few inches to overlap the bed weed barrier.

Figure 33-12 Placement of precast concrete edging. This edging piece may be placed in straight or curved alignments.

Place the blocks end to end in the trench with one side flush with the lawn edge. Turn corners by fanning the block and leaving a small gap at the front or back of the block. Special block is available with shaped ends that interlock or alternate to form smooth straight and curved sections (Figure 33-12). The installation will be more stable if you backfill with a small amount of mortar in place of soil. Backfill the edging, leaving the bed side lower to accommodate mulch.

Concrete Curb Edging. Concrete curbing makes a durable and distinct edge for a planted area. Whether installed by hand or with a curbing machine, concrete provides a low-maintenance edge that blends with many design concepts. A variety of shapes and widths are also available with this choice. Price for curbing may be expensive as a result of equipment rental or hand labor required for forming.

To install curbing, begin by excavating a square, cross-section trench along the perimeter where the curb is to be placed. The depth should match the thickness of the edging selected. Place a small amount of granular backfill in the bottom of the trench to level the base. Construct forms (see concrete installation in Chapter 25) with the top set at the desired finish elevation. Pour concrete into the forms and tap the sides to settle the mixture. Complete filling and use a float or trowel to smooth and finish the top. After the concrete has hardened, remove forms and backfill, leaving the planting bed side lower to accommodate mulch.

If it is available, a curbing machine will speed the placement of curb edging. The curbing machine requires either that a trench be excavated to the depth of the edging or that the finish grade be built up after the edging is completed. No forms are required. A curbing machine places mixed concrete in a uniform shape along the path where the machine is operated. Finishing of the edging's top with a trowel is usually required.

Stone Block or Flagstone Edging. Wall stone or flagstone can also be used for edging planting beds. Using stone requires more extensive site preparation than done for plastic or metal edgings. Stone is more costly than most edgings but is relatively maintenance-free and attractive.

Stone block and flagstone are installed by excavating the trench the same depth as the thickness of the material and 2 inches wider. For irregular-shaped flagstone, excavate the trench the same width as the widest dimension of the stone. Place strips of landscape fabric in the trench before placing stone to reduce weed growth. Place the fabric flush with the lawn edge of the trench and let it extend into the planting bed a few inches to overlap weed barrier in the bed. Place the blocks end to end in the trench with one side flush with the lawn edge (Figures 33-13 and 33-14). With flagstone, select the straightest edge and place that edge along the lawn edge. Flagstone leaves an irregular inner edge with interesting shapes and lines. Turn corners using smaller pieces of stone. Backfill the edging, leaving the bed side lower to accommodate mulch.

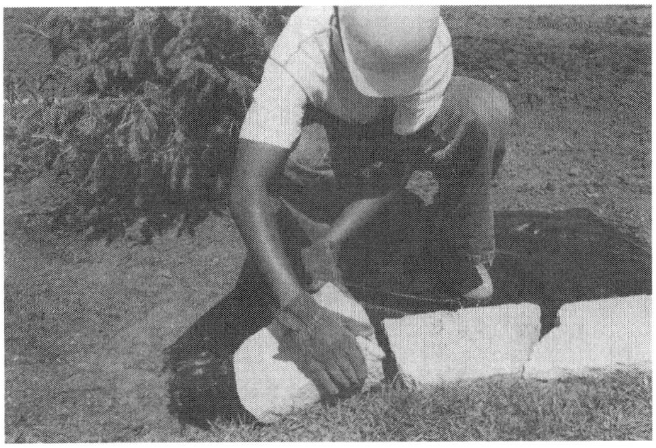

Figure 33-13 Edging with wall stone placed on weed barrier.

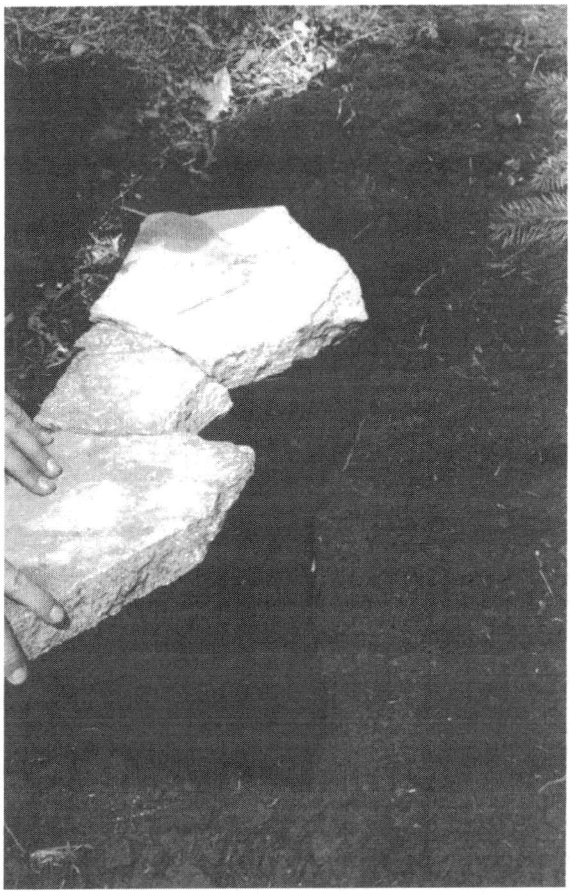

Figure 33-14 Edging with flagstone placed on weed barrier. Straight edge of flagstone is placed along turf edge, with irregular edge facing planting bed. Place edging flush with turf and sloping up into planting bed.

Composite Materials and Bender Board Edging. Bender boards and composite materials can be effective when used as edging for planting beds. Both materials are useful when edging curved applications or when a wood feel is desired. Although there are limitations on how tight a curve can be bent using these materials, they will traverse slopes and rounded edges that cannot be addressed when using wood. Both come in long strips and require decay-resistant wood stakes and rust-resistant fasteners to install.

To install composite materials or bender board, excavate a 6-inch wide trench slightly deeper than the edger width along the perimeter of the planting bed. Install treated 12-inch long 1 × 2 stakes every 18 inches along the desired alignment of the edging (Figure 33-15). The top of the stakes should be driven at least 1 inch below the top of the edging. Beginning at one end, hold the edging material to the stakes and drive galvanized 10d nails through the stake into the edging. If necessary, adjust the elevation of the stake before fastening. Substitute 2-inch rust-resistant screws for nails to minimize disturbance of the stake and to make a stronger connection.

Bender board is turned around corners by allowing the overlapping boards to slide past each other. This will leave one end with staggered boards. If the overlap from the next section does not fit with the staggered boards,

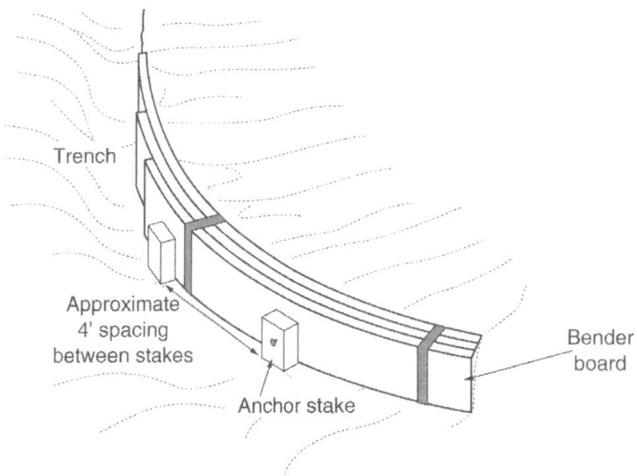

Figure 33-15 Anchoring of bender board.

trim the staggered end before continuing the next section. Composite materials can be left in the sun to improve their bending ability for corners.

Using a hacksaw, trim the edging to the proper length before installing the final section. When sections require jointing, drive stakes at the end of each abutting section. If the sections are manufactured with interlocking joints, connect the pieces and place an additional stake at the joint. Backfill the outside and planting bed side of the edging.

Wood Edging. Relatively inexpensive and low in maintenance once installed, wood presents a natural material choice for edging beds. Wood edgers can be difficult in installations that have undulating slopes and curved edges. Wood edging can also be damaged by mowers and maintenance equipment. Use only treated or decay-resistant lumbers that will contact the soil.

To install wood edging, select a decay-resistant, dimensioned lumber, typically a 2 × 6, and cut to length for each section to be edged. Cut enough 1-foot long 1 × 2 treated stakes to place one at both ends of each edging piece and one every 2 feet along the perimeter. Excavate a vertical trench 8 inches deep along the edging alignment. Place the wood edging in the trench tightly against the vertical side and at the desired elevation. Attach a stake at each end of the edging to stabilize the piece. Holding the stakes tightly against the edging, drive the stakes into the subgrade (Figure 33-16). Hide the tops of all stakes by driving them 1 inch below the top of the edging. Drive form nails through the stake into the edging. Adjust to the desired elevation by prying the edging up with a shovel or driving the stakes down. After edging elevation is set, place additional stakes every 2 feet and nail them to the edging. Backfill on both sides of the edge, leaving the planting side low enough to accommodate mulch.

Turn corners by butting one section of edging into another and end nailing to hold the two pieces together. Joining two sections is strengthened by nailing a treated 1 × 4 stake across the joint on the back side of the two pieces being joined.

An alternative to staked wood edgers is treated 4 × 4s or 6 × 6s as edging material. These edgers require a trench excavated to the same depth and width as the material. Place the material in the trench and backfill. Turn corners by cutting short pieces of material and placing them fanned along the curve alignment. No staking is required.

Figure 33-16 Staking for wood edging. Place end stakes and adjust for level. Joints should overlap a single stake.

INSTALLING PLANTERS

To install plants in interior or in certain exterior applications, planters may be required. Planters come in square, rectangular, or round shapes, with custom shapes available, and are made of wood, metal, terra cotta, fiberglass, and precast concrete. Although typically designed to set on a paved surface without any further anchoring, some planters require anchoring to slabs and others are permanently built into projects.

Prefabricated Planters

Planter installation requires unpacking, possibly assembling, and placing at the appropriate locations throughout the site (Figure 33-17). If the planter is anchored at a specific location, anchor bolts should be placed during the paving portion of the project. When anchor bolts are preplaced, cover with Styrofoam painted a fluorescent color to reduce potential damage from traffic. Because outdoor surfaces are usually sloped for drainage, level placement of planters may require the use of permanent shims. Use a carpenter's level placed on a horizontal surface of the planter to determine the amount of shimming required. Break off a shim the correct thickness, lift the empty planter, and slide the shim underneath. Multiple shims may be required to level in all directions. If planters must be lifted and adjusted several times, use double-stick tape to hold the shims at the correct location on the bottom of planters. Tuck shims under the edge so they are not visible from the side.

Figure 33-17 Planters in an urban plaza. Many planters are placed on pavement without anchors.

Built-In Planters

Landscape projects occasionally make use of built-in planters, which are typically enclosed retaining walls that have been backfilled with planting soil to support plant growth. Walls for planter construction should be constructed using the same techniques described in Section 5. When constructing walls for built-in planters, accommodations for drainage may be required. To drain excess water from the planter, extend a perforated drain tile around the entire interior perimeter of the wall. Connect to an underground tile or storm sewer or drain through an opening in the wall.

INSTALLING TREE GRATES AND TREE GUARDS

Cast metal grids that are placed at openings in walkways where plant material is to be installed, tree grates allow the water and air necessary to sustain plant growth to pass through what would otherwise be a paved surface. Tree grates have enough solid surface that they can support foot traffic. Working in conjunction with tree grates are tree guards, which are metal enclosures that form a protective surrounding for tree trunks. Guards protect trees from damage from contact with vehicles, bikes, and other types of traffic. Tree guards are usually installed with tree grates.

Follow manufacturer's specifications when installing tree grates and tree guards. Installation requires preliminary work during the paving stage of the construction process. Tree grates are placed on a frame that is set into the paving around the plant opening. The paving used to place this frame can be part of the walkway, or it can be a curb poured installed separately from the walk (Figure 33-18). Although the grate frame and a separate curb can be installed after the walk installation is complete, this will require additional forming and delivery of paving materials. The opening for the grate frame needs to be constructed to the correct size and the frame placed at the proper depth for the tree grate to set flush with adjacent paving. Verify with the manufacturer the dimensions of the tree grate prior to forming the walk or curb that will support the frame.

Figure 33-18 Curbing with tree grate in place. This curb was formed and poured separately from the walk and included a lip on which the grate was placed.

Figure 33-19 Tree grate sections bolted together. Sections of guards are placed around the tree and bolted together, then bolted to the tree grate.

Before placing any plant material in the tree grate opening, excavate all undesirable fill material from the hole and replace it with suitable planting soil. After plant material has been installed, the tree grate may be placed on the curbing. Grates come in two or more sections to fit around the tree. If the design requires, bolt the two sections together with rust-resistant hardware. Manufacturers typically design grates so that when the opening is too small for plant material, interior rings can be cut from the grate. Use a cutoff saw with a carbide blade to remove enough inner rings to accommodate plant size. Tree guards come in two pieces and are bolted together and then to the tree grate for stability (Figure 33-19). Use touch-up paint if required to repair any finish damage.

SECTION 8

SUMMARY

Although other elements of sitework create the major functional framework for a design, site amenities create the finishing details of the hardscape. In Section 8, the installation of several common amenities was discussed. Although the variety of site amenity treatments is extensive, the most common installations include use of water as a design feature, bridges, site furniture, play equipment, outdoor kitchens, edgings, and plant protection devices such as tree grates and tree guards.

Because decorative water features are so creatively and diversely used in the landscape, attempting to classify uses of water can be difficult. For the purposes of this text, water-related features were grouped into flexible and rigid liner decorative pools, waterfalls, cascades and fountains. Preparation for these features requires planning the layout to accommodate the topography, electrical sources, water sources, drain installation, and recirculation piping.

Installation of flexible and rigid liner decorative pools is accomplished by marking the location for the pool and excavating a basin into which the liner is placed. Flexible liners can have variable levels and shapes, whereas rigid liners require excavation to the predetermined size and shape. Liners are placed and leveled, then edge treatments are applied to hide the top edge of the pool. Pools are filled and ready to operate. Submersible pumps are used if water is to be recirculated to other basins. Lighting filters and fountains can be added to enhance the installation.

Waterfalls require the construction of one or more basins into which water can fall. A lower basin to receive water is required and, in many waterfalls, an upper basin to supply water is also installed. Decorative pool construction techniques can be used to create the water fall basins. The water source and recirculation mechanism must be designed and tested to ensure that the desired amount of water will circulate into the lower basin. At the top of the falls, an engineered opening, called a weir, controls the amount of water that passes over the falls. If multiple basins or multiple falls are part of the design, the channels between these elements must also be constructed to conduct the proper amount of water. Cascades are constructed in a manner similar to construction of waterfalls. A lower basin captures water that spills down a gently sloped channel. When waterfalls and cascades are constructed using liners, the surfaces and edges are typically covered with landscape material to hide the liner and to create a natural appearance.

Fountains and lighting can be placed in decorative pools as stationary elements or floated onto the water. Each installation requires proper sizing of the pool, a pump motor, and a supply of electricity to the fountain pump. Bridge installation by the landscape contractor is typically restricted to crossings of minor water features. Both custom-built and premanufactured bridges are available to span pools, ponds, and small streams.

Installation of site furniture and premanufactured play equipment begins with the accurate layout of the amenity. Amenities purchased may require assembly according to factory instructions and exact tolerances for placement of anchors and posts. Amenities typically have posts that are either directly buried in the ground, connected to a concrete slab using anchor bolts placed when the slab was poured, or anchored on top of a frost footing. Each anchoring method requires that the posts resist frost action. Certain amenities may require that conduit for supplying electrical wiring or reinforcing be placed by specialty contractors when frost footings are poured. Play equipment also requires the placement of a resilient surfacing below and around the equipment. Some manufacturers require field finishing or touch-up of metal amenities.

The home is enhanced through the addition of amenities such as outdoor kitchens, firepits, and outdoor fireplaces. The great outdoor spaces created through all of the paving and construction receive the final touches when the family can prepare meals, dine, relax, and enjoy the exterior spaces in the same comforts as they do the interior spaces of a home. Outdoor kitchens require extensive planning and complex construction when building a custom cabinet that houses grills, sinks, and refrigerators and often require the expertise of design professionals and specialty contractors. Firepits require the construction of a surround to contain the fire and accommodation of a natural or gas-fueled flame.

Amenities related to plant installation include edgings, planters, tree grates, and tree guards. Natural edging is accomplished by excavating a clean border between planting beds and turf. Permanent edging installation requires excavation of a trench and placement of the edging material flat against the turf side of the trench. Plastic edging is joined using short tubes and anchored using metal stakes driven through the edging. Metal edgings are overlapped and joined with a metal stake driven through a slot in both adjoining pieces. Metal stakes are driven along the length of the edging to secure it. Wood edging, bender board, and composite material are anchored at each end, and at regular intervals, using wood stakes. Other edgings, including bricks, stone, and precast concrete, are installed by laying them edge to edge in the trench and backfilling. Edging can also be accomplished using a curbing machine that lays a shaped bead of concrete in an excavated trench. When planting beds are edged, weed barriers can be installed to reduce unwanted plant growth.

Planters are typically placed in the proper location, filled with soil, and planted. In certain locations, planters may require leveling to match pavement grades. Tree grates require a castin-place concrete curb to support the framework for the grate. The framework is set in the curb and the grate is set in place after plant material is installed. Many frames come in two or more pieces that are bolted together. Tree guards come in two pieces and are placed around the tree, bolted together, and bolted to the tree grate.

SECTION 9

PLANTING

INTRODUCTION

Few landscape projects can be considered complete without the addition of plant material. With endless attention paid to developing a site's hardscape, it is the plant material that truly adds life to a project. To accomplish this phase of the project, contractors must shift their thinking from working with inanimate objects to working with living organisms. Regardless of the planting method they use, contractors must understand the environment in which plants are to be placed. Knowing the soil conditions, how to properly place plants, maintaining appropriate irrigation, and initiating post-planting care programs are the basis of creating longterm, healthy plant installations.

The chapters of this section address planting in two steps: installing plant material and establishing turf areas. Installing plant material will describe the installation of bare-root, container, balled and burlapped, boxed, and machine-moved plant material. This range of methods covers the majority of transplanting methods currently available within the industry. This chapter will also address site preparation, soil amendment, and installation of plants in difficult situations. Also included in this chapter is information regarding more recent additions to the sustainability movement, green roofs and living walls.

Turf establishment includes the starting of lawns, prairies, pastures, and roadsides using seeding, sodding, or plugging/sprigging techniques. Also included in this section are the preparation of the site and specialty seeding techniques such as hydroseeding.

SUSTAINABILITY SUGGESTIONS

- Mulch plantings and planted areas to reduce evapotranspiration and weed growth.
- Encourage the use of Integrated Pest Management (IPM) to maintain plantings.
- Consider naturally occurring and organic soil amendments when modifying the soil.
- Compost any plant trimmings made during this phase of construction if feasable.
- If allowed to select plant material, select native and locally adapted non-invasive plants that are drought tolerant.
- Plant for diversity; include plants that will attract beneficial organisms to the garden to help control pests.
- Space plant material appropriately.
- Select plant material that is disease-resistant.

CHAPTER 34

PLANT MATERIAL INSTALLATION

OBJECTIVES

By reading and practicing the techniques described in this chapter, the reader should be able to successfully complete the following activities:

- Evaluate plants for installation.
- Prepare planting beds.
- Install plants that are bare-root, containerized, balled and burlapped, boxed, and machine moved.
- Care for plants after installation.
- Describe the process for installing green roofs and living walls.

Planting a site is usually reserved for near the end of the landscaping process. Once all the hardscape has been installed, the irrigation is operational, the amenities are complete, and the structures are probably occupied, plant installers are asked to ply their trade. But despite this step being near the end of the process, the impact of plant installation, along with turf establishment, often provides the most dramatic change. The walkways, walls, structures, lights, and other site elements take on meaning once spaces are created, framed, and backdropped with plantings. As dramatic as the initial change might appear, over time the impact of a successful planting will even further enhance the site.

Installing plant material has evolved through the advent of modern plant growing methods and the availability of equipment to dig, move, and install plants. The creation of a site with canopy and bloom is a blend of the work of artists and craftspeople with the laborer, engineer and landscape architect.

RELATED INFORMATION

Information in this chapter is supplemented by instruction provided elsewhere in this text and in other sources. Before undertaking the activities described in this chapter, read the related information in these sources:

- Basic Soils for Landscape Contractors, Chapter 12
- Site Drainage, Chapter 15
- North Carolina Manual of Professional Horticultural Practice

SELECTING PLANT MATERIAL

Quality plantings require quality plants. When working with living organisms such as plant material, landscape contractors need to place the right plant in the right place; otherwise, there will be no successful plantings. Although much of a job's success relies on a designer's ability to choose plants that will culturally and aesthetically perform, determining the right plant will also depend on evaluating the health of the plant material to be installed. Whether inspecting plants in a nursery or as they are set off the delivery truck, completing a stock inspection before purchasing, accepting, or installing plants will boost the chances of success.

The ANSI standards for nursery stock (ANSI Z60. 1-2004) and the American Standard for Nursery Stock, published by AmericanHort, serve as the current minimum standard for evaluating the size, species, and vigor of plant material. Keep in mind that these are minimum standards. Different nurseries have different goals and their standards may vary. They all must meet minimum standards but some may strive to provide the highest quality that goes beyond minimum standards.

When evaluating stock, above ground components to review include the correct species and cultivar, straight trunk, single strong leader,

Figure 34-1 Inspecting the root zone of a container plant.

proper proportion, proper growth for that container size (typically determined by caliper or number of stems/canes), proper number of branches that are evenly spaced around the trunk, absence of pests and diseases, strong branch unions, proper color and healthy, well-shaped leaves, overall good appearance, and similar characteristics. Remove the plant from any metal or plastic container (not applicable for balled and burlapped plants) and inspect the root zone (Figure 34-1). In the root zone, look for girdling roots, dry or dead spots, pests, and moist fibrous roots. Specifications may also include additional plant requirements such as density, specific branching height (for placement along walks and streets) or for plant material that is matched (similar height, form, and branching characteristics).

PREPLANTING CARE

In the world of construction, having materials show up the instant they are required is not the standard. Having materials arrive late can be devastating, but having materials arrive before they are needed creates new problems, especially when those materials are plants. Unlike hardscape that can be set in a secure storage area and largely ignored until used, plant material must be maintained on a daily basis until it is planted.

Initially, contractors should determine whether they will accept plant material prior to installation date. Many plants cannot be stored, and how long those that are held can be stored will depend on the type of plant. Timelines for larger jobs may necessitate that plants be held for several days while the installation work progresses. Trees, shrubs, perennials, and most annuals and ground covers that arrive early can be stored with proper care for up to 2 weeks and show few detrimental effects. This would include plants that are in flats, containerized, balled and burlapped, and boxed. Larger containerized trees and shrubs can be stored much longer. In contrast, bare-root plants require continual moisture and benefit from refrigeration. These plants should be planted immediately upon delivery. Trees that are machine moved are for direct relocation only and

Figure 34-2 Plants staged in a storage area.

cannot be stored. B & B (balled and burlapped) plant material can be stored with proper handling and care. Seed and dry materials can also be stored in a dry, cool place for an indefinite period; but sod should not be ordered or accepted for delivery prior to its scheduled installation. Sod will start to deteriorate immediately and should not be store . In whatever location you store them, all plants should be kept in a secure area to reduce the chances of theft (Figure 34-2).

Whenever plants arrive, insure they have been protected from wind-causing dessication during delivery, and that there is no shipping damage such as scraped bark or broken limbs. To protect plants that arrive early, maintain them in an upright position, keep their roots cool and moist and protect them from physical damage and injury from excess light, heat, and wind. Just as plants are protected during their transport to a site, the storage area must also create a safe growing environment. If possible, storage in an area that is similar to the conditions where the plants will ultimately be placed will help with "hardening off" (the process of plants adapting to new environmental conditions). Place the plants in the storage area and water them thoroughly. Depending on conditions, it may be advantageous to mulch plants to maintain moisture. Set up a temporary irrigation system that will water at least once a day, and add supplemental water when needed. Until you plant them, check the plants on a daily basis to ensure proper moisture, that plants are not setting in water, and that no pest or other physical condition is inflicting damage on them. Once accepted on a job site, plants become the landscape contractor's financial responsibility.

PREPARING SOIL FOR PLANTING

For a plant to survive, it must adapt to its new permanent environment in the soil. To facilitate the plant's survival, many believe that the soil around the plant should be modified to encourage vigorous growth. Others believe that because the plant must eventually adapt to soil present at the new location, little or no soil preparation should be done, except for pH modifications if necessary. This argument over soil preparation for planting has been ongoing for decades, and it will most likely continue well beyond the life of any plant the contractor will install. This text sides with neither position but, instead, provides the information necessary to modify planting beds and planting soil if so required or desired. This information is offered even if the contractor chooses to use unaltered site soil as backfill material when planting.

As noted in Chapter 12, the average content of organic matter in North Carolina soils is often under 2 percent, and a healthy planting soil has 5 percent organic matter. This 5 percent optimum is not always achievable due to various constraints. Ultimately, in many contracting situations, the landscape designer's specifications will determine the soil processes for the project.

Know Your Soil

Before planting activities begin, it is important to understand the type of soil that is present on your site. The North Carolina Department of Agriculture and Consumer Services offers soil testing services, and samples can be analyzed for specific types of plantings (http://www.ncagr.gov/agromoni/sthome.htm). Soils are rarely homogenous across a site, so several samples should be taken to achieve a good understanding of all the site soils. Testing requires time to complete, so submit samples well in advance of beginning work.

Plant Bed Preparation

In fortunate situations you will encounter a site that has uncompacted soils with a hight organic content requiring no special site preparation for installation in the landscape. However, in many cases you will run into soil that has poor characteristics or has been damaged and compacted from construction activities. A landscape contractor should review soil conditions on a site before beginning planting installations. If the soil is damaged and in poor condition, remediation is recommended to enhance the plants survivability. Project specifications may dictate soil preparation and the manner in which it is to occur, but without good soil plants will struggle to perform.

The first situation the landscape contractor should examine is the degree of compaction in the soil. If equipment and traffic have been traversing the planting area it will typically require some degree of restoration before planting. The best solution for heavy compaction is a combination of deep soil ripping and surface tilling. Deep soil ripping can be done with a small backhoe blade or a frost blade. The soil is ripped is a criss-cross pattern to a depth of 18", then the surface is returned to finish grade.

Often times sites are limited in accessibility for larger equipment that can effect this process. Most landscaping tools, at best, reach depths of 6 inches. Deep ripping is often only achievable optimum with additional resources and not always available as a solution to compaction.

Tilling the soil as deeply as feasible will repair compacted surface soils. Note that excessive tillage also damages soil structure, particularly in soils with clay content. Tilling breaks apart the naturally bound peds of soil leaving fine particles of dust that are more subject to erosion. Excessive tillage also breaks apart the biological components of the soil that are present to facilitate soil ped formation and decomposition. Till only enough to blend in amendments and to make the soil more workable.

Preparation may be required for any category of plant material to be installed. Annual and ground cover beds, masses of perennials, decorative grasses, and shrubs do better when landscape contractors prepare the entire root zone area to assist plant growth. To prepare the bed, identify the edge and remove any sod or other plant growth covering the area. By hand, using a garden fork or using a rototiller, till the bed to a depth of 6-12 inches (the deeper the better). Once tilled, spread the pH and fertilizer amendments called for in the soil test. If organic matter is to be incorporated, spread that material evenly over the entire area and till all materials in to a depth of 6 – 12 inches. When complete, rake smooth and lightly compact the soil. Locations for planting trees and shrubs may require the deep soil ripping described above in the locale where plants are to be installed. Lawn areas may require preparation of the entire area to be planted.

Plant Soil Amendments

A wide range of choices exist for backfill soil used in planting. In reference to the argument made in the first paragraph of this section, many people are adamant about backfilling around newly installed plants with the same soil that was removed from the planting hole. Other references will recommend that the site soil be amended with compost or other organic materials and utilized for backfill.

This amended backfill may also include slow-release starter fertilizer and pH adjustment material (Figure 34-3). Although there is no perfect answer, a few characteristics of backfill have been recognized as helping plants establish themselves in a new environment. These characteristics include:

- Backfill that is placed around the plant should be friable and lightly compacted without leaving air holes around the plant.
- Any fertilizer added should be in small quantities and should be slow-release.
- Naturally occurring compounds such as compost can provide essential nutrients without creating fertilizer "burn."
- Do not used 'screened' soils as backfill. Screening of soil, as required by some specifications to reduce clods, damages the soil structure.

INSTALLING PLANTS

Once the site, plant material, and amendments are prepared, installation of the plants can begin.

Figure 34-3 Soil staged to backfill a plant. The soil and amendments have not yet been blended.

Figure 34-4 Placing plants for inspection.

CAUTION

Locate all utilities in the planting area prior any soil disturbance. *Always* call NC811 for location of utilities lines or cables before performing *any* work at a site.

Layout of Planting Areas

Plant installation begins with locating the plants on the site. Several layout methods are available, with the simplest being setting the plants in the locations where they are to be installed (Figure 34-4). This allows the designer to identify any problems and adjust plant locations prior to planting. In more specific situations such as planting beds and ground cover areas, plantings may be laid out using stringlines or lines painted on the ground.

Spacing of plant material is often specified on a planting plan or in a plant schedule. Typical dimensions and terms used include the abbreviation *O.C.*, which stands for "on center" and identifies the distance between the centers of plants; grid spacing, which will identify the spacing between rows and columns of plants; and triangular spacing. Triangular spacing is particular to plant material and is commonly used to position plants to avoid the open space left between plants when installed in a grid pattern. Triangular spacing places the rows slightly closer than the diameter of the plant and offsets the plants in every other row to a position halfway between the plants in neighboring rows.

Excavation of Planting Holes

Excavating a good planting hole is as essential to plant survival as selecting a quality plant. A plant often fails to survive because it was installed too high or low, the planting hole was undersized, or the hole was not properly prepared. To excavate a hole for installing plant material, begin by setting the plant(s) in the desired location. If the plant is small, use spray paint or other material to mark a circle around the container. If the plant is larger (1 gallon and up), mark an *X* over the spot with the legs of the *X* extending at least 2 feet beyond the plant (Figure 34-5). This extra marking will allow you to locate the center of the hole after excavation. If planting in an area where minimal disturbance of the surrounding landscape is desired, cut a 4-foot by 4-foot piece of landscape fabric on which to place excavated soil and to mix backfill (Figure 34-6).

Figure 34-5 Layout of plant material for planting. Where the legs of the *X* cross is the center of the plant. Extending the legs of the *X* beyond the hole allows the center to be located after excavation.

Figure 34-6 Using a drop cloth to store excavation and backfill material.

Figure 34-7 Excavating a planting hole.

Using a shovel or backhoe, dig the hole to the proper diameter (Figures 37-7). Larger plant material (4-inch caliper or larger, 36-inch box or larger) will benefit from using a backhoe to excavate the planting hole. The hole should be at least twice as wide as the rootball and the same shape as the container.

Excavate the hole to the proper depth. Determine the proper depth by measuring either the level of the soil in the container or the distance from the bottom of the root-ball to the soil line on the plant trunk. Once you have excavated the hole, examine the sides of the hole for glazing of any clay soils. If the sides have been smoothed and compacted by excavation, use a mattock to scarify the surface. Place the plant on the undisturbed soil in the bottom of the hole. If you make a mistake on planting depth, it is better to plant too high rather than too low. Fill can be placed around the plant if it is too high; but if the plant is installed too low, it is cannot be corrected.

If the planting is in heavy clay soil, an urban location, or other situation where drainage is poor, consider installing open French drains in the area (see Chapter 15 – Site Drainage/Subsurface Drainage). The drainage tiles should come in contact with the bottom of the planting hole and should drain to daylight at a minimum of 2 percent grade. If it is not possible to run the drainage to daylight, consider excavating one or more sumps in the bottom of the planting hole. Create a sump by excavating a hole 8 inches in diameter and 3 feet deep using a posthole excavator or auger. Fill that hole with large, rounded drainage rock and cover the hole with landscape fabric. The sump(s) will hold excess water away from the root zone in poor draining areas. If the planting location is in heavy clay soil, another technique that can be used is to fill the planting hole with water and wait until the hole drains before planting. If the hole has not drained in 1 day, other options such as sumps or subdrainage should be considered to protect the plant from excess water.

Other situations can arise in a plant installation operation that require special techniques. One such situation is planting on a hillside. Although shrubs and smaller plants are planted with the slope of the hillside, trees will appear out of plumb if similarly planted. To plant trees on a hillside and maintain the trunk in a vertical position, bench the area where the planting hole is placed prior to digging the hole. Benching requires a minor cut and fill operation above and below the center of the planting hole. Excavate on the back half of the planting area

Figure 34-8 Planting on a hillside.

and transfer that soil to fill on the front half (Figure 34-8). Bench an area wide enough to accommodate the planting holc plus an additional 1 foot apron. Then excavate the planting hole in the newly created level area. When the tree is placed, verify that it is on the original soil, not the fill added from above the hole. If the soil is unstable, then you may need to move the hole farther into the hill or possibly build a tree well to create a level planting area.

Installation of plants that are too large for one or two people to move will also require special techniques and equipment. For large plants, one technique is to place a heavy wood plank at the edge of the hole and slide the plant down the plank into the planting hole. A second method is to excavate a small ramp on one side of the planting hole so that the plant can be pulled or rolled into the planting hole. Another technique is lifting the plant and the root-ball supported by a chain sling (Figure 34-9) or tow straps with a skid-steer, backhoe, or crane. Tow straps can be worked under the root-ball/container by lifting one side and sliding a strap under, lowering the plant, and repeating on the opposite side. The forks of a skid-steer can then be positioned under the chains, and the plant can be lifted and placed in the hole. It is important to not damage the root ball during these operations.

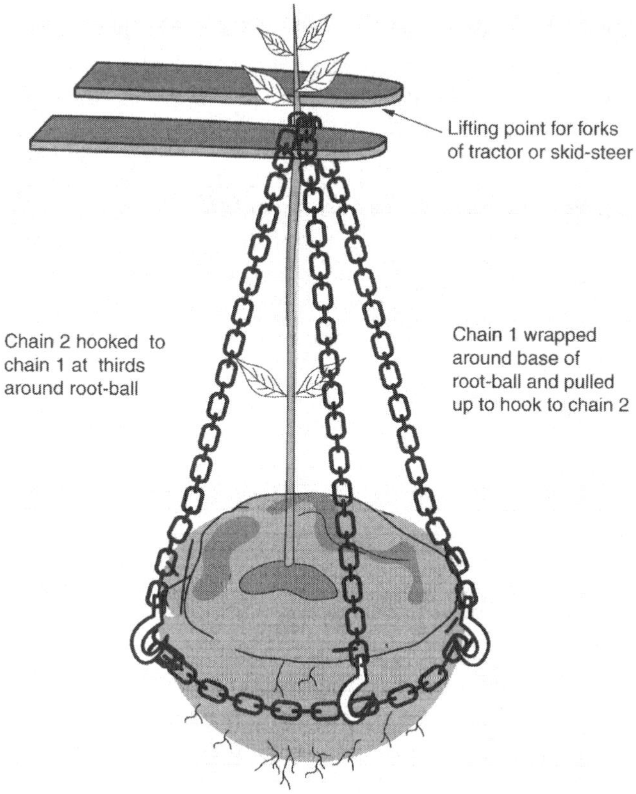

Figure 34-9 Chain sling for lifting heavy objects.

> **CAUTION**
>
> When lifting any plant material, verify that all lifting devices are secure. Never pass under a suspended plant.

Installation of Bare-Root Plants

Bare-root is a common method for supplying contractors with roses, berry plants, small fruit trees, and certain perennials. In simple terms, bare-root is a plant that has had the growing medium removed from the roots. Only certain plants have roots vigorous enough to overcome the removal of soil, but packaging in such a manner greatly reduces the shipping costs for those plants. Bare-root plants can be installed anytime during the year, but installing while the plant is dormant or just emerging from dormancy is the optimum planting time. Before planting bare-root plants, remove the plant from its packaging and remove any sawdust, moss, or other packaging from the roots. Place the roots in a bucket filled with water and a quart of soil, and leave them in this "gravy" mixture for at least 2 hours and up to 24 hours before planting. This technique will rehydrate the roots and help stimulate new growth from the root hairs.

To install bare-root stock, use the following steps (Figure 34-10):

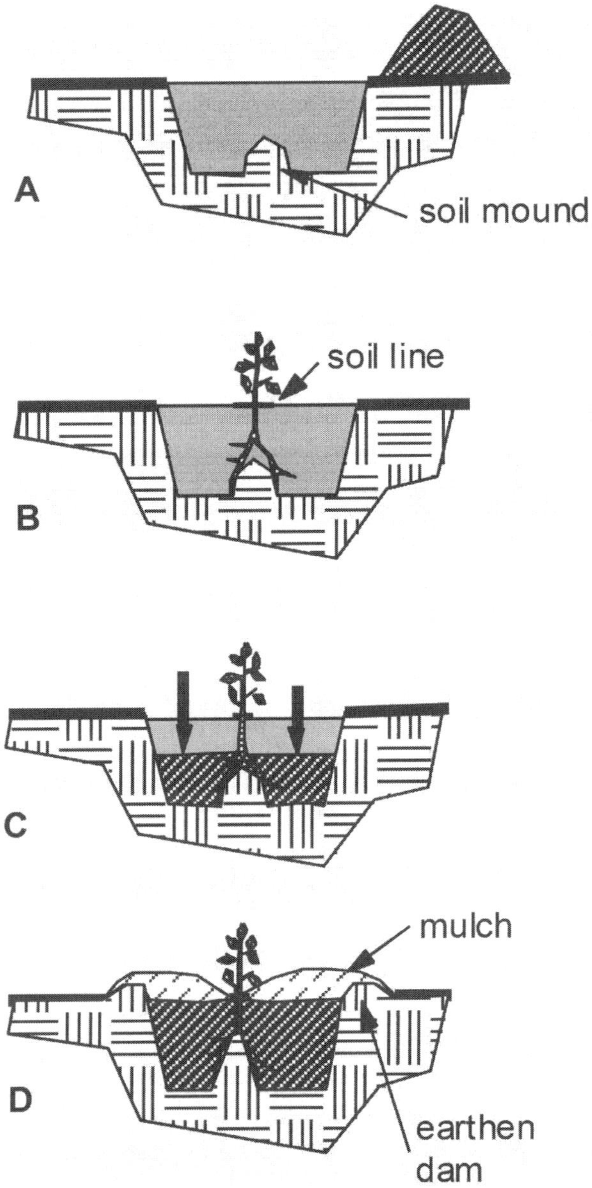

Figure 34-10 Installation of bare-root plant material.

- Excavate the planting hole (A). Slope the sides of the hole and scarify the sides of the hole.
- Amend backfill soil if intending to do so.
- In the center of the hole, create a cone-shaped mound of soil. The height of the cone should be approximately half the depth of the planting hole.
- Remove the plant from the soaking bucket.
- Prune any damaged roots and stems.
- Orient the plant with the best side facing forward (B).
- Spread the roots evenly over the soil cone (Figure 34-11, B).
- Hold the plant at the graft or soil mark while backfilling.
- Gently backfill ½–⅔ of the hole.
- Adjust the planting depth if necessary to assure the plant will be 1 inch above the surrounding grade after planting. Adjust the plant depth by gently pulling up on the plant's trunk.
- Compact the backfill by foot or by using the handle end of a shovel (C).
- Complete the backfilling and compact (D).
- Avoid placing soil on top of the roots and around the collar area of the trunk. The trunk flare should be clearly visible.
- Remaining soil can be used to build a temporary berm around the perimeter of the planting hole, creating a basin for watering.
- Water and mulch the plant.

Installation of Container Plants

Container-grown plant material now dominates the landscape industry. Reasons for growing plants in containers include consistency of growing medium, ease in transplanting, and less weight for shipping. Container stock now accounts for the vast majority of plants installed

Figure 34-11 Bare-root plant with roots spread over soil cone in planting hole.

in landscapes. A wide variety of containers can be found in service, ranging from 2-inch square "cells" in a growing flat to nursery containers of up to 200 gallons.

To install container-grown stock, use the following steps (Figure 34-12):

- Excavate the planting hole (A) no deeper than the container. Slope the sides of the hole and scarify the sides of the hole.
- Amend backfill soil if intending to do so.
- Place the plant near the planting hole.
- Carefully remove the plant from the container (Figure 34-13). For small containers up to 4 inches, place a hand under the container and squeeze the plant out. For larger containers, set the container on its side and grasp the plant by the base of the trunk or stem. Pull to remove the plant. If the plant will not come out of the container, slap the container with the heel of your hand on several sides and pull again. If the plant will still not come out, cut away the container using tin snips.
- Examine the roots and remove or straighten any girdling roots. Scarify the root-ball if compacted root growth exists.
- Set the plant in the hole on undisturbed soil (Figure 34-14, B).
- Orient the plant with the best side forward.

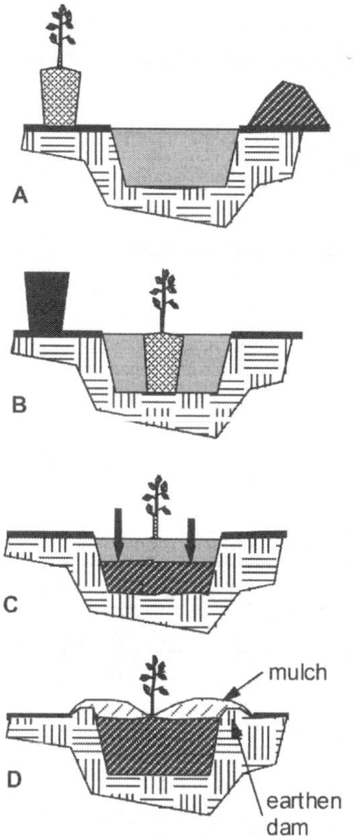

Figure 34-12 (Above) Installation of container plants. **Figure 34-13 (Below)** Removing plant from container.

- Adjust the plant to proper depth by either removing soil under the root-ball with your hand or tipping the plant and adding soil. If the plant is large, you may need to make several smaller adjustments to raise or lower the plant and maintain proper orientation and plumb.

Figure 34-14 Container plant placed in a planting hole.

- Backfill half of the hole and lightly compact with foot or with the handle end of a shovel (C).
- Verify that the plant is at the correct planting depth, slightly above the surrounding grade. Adjust the height of the plant if necessary.
- Complete the backfilling and lightly compact (D).
- Avoid placing soil on top of the root ball and around the collar area of the trunk. The trunk flare should be clearly visible.
- Remaining soil can be used to build a temporary berm around the perimeter of the planting hole, creating a basin for watering.
- Water and mulch the plant.

Installation of Balled and Burlapped Plants

Field-grown plant material is typically harvested using a method called **balling and burlapping,** or B & B. B & B uses one or more large sheets of burlap to protect and contain the root-ball of the excavated plant, often with twine or a metal basket supplementing the burlap containment. Although B & B is reasonably stable, exercise care when handling B & B stock to avoid breaking the root-ball and roots contained within.

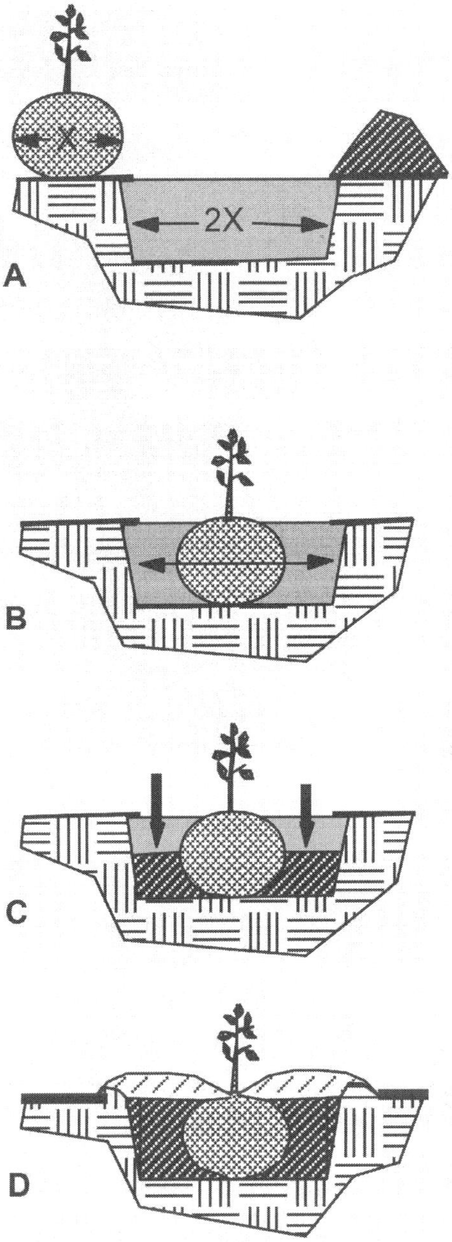

Figure 34-15 Installation of balled and burlapped plants.

To install balled and burlapped stock, use the following steps (Figure 34-15):

- Excavate the planting hole (A) no deeper than the container. Slope the sides of the hole and scarify the sides of the hole.
- Amend backfill soil if intending to do so.

Figure 34-16 Installation of balled and burlapped plants.

Figure 34-17 Installation of balled and burlapped plants.

- Position the plant near the hole and determine the best orientation and depth for the plant. Adjustments are easier to make at this stage, rather than waiting until the plant has been lowered into the hole.
- Place the plant in the planting hole on undisturbed soil (Figure 34-16, B).
- Adjust the depth by leaning the plant to one side and removing or adding soil; repeat for the opposite side. Plants should be installed with the soil line 1 inch above the surrounding grade.
- Once you have properly positioned the plant, cut and remove the twine surrounding the root ball. If the plant is in a wire basket, remove or fold back the top third to half of the basket (Figure 34-17).
- Remove the burlap from the top half of the root-ball using a sharp utility knife. Trim any girdling or damaged roots that are exposed.
- Backfill the hole halfway and lightly compact with your foot or with the handle end of a shove (C).
- Complete backfilling and lightly compact (D).
- Avoid placing soil on top of the root ball and around the collar area of the trunk. The trunk flare should be clearly visible.
- Use extra soil to build a temporary berm around the perimeter of the planting hole, creating a basin for watering.
- Water and mulch the plant.

Installation of Boxed Plants

Trees and larger plants are often grown to certain sizes in containers; and when the root-balls and plants become too massive, they are transferred to large wood boxes. These boxes are specially constructed with a removable bottom, sides that angle outward, and metal straps that hold them intact. Using this method, trees can be grown to large sizes in boxes that are up to 5 feet across or larger.

To install boxed stock, use the following steps (Figure 34-18):

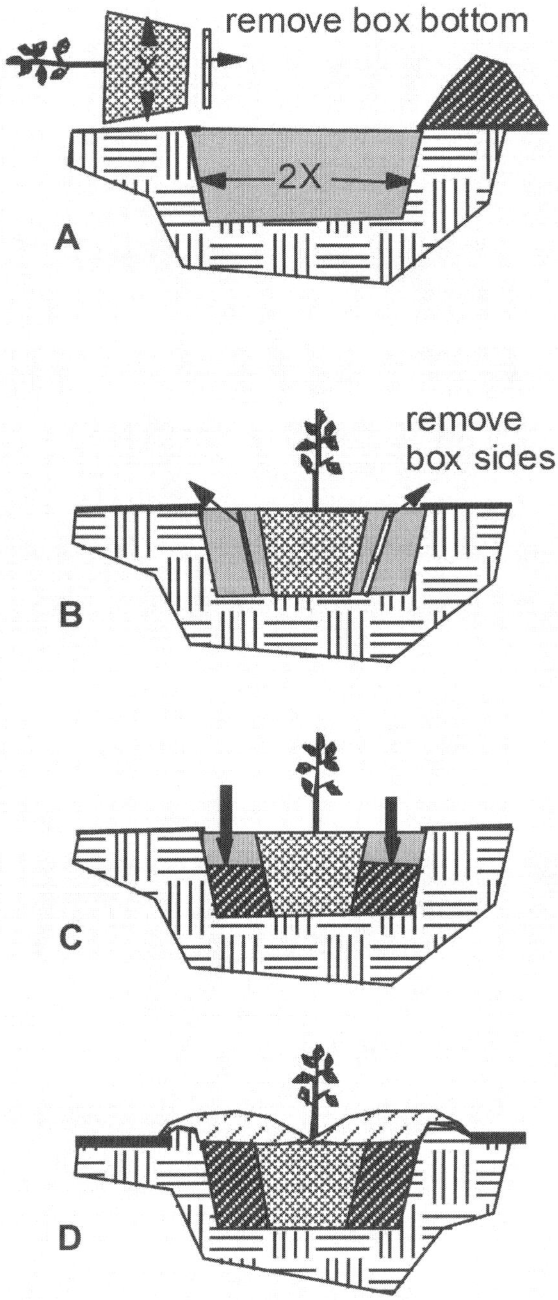

Figure 34-18 Installation of boxed plants.

- Excavate the planting hole (A) no deeper than the container. Slope the sides of the hole and scarify the sides of the hole
- Amend backfill soil if intending to do so.
- Position the plant near the hole and determine the best orientation and planting depth for the plant. Adjustments in depth and hole size are easier to make at this stage, rather than after the plant is in the hole.
- Tilt the plant on one side of the container using caution not to damage any branches or canopy.
- Remove the bottom of the box with pry bars and hammer.
- Lower the plant into the hole on undisturbed soil (B).
- Adjust the depth if necessary to place the soil line approximately 1 inch above the surrounding grade. This can be done by leaning the box one direction and adding or removing soil. Then lean the box the opposite direction and add/remove soil. Repeat until you attain the correct planting depth.
- Orient the plant to the desired position.
- Using tin snips, cut the wire bands holding the sides of the box. Several cuts may be required to free the sides from each other.
- Remove the sides and lift them out of the planting hole. If necessary, twist the side to loosen it from the root-ball.
- Trim any girdling and damaged roots that can be reached. Scarify areas of the rootball where compacted root growth is present.
- Backfill the hole halfway and lightly compact using the handle end of a shovel (C).
- Complete the backfilling and lightly compact (D).
- Avoid placing excess soil on top of the root ball and around the collar area of the trunk. The trunk flare should be clearly visible.
- Remaining soil can be used to build a temporary berm around the perimeter of the planting hole, creating a basin for watering.
- Water and mulch the plant.

Installation of Machine-Moved Plants

Situations will arise when large plants are in the incorrect location. As a result of construction, expansion, or other activities, you may need to move plants that are too large to hand-dig. In these instances, you will need the services of a **tree spade** (Figure 34-19), a hydraulic-operated excavation tool that is mounted on a truck or towed by a tractor. Tree spades typically have four large triangular blades that are pressed into the ground surrounding a plant, coming to a point directly below the tree. Once you have completely inserted them into the ground, the blades sever all roots and cut the soil, allowing the tree to be lifted out of the ground by the hydraulic arms of the tree spade. The plant is then transported to its new location where the process is reversed and the tree is planted in a predug hole. Although expensive to own and operate, tree spades can prove invaluable when moving important plants or substantial quantities of large plant material.

> **CAUTION**
>
> Locate all utilities, overhead and underground, before operating a tree spade. Verify that the tree spade equipment can negotiate the route between excavation and planting sites.

To machine move a plant, use the following steps:

- Begin by using the tree spade to excavate a hole where the plant is to be moved. Scarify the sides of the hole.
- Deposit the soil plug from this hole next to where the tree is removed, or dispose of the soil elsewhere on site.
- Amend backfill soil if intending to do so.
- Position the tree spade around the plant to be moved and remove the plant from the ground. The process for operating the equipment will vary, depending on the manufacturer, but typically involves closing the blades around the plant, lowering each blade in small increments until completely lowered, then lifting the plant from the ground.

Figure 34-19 Tree spade removing a tree.

- Transport the plant to the planting site.
- Position the tree over the hole and lower it into the ground.
- Remove the tree spade.
- Backfill any voids left between the root-ball and the planting hole. If the tree was not set squarely into the hole, there may be significant voids.
- Remaining soil can be used to build a temporary berm around the perimeter of the planting hole, creating a basin for watering.
- Water and mulch the plant.

Watering

Initial watering is very important for the quick recovery of plants from the shock of trans-plant. Using a low pressure hose, fill the area enclosed by the planting berm with water and allow this to slowly percolate through the soil. Repeat until the root ball and surrounding soil is thoroughly watered.

Mulching

Of all the postplanting activities, mulching is probably the most valuable in protecting the plant's health. Mulching holds moisture near the root zone, reduces competition from weeds, and keeps mechanical equipment such as mowers and string trimmers away from the new plant. If not specified, select natural mulch that is heavy enough to stay in place and slowly degrade to compost. Choices that work well in planting situations include bark, shredded bark, wood chips, pine needles and coarse compost. If the plant is planted singly in an open area, place mulch around the new plant in a circle that is 18–24 inches diameter and 2–3 inches thick. Pull the mulch away from direct contact with the trunk of any trees to prevent decay. If plantings are placed in a bed, mulch the entire bed to a depth of 2–3 inches, also keeping mulch away from the trunk of trees and larger shrubs. Separate the mulch from surrounding areas by cutting a trench as discussed in Chapter 33 – Edging.

Staking

Research suggests that most trees do not require any form of stabilization (staking) and that staking can be detrimental to the tree. Guy materials can damage the trunk, while too much stabilization can prevent the tree canopy from movement in the wind, a process that helps strengthen the base of the tree for long-term stability. There are situation, such as extremely sandy soil, very windy conditions and containerized trees in soilless medium where stabilization may be required to keep a newly planted tree upright while it roots in. In most cases, B & B trees do not require staking. When staking may be required due to specifications or planting conditions, two techniques are most common. The first involves two or three long wood stakes, usually 2 inches x 2 inches, firmly driven into the ground outside of the planting hole. The top of the stake is approximately 3 feet above grade. A web fabric tape is tied to the stake and looped from each stake around the trunk, near the top of the stake, in a figure-eight pattern (Figure 34-20). The tape is not actually wrapped around the trunk and the tape is not taut, so as not to damage the trunk.

The second method uses three or four short wood stakes, driven firmly into the ground outside of the planting hold. The web fabric is tied to the stakes and looped in figure-eight fashion just above the first limbs of the tree. Other materials may be used for the guys, so long as the web material is used for looped portion.

Hardware for either of these methods is often available in pre-packaged kit forms. Whichever method is used, the stakes should remain on the tree no longer than one growing season. Research continues in this area, and landscape contractors should stay abreast of this research as new techniques and practices develop.

Wrapping

Although a standard practice in the past, trunk wrapping is no longer a general recommendation as it has been found to possibly cause more problems than it solves. As with tree staking, research continues in this area and the landscape contractor should keep abreast of latest recommendations and methods.

GREEN ROOFS AND LIVING WALLS

One of the landscape-related innovations of the green movement has been the integration, or reintegration, of plant material with the structure. Although this movement began many years ago, the concept of placing plant material on the roofs and walls of structures to save energy and improve the environment has gained new momentum in the past few decades. With more innovations undoubtedly to come, the focus for the current era is on creating living environments on rooftops, also called green roofs.

The idea is simple: Replace or cover composite roof materials and mechanical equipment with meadows and living habitats that take in rather than shed water, that absorb rather than reflect heat, and that support life rather than defying it (Figure 34-21). In implementation, however, the idea is not quite so simple, even though the concept that plants can replace tar on roofs has become plausible. More recently the same philosophy has been applied to

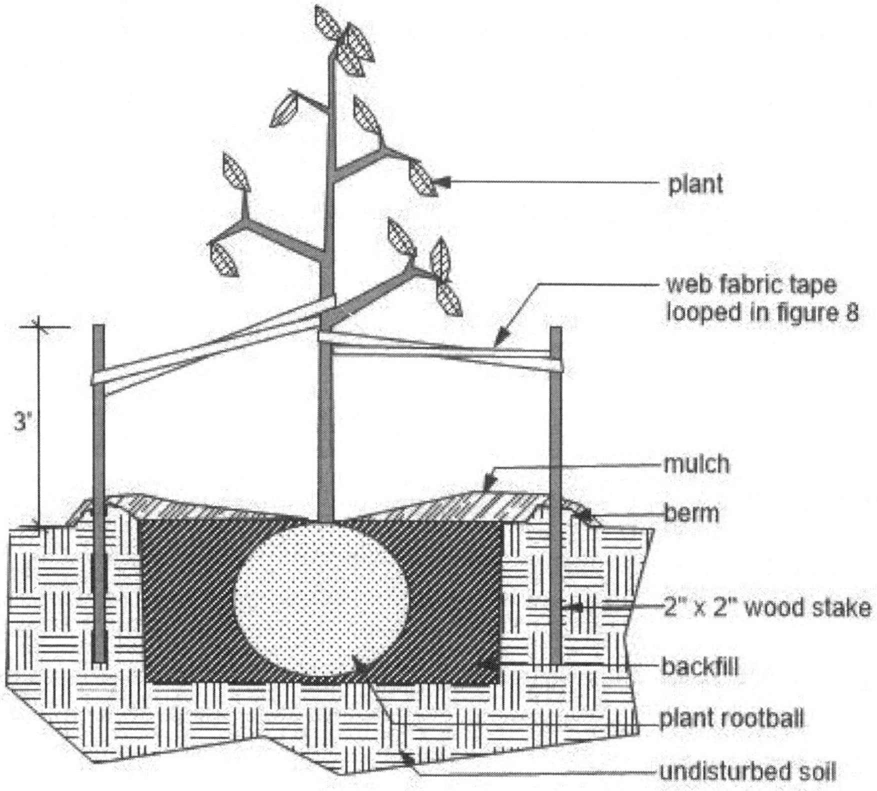

Figure 34-20 Staking a newly planted tree.

Figure 34-21 An extensive green roof with grasses and perennial plantings.

the vertical surfaces of structures, both inside and out. Creating a wall out of living plants performs many of the same functions that plants on a roof accomplish, typically on a smaller and more attainable scale (Figure 34-22). Although the technology is specialized and ever-evolving, this text must mention the new frontiers facing landscape contractors on the roofs and walls of the structures they now work around.

Green Roofs

Green roof technology requires high levels of engineering, as well as integration of several trades, to be successfully accomplished. Not only must the success of the plant material be considered, but also the structural stability of the building and the protection of the occupants from a porous roof.

Green roofs can be categorized as either extensive or intensive installations. Extensive green roofs are characterized as having 1–6 inches of soil and would typically support succulents and low-growing plant material.

Figure 34-22 A living wall installation in a patio area.

Intensive green roofs have 6–24 inches of soil and are capable of hosting a wider range of plant life. As expected, both extensive and intensive green roofs require enhancement of the building's structure to support the weight of growing medium and plant material, as well as improved waterproofing installations. Above the structural and waterproofing elements, both types of green roofs typically have membranes that prevent the chance of root penetration into the structure, an additional drainage layer for the planted portion of the roof, and growing media with plants. Drainage for the planting media may be granular material such as pumice or could be constructed of manufactured drainage systems.

Irrigation for the green roof is typically composed of drip systems, emitter tubes, or subsurface irrigation that can deliver water directly to the plant roots. Occasionally, an overhead system with low-rise sprinkler heads is used, but in general the overhead systems are not as effective in providing water to the root zone. The distribution system will often be above grade, perhaps even surface mounted. Even the "soil" in which green roof plants are growing is not a traditional soil but a blend of lightweight components similar in nature to the mix used in container plantings. Two general methods for installing plants include (1) planting directly into a layer of media and (2) growing plants in modular trays with several cells and then transferring the cells to the roof for permanent installation. For green roofs, the plants are mostly succulents, including sedums, mosses, grasses, and short flowering plants. For intensive roofs, trees and shrubs, as well as perennials, vines, forbs, and the full range of smaller plants, are available. Plants that have reduced water demands are priorities for each type of roof.

Because of the many specialized activities, the role of the landscape contractor in green roof installation will be far from traditional. It is possible that the landscape contractor may find a role in growing the plants, placing modular trays, mixing and placing the media, installing the irrigation system, or installing the plants. Much of the work will be done by hand and without the benefits of large equipment; and with the extreme growing conditions, the warranty requirements will be continually evolving.

Living Walls

Living wall technology and its adoption into the everyday landscape may not be as extensive as green roofs, but the two technologies share many of the same environmental benefits. Living walls help clarify the air; they can reduce noise and pollution, in addition to absorbing heat and protecting structures from environmental stresses. Living walls also have two general categories: (1) green walls, composed of plants that are directed up walls on support networks, and (2) living walls, which are vertical installations of plant material in growing medium. Although green walls would be considered primarily an exterior technique, they can be either an interior or exterior application.

Green walls consist primarily of planting space or containers in which to grow plants, often positioned on the ground or in lower levels of structures, and a framework on which plants can grow. This framework can be as simple as a latticework fastened to a house wall or as extensive as a wire or fencing network anchored to the walls of a large office building. The plant materials, often vining plants, are grown in the lower levels and encouraged to extend up the growing framework. The presence of a plant buffer serves to absorb light and heat, hence cooling the structure. Although not without challenges, including maintenance and habitat for undesired wildlife, green walls can producc measurable environmental benefits.

Living walls are a fabricated environment in which panels with upward angled cells are filled with growing medium and planted with species such as sedums, vegetables, grasses, succulents, and similar plants. Each of these panels has a channel running across the top to accommodate drip or emitter hose irrigation. These panels are then hung on a framework that provides the vertical support. At the bottom of the wall is a channel to collect excess runoff from the panels.

Manufacturers of living wall panels provide kits with the framework, panels, and irrigation equipment necessary to plant and assemble a wall. Although attractive and environmentally sound, living walls are somewhat limited in height by the framework in which they are hung. To scale larger structures, extensive support systems for the panels must be constructed. Living walls are well suited to patios, lanais, interior courtyards, and exterior applications in milder climates.

PROTECTION AND MAINTENANCE UNTIL ACCEPTANCE

As in other portions of landscape construction, the protection and maintenance of finished work until final acceptance is usually the responsibility of the contractor or subcontractor. As mentioned previously, when working as a subcontractor, know your responsibilities before you begin work. It may be advisable to set up barriers and to post warning signs to prevent the unintentional damage to a newly installed landscape.

Planting maintenance until final acceptance may also be required. This would include watering, mulching, maintenance of bed edges, etc; any standard landscape management practice may be required.

CHAPTER 35

TURF ESTABLISHMENT

OBJECTIVES

By reading and practicing the techniques described in this chapter, the reader should be able to successfully complete the following activities:

- Prepare an area for lawn and low maintenance turf.
- Install lawn and low maintenance turf using seeding, sodding, sprigging/plugging, and-hydroseeding methods.

In many cases, much of a site's planted area is covered with lawn. Used as athletic fields, picnic areas, natural areas, or negative spaces to balance the larger plant material, these largescale areas create the bulk of the visual landscape. To describe every different type of open space planted with grass and forb species, and the slight nuances used to establish each, could take an entire text. To simplify the description of establishment methods, two general types of areas, lawn and low maintenance turf areas, are considered in this chapter. Although this may be a significant overgeneralization, most establishment techniques can be applied to one or both of these general categories. These two areas and their descriptions are as follows:

- Lawn Areas. Lawns are used in the landscape primarily for aesthetics or to create a soft groundcover for active and passive use for athletic purposes. Although a variety of plants may be utilized, the vast majority of spaces are composed of lawn grass species. Plants in lawn areas are typically short sod-forming grasses that are mowed and granted a high level of maintenance such as irrigation, fertilization, and related cultural practices. Typical plant species would include Kentucky bluegrass, fescues, ryes, Bermudagrass, zoysia, buffalo, and bent grasses.
- Low maintenance turf areas. This large group could include spaces labeled as meadows, pastures, and roadsides, as well as other similar types of spaces. These areas typically include a mixture of grasses, either pasture or native, and forbs to create attractive and diverse habitats while providing erosion control and site protection (Figure 35-1). Low maintenance turf areas could also include lawn grasses that are left unmown or in masses of decorative grasses. Few of these spaces are mowed regularly or require mowing as a result of the use of the space. Typical plant species would include native forbs, clovers, vetches, trefoils, and a wide range of pasture and native grasses.

Although there are many visual benefits to each of these areas, low maintenance turf areas spaces are often home to a vast diversity of species that help pollinate flowers, control pests, and provide an important link in nature's food chain. Lawn areas create the ideal exterior surface on which to play.

Each of these spaces requires techniques for establishment that are much different than the planting of the more ornamental landscape. No one would consider raising all of the plants for a lawn in a container. Instead, these spaces require planting methods that can deliver large quantities of plants in an economical and efficient manner. Those demands have led to the development of several planting methods common to the large-scale open spaces. Seeding, sodding, using sprigs and plugs, and hydroseeding are the methods by which most lawn and natural areas are established.

Figure 35-1 A low maintenance turf area of unmown grasses serves as an attractive and reduced-maintenance entry to a facility.

Establishment of low maintenance turf areas differs significantly from the establishment of lawn areas. Where lawn establishment is expected quite quickly, low maintenance area, depending on the seed mix utilized, can take several seasons to fully mature. Expectations of 'instant' meadows are often not met due the to the nature of the species and seeding rates.

RELATED INFORMATION

Information in this chapter is supplemented by instruction provided elsewhere in this text and in other sources. Before undertaking the activities described in this chapter, read the related information in these sources:

- Site Grading, Chapter 13
- Site Drainage, Chapter 15
- Erosion Control, Chapter 16
- Plant Material Installation, Chapter 34
- North Carolina Manual of Professional Horticultural Practice
- Publications available through North Carolina State University Extension Service at http://www.lawnfiles.ncsu.edu/
- Appendix G 'Carolina Lawns'

SELECTING PLANT MATERIAL

Any successful planting project begins with selection of quality plant material, and the same is true for the installation of lawn and reduced-maintenance grass areas. Whether picking seed, selecting sod, revegetating a roadside, or determining what native grasses and forbs are best for your low maintenance turf, you will note the qualitative differences in the products available.

Selecting Species and Cultivars

Numerous factors must be considered when selecting a seed species and cultivar. The first is to determine the type of planting to be undertaken. If planting a low maintenance turf or roadside, your choices of species may be restricted to those specified or appropriate to a specific region, with a limited number of cultivars available. For low maintenance turf areas and lawn areas, the number of species and cultivars can be extensive. Key factors to consider when selecting seed should include the following:

- Climate and Conditions. Most species and cultivars, particularly the LAWN grasses, have particular ranges of heat and cold tolerances. Although reduced-maintenance grasses and species often grow in wide ranges, lawn grasses are classified to their success in cool season and warm season areas, as well as in arid versus humid areas. Most species will have -limitations on whether they will be successful in sun or shade, and many are intolerant of salt levels found in regional soils. It will also be -necessary to consider the availability of irrigation and the type of soil.
- Intended Use. Although the classification of the planting suggests types of plant material that will work best, understanding whether the desire is to support heavy traffic and rigorous play such as a golf course versus occasional strolls and low-impact traffic of a park will lead to smarter species choices. Both aesthetic and functional concerns play a role in selecting a mix of species and cultivars that provide a tight, manicured look or a natural, rough-hewn presentation.
- Regional Seeds. Although lawn, pastures, and roadside plant material have only moderate sensitivity to where they are grown and planted, low maintenance turf areas and native plantings are best purchased from a grower within the same region as where they are to be planted. Seed and herbaceous materials imported from foreign regions sometimes struggle to survive outside their adapted conditions.
- Maintenance Level. The amount of care intended for the planting will play a -significant role in selecting species. Roadsides, low maintenance turf areas, and low maintenance turf areass are typically planted and left unattended, often for the lifetime of the project. Selection of plants with high-maintenance requirements and inability to adapt to conditions will lead to quick failure. lawn areas, however, are the most highly maintained areas of the landscape. Support from irrigation, fertilization, aeration, and other cultural activities allows selection of a higher -maintenance plant.
- Blending and Mixing of Species/Cultivars. In many areas of North Carolina, single species lawns are the norm. An exception to this is the mix of tall fescue and bluegrass in some cool season areas. It would be uncommon for any of the categories of low maintenance grass areas to be composed of a single species and/or cultivar. For roadside plantings, it is normal to blend a substantial number of forbs (often half) with grasses to create the desired textures and survival rates. Pastures and low maintenance turf areas can often be composed of 75% grass species with forbs rounding out the balance of the mixture. Within each of these categories, the blend of grass and forb types will include several species suited to the aesthetic and functional concerns of the project.

Selecting Seed

Seed is one of the most rigorously evaluated plant products available to the landscape contractor. In addition to selecting the species and cultivars, the contractor must be able to evaluate the product label. In the case of lawn grasses, label information will provide a veritable history of the product. In other grass types, including pasture and native grasses, the information may not be as extensive but can still provide valuable help in verifying suitability for a project. Information typically available when evaluating the label of seed products include those items listed below:

- Germination Rate. Explains what percent of the seed actually germinated during tests.
- Pure Live Seed. The actual percentage of desired grass seed that is expected to germinate.
- Lot number.
- Name and address of labeler.
- Kind and variety of lawn grass seed, listed in order of predominance. This will identify the percentages, by weight, of each species and cultivar included in the blend.
- Percentage of other crop seed.
- Percent by weight of weed seed.
- Percent of undesirable grass seed.
- Percent by weight of inert matter.
- Date on which germination test was conducted.

In North Carolina, all seed must meet or exceed the standards of the North Carolina Seed Law

PREPARING THE SITE

Site preparation will be one of the critical steps in establishing any seeded or sodded area. As in planting, the site preparation for turfgrass establishment is often dictated by project specifications. Optimum soil conditions as previously described may not be obtainable. Begin by clearing the site of any debris and perennial weeds; then complete the rough grading to mirror the desired finish grade. Respread any topsoil saved during earlier grading steps to establish the finish grade. In situations where planting is to be on existing grade or where topsoil is to be spread, surface tilling should be performed. Surface tilling is a process of loosening the top few inches of soil using a toothed cultivator pulled behind a tractor. When spreading topsoil, this can be performed before topsoil distribution. Note that excessive tillage damages soil structure, particularly in soils with clay content. Tilling breaks apart the naturally bound peds of soil leaving fine particles of dust that are more subject to erosion. Excessive tillage also breaks apart the biological components of the soil that are present to facilitate soil ped formation and decomposition. Till only enough to make the soil more workable.

Desirable soils for any lawn area are clay loam, loamy or sandy loam soils placed in a lift of 4–6 inches. Any amendments that are planned should be added during tilling operations. Blending a starter fertilizer with the ratio of 1-1-1 (e.g., an 8-8-8 or 16-16-16 grade fertilizer) into the topsoil will provide an additional boost to lawn plants immediately after planting.

Grade the surface to a smooth finish that is free of bumps or clods, following the proposed contours as closely as possible. For seeded areas, the grade should be finished to the exact finish grade; for sodded areas, the grade should be 1 inch below the finish grade to allow for the soil carried with the sod. Before sodding, lightly roll the surface to further level the grade. If any edgers are to be installed, they should be placed after grade preparation and before planting operations begin (Figure 35-2).

INSTALLATION

Several methods are available for installation of lawn and related seeded materials. Sowing seed is the standard for most large sites, with sodding common for smaller areas or for installations that require instant lawn. With warm season grasses, plugs or sprigs are available for establishing lawn areas. Hydroseeding is a popular method for establishing lawn and lowmaintenance grass areas. Seeding, sodding, and plugs/sprigs are common for lawn grasses, whereas seeding is traditional for natural areas such as low maintenance turf areas. Hydroseeding is often used in areas where seeding equipment will have difficulty accessing the site.

Seeding

Seeding is a common method for establishing a wide range of spaces and is the preferred method for pastures and low maintenance turf areas.

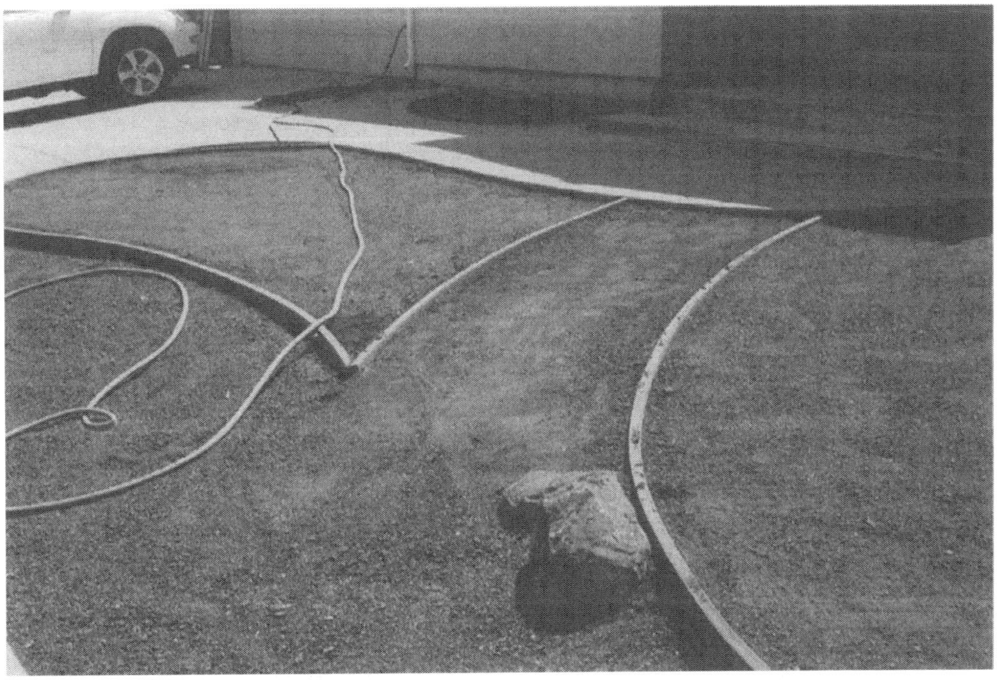

Figure 35-2 A site prepared for sod. The grading has been completed and the edger installed. Note that the soil grade has been left below the top of the edger to accommodate the thickness of the sod.

Large spaces planned for lawn are also candidates for seeding operations. Based on the climate, seeding operations may be limited to seasons and grass species where the chances for seed success are the highest. Optimum seeding times for warm season grasses are between March 1 and July 1, cool season grasses from mid-August to mid-September. Regardless of the method of installation, irrigation, either permanent or temporary, should be ready to supply water to the site if natural rainfall cannot perform that function.

Seed application can be accomplished by hand sowing, using a drop spreader or using a broadcast spreader. The last two pieces of equipment may be smaller hand-operated units or can be larger tractor-towed implements. It is important to test the seeding equipment to assure proper application rate for the type of seed being sown. Small seed can readily pass through an improperly set opening, and large seed may not make it out of the hopper. For seeding projects that have seeds of significantly differing sizes, you may need to make multiple applications with the equipment appropriately set for each pass.

Divide the seed to be installed into two equal portions. Fill your seeding equipment with one portion and begin at one edge of the project. Apply seed in even passes over the entire site, with only slight overlap between passes. When you have covered the site, repeat the process in runs that are perpendicular to the original direction (Figure 35-3). Lightly rake the site and then roll with a water-filled drum roller to improve seed contact with the soil. Water the seed using a light irrigation, stopping when water begins to run off the lower side of the site. To reduce loss of seed as a result of erosion and to preserve moisture, spread straw mulch over the newly seeded surface. Germination will vary, depending on the species.

The newly seeded, and then germinated, lawn must be maintained until the area is established. Maintenance will include minimizing compaction on the surface and irrigating every 1–2 days. Irrigation amounts will depend on site conditions,

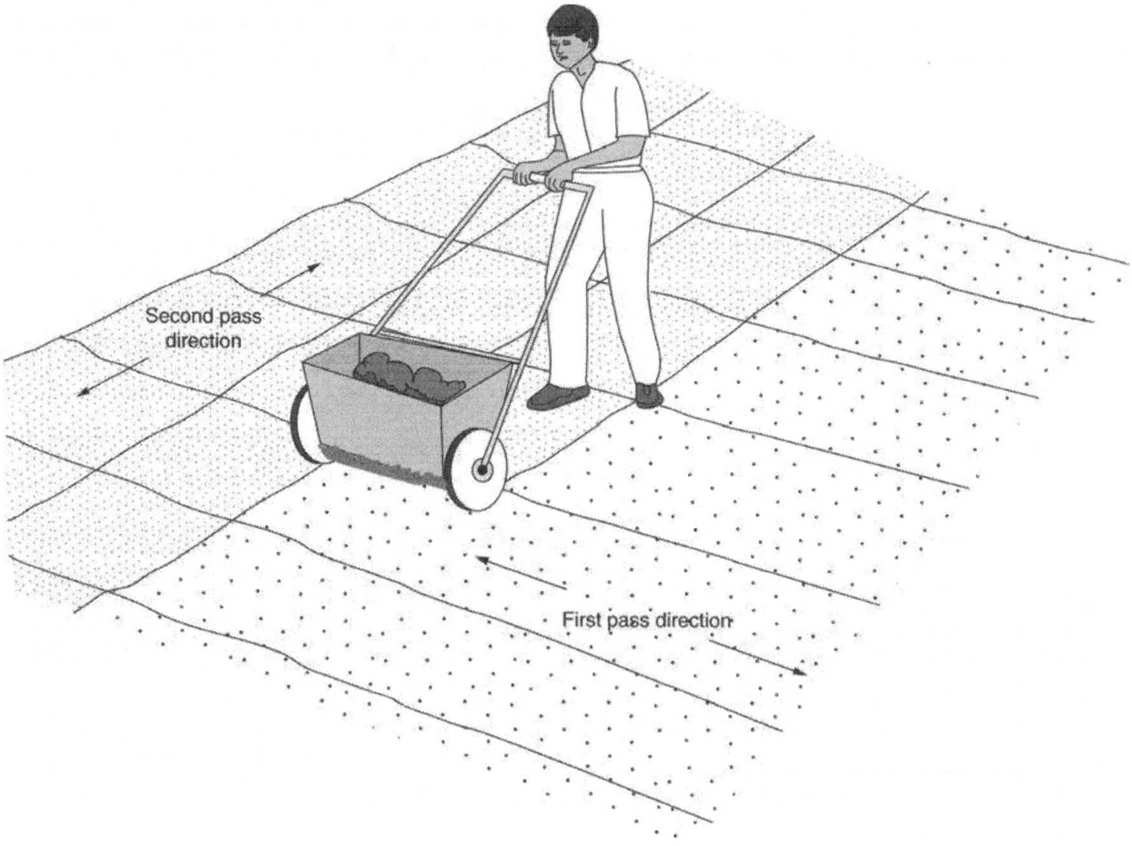

Figure 35-3 Seeding in two passes running perpendicular to each other.

but enough water should be applied to keep the surface slightly moist and to avoid newly germinated seed from completely drying out. In the case of lawn grass, once the grass has reached its normal maintained height, the initial mowing can be performed. At this time, set the watering to a normal irrigation schedule and perform regular maintenance.

Installing Sod

Although a contractor may find occasional vendors selling "native grass" or "wildflower" sod, lawn is the primary category to use sod as an establishment method. Optimum sodding schedules are the same as those for that same grass species, but more latitude exists when sodding.

To sod a prepared site, select a beginning point that will allow sod to be installed in a straight row. This may be next to a walkway, edger, or a chalk line snapped through an irregular-shaped area. Beginning at the edge of a space will reduce the chances of significant trimming of sod along the entire perimeter. It is also beneficial, though not required, to begin sod placement at the bottom of a hill. Although sod on a hillside can be staked, the stability of the installation will be increased if the sod follows the contour of the hill, as opposed to running top to bottom.

Sod typically comes in rolls about 4 feet long or in pieces that are folded in half. Unroll or unfold the first piece and place it on the base (Figure 35-4). Check the piece for edges that have torn or curled under. Unroll curled edges before placing them. Reject damaged pieces and save them for trimming areas where smaller pieces will be adequate. If necessary, adjust the position of the piece by grasping the long edges and sliding or turning it until it is straight and snug against any edge or pavement. Continue placing pieces end-to-end to install the initial

Figure 35-4 Placing sod. Note the joints at the ends of the pieces are staggered.

row. Each subsequent piece should be butted tightly up to the previous piece.

If additional labor is available, part of a crew can be placing sod while other members can be carrying sod and staging it near where future pieces will be installed. Begin the second row of sod by cutting a half piece to stagger the joints with the previous row. To the greatest extent possible, avoid joints that align between rows. An alternative to placing sod by hand is to purchase large rolls of sod that are installed using a tractor. The rolls attach to the hydraulic lift of the tractor and are positioned at the starting point; and as the tractor moves slowly forward, the sod is unrolled and slid into position. This method requires special equipment and sod providers, but it can save time if sodding a large area such as an athletic field.

Trimming can be done by placing the sod piece in position and allowing it to overlap the edge where it is to be cut. Cut the sod using a shovel, utility knife, serrated bread knife, or other sharp kitchen knife (Figure 35-5). Roll the sod with a drum roller half filled with water to improve the contact between the sod and the soil (Figure 35-6). As long as the sod is stable, rolling can be performed on the installed sod behind the installation operation. Sod placed on hillsides may require staking to keep it in position during storms and irrigation.

Stakes are metal U stakes or wood pegs that are driven through the sod into the subgrade below. Place two to three stakes along the upper side of the sod pieces. After you have completed the installation, or at the end of a day, thoroughly water the entire installation.

Until the sod is rooted, avoid traffic over the sod and water it daily to prevent the pieces from drying out. Once the sod is rooted in, which can take from 5 days to 2 weeks, depending on conditions, you can begin mowing and regular maintenance operations. To check for rooting, grasp the blades of grass from a piece of the sod and gently lift. If it has rooted, the sod will resist lifting.

Figure 35-5 Trimming sod.

Figure 35-6 Rolling newly placed sod with a drum roller.

Installing Plugs or Sprigs

Plugs and sprigs are an establishment method used with warm season species. **Sprigs** are short sections of lawn grass stems with at least one or two nodes capable of rooting. **Plugs** are small circles or squares of sod, usually about 2 inches in diameter, with roots, stems, leaves, and a small "plug" of soil. Both methods are effective at establishing a lawn for grass species that are vigorous rooters from plant crowns and rhizomes.

To establish a lawn area using sprigs, begin by lightly watering the prepared area. Broadcast or place the sprigs evenly. Bermudagrass and zoysiagrass are sprigged at a rate of 3 to 10 bushels per acre, depending on how fast cover is required. St Augustinegrass is rarely sprigged. Rake the surface lightly and then roll with a drum roller half filled with water. Verify that all sprigs are making good contact with the soil. Large installations may utilize a tractor with a disc attachment to lightly disc the sprigs into the top ½ to 1 inch of soil. To establish a lawn using plugs, excavate a checkerboard pattern of small holes every 6–12 inches across the prepared subgrade. The holes should be the same diameter as the plugs. Place a plug in each hole and then roll with a drum roller half filled with water. Verify that all plugs are flush with the surrounding soil.

Until the lawn area is completely established, minimize traffic across the lawn and water it regularly. Allowing springs and plugs to dry out can result in planting failure. Establishment should occur in 2–3 weeks as the plants spread to fill the voids between starts.

Hydroseeding (with Hydromulch)

Hydroseeding will require specialized equipment and materials to establish roadsides, low maintenance turf areas, low maintenance turf areass, and lawn in hard-to-work areas. This method is particularly effective for steep slopes and areas where equipment cannot operate and can also be an effective way to seed and mulch large areas. Additional information regarding hydromulching, which often works in concert with hydroseeding to create a vegetative cover, can be found in Chapter 16 ("Protecting the Site from Surface Erosion").

To hydroseed, prepare the subgrade in a similar manner to all previous establishment methods, if possible. If you cannot access a site and if the expectation for quality growth is not high, you can perform hydroseeding over rough-graded sites.

A wide range of equipment options are available for implementing a hydroseeding project. Small units are mounted in the beds of trucks, whereas larger units are built on tractor-drawn trailers. All contain a hopper in which the components of hydroseeding are mixed, a powerful pump for spraying the mixture, and a discharge gun or hose used to distribute the mix. The components, with percentages determined by manufacturer's specifications, include water, seed of almost any type, water-soluble fertilizer, a tackifier, and, in most cases, a dyed mulch. The mulch can be wood fibers, paper, or a bonded matrix product with dye added to assist the applicator in determining where the product has been sprayed. The tackifier is typically a polyacrylamide that thickens and lubricates the mixture, holding the hydroseeded components in place for several days until the crop has germinated and is self-anchoring.

In the hopper of the hydroseeder, add the water, seed, fertilizer, and mulch (if desired). Add the tackifier last. If the equipment has mixing capabilities, let the mixture blend for a short while. Start the pump and, using the nozzle or hose, spray the mixture on the site beginning at the highest point and working evenly to the bottom of the site. Spray slowly enough to obtain an even cover over the subgrade. If using a discharge gun applicator, you may need to move the unit to gain access to the entire site. If applying by hose, plan your route so the application can be continuous and even. Overspray on paved areas can create slippery surfaces; so, when seeding operations are finished, remove overspray by washing with pressurized water or by spreading rock salt over the area to absorb the moisture. Seed installed in this method typically establishes in 5–7 days, but pregerminating by soaking the seed in water for

1–2 days prior to application can speed the process. Avoid traffic and maintain irrigation for the site until the crop has been established. Once the crop is established, start routine maintenance.

PROTECTION AND MAINTENANCE UNTIL ACCEPTANCE

As in other portions of landscape construction, the protection and maintenance of finished work until final acceptance is usually the responsibility of the contractor or subcontractor. As mentioned previously, when working as a subcontractor, know your responsibilities before you begin work. It may be advisable to set up barriers and to post warning signs to prevent the unintentional damage to a newly installed landscape.

Lawn maintenance until final acceptance may also be required. This would include watering, mowing, maintenance of bed edges, etc; any standard lawn management practice may be required.

REFERENCE

This Chapter focuses on installation methods. Refer to Appendix G, titled Carolina Lawns, published by the North Carolina Extension Service for extensive information on lawn selection, installation and management.

SECTION 9

SUMMARY

No landscaping project can be considered complete until the green element has been added. Installation of plant material is the most environmentally friendly portion of a trade dedicated to improving living environments. Trees, shrubs, flowers, perennials, and ground covers provide the finishing touches that bring a project to life.

In this section, the installation of plant material was covered, as well as the establishment of lawn and low maintenance turf areas-like spaces. In both chapters, the importance of selecting quality plant material and good site preparation were emphasized. Planting techniques reviewed included bare-root, containerized, balled and burlapped, and boxed plants. The moving of trees by machine, more specifically a tree spade, was also introduced. Once plants are installed, the post-planting care methods of watering, mulching and staking were presented. For the establishment of lawn and low maintenance turf areas areas, the selection of plant material and preparation of the site were discussed. lawn areas are generally described as spaces with primarily lawn grass species that are mowed and maintained for aesthetic and athletic purposes. The term "low maintenance turf areas" was used to generally describe areas such as pastures and roadsides where a mixture of grasses and forbs are present and mowing is seldom encouraged. Establishment of lawn areas via seed, sod, sprigs/plugs, and hydroseeding was covered, with seeding and hydroseeding applicable to both lawn and low maintenance turf areas. Establishment times for low maintenance turf areas are often much longer than those of lawn areas.

Sustainability concepts were introduced in the form of green roofs and living walls. Green roofs are rooftops that are planted with specialty plant material in an attempt to absorb water, reduce heat islands, and improve the environment. Living walls are vertical installations of plants that improve air quality and also add ambiance to the environment. The importance of maintenance and protection of the landscape until final completion and acceptance was reiterated.

Appendix A

NOTE: THE FOLLOWING IS AN EXAMPLE OF A SPECIFICATION STYLE. IT IS NOT INTENDED FOR CONSTRUCTION AND SHOULD NOT BE USED FOR ANY PROJECT WITHOUT BEING REWRITTEN TO FIT A SPECIFIC PROJECT

EXAMPLE MATERIAL AND WORKMANSHIP SPECIFICATION FOR SEEDING PROJECT

Section 02900 Seeding

Part 1—General Information

1.1 Description of work.

A. Work included: Provide all labor, materials, equipment, and incidentals necessary to complete topsoil preparation, fertilization, seeding, and mulching where shown on the drawings, as specified herein, and as needed for a complete and proper installation.

B. Related documents:

1. Documents affecting work of this section include, but are not necessarily limited to, General Conditions, Supplementary Conditions, and Sections in Division 1 of these Specifications.

1.2 Quality assurance.

A. Use adequate numbers of skilled workers who are thoroughly trained and experienced in the necessary crafts and who are completely familiar with the specified requirements and the methods needed for proper performance of the work of this section.

B. Seed, fertilizer, and soil conditioners shall be commercial grade.

1.3 Product handling.

A. Comply with pertinent provisions of Section 1640, Product Storage and Handling.

Part 2—Products

2.1 Grass seed.

A. Provide mixture consisting of the following proportions by weight:

1. Kentucky Bluegrass—10% by weight.

2. Tall Fescue – 90% by weight.

B. Lime: Finely ground agricultural limestone containing not less than 85% calcium and magnesium carbonates.

C. Fertilizer: Free-flowing granular type of uniform composition containing by weight the following:

1. 5% Nitrogen, with 50% of this total organic.
2. 10% Available Phosphoric Acid.
3. 5% Potash.

D. Mulch: Wheat straw.

E. Water: Available at site.

Part 3—Execution

3.1 Preparation of topsoil.

A. Deposit additional topsoil as may be required to correct all settlement and erosion.

B. Apply fertilizer at an approximate rate of 10 pounds per 1,000 square feet over area.

C. Thoroughly and evenly incorporate fertilizer with the soil to a depth of 3 inches by disking or other approved method. In areas inaccessible to power equipment, use hand tools.

D. Prepare seed bed in accordance with acceptable horticultural practices. Leave area smooth with a loose, friable seed bed.

E. Remove roots, sticks, clods, rocks, stones, etc. of golf ball size or larger.

3.2 Seeding.

A. Apply seed uniformly and evenly over entire area.

B. Seed may be drilled or broadcast. If broadcast, lightly cover seed.

C. Apply grass seed at a rate of 3 pounds per 1,000 square feet.

D. Roll lightly to firm seed bed and cover with mulch.

3.3 Maintenance.

A. Soak seed bed at initial watering. Maintain damp seed bed through germination period, watering as necessary.

B. Contractor shall be responsible for the repair and reseeding of all eroded areas and areas that fail to show a uniform stand of grass and ground cover.

C. Reseed those areas that do not produce proper stand within first year after seeding.

End of Section 02900

EXAMPLE PERFORMANCE SPECIFICATION FOR SEEDING PROJECT

Section 02900 Seeding

Description of work.

Contractor shall provide all labor, materials, equipment, and incidentals necessary to provide a complete and proper seeding installation. Installation shall include topsoil preparation and modification, fertilization, seeding, and mulching where shown on the drawings and in all other areas on the site disturbed by construction activities.

Work in related documents.

Other contract documents that relate to this section include, but are not necessarily limited to, General Conditions, Supplementary Conditions, Sections in Division 1 of these Specifications, and Planting and Seeding Plans.

Quality assurance.

Contractor shall provide a vigorous, viable, weed-free turf cover composed of no less than 100 grass plants per square foot at the time of acceptance of the project by owner. Cover crop species will not be considered as part of this assurance.

Products.

Turf shall be composed approximately equal parts of three species of Kentucky Bluegrass and one species of fine textured fescue. Cover crop species may be added as required. All turf species used shall be locally adapted cultivars.

Installation requirements.

Installation shall be coordinated with other site and building construction activities. Installation will be in accordance with recognized horticultural standards. Any soil modifications and finish grade corrections required will be the responsibility of the contractor. Any work disturbed by construction, erosion, or other means prior to final acceptance of project by owner will be repaired at contractor's expense.

Warranty.

Contractor shall warranty the turf completely for 30 days following acceptance by owner. Contractor shall warranty trueness of species for a period of 1 year following acceptance by owner.

End of Section 02900

EXAMPLE LANDSCAPE SPECIFICATIONS

Specification content and layout will vary from one design professional to another. Following are sample specifications written for a variety of landscape related activities that can be used to compare and review the styles used by landscape architects, architects, and engineers.

SECTION 02277

LIMESTONE WALL

McCORKLE RESIDENCE PROJECT
BUENA VISTA UNIVERSITY
STORM LAKE, IOWA

PART 1 GENERAL

1.01 WORK INCLUDED

A. Limestone dry laid edges/walls.

1.02 ENVIRONMENTAL REQUIREMENTS

A. Maintain materials and ambient air to 40 degrees F (5 degrees C) minimum prior to, during, and 48 hours after completion of work.
B. At the end of working day, or during rainy weather, cover exposed stone work with non-staining waterproof coverings, securely anchored.

PART 2 PRODUCTS

2.01 ACCEPTABLE STONE SUPPLIER

A. Quarried and supplied by Weber Stone Co., Inc. Anamosa, IA

2.02 STONE

A. Stone: native Iowa limestone
B. Size: as indicated on the drawings

2.03 STONE FABRICATION

A. Form external corners to irregular joint profile. Clean jagged corners from stone in preparation for setting.
B. Slope exposed top surfaces of stone for natural wash.

PART 3 EXECUTION

3.01 INSPECTION

A. Verify that support work and site conditions are ready to receive work of this Section.
B. Verify that items built-in under other Sections are properly located and sized.
C. Beginning of installation means acceptance of existing conditions and support work.

3.02 PREPARATION

A. Establish lines, levels, and coursing. Protect from disturbance.
B. Clean stone prior to erection. Do not use wire brushes or implements which can mark or damage exposed surfaces.

3.03 INSTALLATION

A. All stone work shall be installed with the following guidelines:
   1. Erect stone in accordance with stone supplier's instructions.
   2. When required, split stone at site to produce clean faces and to fit opening dimensions.
   3. Arrange stone pattern to provide variable joint sizes throughout. Joints between stones on the same course shall be no greater than 3/4" in all walls. Space between courses shall be a maximum of 1/2". Stone courses shall be as dimensioned ±1/2".
B. Dry Laid Walls
   1. Clinkers, or shims, shall be of the same stone as the wall. Use as few shims as necessary to make the wall structural.
   2. Place backfill rock and fabric as the wall is laid up.

3.04 CLEANING
A. Clean soiled surfaces with cleaning solution.
B. Use non-metallic tools in cleaning operations.

END OF SECTION

Figure A-1 Sample technical specification for stone wall. (Courtesy of Dunbar Jones Partnership, Des Moines, IA)

Source: Delmar/Cengage Learning

SECTION 02518

INTERLOCKING CONCRETE PAVERS

McCORKLE RESIDENCE PROJECT
BUENA VISTA UNIVERSITY
STORM LAKE, IOWA

PART 1 GENERAL

1.01 WORK INCLUDED

A. Concrete paver units.
B. Sand bed and sand joint filler.

1.02 RELATED WORK

A. Section 03001 – Concrete.

1.03 REFERENCE STANDARDS

A. ASTM C936: Specification for Solid Interlocking Concrete Paving Units.
B. ASTM C140: Method of Sampling and Testing Concrete Masonry Units.
C. ASTM C136: Method for Sieve Analysis for Fine and Coarse Aggregates.
D. ASTM C33: Specification for Concrete Aggregates.

1.04 SUBMITTALS.

A. If manufacturer is different from one indicated below, submit samples of concrete paving units to indicate color and shape selections. Color will be selected by Landscape Architect from manufacturer's available colors.
B. Submit sieve analysis for grading of bedding and joint sand.
C. Submit test results from an independent testing laboratory demonstrating compliance of paving units to requirements of Section 2.02 A below.
D. Submit manufacture's installation instructions if different from Article 3.02.

1.05 MOCK UPS

A. Install a 7 ft. x 7 ft. paver area as described in Article 3.02. This area will be used to determine surcharge of the sand layer, joint sizes, laying pattern(s), color(s), and texture of the job. This area shall be the standard from which the work will be judged.

B. For smaller projects, a mock-up may not be necessary. In order to determine the amount of settlement of the pavers after compaction, a paver shall be placed on approximately 1 inch of bedding sand, and tapped solidly several times with a rubber mallet. The difference in height of the paver from the base from before compaction to after compaction shall be used to determine the height of the stringlines for proper grade.

1.06 DELIVERY, STORAGE AND HANDLING

A. Deliver concrete pavers to the site in steel band, plastic banded, or plastic wrapped cubes capable of transfer by forklift or clamp lift. Unload pavers at job site in such manner that no damage occurs to the product.

Figure A-2 Sample technical specification for concrete pavers. (Courtesy of Dunbar Jones Partnership, Des Moines, IA)

Source: Delmar/Cengage Learning.

B. Cover sand with waterproof covering to prevent exposure to rainfall or removal by wind. Secure the covering place.
C. Coordinate delivery and paving schedule to minimize interference with normal use of buildings adjacent to paving.

PART 2 PRODUCTS

2.01 ACCEPTABLE MANUFACTURERS

A. Manufacturer: UNILOCK-Chicago
301 East Sullivan Rd.,
Aurora, IL 60504
Phone: (630) 892-9191
Fax: (630) 892-9215
e-mail: chicago@unilock.com

B. Pavers
1. Paver style: Hollandstone
2. Color: Buff and Charcoal
2. Paving Pattern: Herringbone

C. Other Manufacturers are acceptable if they are members of the CONCRETE PAVER INSTITUTE. If another manufacturer is selected, 25 pavers of each color of each size shall be submitted for approval by the Landscape Architect.

2.02 MATERIAL

A. Pavers: 4"x8"x2 3/8" inch nominal size; selected from manufacturer's standard range. Pavers shall meet the minimum material and physical property set forth in ASTM C936, Standard Specification for Interlocking Concrete Paving Units. Efflorescence shall not be a cause of rejection.
B. Sand for Leveling Base: Clean, non-plastic, and free from deleterious or foreign matter. The sand shall be natural or manufactured from crushed rock. Limestone screenings or stone dust that do not conform to ASTM C33, as specified in the following table, shall not be used.

Bedding Sand Grading Requirements

Sieve Size	Mass Percent Passing
9.5mm	100%
4.75mm	95-100%
2.36mm	85-100%
1.18mm	50-85%
600μm	25-60%
300μm	10-30%
150μm	2-10%

C. Sand for Joint Fill: Base: Clean, non-plastic, and free from deleterious or foreign matter, conform to ASTM C144, as specified in the following table.

Joint Sand Grading Requirements

Sieve Size	Natural Sand Percent Passing	Manufactured Sand Percent Passing
4.75mm	100%	100%
2.36mm	95-100%	95-100%
1.18mm	70-100%	70-100%
600μm	40-75%	40-75%
300μm	10-35%	20-40%
150μm	2-15%	10-25%
75μm	0%	0-10%

Figure A-2 (*continued*)

D. Edge restrains shall be along all unrestrained paver edges and supported on a minimum of 6" of aggregate base.

Acceptable manufacturer: Pave Tech, Inc.
P.O. Box 31126
Bloomington, MN 55431
Phone (612) 881-5773
Fax (612) 881-2169

PART 3 EXECUTION

3.01 INSPECTION

A. Verify that base is dry, uniform, even and ready to support sand, pavers and imposed loads.
B. Verify gradients and elevations of base are correct.
C. Beginning of installation means acceptance of substrate.

3.02 INSTALLATION

A. The paving brick installer/contractor must have related experience in installation of concrete paving bricks.
B. Ensure that pavers are free of foreign material before installation.
C. Spread sand evenly over concrete base surface to maximum thickness of 1-1/2 inches.
D. Screed sand to level and even surface, properly accounting for compaction of sand.
E. Place paver units in patterns as shown on drawing, from reference edge.
F. Place half units or special shaped units at edges and interruptions. Maintain evenly spaced joints not to exceed 1/8".
G. Tamp and level paver units with mechanical vibrator until units are firmly bedded, level, and to correct elevation and gradient.
H. Sprinkle sand over surface and sweep into joints. Re-cover joints with additional sand until firm joints are achieved. Remove excess sand.
I. Pavers after tamping must be 1/8" to 1/4" above adjacent edge restraints.

3.03 SAMPLING AND TESTING.

A. Two pavers from each pallet shall be sampled and tested in accordance with ASPM C140.
B. Rejection: In case the shipment fails to conform to the specified requirements, the manufacturer may sort it, and new test units shall be selected at random by the purchaser from the retained lot and tested at the expense of the manufacturer. In case the second set of test units fail to conform to the specified requirements, the entire lot shall be rejected.
C. The expense of inspection testing shall be borne by the purchaser, unless otherwise agreed.

END OF SECTION

Figure A-2 (*continued*)

SECTION 02495
LANDSCAPE ACCESSORIES

RIVER TERRACE
IOWA MEMORIAL UNION
UNIVERSITY OF IOWA

IOWA CITY, IOWA

PART 1 GENERAL

1.01 CONDITIONS OF THE CONTRACT

A. The other Contract Documents compliment the requirements of this Section. The General Requirements apply to the work of this Section.

1.02 SCOPE

A. Furnish and install work, including but not limited to:
   1. Metal Edging
   2. Shredded Hardwood Mulch

1.03 SUBMITTALS

A. Submit manufacturer's product data for each type of factory fabricated accessory required, including finish indicated.

1.04 DELIVERY, STORAGE AND HANDLING

A. Deliver, store and handle landscape accessories to prevent damage and deterioration.

PART 2 PRODUCTS

2.01 MATERIALS

A. Metal Edging:
   1. Metal edging shall be 3/16" x 4' stainless steel edging. Submit manufacturer or fabricator for approval.

B. Shredded Hardwood Mulch:
   1. Provide shredded hardwood mulch in all planters, plant saucers, and planting beds to a 4" minimum depth or as shown on details.

C.. Trash Receptacles:
   1. Manufacturer: Forms+Surfaces
      Box 5215
      Santa Barbara, CA 93150
      (805)969-7721 FAX(805)565-1578
   2. Versit Series stainless steel
      Model #AE 7581

PART 3 EXECUTION

3.01 PREPARATION

Figure A-3 Sample technical specification for landscape accessories. (Site amenities, courtesy of Dunbar Jones Partnership, Des Moines, IA)

Source: Delmar/Cengage Learning.

A. Remove loose material and debris from base surface before placing landscape accessories.
B. Locate and layout all landscape accessory items. Obtain Landscape Architect/University Representative's acceptance of layout prior to installation.

3.02 INSTALLATION

A. Metal Edging:
   1. Install metal edging as shown on the drawings.
   2. Install per manufacturer's recommendations.
B. Shredded Hardwood Mulch:
   1. Install shredded hardwood mulch in all planters, plant saucers, and planting beds, as shown on the drawings, to a 4" minimum depth or as shown on details.
C. Trash Receptacles:
   1. Bolt to concrete.

3.03 CLEANING

A. Perform cleaning during installation of the work and upon completion of the work. Remove from site all excess materials, debris, and equipment. Repair damage resulting from landscape accessories work.

END OF SECTION

Figure A-3 (*continued*)

SECTION 02514

PORTLAND CEMENT CONCRETE PAVING

IOWA CITY WATER DIVISION
WATER TREATMENT PLANT – PHASE 3

IOWA CITY, IOWA

PART 1 GENERAL

1.01 WORK INCLUDED
- A. Concrete sidewalks, curbs and gutters.
- B. Surface finish.
- C. Curing.

1.02 RELATED WORK
- A. Section 01050 - Field Engineering.
- B. Section 02200 - Earthwork.
- C. Section 02618 - Pavement Marking.

1.04 REFERENCES
- A. ASTM C33 - Concrete Aggregates.
- B. ASTM C94 - Ready Mixed Concrete.
- C. ASTM C150 - Portland Cement.
- D. ASTM C260 - Air-Entraining Admixtures for Concrete.

1.05 QUALITY ASSURANCE
- A. Perform work in accordance with ACI 301.
- B. Obtain materials from same source throughout.

1.06 REGULATORY REQUIREMENTS
- A. Conform to applicable codes for paving work on public property.

1.07 TESTS
- A. Testing and analysis will be performed under provisions of Section 01400.
- B. Tests of cement and aggregates will be performed to ensure conformance with requirements stated herein.
- C. Three concrete test cylinders will be taken for every 50 or less cu yds of each class of concrete placed each day.
- F. One additional test cylinder will be taken during cold weather and be cured on site under same conditions as concrete it represents.
- G. One slump test will be taken for each set of test cylinders taken.

1.08 SUBMITTALS
- A. Include data on joint filler, admixtures. and curing compounds.
- B. Submit manufacturer's instructions under provisions of Section 01300.

PART 2 PRODUCTS

2.01 CONCRETE MATERIALS
- A. Minimum of 4000 psi compressive strength at twenty-eight days..
- B. As specified in Section 03001.
- C. Water: Clean and not detrimental to concrete.

Figure A-4 Sample technical specification for concrete paving. (Courtesy of Dunbar Jones Partnership, Des Moines, IA)

Source: Delmar/Cengage Learning.

2.02 FORM MATERIALS
Conform to ACI 301.

2.03 REINFORCEMENT
A. As specified in Section 03001.

2.06 CONCRETE MIX
A. Mix concrete in accordance with ASTM C94.

PART 3 EXECUTION

3.01 INSPECTION
A. Verify compacted subgrade is ready to support paving and imposed loads.
B. Verify gradients and elevations of base are correct.
C. Beginning of installation means acceptance of existing conditions.

3.02 PREPARATION
A. Moisten base to minimize absorption of water from fresh concrete.
B. Notify Landscape Architect minimum 24 hours prior to commencement of concreting operations.

3.03 FORMING
A. Place and secure forms to correct location, dimension, and profile.
B. Assemble formwork to permit easy stripping and dismantling without damaging concrete.
C. Place joint fillers vertical in position, in straight lines. Secure to formwork during concrete placement.

3.04 REINFORCEMENT
A. Place reinforcement at mid-height of slabs-on-grade.
B. Interrupt reinforcement at expansion joints.
C. Provide doweled joints at interruptions of concrete with one end of dowel set in capped sleeve to allow longitudinal movement.

3.05 FORMED JOINTS
A. Place control joints at a maximum of 12 foot intervals to correct elevation and profile. See plans for locations. Align curb, gutter, and sidewalk joints.
B. Place joint filler between paving components and building or other appurtenances.

3.06 PLACING CONCRETE
A. Place concrete in accordance with ACI 301.
B. Hot Weather Placement: ACI 301.
C. Cold Weather Placement: ACI 301.
D. Ensure reinforcement, inserts, embedded parts and formed joints are not disturbed during concrete placement.
E. Place concrete continuously between predetermined construction joints. Do not break or interrupt successive pours such that cold joints occur.

3.07 FINISHING
A. Finish as indicated on the plans.
B. Place curing compound on exposed concrete surfaces immediately after finishing. Apply in accordance with manufacturer's instructions.

3.08 FIELD QUALITY CONTROL

A. Field inspection and testing will be performed under provisions of Section 01400.
B. Maintain records of placed concrete items. Record date, location of pour, quantity, air temperature, and test samples taken.

3.09 PROTECTION
A. Immediately after placement, protect concrete under provisions of Section 01500 from premature drying, excessive hot or cold temperatures, and mechanical injury.

END OF SECTION

Figure A-4 *(continued)*

Appendix B

CONSTRUCTION SPECIFICATION INSTITUTE MASTERFORMAT™ NUMBERING SYSTEM FOR SPECIFICATIONS

Following is one of the typical formats used when numbering specifications for construction documents. This system is a standard for classifying work in the construction industry. Occasionally design professionals will modify the number of zeros used, but the lead number seldom changes. Most work related to landscape contracting is located in Division 32, but contractors are urged to review the entire set of construction documents for items related to their work. As of this writing, this format is being reviewed for possible changes and revisions.

Division 1—General Requirements

Division 2—Site Construction

Division 3—Concrete

Division 4—Masonry

Division 5—Metals

Division 6—Wood

Division 7—Thermal and Moisture Protection

Division 8—Doors and Windows

Division 9—Finishes

Division 10—Specialties

Division 11—Equipment

Division 12—Furnishing

Division 13—Special Construction

Division 14—Conveying Systems

Division 21—Fire suppression

Division 22—Plumbing

Division 23—HVAC

Division 26—Electrical

Division 27—Communications

Division 28—Security

Division 31—Earthwork

Division 32—Exterior improvements

Division 33—Site Utilities

Division 34—Transportation

Division 35—Waterway and marine

Appendix C

MEASUREMENT CONVERSIONS

As contractor purchase, calculate, and build with the variety of materials used in landscape construction, they will encounter many situations that require conversion from one standard to another. Commonly used conversions are listed here.

Linear:

12 inches	= 1 foot
36 inches	= 1 yard
3 feet	= 1 yard
5,280 feet	= 1 mile
1,760 yards	= 1 mile

Weights:

16 ounces	= 1 pound
2,000 pounds	= 1 ton

Liquid Measure:

16 fluid ounces	= 1 pint
128 fluid ounces	= 1 gallon
2 pints	= 1 quart
8 pints	= 1 gallon
4 quarts	= 1 gallon

Area:

144 square inches	= 1 square foot
9 square feet	= 1 square yard
43,560 square feet	= 1 acre
100 square feet	= 1 square (sod and shingles)
640 acres	= 1 square mile

Volume:

1,728 cubic inches	= 1 cubic foot
27 cubic feet	= 1 cubic yard

Inch/Decimal Equivalents:

1 inch	= .08 feet
2 inches	= .17 feet
3 inches	= .25 feet
4 inches	= .33 feet
5 inches	= .41 feet
6 inches	= .50 feet
7 inches	= .58 feet
8 inches	= .66 feet
9 inches	= .75 feet
10 inches	= .83 feet
11 inches	= .92 feet

Comparative Volume/Weight:

1 cubic foot water	= 64 pounds
1 cubic foot water	= 7.48 gallons
1 gallon water	= .134 cubic feet
1 cubic foot soil	= approx. 90 pounds
1 cubic foot dry sand	= approx. 100 pounds
1 cubic foot aggregate	= approx. 140 pounds
1 cubic yard soil	= approx. 2,400 pounds
1 cubic yard dry sand	= approx. 2,700 pounds
1cubic yard aggregate	= approx. 3,780 pounds

Metric Conversions:

1 inch	= 25.4 millimeters (mm)
1 inch	= 0.025 meters (m)
1 foot	= 0.30 meter
1 yard	= 0.914 meter
1 millimeter (mm)	= 0.0393 inch
1 meter (m)	= 3.28 feet
1 meter (m)	= 39.37 inches
1 meter (m)	= 1.093 yards
1 square inch	= 654.16 millimeters squared (mm^2)
1 square foot	= 0.092 meter squared (m^2)
1 square meter (m)	= 10.76 square feet
1 hectare	= 2.471 acres
1 cubic inch	= 16,387 cubic millimeters (cm^3)

1 cubic foot	= 0.0283 cubic meter (m^3)
1 cubic millimeter (mm^3)	= 0.00006102 cubic inch
1 cubic meter (m^3)	= 35.314 cubic feet
1 cubic meter (m^3)	= 1.3079 cubic yards
1 fluid ounce	= 28.41 milliliter (mL)
1 gallon	= 4.54 liters (L)
1 milliliter (mL)	= 0.03519 fluid ounce
1 liter (L)	= 0.2199 gallon
1 gram (g)	= 0.0352 ounce
1 kilogram (kg)	= 2.204 pounds
1 tonne (t) (1000 kg)	= 2204.6 pounds
1 kilogram per cubic meter ($1kg/m^3$)	= 0.0622 pounds per cubic foot
1 pound per cubic foot	= 16.108 kilograms per square meter (kg/m^3)

Appendix D

SUPPLEMENTAL MATH FORMULAS

Included in this appendix are construction-related math calculations that serve specific but uncommon purposes. Formulas are provided for calculating the heights of objects, quantities of rip rap, the length of closed or open french drains, edge restraint, contraction joint spacing in concrete, and wood material calculations.

Determining the Heights of Objects

When it is necessary to determine the height of objects such as trees and buildings, two quick processes can be used. A third process involving trigonometric functions is also available, but this process requires special measurement equipment.

Estimating Object Heights. One method to determine heights that has a relatively high margin of error (approximately 10%) is to estimate heights. To estimate heights, select a ruler or similar object that is approximately 1-foot long. Hold the object at arm's length and align the bottom of the ruler with a point at the bottom of the object for which you need to know the height. This point is labeled the beginning point. Walk toward or away from the object until the top of the ruler aligns with the top of the object directly above the beginning point. Still holding the ruler at arm's length, turn the ruler 90 degrees so that it is horizontal with the ground. Align the end of the horizontal ruler with the beginning point. Scan to the other end of the ruler and identify a second point on the ground that corresponds with that end of the ruler. On the ground, measure the distance between the beginning point and the second point. This distance is the approximate height of the object.

Using a Formula to Calculate Object Heights. You can use a simple ratio to calculate object heights if you have enough light to cast shadows. This calculation will have some degree of error (probably less than 10%). To perform this method, measure the length of the shadow for the object you need to determine the height. Then measure your height and your shadow length. It is easier to perform the math if all of your measurements are in feet and tenths. Insert the measurements into the following formula:

(Your height × Shadow length of object) divided by Your shadow length = Height of object

An example of this calculation is shown in Figure D-1.

Using Trigonometry to Calculate Object Heights. If you need a more precise determination of height, then use the formulas from trigonometry. To perform this calculation you will need measurements of your distance from the object and the measurement of the angle between the ground and the top of the object, or the angle of elevation.

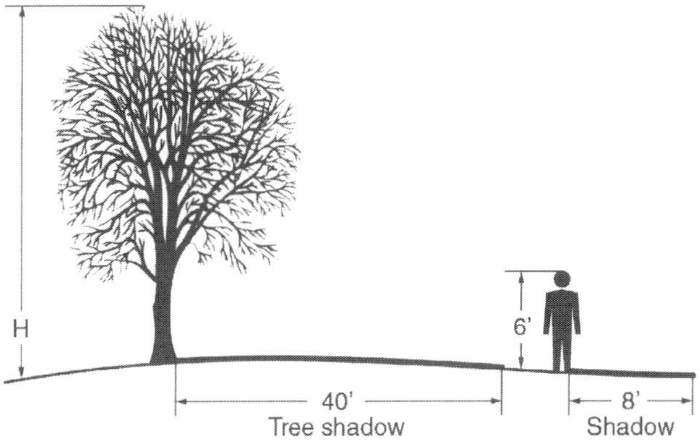

$$\frac{6 \times 40}{8} = H$$

$$\frac{240}{8} = 30'$$

H= Tree height

Figure D-1 Calculating the height of an object using a ratio.

When performing this work, you must be on a level horizontal plane from the bottom of the object you are measuring. Angles of elevation can be measured using a surveyor's transit. When you have these two measurements, insert them into the following formula:

Distance from object × tangent of angle of elevation (from Table D-1) = Height of object

An example of this calculation is shown in Figure D-2.

Calculating Length of French Drains

French drains are sized according to the length of trench required to store water currently pounding on the surface. If your work is located in areas where drainage problems are serious or surface storm water storage is required, consult a design professional who is familiar with calculating water storage based on storm intensity, rainfall amounts, runoff coefficients, and allowable outflow to address the problem. If the drainage problem does not create a hazard to life or property, then you can approximate french drain size. Before performing this calculation, observe the drainage area during a rain to estimate the area and depth of the pond. Use the following steps to determine the length of the french drain (Figure D-3):

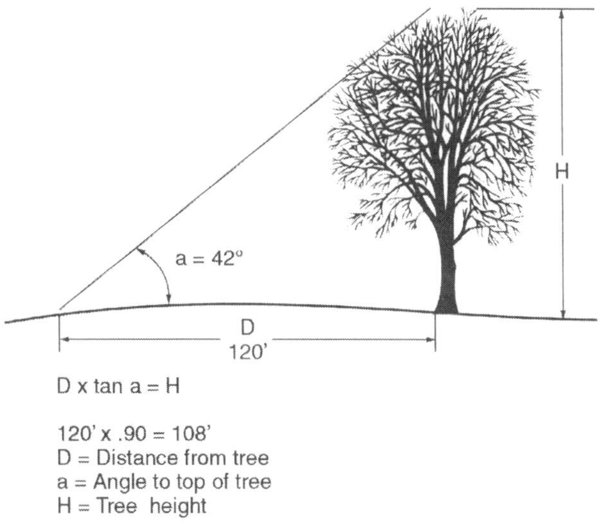

Figure D-2 Calculating the height of an object using a trigonometric formula.

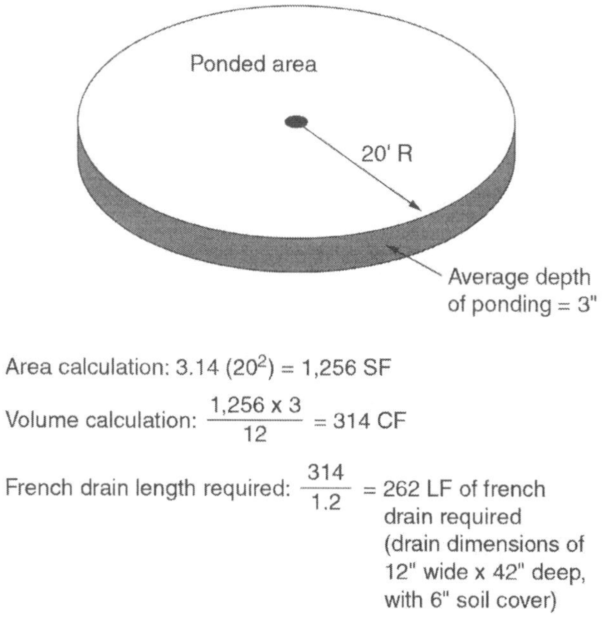

Figure D-3 Calculating length for french drains.

- Estimate the CF of water that requires storage (volume calculation for ponded area).
- Divide the CF of storage by 1.2 (one and two-tenths).

The answer is the length of trench required to store water. The division factor used in the second step provides an answer that is based on the trench that is 12 inches wide, 42 inches deep, and has 6 inches of soil cover. Trenches that have different dimensions will require a different division factor. As trench dimensions diminish, the factor value decreases; as trench dimensions increase, the factor value increases.

Edge Restraint Calculations

The amount of edge restraint required for a project is determined by calculating the perimeter of the area being edged. Most edging is purchased by linear foot, and the perimeter measurement will be adequate. Stone edging materials are ordered by the tonnage, similar to wall material. To determine the tonnage required, calculate the square feet of edging and divide by the number of square feet per ton for stone.

Table D-1 Natural tangents

Angle (in degrees)	Tangent	Angle (in degrees)	Tangent	Angle (in degrees)	Tangent
0	.000	30	.577	60	1.732
1	.017	31	.600	61	1.804
2	.034	32	.624	62	1.880
3	.052	33	.649	63	1.962
4	.069	34	.674	64	2.050
5	.087	35	.700	65	2.144
6	.105	36	.726	66	2.246
7	.122	37	.753	67	2.355
8	.140	38	.781	68	2.475
9	.158	39	.809	69	2.605
10	.176	40	.839	70	2.747
11	.194	41	.869	71	2.904
12	.212	42	.900	72	3.077
13	.230	43	.935	73	3.270
14	.249	44	.965	74	3.487
15	.267	45	1.000	75	3.732
16	.286	46	1.035	76	4.010
17	.305	47	1.072	77	4.331
18	.324	48	1.110	78	4.704
19	.344	49	1.150	79	5.144
20	.363	50	1.191	80	5.671
21	.383	51	1.234	81	6.313
22	.404	52	1.279	82	7.115
23	.424	53	1.327	83	8.144
24	.445	54	1.376	84	9.514
25	.466	55	1.428	85	11.430
26	.487	56	1.482	86	14.300
27	.509	57	1.539	87	19.081
28	.531	58	1.600	88	28.636
29	.554	59	1.664	89	57.290

Calculating Contraction Joint Spacing in Concrete

When tooling or sawing contraction joints in concrete, the spacing is important to control cracking in the surface. To determine an approximate horizontal distance between contraction joints, use the following formula:

- Multiply the thickness of the concrete times 12.
- The answer is a typical spacing (in inches) between joints.

This formula produces an approximate spacing. Other considerations for locating joints include width, shape, and configuration of paved areas.

WOOD MATERIAL CALCULATIONS

Ordering wood materials requires an item count for each size of structural member used. The most efficient method for performing this count is to prepare a plan for the project and make a list of all types of lumber pieces, hardware, and connectors required. Count the number required, paying special attention to those members that will require specific lengths.

The concept of board foot is sometimes used when referring to lumber. One board foot is the equivalent of a 1 foot × 1 foot × 1 inch piece of wood and is a calculation lumber suppliers use when purchasing and pricing wood. Materials in landscape applications seldom use this method for ordering, but the term may appear on billing statements. To calculate board feet, multiply the width of the board, in inches, by the thickness of the board, in inches, by the length of board, in feet, then divide the answer by 12. Dimensions less than 1 inch are considered as 1 inch.

Appendix E

SAMPLE BID FORMS

Following are sample forms that businesses use to bid landscape construction and maintenance work. Forms will vary significantly based on the type of bid to submit.

The Village Gardener
2975 Fair Oaks Avenue
Redwood City, CA 94063
(650) 306-9449
(650) 306 9473 (FAX)

Estimate

DATE	ESTIMATE NO.
4/21/2003	288

NAME / ADDRESS

P.O. NO.	PROJECT

QTY	DESCRIPTION	COST	TOTAL
	Renovate existing irrigation system		
	Front yard:		
	Valve box at right side of house - Raise Hosebib 12"		
4	Weathermatic 1" valve - replace 4 valves (serve front lawn/yard)	185.00	740.00
65	Ln. ft. 1" PVC pipe	3.50	227.50
2	Rainbird nozzle - replace 2 nozzles and check additional 16 for lawn)	3.00	6.00
6	Rainbird 12" pop-up sprinkler - replace in front right side planter	40.00	240.00
6	Rainbird 12" pop-up sprinkler - add to planter beds on right and left side (of door) against house	40.00	240.00
5	Rainbird 12" pop-up sprinkler - at left side lawn change 4 plus add 1	40.00	200.00
	Subtotal		1,653.50
	Valve box at left side of driveway		
1	Weathermatic 1" valve - replace and remove 1 - only 1 valve needed with pop up sprinklers, remove bubblers	185.00	185.00
3	Rainbird 12" pop-up sprinkler - change	40.00	120.00
16	Man hour(s) of labor	40.00	640.00
	Subtotal		945.00
	Backyard (4 valves):		
	Valve box in lawn area-		
6	Rainbird 12" pop-up sprinkler - lawn	40.00	240.00
1	Weathermatic 1" valve - new for drip	185.00	185.00
9	Hunter 6" PGP adjustable pop-up sprinkler - replace PGP's - main lawn area (serviced by 2 valves)	65.00	585.00
16	Man hour(s) of labor	40.00	640.00
Estimate is valid for 90 days		**Total**	

Page 1

Figure E-1 Sample bid form for irrigation work. (Courtesy of Frank Niccoli, The Village Gardener, Redwood City, CA)

Source: Delmar/Cengage Learning

The Village Gardener
2975 Fair Oaks Avenue
Redwood City, CA 94063
(650) 306-9449
(650) 306 9473 (FAX)

Estimate

DATE	ESTIMATE NO.
4/21/2003	288

NAME / ADDRESS

P.O. NO.	PROJECT

QTY	DESCRIPTION	COST	TOTAL
	Subtotal		1,650.00
	Sideyard (3 valves):		
7	Rainbird 12" pop-up sprinkler - additional for areas not met with water (on rose garden) + remove drip system from sprinkler valve	40.00	280.00
1	Weathermatic 1" valve - add for Arbutus area and planter at gate/fence area	185.00	185.00
1	Rainbird nozzle - change to center strip	3.00	3.00
6	Man hour(s) of labor	40.00	240.00
	Subtotal		708.00

Estimate is valid for 90 days	**Total**	$4,956.50

Page 2

Figure E-1 (*continued*)

Proposal Page # ______ of ______ pages

M. WILSON LANDSCAPE CONTRACTING

Proposal Submitted To: WALTER ANDERSON		Job Name FENCING	Job # —
Address 2855 H. AVE		Job Location SITE	
WILLIAMSBURG, IA 52361		Date 4/22/02	Date of Plans SAME
Phone #	Fax #		Architect M. WILSON

We hereby submit specifications and estimates for:

60 LF REDWOOD ALTERNATING BOARD WOOD FENCE – 6' HIGH
7 – 8' PANELS AND 1 – 4' PANEL

MATERIALS: (ALL CONSTRUCTION HEART REDWOOD)

– 8 BAGS SACRETE @ \$3/EACH	\$ 24 –
– 9 4x4 – 10' @ \$36/EA.	324 –
– 8 2x8 – 8' @ \$18/EA	144 –
– 16 2x4 – 8' @ \$8/EA	128 –
– 105 1x8 – 6' @ \$11/EA	1155 –
– 64 1x1 – 8' @ \$5/EA	320 –
– 5 LBS 8d GALV. NAILS @ \$3/EA	15 –
EQUIPMENT RENTAL – POWER AUGER, 1 DAY	\$ 150 –
LABOR – 48 HOURS (2 PERSON CREW) @ \$40/HR	\$1920 –

We propose hereby to furnish material and labor — complete in accordance with the above specifications for the sum of:

\$ 4180.00 (FOUR THOUSAND ONE HUNDRED EIGHTY AND NO/100) Dollars

with payments to be made as follows: HALF UPON ACCEPTANCE, HALF UPON COMPLETION

Any alteration or deviation from above specifications involving extra costs will be executed only upon written order, and will become an extra charge over and above the estimate. All agreements contingent upon strikes, accidents, or delays beyond our control.

Respectfully submitted Michael Wilson

Note — this proposal may be withdrawn by us if not accepted within 7 days.

Acceptance of Proposal

The above prices, specifications and conditions are satisfactory and are hereby accepted. You are authorized to do the work as specified. Payments will be made as outlined above.

Signature ______________________

Date of Acceptance ______________________ Signature ______________________

NC3819 MADE IN USA

Figure E-2 Sample bid for fence installation.

Source: Delmar/Cengage Learning

Appendix F

RESOURCES

To further supplement the information provided in this text, several organizations related to the construction and design of landscapes are listed in this appendix. This list is for reference only and is not an endorsement of the associations' products or views. This list is current as of August 2009, but changes often occur in the contact information. Addresses and phone numbers are shown as presented in literature and on Web sites. Some organizations require membership or payment of a fee before you can obtain information from them.

Professional Associations

The National Association of Landscape Professionals (Formerly PLANET)

950 Herndon Parkway, Suite 450

Herndon, VA 20170

800-395-2522

www.landscapeprofessionals.orgAmericanHort

Columbus Ohio:

2130 Stella Court

Columbus, Ohio 43215 USA

614-487-1117

Washington DC:

529 9th St. NW, Suite 800

Washington, DC 20004 USA
www.americanhort.org

Association of Professional Landscape Dsigners

2207 Forest Hills Drive

Harrisburg, PA 17112

717-238-9780 www.apld.com

American Society of Landscape Architects

636 Eye Street, NW

Washington, DC 20001-3736

202-898-2444 www.asla.org

The American Institute of Architects

1735 New York Ave., NW

Washington, DC 20006

800-AIA-3837 www.aia.org

Portland Cement Association

5420 Old Orchard Road

Skokie, IL 60077

847-966-6200

Interlocking Concrete Paving Institute

14801 Murdock Street, Suite 230

Chantilly, VA 20151

703-657-6900 www.icpi.org

Professional Grounds Maintenance Society

720 Light Street

Baltimore, MD 21230

410-223-2861

National Concrete Masonry Association

13750 Sunrise Valley Drive

Herndon, VA 20171-3499

800-455-4322

The Construction Specifications Institute
110 South Union Street, Suite 100
Alexandria, VA 22314
800-689-2900

The Southern Pine Inspection Bureau
P.O. Box 10915
Pensacola, FL 32524-0915
850-434-2611

International Wood Products Association
4214 King Street, West
Alexandria, VA 22302
703-820-6696

Appendix G

CAROLINA LAWNS PUBLICATION

Courtesy North Carolina State University Cooperative Extension Service

Carolina Lawns

A Guide to Maintaining Quality Turf in the Landscape

Lawns are smooth, living carpets that add beauty and recreational space to your home. The benefits of a healthy lawn go beyond the obvious. As your grass grows, it helps the environment by stabilizing soil and reducing air pollution, noise, heat, dust, and glare. Surveys show that an attractive, well-landscaped lawn can even add to the value of your home.

To reap the rewards of a handsome lawn, take great care in the selection, establishment, maintenance, and renovation of your lawn grass. By making the proper choices, you can create a durable lawn that will grow with minimal maintenance and pesticide use.

Recommendations for the use of agricultural chemicals are included in this publication as a convenience to the reader. The use of brand names and any mention or listing of commercial products or services in this publication does not imply endorsement by the North Carolina Cooperative Extension Service nor discrimination against similar products or services not mentioned. Individuals who use agricultural chemicals are responsible for ensuring that the intended use complies with current regulations and conforms to the product label. Be sure to obtain current information about usage regulations and examine a current product label before applying any chemical. For assistance, contact your county Cooperative Extension agent.

Professional lawn care companies may use a maintenance schedule that differs from what is described in this publication, and it may be equally effective.

Contents

What To Plant

Whether you are establishing a new lawn or renovating an existing one, deciding which type of grass to plant will be the first step. No one type of grass is best suited to all situations. A number of factors should be considered before deciding which lawn grass to plant. Your decision should be based on region, climate, intended use or wear at the site, and desired appearance.

Find your region in the map in Figure 1. Both cool-season (northern) and warm-season (southern) grasses are grown in North Carolina (Table 1, page 5). Cool-season grasses grow best in the spring and fall and less actively in the summer. They stayreasonably green in the winter. Tall fescue, Kentucky bluegrass, fine fescue, and perennial ryegrass are common types of cool-season grasses. Table 3 (page 9) rates the performance of various cultivars of these grasses in North Carolina. Warm-season grasses are slow to green up in the spring, grow best in the summer, and go dormant after the first heavy frost. Table 4 (page 10) lists many warm-season cultivars.

Table 1. Responses to Soil Temperature for Cool and Warm-season Grasses

Event	**Temperature at Which Event Occurs**	
	Cool-season Grasses	**Warm-season Grasses**
Shoot growth ceases due to heat	90°F	120°F
Root growth ceases due to heat	77°F	110°F
Maximum temperature for root growth of any consequence	70°F	N/A
Optimum shoot growth	60 – 75°F	80 – 90°F
Optimum root growth	50 – 65°F	75 – 85°F
Expected spring root decline triggered	N/A	64°F Roots turn brown and die within 1 or 2 days. This decline occurs only if a very cold winter is followed by a rapid spring warm-up.
Shoot growth ceases due to cold	40°F	N/A
Root growth ceases due to cold	33°F	50°F Root growth begins to slow below this temperature. Chilling injury resulting in discoloration is possible. Initiation of dormancy results in discoloration
Low temperature kill possible	If temperature drops rapidly below 20°F	25°F

Also consider the characteristics of each site and your goals to determine which types of grass are appropriate. Choose the grass that best meets your preference for color, density, and texture. Choose a tough, aggressive, wear-tolerant grass where heavy traffic is expected. And consider the amount of time, effort, and money you are willing to spend for turfgrass maintenance.

Cool-season Grasses

Tall fescue, Kentucky bluegrass, perennial ryegrass, and fine fescues—such as creeping red, chewings, and hard—are cool-season perennial grasses used for lawns, mostly in the mountain and piedmont regions of North Carolina. Unlike warm-season grasses, cool-season grasses remain green throughout most of the winter. They are better adapted to the mountains and piedmont. These grasses perform best in spring and fall and have a tendency to show signs of stress in the summer. This is especially true as you move toward the coastal plain. Cool-season grasses are best seeded in early fall, but fair results may be obtained from seeding in early spring (mid-February to late March in the piedmont). Generally, late winter or spring seeding of these grasses is not recommended.

Tall fescue is best adapted to the mountains and piedmont but can be successfully maintained on the heavy silt loams in the coastal plain. It is a reliable performer and easily started from seed. It is the best grass to plant if you want a year-round green lawn. Tall fescue thrives in sun or medium shade. It will not perform well in full sun in the coastal plain, especially if the soil is sandy. It can be seeded by itself or mixed with Kentucky bluegrass, fine fescue, or both, particularly where shade is a concern. Tall fescue is a bunch-type grass, so damaged or bare areas will need to be re-seeded. It exhibits good disease resistance, drought tolerance, and cold tolerance; tolerates moderate traffic; and persists with minimum care. Several improved tall fescue cultivars have been developed that are more shade tolerant, denser, and finer textured than Kentucky 31, a commonly used older cultivar. These characteristics become more evident as the turf matures and the maintenance level increases. Research has shown that some of these improved cultivars also have darker green color, improved disease tolerance, lower growth habit, better wear tolerance, and drought tolerance.

Experts recommend that a blend of two or three cultivars be planted rather than seeding just a single cultivar. This broadens the genetic base and gives the turf a better chance of withstanding a variety of challenges. Use a seeding rate of 6 pounds per 1,000 square feet (sq ft). Don't assume more is better. Higher seeding rates can result in weak, thin stands that are more susceptible to disease and high temperature stress.

The tall fescues perform best when mowed at a height of 3 inches, and should never be mowed shorter than 2.5 inches. Tall fescue may turn brown, yet can often survive short periods of drought. Under certain circumstances, some tall fescue may be lost if a drought exceeds three weeks. To maintain a green lawn, it is best to irrigate, if possible, during periods of drought.

Kentucky bluegrass produces a high-quality, medium- to fine-textured turf, at least when grown in the right climate. In North Carolina, it is well suited for the mountains and can be grown in combination with tall fescue in the piedmont. It is not suitable for use in the coastal plain. Kentucky bluegrass prefers fertile, limed, well-drained soils in sun or light shade. Excellent sod results from rhizomes (underground stems) that spread, with most cultivars recuperating from and tolerating pest control measures and moderate levels of traffic. Many new cultivars with improved color, texture, and pest resistance are now commercially available.

As with most cool-season grasses, it is best to broaden the genetic base by planting a blend of two to three cultivars rather than seeding a single cultivar. It is also common for Kentucky bluegrass to be seeded in combination with tall fescue. The tall fescueenhances drought and heat tolerance, whereas the Kentucky bluegrass provides finer texture and greater recuperative potential. Generally, Kentucky bluegrass grows better than tall fescue in moderate shade. When mixed with tall fescue, Kentucky bluegrass tends to dominate where the soil is limed and the turf is adequately fertilized and mowed fairly short.

Kentucky bluegrass should be mowed at a height of 1.5 to 2.5 inches when planted alone. It should be mowed at 2.5 inches or higher when mixed with tall fescue. Seeding rates range from 1 to 2 pounds per 1,000 sq ft. Higher rates can result in weak, thin stands that are more susceptible to disease and high temperature stress.

Even though Kentucky bluegrass may turn brown during a two to four-week summer drought, it is not necessary to irrigate. Kentucky bluegrass recovers well from most droughts, and watering will often increase disease problems.

Fine fescues include creeping red, chewings, and hard fescue. The name is derived from the very finely textured leaves, which are almost as fine as pine needles. Noted for tolerance to shade, drought, and poor soil conditions compared to other cool-season grasses, fine fescues are often included with tall fescue or Kentucky bluegrass when planted in the shade or subject to low maintenance. They are best adapted to the mountains but can be grown in the piedmont. They should not be used in the coastal plain. They may not persist insunny locations exposed to high temperature extremes, excessive soil moisture or humidity, or heavy traffic.

Fine fescue seed should be mixed with Kentucky bluegrass because most of the fine fescues are bunch type and do not have the ability to spread. New seedlings establish quickly due to excellent seedling vigor. Seed fine fescue at 1.5 pounds per 1,000 sq ft when mixed with either tall fescue or Kentucky bluegrass.

Fine fescue should be mowed at 1.5 to 2.5 inches when mixed with Kentucky bluegrass but at 2.5 inches or higher when mixed with tall fescue.

Perennial ryegrass is similar in appearance to Kentucky bluegrass, but is only adapted to the mountains. In North Carolina it is never seeded alone but always mixed with Kentucky bluegrass. These grasses complement each other because perennial ryegrass establishes faster than Kentucky bluegrass, and Kentucky bluegrass has the ability to spread and fill in damaged areas.

A mix of Kentucky bluegrass and perennial ryegrass should be seeded at the rate of 2.5 pounds per 1,000 sq ft, with Kentucky bluegrass making up 60 percent of the mix by weight.

Perennial ryegrass should be mowed at 1.5 to 2.5 inches when mixed with Kentucky bluegrass.

Annual ryegrass is used only when a temporary turf cover is needed. It is *never* recommended for permanent lawn mixtures because it dies in late spring, when temperatures approach 80ºF or higher. It is sometimes found in inexpensive commercial seed mixtures but should be avoided. Because annual ryegrass is an annual, it must be re-seeded each fall. Annual ryegrass has been used by some homeowners to provide winter color for bermudagrass lawns. It is never recommended for overseeding other warm-season grasses.

Warm-season Grasses

Bermudagrass, zoysiagrass, centipedegrass, St. Augustinegrass, carpetgrass, and bahiagrass are clas-sified as warm-season perennial grasses. All except bahiagrass are mostly recommended for lawns in the piedmont and coastal plain of North Carolina. They grow best in the summer, go dormant in the fall at the first heavy frost, turn brown, and then green up slowly the following spring. For this reason, they usually perform better the farther east and south you go in those regions. Warm-season grasses are best planted in late spring and early summer. Unlike cool-season grasses, some warm-season grasses must be planted either by and slow-growing. They are very slow to establish from plugs, often taking three years for total coverage when sod or other vegetative means because seeds either are not available or do not result in uniform stands. Warm-season grasses are usually seeded or planted as a single variety (monoculture) rather than in blends and mixtures.

Bermudagrass spreads by stolons and rhizomes, and it can invade flowerbeds and other areas because it has runners that spread rapidly both above and below ground. But bermudagrass is extremely drought tolerant, grows rapidly on any type of soil except where drainage is poor, and makes a good turf if fertilized and mowed low and often. Cultivar texture ranges from coarse to fine, and it forms a dense, durable surface when grown in full sunlight. The majority of cultivars will not tolerate shade. Bermudagrass is well adapted to sandy soils. Bermudagrass establishes quickly, withstands wear and traffic, and recovers rapidly from injury.

Most finely textured, high-quality turf-type bermudagrasses are planted using sod, sprigs, or plugs. Common bermudagrass, which is the most coarsely textured, can be seeded. Several newer cultivars, however, can also be seeded that have a medium texture. Bermudagrass should be seeded at 1 to 2 pounds per 1,000 sq ft.

Bermudagrass lawns perform best when mowed at 0.75 to 1 inch using a reel mower. However, good performance can be achieved with a rotary mower with sharp blades set as low as possible without scalping. Uneven ground can make mowing below 1 inch difficult. For this reason, a 1- to 2-inch mowing height is recommended when using a rotary mower. For best results, bermudagrass should be mowed often (at least twice per week), especially at the lower mowing heights.

Zoysiagrass spreads by stolons and rhizomes, but it is easier to keep out of flowerbeds than bermudagrass. Zoysiagrass produces a very dense, wear-tolerant lawn that grows well in full sun and light shade. It has stiff leaves that produce a very dense turf, which peopleoften describe as feeling like "walking on a cushion." Zoysiagrass grows more slowly than bermudagrass, and thus requires less frequent mowing. But because the leaves are stiff, mowing can be difficult unless the mower blades are sharp. The finer-textured zoysiagrasses ideally should be mowed with a reel mower, whereas the coarser-textured zoysiagrasses can be mowed with a rotary mower. Zoysiagrass is very drought resistant. It rarely needs irrigation to survive in North Carolina.

Zoysiagrass cultivars were once limited to two cultivars: Meyer and the finer textured Emerald. These cultivars must be planted vegetatively, and are low- planted on 12-inch centers. These older cultivars can become thatchy—puffy due to an accumulation of dead, dying, decaying plant residue at the soil surface. This is especially so when these grasses are mowed high and infrequently or heavily fertilized. Thatch may need to be removed every two to three years, but care should be taken because the recovery rate of these cultivars is very slow.

In the last 20 years, a number of zoysiagrass cultivars have been released. These cultivars, such as El Toro, Crowne, Palisades, Empire, and Jamur, are coarser in texture (similar to newer tall fescues) and are quicker to establish and recover from injury. They are not as cold tolerant as Meyer and should not be mowed as short as Emerald and Meyer. Cavalier, Zeon, and Zorro are new zoysiagrass cultivars with a moderate growth rate and a fine texture similar to Emerald. Cold tolerance of zoysia is not a problem in North Carolina's piedmont and coastal plain.

A few cultivars of zoysiagrass, such as Compadre, Zenith, Zen 100, and Zen 300CS, can be seeded. These coarse-textured zoysiagrasses are typically mowed with a rotary mower.

Centipedegrass spreads by stolons. Centipedegrass is a slow growing, apple-green, coarsely leaved turfgrass that is best used as a low maintenance, general purpose turf. It requires little fertilizer once established (0.5 to 1 pound of nitrogen per 1,000 sq ft per year) and infrequent mowing, and it grows well on acidic soils in full sun to partial shade. It does not tolerate traffic, compaction, high soil pH, high soil phosphorus, excessive thatch, drought, or heavy shade.

Centipedegrass is slow to establish and may take two to three years when seeded. It should be mowed when it attains 1 inch in height and no higher than 1.5 inches. Centipedegrass can become thatchy, especially when mowed high and infrequently or when heavily fertilized. Thatch may need to be removed every two to three years, but care should be taken because the stems can easily be torn from the ground, leaving bare spots.

TifBlair, an improved cultivar from the University of Georgia, is quicker to establish and more cold tolerant then common centipedegrass. It also retains its green color later in the fall.

St. Augustinegrass spreads by stolons. St. Augustinegrass is a fast-growing turfgrass best adapted to the coastal plain. It has a medium- to dark-green color and very coarsely textured leaves. With proper maintenance, it will provide a dense, lush lawn. St. Augustinegrass is very shade and salt tolerant but is considered the least cold tolerant lawn grass. The cultivar Raleigh has the best cold tolerance and is well adapted for the eastern side of the piedmont and the western side of the coastal plain.

Seed is unavailable, so cultivars must be vegetatively planted. St. Augustinegrass grows best in fertile, well-drained soils.

Because St. Augustinegrass is fast growing, it needs to be mowed frequently at 2.5 to 4 inches during the growing season using a rotary mower. It should never receive more than 4 pounds of nitrogen per 1,000 sq ft annually. At high rates of fertilization and irrigation, thatch buildup may become a problem. St. Augustinegrass is not tolerant of heavy traffic, compaction, or cold weather.

Carpetgrass spreads by stolons. Carpetgrass is a slow- and low-growing, medium-green, coarsely textured lawngrass. It produces a low maintenance, general purpose turf. Carpetgrass resembles St. Augustinegrass and centipedegrass and is often mistaken for centipedegrass but has broader leaves. It grows well in full sun to moderate shade and performs well in wet, shaded, acid soils where other lawngrasses may not grow. It grows best in full sunlight when daytime temperatures are between 60 and 90ºF, and does not tolerate cold, drought, salt, or traffic. Carpetgrass requires only 1 pound of nitrogen per 1,000 sq ft annually, and needs to be mowed only infrequently at 1.5 inches.

Bahiagrass spreads by stolons and rhizomes. Bahiagrass is never recommended as a lawn grass because of its open canopy, unsightly seedheads, and difficulty in mowing. It is best used on roadsides where appearance is not a concern and low maintenance is the rule.

A comparative chart of principal lawn grasses used in each region is provided in Table 2 (page 8). Study the chart to help select the appropriate grass for the site and the intended use of the lawn. This information is based on cultivar (variety) trials and observations by turfgrass researchers at North Carolina State University.

The NC State TurfFiles Turf Select Decision Aid program (http://www.TurfFiles.ncsu.edu/turfselect/) is a free online tool designed to guide homeowners through the turf selection process. Cultivar performance recommendations are based on overall quality ratings for each of these commercially available varieties. The National Turf Evaluation Program (NTEP) trial research results have been consolidated into an easy-to-use question-and-answer program that provides proven grass types and cultivars suitable for your region and use.

Establishing a New Lawn

Establishing a healthy, attractive lawn means planting the best grass for your site at the right time and in a careful manner. Grass can be seeded or established using vegetation in the form of sprigs, plugs, or sod. The type of grass and the planting method you select will determine the best time of year to plant. Site and soil preparation, including fertilization, are especially important.

Site Preparation

Preparing the site involves removing weeds and debris, planning for drainage, and grading the site.

1. Control perennial weeds with a nonselective herbicide. Hard-to-control weeds may require the services of a professional.
2. Remove debris. Insist that the builder ***not*** use the site as a dumping ground for paint, concrete, and other materials.
3. Plan for easy maintenance and a pleasing appearance. Avoid terraces, steep grades, poorly drained areas, and heavily shaded spots.

4. Install tile drain in poorly drained areas. Get professional advice about the type of drain and installation.
5. Remove the topsoil (usually 4 to 8 inches) and stockpile it nearby if grading is needed. (If bringing topsoil from other sites, be cautious. It may contain hard-to-control weeds or weed seeds.)
6. Build protective walls to save trees if the finalgrade is to be appreciably higher than the present level.
7. Shape the underlying subsoil to the desired contour, and redistribute topsoil uniformly above the subsoil. A 2 to 3 percent slope is needed for proper drainage away from buildings. Make certain the soil is firmed after shaping. There should be no visible footprints after walking on it.
8. Water the area to enhance settling. Fill areas that settle unevenly to avoid standing water.
9. If possible, mix 1 to 2 cubic yards of peat moss or compost per 1,000 sq ft into the top 6 to 8 inches of subsoil if planting in heavy clay or very sandy soils. Clay soils are prone to compaction and require frequent aerification (removal of soilcores).

Soil Preparation

Well-prepared soil with adequate nutrients for growing grass encourages the development of a healthy lawn.

1. Take soil samples from the front yard and the backyard to determine soil pH and nutrient requirements. A single soil test may be all that is necessary if there are no obvious differences in soil texture, terrain, or troubled areas of the front yard and backyard. If the soils seem different, collect soil samples to a depth of 3 to 4 inches from several (10 to 15) locations and mix them together to produce a composite sample. Send approximately 1 cup of the air-dried soil sample to the NCDA & CS Agronomic Division Soil Testing Services, 1040 Mail Service Center, Raleigh NC 27607. Boxes and forms can be obtained at your county Cooperative Extension center or at the Agronomic Division office in Raleigh. Allow several weeks for the results to be returned.
2. Based on the soil test report recommendations or the fertilization guidelines presented below, incorporate lime and fertilizer into the top 6 to 8 inches of the soil using a disk or rototiller. Regardless of the region, a deeper root system is able to extract more moisture and nutrients from the soil, improving drought tolerance and overall health of the plant.
3. Rake or harrow the site to establish a smooth and level final grade. Soil particles should be no larger than marble size, and pea gravel size is even better. Hand raking is the best way to level the soil and work out hills and hollows. Allow time for rain or irrigation to settle the soil, and roll or cultipack lightly to firm the soil before planting seed, sprigs, plugs, or sod. Hand rake again to break up the crusty surface before planting.

Fertilization

As recommended above, it's best to submit a soil sample for testing when establishing a new lawn to determine how much lime and fertilizer should be added to your soil. This is especially important if you are planting centipedegrass. It prefers acidic soils and low levels of phosphorus and may not require the addition of lime and phosphorus.

Fertilize before planting. Apply fertilizer and lime when the soil is prepared based on these guidelines:
If you obtained a soil test: Apply the amount of lime and fertilizer recommended for your soil by the soil testing laboratory. For additional informationabout interpreting a soil test, visit this Web site: http://www. ncagr.com/agronomi/uyrst.htm
If you did not obtain a soil test: Follow these recommendations for all grasses except centipedegrass.

Table 2. Characteristics of Principal Lawn Grasses Grown in North

Lawn grass	Can Be Seeded?	Tolerance					Appearance		Preferr	Rate of Establish-	Maintenance		
		Shade	Heat	Cold	Drought	Wear	Color	Texture			Cutting Height (in.	Fertilizer (lb N/1,000 sq ft/yr)	Mowing Frequency**
MOUNTAINS													
Kentucky bluegrass	Yes	4	3	5	4	4	Med-dark	Medium	Fall	Moderate	1.5 – 2.5	2 –3	Medium
Kentucky bluegrass/fine fescue mix	Yes	4	3	5	4	3	Med-dark	Fine-med	Fall	Moderate	1.5 – 2.5	2 –3	Medium
Kentucky bluegrass/tall fescue mix	Yes	4	4	5	5	5	Med-dark	Med-coarse	Fall	Fast	2.5 – 3.5	2 – 3	High
Kentucky bluegrass/tall fescue/ fine fescue mix	Yes	5	4	5	5	5	Med-dark	Med-coarse	Fall	Fast	2.5 – 3.5	2 – 3	High
Kentucky bluegrass/ perennial ryegrass mix	Yes	4	3	5	4	5	Med-dark	Medium	Fall	Fast	2 – 3	2.5 – 3.5	Med-high
Tall fescue	Yes	4	4	5	5	5	Medium	Med-coarse	Fall	Fast	2.5 –	2.5 –	High
											3.5	3.5	
PIEDMONT													
Bermudagrass (common)	Yes	1	5	1	6	6	Medium	Medium	Spr–sum	Fast	0.75 – 2	4 –4.5	Med-high
Bermudagrass (hybrid)	No	1	5	2	6	6	Light-dark	Fine	Spr–sum	Moderate	0.75 – 2	3 – 6	High
Bahiagrass	Yes	4	4	2	6	4	Med-dark	Coarse	Spr–sum	Moderate	2 – 4	1	High

Centipedegrass	Yes	4	4	2	4	1	Light	Coarse	Spr–sum	Slow	1 – 1.5	1 – 2	Low
Kentucky bluegrass/tall	Yes	4	4	5	5	5	Med-dark	Med-coarse	Fall	Fast	2.5 –	2 –	High
fescue mix											3.5	4	
Kentucky bluegrass/tall fescue/ fine fescue mix	Yes	5	4	5	5	5	Med-dark	Med-coarse	Fall	Fast	2.5 – 3.5	2 – 4	High
St. Augustinegrass	No	5	5	2	4	1	Med-dark	Coarse	Spr–sum	Moderate	2.5 – 4	2 – 3	Med-high
Tall fescue	Yes	4	4	5	5	5	Medium	Coarse	Fall	Fast	2.5 – 3.5	2 – 4	High
Zoysiagrass	Yes	4	5	4	6	4	Med-dark	Fine-med	Spr–sum	Very slow	0.75 – 2	1 – 3	Low-med
COASTAL PLAIN													
Bermudagrass (common)	Yes	1	5	1	6	6	Medium	Medium	Spr–sum	Fast	0.75 – 2	3 – 4.5	Med-high
Bermudagrass (hybrid)	No	1	5	2	6	6	Light-dark	Fine	Spr–sum	Moderate	0.75 – 2	3 – 6	Very high
Bahaiagrass	Yes	4	5	2	6	4	Med-dark	Coarse	Spr–sum	Moderate	2 – 4	1	High
Centipedegrass	Yes	4	4	2	4	2	Light	Coarse	Spr–sum	Slow	1 – 1.5	1 – 2	Low
St. Augustinegrass	No	5	5	2	4	2	Med-dark	Coarse	Spr–sum	Moderate	2.5 – 4	2 – 4	Med-high

Tallfescue	Yes	4	4	5	5	5	Medium	Coarse	Fall	Fast	2.5 – 3.5	2 – 4	High
Zoysiagrass	Yes	4	5	4	6	4	Med-dark	Fine-med	Spr–sum	Very slow	0.75 – 2	2 – 4	Low-high

Key for tolerance ratings: 6—Excellent 5—Very good 4—Good 3—Fair 2—Poor 1—Very poor Abbreviations: Med—Medium, Spr—Spring, Sum—Summer

Note: Some improved cultivars are better adapted and more pleasing in appearance than the comparison rating provided for a given lawn grass. Check with your county Cooperative Extension center concerning specific cultivars that have characteristics of interest to you. See Table 5 for suggested months of establishment.

*Establishment rate is dictated by planting dates, seeding and planting rate, intensity of culture, and environment.

** Mowing frequency is dictated by season, intensity of management, and use.

Table 3. Cool-season Grass Cultivars with Excellent Performance in North Carolina

Grass Type			Cultivar Name		
Tall fescue	2nd Millenium Avenger Barlexas Barlexas II Barrera Barrington Biltmore Bingo Bonsai Bravo Cayenne Constitutio n Coyote Davinci Desire	Dominion Dynasty Endeavor Escalade Falcon II Falcon IV Fidelity Finesse II Fireaza Firebird Focus Grande II Greenkeep er Greystone	Hunter Inferno Jaguar 3 Justice Kalahar i Kitty Hawk 2000 Legitimate Lexington Magellan Masterpiece Matador Millennium Millennium	Olympic Gold Padre Picasso Plantation Proseeds 5301 Prospect Pure Gold Quest Rebel Exeda Rebel Sentry Rebel IV Regiment	Scorpion Serengeti Signia Silverstar Southern Choice II Stetson Tarheel Titan ltd Titanium Tracer Ultimate Watchdo g Wolfpack
Kentuck y bluegras s	Alpine Apollo Arcadia* Arrow Award Awesome Bariras Baronie Bedazzle d Bewitche d Beyond	Blackstone Blueberry Bodacious Boomeran g Bordeaux Boutique Brilliant Cabernet Champagn e Champlain Chicago	Eagleton Envicta Everest Everglade Excursion Freedom II Hallmark Impact Jefferson Jewel	Langara Liberator Limousine Midnight Moonlight Nuglade Odyssey Prosperity Quantum Leap	Rambo Rita Royce Rugby Showcas e Sonoma Skye Total Eclipse Unique Washingto
Fine fescue	Ambassad or Berkshire Cardinal Class One Compass*	DP Edgewood * Firefly Fortitude Garnet Gotham	Jasper II Musica* Oxford Pathfinde r Predator*	Quatro Razor* Reliant IV*	Scaldis Spartan II Seabreez e Zodiac
Perenni al ryegras s	Accent II Allstar 3 Apple GL Brighstar SLT Caddieshack II Charismatic II Citation Fore Dart	Fiesta 4 Fiji Goalkeeper II Grand Slam 2 Harrier Headstart 2 Homerun Inspire Keystone II	Line Drive GLS Majesty II Manhattan 5 GLR Monterey 3 Nexus Palace Palmer III Palmer IV Panther	Paragon GLR Pentium Phenom Pianist Pinnacle II Pizzazz Premier Primary	Quicksilver Repell GLS Revenge GLX Secretariat II Silver Dollar Transforme r Top Gun

A rating of *excellent* means that the cultivar was not significantly different from the top performing cultivar regarding overall quality.

*These cultivars have not been tested in North Carolina but have performed well in surrounding states.

Table 4. Performance of Warm-season Grass Cultivars in North Carolina

Grass Type	Cultivar	Comments
Bermudagrass , seeded cultivars	Arizona Common Mohawk Numex Sahara Savannah Southern Star Sunbird Sundevil II Sunstar Transcontinent alYukon Riviera Princess	These cultivars are available as seed and will produce acceptable quality under proper management. They closely resemble common bermudagrass in its coarse texture and light-green color. **Transcontinental, Yukon, Riviera,** and **Princess** are finer textured and denser than other seeded cultivars. **Riviera** and **Yukon** are noted for cold tolerance and are more likely to survive in the western and northern parts of the state. *Note:* Seeded cultivars are grasses that do produce viable seed, which can be harvested and sold for use.
Bermudagrass, vegetative cultivars	Aussie Green Celebration GN-1 Patriot Tifsport Tifton 10 Tifway	These cultivars produce excellent quality grass under proper management. They possess dark-green color, fine leaf texture, and dense growth habits. They are typically considered as high maintenance grasses and must be mowed with a reel mower at a height of 0.5 to 1 inch to achieve high quality. These grasses are primarily suited for use on golf courses as well as high-end athletic fields and home lawns. **Tifsport** performs best at 1 to 2 inches. *Note:* Vegetative cultivars are only available as sprigs, plugs, or sod. This is because they are either sterile grasses that do not produce viable seed, or they may produce seed that does not retain characteristics true to the cultivar. Vegetative cultivars must be purchased from a sod farm that carries the variety.
Centipedegrass	Common Tifblair	**Tifblair** is an improved cultivar that exhibits better cold tolerance compared to **Common**.
St. Augustinegrass	Common	**Raleigh** is noted for its improved cold tolerance compared to **Common** St. Augustinegrass.
Zoysiagrass, coarsely textured varieties	Compadre Crowne El Toro Empire Jamur Meyer Palisades Zenith	Seed is available for **Compadre** and **Zenith**.
Zoysiagrass, finely textured varieties	Cavalier Diamond Emerald Zeon Zorro	

Because the release and evaluation of turfgrass cultivars changes rapidly, you are encouraged to contact the Cooperative Extension center in your county for the latest information on grass characteristics and selection (http://www.NCSU TurfFiles.ncsu.edu/turfSelect/).

1. Apply 75 pounds of ground limestone per 1,000 sq ft.
2. Apply a starter type fertilizer (one that is high in phosphorus) based on the type of grass and the planting method. Fertilizer bags have a three-number system indicating the primary nutrients, such as 8-8-8 or 5-10-10. These numbers denote the N-P-K ratio—the percentage of each nutrient in a fertilizer. The percentages are always noted in the following order:

N Nitrogen for green color and growth.

P_2O_5 Phosphorus for good establishment and rooting.

K_2O Potassium to enhance pest and environmental stress tolerance.

Somc common examples of starter type fertilizers required for a 1,000 sq ft area include 40 pounds of 5-10-10, 20 pounds of 10-20-20, or 16 pounds of 18-24-6. For sandy soils, typical to the coastal plain and sandhills of North Carolina, fertilizer rates should be increased by 20 percent.

Fertilize after planting. Apply fertilizers uniformly and with care using a centrifugal (rotary) or drop-type spreader. Apply half the fertilizer in one direction and the other half moving at right angles to the first pass to ensure thorough and uniform coverage (See Figure 3). *For seeded lawns:* Fertilize the new seedlings approximately six to eight weeks after emergence. For more specific maintenance information on your grass type, refer to the NC State TurfFiles Maintenance Calendars at the Web sites listed under "For More Information" at the end of this publication. Use a complete N-P-K turfgrade fertilizer that provides about 1 pound of nitrogen per 1,000 sq ft or the amount recommended on your soil test. The fertilizer should have a 3-1-2 or 4-1-2 analysis (for example, 12-4-8 or 16-4-8), and one-fourth to one-half of the nitrogen should be a slow-release form.

For vegetatively planted warm-season grasses: Fertilize throughout the first growing season to encourage faster spread. Every three to four weeks during the growing season, add 0.5 to 1 pound of nitrogen per 1,000 sq ft until the plants have completely covered the desired lawn area.

To help reduce turf loss: Avoid high nitrogen fertilization of cool-season grasses in the late spring or summer and of warm-season grasses in the fall or winter. If higher nitrogen fertilization is applied, there may be a greater occurrence of diseases.

When to Plant

Cool-season grasses

Seeding: Cool-season grasses are best seeded from mid-August to mid-September, depending on location (see Table 5, page 13). Seeding beyond these dates increases the chance of failure caused by winter injury. Spring or late-winter seedlings are often less than satisfactory because the seedling roots do not have time to become well established before the heat and drought of summer. If seeding of a cool-season grass is not

How to Determine Fertilizer Requirements

To apply 1 pound of nitrogen per 1, 000 sq ft:
Divide 100 by the first number on the fertilizer bag to determine the amount of product to be used per 1,000 sq ft.
Example: A 16-4-8 fertilizer. 100 divided by 16 equals 6.25. Therefore, 6.25 pounds of fertilizer per 1,000 square feet will deliver 1 pound of nitrogen.
To apply 0.5 pound of nitrogen per 1, 000 sq ft:
50 divided by the first number on the fertilizer bag equals the amount of product to be used per 1,000 sq ft.
Example: A 10-10-10 fertilizer. 50 divided by 10 equals 5. Therefore, 5 pounds of fertilizer per 1,000 sq ft will deliver 0.5 pound of nitrogen.

Table 5. Planting Dates and Rates for Cool- and Warm-season Grasses in North Carolina

Lawn Grass	Optimum Planting Date*	Planting Rate per 1,000 Square Feet		
		Seed (pound s)	Sprigs for Space Planting	Sprigs for Broadcast (bushels)
MOUNTAINS				
Kentucky bluegrass	Aug. 15 to Sept. 1	1.5 to 2	–	–
Kentucky bluegrass/ fine	Aug. 15 to Sept. 1	1.5 + 1.5	–	–
Kentucky bluegrass/ tall	Aug. 15 to Sept. 1	1 + 5	–	–
Kentucky bluegrass/tall fescue/ fine fescue mix	Aug. 15 to Sept. 1	1 + 5 + 1	–	–
Kentucky bluegrass/ perennial ryegrass	Aug. 15 to Sept. 1	1.5 + 1	–	–
Tall fescue	Aug. 15 to Sept. 1	6	–	–
PIEDMONT				
Bermudagrass	April to July a	1 to 2	0.75	3 to 10
Bermudagrass (hybrid)	April to July	–	0.75	3 to 10
Bahiagrass	March to June	5	–	–
Centipedegrass	March to July	0.25 to 0.50	1 to 2c	–
Kentucky bluegrass/ tall	Sept. 1 to Sept. 15	1 + 5	–	–
Kentucky bluegrass/ tall fescue/ fine fescue mix	Aug. 1 to Sept. 1	1 + 5 + 1	–	–
St. Augustinegrass	April to July	–	1.0	1
Tall fescue	Sept. 1 to Sept. 15	6	–	–
Zoysiagrass	April to July a	1 to 2	1 to 2c	3 to 10
COASTAL PLAIN				
Bermudagrass	April to July	1 to 2	0.75	3 to 10
Bermudagrass (hybrid)	March to July a	–	0.75	3 to 10
Bahaiagrass	March to June	5	–	–
Centipedegrass	March to July	0.25 to 0.50	1 to 2c	–

St. Augustinegrass	April to July	–	–	–
Tall fescue	Sept. 15 to Oct. 15	6	–	–
Zoysiagrass	March to July a	1 to 2	1 to 2c	3 to 10

*Seeding beyond these dates increases the chance of failure. Sod consisting of cool-season grasses can be installed any time the ground is not frozen. Warm-season grasses can be installed as long as soil temperature exceeds 55°F.

[a] For best results, choose earlier dates when using vegetative material.

[b] 1 square yard of turf pulled apart is equivalent to 1 bushel of sprigs.

[c] Often plugged using 3 square yards of turf cut into 2-inch squares on 12-inch centers to plant 1,000 sq ft

accomplished in the fall, your best alternative date for the piedmont is mid-February to early March. Coastal plain areas would be seeded two weeks earlier, whereas the mountain areas would be seeded two weeks later.

If you plan to seed a cool-season grass in the fall, such as tall fescue or Kentucky bluegrass, and your lawn site is ready for seeding in late March, April, May, or June, you can obtain a temporary cover by seeding annual ryegrass. Fertilize with 75 pounds of ground limestone and 15 pounds of a 0-10-20 fertilizer per 1,000 sq ft. Another alternative is to seed annual ryegrass at 1.5 to 2 pounds per 1,000 sq ft, fertilized with 15 to 20 pounds of 10-10-10 fertilizer per 1,000 sq ft. Instead of following the above suggestions, you may wish to seed the desired cool-season grass. This procedure may succeed in some years, but in any event will give you ground cover until fall, even if all of the grass dies.

Sodding: You may successfully install a cool-season grass sod anytime in the cooler portions of the growing season when the ground is not frozen.

Warm-season grasses

Seeding: Warm-season grasses may be seeded successfully between March 1 and July 1, depending on the species used. See Table 5 for different species and locations.

Sodding: Warm-season grasses are best established by sodding at the same dates suggested for seeding, about April until July 1. Sod will not produce roots unless the soil temperature exceeds 55°F for several weeks. Professional sod installers have been successful in establishing lawns beyond those dates, but care must be given to ensure that the soil does not dry out.

Vegetative: Warm-season grasses may be planted vegetatively (by sprigs or plugs) from March through July.

How to Plant

Lawns can be established by seeding, sodding, or vegetative planting (sprigs or plugs). Buying poor-quality seed or plants often results in less-than-satisfactory performance, pest problems, and general disappointment. Selection of seeds or plants is especially important when establishing a lawn. Read the information on the seed tag carefully, and make sure you purchase seed with no noxious weed seed and low levels of other crop seed. One way to be sure you have seed or planting material that is true to type, free of noxious weed seed, and contains low levels of other crop seed, is to purchase certified seed or sod. A blue certified tag indicates that the seed or plants have met certain standards to assure high quality and low levels of contaminants. The North Carolina Crop Improvement Association (NCCIA) offers a list of certified seed producers on its Web site: http://www.nccia.ncsu.edu/.

Seeding is usually the fastest, most economical method of establishing grasses. To ensure uniform coverage, use a centrifugal (rotary) or drop-type spreader.

Apply half the seed in one direction and the other half moving at right angles to the first pass (see Figure 3). Lightly cover the seed by hand raking or dragging with a mat or span of chain-link fence. Roll the soil lightly to firm the surface, and provide good seed-to-soil contact.

Mulch grass seed with weed-free small-grain straw or hay. Use one bale per 1,000 sq ft for warm-season grasses and one to two bales for cool-season grasses. This will help conserve moisture, control erosion, and reduce surface crusting until establishment. Once in place, stabilize the mulch by rolling or watering. Twine netting can be used if wind displacement is a problem. If applied evenly and lightly, these materials need not be removed.

Vegetative planting is necessary for some grasses that do not produce viable seed (seed that will germinate). When this method is used, the planting material must be kept fresh and moist from removal site to plantingarea. Keep planting material moist until established.Fertilize with 0.5 to 1 pound of nitrogen per 1,000 sq ft every one to three weeks for the fastest spread. Here are the methods most useful in lawn areas:

Space planting is the planting of separate shoots or sprigs (runners, cuttings, or stolons) at regular spacings. This labor-intensive method is best used for planting small areas. Spacing is determined by how fast the grass will spread, how fast you want it to cover, and how much material you have available. The closer the spacing, the faster the lawn will become established (see Figure 4).

Broadcasting is the uniform distribution of sprigs (cut stems) over the entire area. The sprigs are pressed into the top 0.5 to 1 inch of soil by hand or by using an old disk set straight, special planter, cultipacker, or roller. Large areas planted with bermudagrass or zoysiagrass sprigs require a minimum of 3 to 5 bushels (yards) of sprigs per 1,000 square feet and 5 to 10 bushels (yards) for extremely fast cover. St. Augustinegrass is seldom established through broadcasting because the stems are too sensitive.

Plugging is planting individual pieces (2 inches or larger) of sod on 6-inch or 12-inch centers. This is an excellent way to introduce a more adapted lawn grass into an old lawn in an effort to replace old grass by crowding out. Zoysiagrass, St. Augustinegrass, and centipedegrass are often planted by plugging.

Sodding is placing sod stripped from one site to another for an "instant" lawn. Lay sod as soon as possible after it has been harvested to prevent injury.

1. Make sure the soil is moist (but not overly wet) before laying sod. Irrigating the soil several days before delivery is often adequate.
2. Install the sod within 24 hours of delivery. Plan to unstack and unroll the sod if it cannot be laid within 48 hours.
3. While installing, keep sod in the shade to lessen the chance of heat buildup.
4. Start sodding from a straight edge (driveway or sidewalk), and butt strips together, staggering them in a bricklike pattern (See Figure 5).
5. Avoid stretching sod. Use a knife or sharp spade for trimming to fit irregularly shaped areas.
6. Lay sod lengthwise across the face of slopes, and peg or stake the pieces to prevent slippage.
7. After the sod has been placed, roll the lawn to ensure good sod-to-soil contact. Then begin watering.

For a complete list of North Carolina sod producers and the varieties they carry, visit the North Carolina Sod Producers Association Web site: http://www. ncsod.org.

Again, to ensure high quality and better chance for success, it is highly recommended that certified sod be used. A list of producers growing certified sod can be found on the NCCIA Web site: http://www.nccia. ncsu.edu/.

The times and rates for planting vegetative grasses are given in Table 5.

Caring for a New Lawn

Irrigating

To prevent drying of planting material, keep the top 1.5 inches of the soil moist. This may require light watering two or three times a day for 7 to 21 days. Bluegrass takes 7 to 14 days longer to germinate than other cool-season grasses. As the seedlings grow and root, water less often but for longer periods. For mixtures containing bluegrass, do not make the mistake of decreasing water as soon as the seedlings appear. Continue watering until the bluegrass seedlings emerge. After the third mowing, water to a depth of 6 to 8 inches about once a week or when needed.

Mowing

Begin mowing as soon as the grass is 50 percent higher than the desired height. For example, mow tall fescue back to 3 inches when it reaches 4.5 inches. The frequency of mowing is governed by the amount of growth, which depends on temperature, fertility, moisture conditions, the season, and the natural growth rate of the grass. The suggested height of cut is given in Table 2. The homeowner should cut often enough that less than 50 percent of the total leaf surface is removed. Use a mower with a sharp blade. To reduce the danger of spreading disease and injuring the turf, mow when the soil and plants are dry. If clippings are heavy enough to hold the grass down or shade it, catch them or rake and remove them. Otherwise, do not bag the clippings. Allow them to fall into the turf where they will decay and release nutrients. This may reduce the need for fertilizer by 20 to 30 percent.

Pest Control

Fungicides and insecticides are rarely needed on new lawns, and different planting methods require different pest control methods. If pesticides are used, always read and follow label directions.

Seeding. Siduron (Tupersan 50WP) may be applied to cool-season grasses at the time of spring seeding for selective pre-emergence control of some annual grassy weeds like crabgrass. Other herbicides may be applied to young seedlings during establishment. Get the latest recommendations by visiting the NC State TurfFiles Web site.

Broadleaf weeds are common in new seedings. However, many will be controlled with frequent mowing at the proper height. After the lawn has been mowed three times, remaining weeds may be controlled using the minimum label rate of a broadleaf herbicide. The particular herbicide used depends upon the weeds present and the tolerance of the turfgrass to the herbicide.

Space-planting sprigs, broadcasting sprigs, and plugging. Atrazine (AAtrex) or simazine (Princep) may be applied for control of certain annual grass and broadleaf weeds when sprigging bermudagrass, centipedegrass, St. Augustinegrass, and zoysiagrass. Do not apply these herbicides over the rooting areas of trees and ornamentals that are not listed as being tolerant on the herbicide label.

Sodding. Pre-emergence herbicides, such as siduron (Tupersan) and bensulide (Betasan), can be applied for annual weedy grass control after sodding cool- and warm-season grasses.

Maintaining An Established Lawn

Consider your lawn established when you have mowed it three times. Lawn Care Maintenance Calendars for specific grass types are available online through the NC State TurfFiles Web site: http://www.TurfFiles. ncsu.edu.

Irrigating

Improper irrigation of lawns results in wasted water, added cost, and unhealthy plants. Water should be applied only when a reasonable portion of the lawn shows signs of moisture stress. A dark bluish-gray color; footprints that remain some time after walking; and wilted, folded, or curled leaves are indications that it is time to water. A delay in watering at the firstsigns of wilt will generally not result in permanent damage unless the turf is being allowed to go dormant.

If irrigation is not available or desirable, then an alternative to irrigating is to allow the turf to go semidormant to dormant. Tall fescue, bermudagrass, and zoysiagrass are tolerant of drought if allowed to go dormant. An irrigation water management program is available online through the NC State TurfFiles Web site: http://www.turffiles.ncsu.edu/tims/. General watering recommendations include the following:

1. Water in the early morning if possible. This is the preferred time to water because it reduces the risk of disease, water loss through evaporation, and improper water distribution. Also, the demand for water by industry and municipalities is usually low at this time.
2. Water established lawns to a depth of 6 to 8 inches to encourage deep rooting. Usually, 1 inch of water per week is adequate. Ideally, this would not be applied in one application. Applying 0.5 inch of water every three to four days is adequate for most situations.
3. Use cans or a rain gauge to determine how much water is being delivered in a certain period of time. It takes 640 gallons of water to apply 1 inch of water per 1,000 sq. ft. Because clay soils accept water slowly, water should be measured to prevent wasteful runoff. Water clay soils until runoff is about to occur. Wait 30 minutes for the water to be absorbed. Then apply more water until the desired depth or amount is achieved. This same technique can be used on slopes and compacted soils. Few lawns established on clay soils can absorb more than 0.5 inch of water per hour. Sandy soils require more frequent watering. Applying 0.5 inch of water every third day is usually sufficient. Adjust any automatic irrigation system to supplement rainfall so that the lawn is not over-watered.

Take certain precautions if you do not plan to irrigate throughout the summer. Slowly ease a lush, actively growing lawn into dormancy. This can be accomplished by allowing the drought stress symptoms to appear between infrequent irrigation cycles, by mowing high, and by not over-fertilizing with nitrogen. Brown, withered leaves are normal signs of dormancy, so do not be alarmed by them. If the lawn is conditioned for this stress and has a reasonable level of maintenance, it should survive without permanent damage. Most turfgrasses can withstand 3 to 6 weeks (or longer) without rainwater or irrigation and exhibit minimal or no damage, depending on the situation.

In the absence of rain, water dormant lawns with a minimal amount (about 0.25 inch) every three weeks to keep the growing points hydrated. It is difficult to maintain vibrant green color in cool-season grasses during the summer. Irrigation helps maintain color, but may also increase the risk of disease. For this reason, it is particularly important that cool-season grasses not be overwatered.

Mowing

Use either a rotary (centrifugal) or reel (cylinder) mower. The reel mower is preferred if grasses are cut to less than 1 inch.

1. Keep the mower blades sharp and balanced. The cleanest cut and best mowing are obtained when the mower blades are sharp. Dull mower blades reduce lawn quality by tearing instead of cleanly cutting the grass. Tearing creates many ragged leaf ends that quickly wither and bleach and are easy ports of entry for disease. Using a sharp mower isespecially important for difficult-to-mow grasses, such as zoysiagrass, bahiagrass, and certain types of perennial ryegrass cultivars. A properly sharpened and balanced mower blade will also reduce mower vibration, lengthen mower life, and reduce fuel consumption by as much as 22 percent.
2. Mow at the proper height. The frequency of mowing is governed by the desired

grass height and by the amount of growth, which depends on temperature, fertility, moisture conditions, season, and the natural growth rate of the grass. In most instances, this may amount to biweekly and weekly mowing. To maintain a high-quality lawn, turfgrass should be cut often enough that less than 50 percent of the leaf surface is removed with each mowing. The proper mowing heights are presented in Table 2. If the lawn gets too high during wet seasons, raise the mower and cut off a fourth to a half of the present growth. Then lower the mower to its proper height and mow again in a day or two.

3. Leave clippings to decompose when they are short. Most homeowners bag lawn clippings because they think that the clippings add to the buildup of thatch, which can be harmful to the lawn. Actually, thatch is made up of roots, stems, and the lower portions of leaves that are below the mower blade. Frequent mowing, mowing when the grass is dry, and proper fertilization are the best ways to reduce thatch buildup. Though studies have shown that a lawn of 1,000 square feet can produce 500 pounds of clippings in one growing season, these clippings contribute very little to thatch. In fact, clippings that remain on the lawn quickly decompose and release valuable nutrients. Fertilizer use can be reduced by 20 to 30 percent.

4. Rake, bag, and remove the clippings when mowing is delayed. If prolonged periods of rainfall prevent mowing, clippings may be long enough to shade or smother the grass. In this case, rake, bag, and remove the clippings. Collected clippings can be used as mulch around trees and shrubs or added to compost. Because yard trash accounts for 20 percent of the waste in our overflowing landfills, legislation has been passed that bans depositing yard trash in most public landfills. Homeowners must now look for other alternatives. Contact your county Cooperative Extension center for information about composting yard trash and other uses for this material.

Fertilizing

A soil test should be made at least every two to three years to determine the amounts of lime, phosphorus, and potassium needed by your established lawn. See page 11 for the method used to obtain a good soil sample. A complete fertilizer with an N-P-K ratio of 4:1:2 or 4:1:3 can be used in lieu of a soil test, but it is a poor substitute.

Determine the amount of fertilizer, ratio of nutrients or fertilizer elements, and time of application based on the grasses being grown. See Table 6a, b, or c, depending on your region (pages 18 and 19), to determine the amount of nitrogen fertilizer to apply and the time of application.

Cool season grasses. Avoid any nitrogen fertilization of cool-season grasses, such as tall fescue, after the February application until September for the central piedmont.

If one additional application of nitrogen is made between these dates to improve the color, the rate should not exceed 0.5 pound of nitrogen per 1,000 square feet. This nitrogen should be applied in the central piedmont no later than April 15 (two weeks earlier in the coastal plain and two weeks later in the mountains). This application will not improve the longevity of tall fescue but will enhance its green color.

The application of high rates or repeated low rates of nitrogen to cool-season grasses in the spring or summer greatly increases the severity of brown patch (*Rhizoctonia* species), which can kill the grass and should be avoided. If spring or summer nitrogen applications, or both, are applied to tall fescue, fungicide applications may be necessary to reduce disease symptoms.

Warm-season grasses. Avoid fall or winter applications of nitrogen to reduce winter injury.

Lime. Most soils in North Carolina are acidic and often require the application of lime to sweeten the soil. For most turfgrasses, except centipedegrass, soil pH should be between 6.5 and 7.0 for optimum nutrient availability. Centipedegrass requires more acidic soil with a pH close to 5.5. Lime may be put on any time during the year. Winter is usually best, however, because there is less traffic. Gentle winter rains minimize runoff, and alternate freezing and thawing help incorporate lime into the soil.

Fertilizers and lime should be applied uniformly with a centrifugal (rotary) or drop-type spreader. Apply half the fertilizer in one direction and the other half moving at right angles to the first pass to ensure uniform coverage (see Figure 3).

Coring (Aerification)

Soils that are subject to heavy traffic are prone to compaction. Coring will alleviate this condition. Use a device that removes soil cores. Chop up the cores, and, if possible, distribute them by dragging with a span of chain-link fence or a mat.

Coring should be accomplished when the lawn is actively growing so that it can recover from anyinjury. Core cool-season grasses in fall or early spring. Core warm-season grasses in late spring or early summer. Some lawn care and landscape companies offer coring service if rental equipment is not available.

Power Raking (Verticutting)

Sod-forming grasses, such as Kentucky bluegrass, bermudagrass, zoysiagrass, St. Augustinegrass, and centipedegrass, tend to build up thatch when they are heavily fertilized and watered. When thatch exceeds 0.75 inch, lawns should be power raked and cored. A light power raking is better than trying to remove too much debris at one time. When not excessive, thatch buildup can be removed from warm-season grasses by cutting as closely as possible at spring green-up and then raking by hand. To avoid seriously injuring the lawn, a 3-inch blade spacing is required to remove thatch from centipedegrass and St. Augustinegrass. Some lawn care and landscape companies have specialized equipment and offer power raking services.

Renovating a Lawn

Lawn renovation refers to any procedure beyondnormal maintenance (short of soil modification) required to upgrade an existing lawn. A deteriorated lawn is often a symptom of some underlying problem. Failure to identify and correct the exact problem can lead to further lawn deterioration and the need for repeated renovation. These are some of the major causes of turf deterioration:

- poor establishment procedures
- improper lawn management
- poorly adapted lawn grasses
- improper nutrient balance
- excessive thatch buildup
- disease, insect, or weed infestation

The problems that caused the lawn to deteriorate must be corrected before the renovation process begins.

When to Renovate

Late summer to early fall is the best time to renovate cool-season lawns. Warm-season lawns are best renovated in late spring to early summer. Attempts to upgrade existing lawns when conditions are not conducive to good growth are difficult at best.

Weed Control

The first step in lawn renovation is the control of undesirable vegetation that will compete with newly planted grasses. Some weeds growing in small areas may be controlled by hand weeding or removal using a small hoe, rake, or shovel. Hard-to-control weeds, such as perennial grasses with underground shoots or weeds in large areas, are best controlled with herbicides.

Spray most postemergence broadleaf herbicides four to six weeks before seeding. Most selective postemergence herbicides that control annual grassy weeds, such as crabgrass, should also be applied at least four weeks before seeding.

To control perennial grassy weeds, undesirable turfgrasses, annual grasses, and broadleaf weeds, spray the nonselective herbicide glyphosate (various trade names, such as Roundup or Kleenup). However, it will take several applications spaced three to four weeks apart to completely control bermudagrass. If perennial grassy weeds like bermudagrass are scattered throughout, consider killing the entire lawn.

When using glyphosate, do not disturb the soil or plants before treatment. Tillage or renovation techniques such as vertical mowing, coring, or slicing should be delayed for seven days after application to allow proper movement of the herbicide into underground parts of the weeds.

Table 6a. Suggested Maintenance Fertilization of Established Lawns in the Coastal Region

Lawn Grass Type	Fertilization	Monthly Application Rate (lb N/1,000 sq ft)												Total lb
		J	F	M	A	M	J	J	A	S	O	N	D	N Per 1,000
Bermudagrass	Basic				1		1		1					3
	High				1	1	1	1	1	1				6
Centipedegrass	Basic					1								1
	High					1			1					2
Tall fescue	Basic		0.5							1		0.5		2
	High		1	0.5						1	1	0.5		4
St. Augustinegrass	Basic					1			1					2
	High				0.5	1	0.5	1	0.5	0.5				4
Zoysiagrass (Emerald and Meyer	Basic					1			1					2
	High				1		1		1					3
Zoysiagrass (other	Basic					1			1					2
	High				1	0.5	1	0.5	1					4

Table 6b. Suggested Maintenance Fertilization for Established Lawns in the Piedmont

Lawn Grass Type	Fertilization	Monthly Application Rate (lb N/1,000 sq ft)												Total lb
		J	F	M	A	M	J	J	A	S	O	N	D	N Per 1,000
Bermudagrass	Basic					1		1		1				3
	High				1	1	1	1	1	1				6
	Basic					1								1

	High					1			1					2
Tall fescue	Basic		0.5							1		0.5		2
	High		1	0.5						1	1	0.5		4
Kentucky bluegrass	Basic		0.5							1		0.5		2
	High		1	0.5						1	1	0.5		4
Kentucky bluegrass/ fine	Basic		0.5							1		0.5		2
	High		1	0.5						1	1	0.5		4
Kentucky bluegrass/ tall	Basic		0.5							1		0.5		2
	High		1	0.5						1	1	0.5		4
Kentucky bluegrass/ tall fescue/fine fescue mix	Basic		0.5							1		0.5		2
	High		1	0.5						1	1	0.5		4
Kentucky bluegrass/ perennial ryegrass	Basic		1							1		1		3
	High		1	0.5						1	1	0.5		4
St. Augustinegrass	Basic					1			1					2
	High					1		1		1				3
Zoysiagrass (Emerald and Meyer	Basic					1								1
	High				1			1						2
Zoysiagrass (other	Basic					1		1						2
	High				1		1		1					3

Table 6c. Suggested Maintenance Fertilization of Established Lawns for the Mountains

Lawn Grass Type	Fertilization	Monthly Application Rate (lb N/1,000 sq ft)												Total lb
		J	F	M	A	M	J	J	A	S	O	N	D	N Per 1,000
Bermudagrass	Basic					1		1						2
	High					1	1	1	1					4
Tall fescue	Basic			0.5					1		0.5			2
	High			1					1		1			3
Kentucky bluegrass	Basic			1					1					2
	High			1					1		1			3
Kentucky bluegrass/ fine	Basic			1					1					2
	High			1					1		1			3
Kentucky bluegrass/ tall	Basic			1					1					2
	High			1					1		1			3
Kentucky	Basic			1					1					2

bluegrass/tall	High			1					1		1			3
Kentucky bluegrass/	Basic			1					1		0.5			2.5
perennial ryegrass	High			1					1	1	0.5			3.5
Zoysiagras	Basic					0.5			0.5					1
s (all	High					1		1						2

Young and actively growing weeds are easiest to control, so make sure that the soil is moist several days before application. Carefully read and follow directions and precautions on the herbicide labels. Treat only those areas that need it.

Preparation for Seeding

Preplanting renovation procedures are designed to create the optimum environment for the establishment of newly planted grasses. This process includes the following steps:

1. Reduce competition from existing grasses and remove unwanted vegetation, including thatch.
2. Apply the required fertilizer and lime.
3. Prepare a good seedbed.

Reduce competition. Set the rotary or reel mower at the lowest setting, mow, and collect the clippings. Remove all undesirable vegetation, dead grass, thatch, and weeds so that the soil is exposed. This maynot be necessary if a slit seeder is used. A rake or hoe is ideal for small areas. Several passes with a dethatcher (power raker or vertical mower) is usually the best choice for large areas. If thatch is excessive, it may be necessary to make another pass with a dethatcher after mowing. Both mowing and dethatching reduce plant competition and enhance light penetration for good germination and fast establishment.

Apply fertilizer and lime. Uniformly apply needed fertilizer and lime based on soil test results. Hand application is fine for small areas, but a rotary or droptype spreader should be used on large areas to ensure uniform application.

Prepare a good seedbed. In small bare spots, loosen the top 4 to 6 inches of the soil with a rake, hoe, or shovel. On soils difficult to loosen with hand equipment, loosen the top 2 to 3 inches for good to excellent results. Fill in low areas, and smooth the surface so clods are smaller than marbles. Large areas and areas that contain 50 percent desirable grasses are best prepared for seeding by using a piece of equipment (such as an aerator or coring machine) that brings small soil cores to the surface. This will bring soil to the surface with minimal disruption and create an environment for good seed-to-soil contact. Core in several directions, allow plugs to dry, and then pulverize them with a mower, dethatcher, or span of chain link fence. Because tines have a difficult time penetrating dry, compacted soils, coring is best achieved when the soil is damp.

Seeding

Bare spots larger than 4 inches in diameter should be replanted. Smaller areas tend to fill innaturally, provided the lawn grass is capable of spreading. Tall fescue and perennial ryegrass exhibit a bunch-type growth habit and are incapable of spreading. Choose a blend or mixture that is compatible with the environment and the existing lawn.

To ensure uniform coverage, use a rotary or droptype spreader, applying half the seed in one direction and the other half at right angles to the first pass. Incorporate seed and fertilizer into the top 1/8-inch of soil by lightly pulling a leaf rake over loosened soil or running a vertical slicer over areas that were just power raked and cored.

A slit seeder, consisting of a vertical grooving seeder and seed box, can be used to drill seed to ensure good seed-to-soil contact with minimum disruption. Seed should be drilled in a diamond-shaped pattern. Dry, compacted soils, obstructions such as rocks and trees, and excessive slopes may limit the usefulness of a slit seeder. Bare areas that are seeded should be mulched to enhance germination.

Plugging

Plugging can be used for those grasses that spread laterally—not bunch-type grasses such as tall fescue, ryegrass, bahiagrass, and fine fescue. Place plugs on either 6-inch or 12-inch centers, depending on the desired establishment speed. Use a plugging device to remove plugs of soil from bare areas, and switch them with plugs collected from healthy areas. Apply a starter-type fertilizer, such as 10 pounds per square feet of 5-10-10 fertilizer.

Sprigging Large Areas

Large areas of 15,000 sq ft or more can be sprigged using this method, which is often reserved for bermudagrass. Rototill the recommended amount of fertilizer and lime, indicated by soil test results, or apply lime at 75 pounds per 1,000 sq ft and 10-10-10 fertilizer at 20 pounds per 1,000 sq ft to the area to be sprigged. Spread sprigs over the surface using rates provided in Table 5 for new areas. Press them into the top 0.5 to 1 inch of soil using an old disk set straight, special planter, cultipacker, or roller. Roll the area to firm the soil and ensure sprig-to-soil contact.

Care After Planting

Keep renovated areas moist with light sprinklings several times a day. As the seedlings, plugs, or sprigs grow, continue to decrease the frequency of waterings while increasing the duration to promote deep rooting. After the third mowing, water to a depth of 6 inches.

Mow the area as you normally would, using a sharp blade. But continue to severely stunt existing vegetation by mowing short until desirable grasses have germinated and the desired mowing height is achieved. This will reduce the competition for new seedlings.

Fertilize the new seedlings of cool-season grasses as described for "fertilize after planting" in the section on *Fertilization* (page 12). Use the example provided in that section to determine how much fertilizer to use.

Warm-season grasses can be fertilized every four weeks until coverage is complete. Use a complete N-P-K fertilizer that provides about 1 pound of nitrogen per 1,000 sq ft. Twice-monthly applications of a nitrogen-only fertilizer that provides about 0.5 pound of nitrogen per 1,000 sq ft may help warm-season grasses fill in more rapidly. Keep unnecessary traffic off the renovated lawn until it is wellestablished.

Integrated Pest Management

People are becoming more aware of and concerned about the effects of chemicals on our environment. Research indicates that pesticide use poses a minimal threat to the health of humans, animals, and the environment. But because we can't be certain, many people choose to avoid pesticides. So how would you handle a pest problem that is destroying the appearance of your lawn? Do you use pesticides, change cultural practices, or both?

The balanced use of all available control methods is called *integrated pest management* (IPM). The idea is simple. All available prevention and control methods are used to keep pests from reaching damaging levels. Pesticides are used only when necessary.

Planting the best-adapted grass and then watering, mowing, and fertilizing it properly form the basis for integrated pest management. Keeping the lawn healthy enables it to tolerate low levels of pests and makes the area a good habitat for beneficial organisms that help control pests. To best use natural controls, it is important to develop a sound understanding of the biology and ecology of the lawn environment. Fortunately, many books and other educational materials are now available to assist the homeowner. Also, many companies offer materials for organic lawn care. These range from nematodes that attack caterpillars to traps and repellents. Some of these are quite effective, whereas the effectiveness of others has not been documented. As each product is tested and proven to be effective, it will be added to the list of available options for turf pest management. In the meantime, if chemical control is necessary, select the safest effective pesticide and follow label recommendations. Chemicals should be applied when the pest is most susceptible. Treat only those areas in need, and regard pesticides as only one of many tools available in lawn care. Integrated pest management can be successful, but homeowners must realize that more time and labor are required and high expectations may not be met when pest pressures and environmental conditions are severe.

Glossary

Active ingredient
The chemical in a pesticide that controls the target pest.

Aerification
Removal of soil cores from a turf with hollow tines or spoons.

Annual
A plant that starts from seed and completes its life cycle within the same growing season.

Auricle
A claw-like appendage projecting from the collar of the leaf.

Biennial
A plant that starts from seed and requires two years to complete its life cycle.

Blade
The flat portion of the grass leaf above the sheath.

Blend, seed
A combination of two or more cultivars of the same species, for example Rebel and Falcon tall fescue.

Broadcast
Uniform application to an entire area.

Broadleaf plants
Plants with flattened leaves; dicots, plants that possess two seedling leaves.

Bud leaf
First emerged leaf of a grass plant.

Bunchgrass, bunch-type growth
Plant development in the absence of rhizome and stolon production; a nonspreading grass.

Cool-season grasses
Turf species that have optimum growth at temperatures between 60 and 75°F.

Coring
See aerification.

Creeping growth habit
Plant development at or near the soil surface that results in lateral spreading by rhizomes, stolons, or both.

Crop seed
Any seed grown for profit, often including undesirable grassy weeds, such as orchardgrass.

Crown
The portion of a grass plant that includes the stem apex, unelongated internodes, and lower nodes from which secondary roots begin.

Cultivar
A cultivated variety of a species, such as K-31 and Rebel.

Cultivation
In turf, the working of the soil without the destruction of the turf.

Dormancy
The resting stage of a plant or ripe seeds during which nearly all manifestations of life come to an almost complete stand- still.

Herbicide, contact
Herbicide that injures only those portions of a plant with which it comes into contact.

Herbicide, nonselective
Herbicide that kills or injures all plants. Some plant species may exhibit more tolerance than others. Examples include glyphosate (Roundup, Touchdown Pro), and glufosinate (Finale).

For More Information

This and the following Extension publications about lawns are available on the NC State TurfFiles Web site: http://www.TurfFiles.ncsu.edu/. Or contact your county Cooperative Extension center for copies.

Tall Fescue Lawn Maintenance Calendar (AG-367)
http://www.turffiles.ncsu.edu/articles/tf0017.aspx

Centipedegrass Lawn Maintenance Calendar (AG- 381)
http://www.turffiles.ncsu.edu/articles/tf0019.aspx

Bermudagrass Lawn Calendar (AG-431)
http://www.turffiles.ncsu.edu/articles/tf0016.aspx

Zoysiagrass Lawn Calendar (AG-432)
http://www.turffiles.ncsu.edu/articles/tf0020.aspx

Diseases of Warm-Season Grasses (AG-360)
http://www.turffiles.ncsu.edu/articles/tf0033.aspx

Controlling White Grubs in Turf (AG-366)
http://www.turffiles.ncsu.edu/articles/tf00506.aspx

Carolina Lawns
http://www.turffiles.ncsu.edu/articles/tf4175.aspx

Herbicide, postemergence (POST)
Herbicide that needs to be applied after weeds emerge to be effective.

Herbicide, pre-emergence (PRE)
Herbicide that needs to be applied before weeds emerge to be effective. Can be applied before or after turf establishment. Rainfall or irrigation is often needed to move the chemical into the top few inches of the soil for best activity.

Herbicide, selective
Herbicide that kills or injures some plants without harming others.

Herbicide, systemic
Herbicide that is taken up through contact with the leaves or through the soil (via contact with the roots) and is moved throughout the plant to kill the whole plant.

Inflorescence
The flowering portion of a plant.

Larva
A stage in the development of certain insects, caterpillars (butterfly larva), or grubs (beetle larva).

Ligule
A thin projection from the top of the leaf sheath in grasses; it may be a fringe of hairs, membranous, or absent.

Mixture, seed
A combination of seeds of two or more species, for example Kentucky bluegrass and perennial ryegrass.

Nematode
A microscopic, worm-like organism.

Nitrogen, quick release
Readily available sources of nitrogen that exhibit fast turf greening, short residual, and high burn potential, such as ammonium nitrate.

Nitrogen, slow release
Slowly available sources of nitrogen that exhibit slow turf green-up, long residual, and low burn potential, such as IBDU, urea formaldehyde.

Node
A joint where leaves, roots, branches, or stems arise.

Nymph
A stage in the development of certain insects where the young resemble the adult in form, eat the same food, and reside in the same environment.

Pathogen
The causal agent of disease.

Perennial plant
A plant that may or may not start from seed, may or may not produce seed, and lives more than two years.

Raking, power
Removal of debris with rapidly rotating vertical tines or brush.

Rhizome
An underground creeping stem that can produce roots and shoots at each node.

Scalping
Excessive removal of turf leaves by close mowing. Results in a brown, stubbly appearance.

Sclerotia
Seed-like, compact masses of fungal tissue that allow fungi to survive unfavorable conditions.

Seed, certified
A seed lot inspected to meet minimum standards and to ensure trueness to type for a given cultivar.

Sheath
The basal portion of the leaf surrounding the grass stem. In grass plants, it is usually split with overlapping edges.

Slicing
Penetration of turf in a vertical plane by a series of solid flat tines.

Spiking
Penetration of turf in a vertical plane by series of solid round tines.

Sprig
A stolon or rhizome used to establish turf.

Stolon
An above-ground creeping stem that can produce roots and shoots at each node.

Symptom
The visual characteristics associated with a given disease.

Thatch
A tightly intermingled layer of undecomposed roots, stems, and shoots located between the soil surface and the green vegetation of the turf grass.

Tiller
A grass plant shoot arising in the axes of leaves in the unelongated portion of the stem.

Tolerance, turf
Ability of a turf species to withstand application of a pesticide (herbicide) at the normal dosage without being killed or injured. Specific tolerance may be associated with an anatomical or physiological characteristic in the plant.

Topdressing
A sand or prepared soil mix applied to the turf to help smooth the surface, enhance establishment, and reduce thatch buildup.

Tuber
An underground stem modified for food storage that is attached to the root system as found in yellow nutsedge.

Turf
A covering of mowed vegetation, usually a grass.

Turfgrass

A species or cultivar of grass, usually of spreading habit, which is maintained as a mowed turf.

Warm-season grasses

Turf that has its optimum growth at temperatures between 80 and 95°F.

Weed

A plant growing where it is not wanted.

Wetting agent

A chemical that aids in liquid-to-surface contact.

Edited by

Arthur H. Bruneau, *Crop Science Professor Emeritus (Turf)*
Grady L. Miller, *Crop Science Professor (Turf)*
Charles H. Peacock, *Crop Science Professor (Turf)*

Contributing Authors

Arthur H. Bruneau, *Crop Science Professor Emeritus (Turf)*
Fred H. Yelverton, *Crop Science Extension Specialist (Weed Management)*
Lane P. Tredway, *Plant Pathology Extension Specialist* Rick L. Brandenburg, *Extension Entomology Specialist* Dan C. Bowman, *Crop Science Turf Research*
Charles H. Peacock, *Crop Science Extension Specialist (Turf)*
Grady L. Miller, *Crop Science Extension Specialist (Turf)*
Richard J. Cooper, *Crop Science Turfgrass Management Specialist* Casey W. Reynolds, *Crop Science Research Technician* Douglas S. Chamblee, *Crop Science Emeritus Faculty* Matthew Martin, *Crop Science Extension Associate*

30,000 copies of this public document were printed at a cost of $11,704, or $.39 per copy.

Published by

NORTH CAROLINA COOPERATIVE EXTENSION SERVICE

Appendix H

NORTH CAROLINA GS 89D

NORTH CAROLINA LANDSCAPE CONTRACTORS LICENSURE LAW

§ 89D-1. (Repealed effective August 1, 2015) Certificate required.

On and after December 1, 1975, it shall be unlawful for any person, partnership, association or corporation in this State to use the title "landscape contractor," or to advertise as such without first obtaining a certificate issued by the North Carolina Landscape contractors' Registration Board under provisions of this Chapter. (1975, c. 741, s. 1; 2014-103, s.3(a).)

§ 89D-2. (Repealed effective August 1, 2015) Definition.

A "landscape contractor" within the meaning of this Chapter is any person, partnership, association or corporation who for compensation or valuable consideration or promise thereof engages in the business requiring the art, experience, ability, knowledge, science and skill to install, plant, repair and maintain gardens, lawns, shrubs, vines, bushes, trees and other decorative vegetation including the grading and preparation of plots and areas of land for decorative treatment and arrangement; who constructs or installs garden pools, fountains, pavilions, conservatories, hothouses and greenhouses, incidental retaining walls, fences, walks, drainage and sprinkler systems; or who engages in incidental construction in connection therewith, or does any part thereof in such a manner that, under an agreed specification, an acceptable landscaping project can be executed. (1975, c. 741, s. 2; 2014-103, s.3(a).)

§ 89D-3. (Repealed effective August 1, 2015) Application of Chapter.

The provisions of this Chapter shall not apply to and shall not include any person, partnership, association or corporation who shall perform any of the acts aforesaid in G.S. 89D-2 with reference to any property, so long as that person, partnership, association or corporation shall not use the title "landscape contractor." (1975, c. 741, s. 3; 2014-103, s.3(a).)

§ 89D-4. (Repealed effective August 1, 2015) Landscape Contractors' Registration Board created; membership; compensation; power, etc.

(a) There is created the North Carolina Landscape Contractors' Registration Board (hereinafter called the Board) which shall issue registration certificates of title to landscape contractors. The Board shall be composed of nine members appointed as follows: Two by the Governor to represent the public at large; two by the Commissioner of Agriculture; two practicing nurserymen operating a nursery certified by the North Carolina Department of Agriculture and Consumer Services Plant Pest Inspection Program appointed by the Board of Directors of the North Carolina Association of Nurserymen, Inc.; two registered landscape contractors in the business of landscape contracting appointed by the Board of Directors of the North Carolina Landscape Contractors' Association, Inc.; and one registered landscape architect appointed by the Board of Directors of the North Carolina Chapter of the American Society of Landscape Architects. All appointments shall be for three-year terms and no member shall serve more than two complete consecutive terms.

Any vacancy on the Board created by death, resignation or otherwise shall be filled for the unexpired term by the initial appointing authority and all members shall serve until their successors are appointed and qualify.

(b) From its funds, the Board shall pay its members at the rate set out in G.S. 93B-5: Provided, that at no time shall the expense exceed the cash balance on hand.

(c) The Board shall have power to make such rules and regulations as are not inconsistent with the provisions of this Chapter and the laws of North Carolina. The Board shall not make rules or regulations regulating commissions, salaries, or fees to be charged by registrants under this Chapter. The Board shall adopt a seal for its use, which shall bear thereon the words "North Carolina Landscape Contractors' Registration Board."

(d) The Board may employ a secretary-treasurer and such clerical assistance as may be necessary to carry out the provisions of this Chapter and to put into effect such rules and regulations as the Board may promulgate.

The Board shall fix salaries for employees and shall require employees to make good and sufficient surety bond for the faithful performance of their duties.

(e) The Board shall be entitled to the services of the Attorney General of North Carolina in connection with the affairs of the Board or may, on approval of the Attorney General, employ an attorney to assist or represent it in the enforcement of this Chapter, but the fee paid for such service shall be approved by the Attorney General. (1975, c. 741, s. 4; 1983, c. 108, s. 1; 1997-261, s. 109; 2014-103, s. 3(a).)

§ 89D-5. (Repealed effective August 1, 2015) Application for certificate; examination; renewal.

(a) Any person, partnership, association or corporation hereinafter desiring to register and be titled as a landscape contractor shall make written application for a certificate of title to the Board on such forms as are prescribed by the Board. Each applicant for a certificate of title as a landscape contractor shall be at least 18 years of age. Prior to July 1, 1976, each applicant for a certificate shall have been actively engaged as an untitled landscape contractor for at least one year prior to date of application. After July 1, 1976, an applicant shall furnish evidence satisfactory to the Board of three years' experience in landscape contracting or the completion of a study or combination of study and experience in landscape contracting equivalent to three years' experience under a landscape contractor.

(b) Any person who applies to the Board to be registered and titled as a landscape contractor shall be required to take an oral or written examination to determine his qualifications. Each application for registration by examination shall be accompanied by an application fee of seventy-five dollars ($75.00).

The Board shall compile a manual from which the examination will be prepared. The examination fee shall not exceed seventy-five dollars ($75.00). Any one failing to pass an examination may be reexamined upon payment of the same fee as that charged to persons taking the examination for the first time, in accordance with such rules as the Board may adopt pertaining to examinations and reexaminations.

If the results of the examination are satisfactory, the Board shall issue the applicant a certificate authorizing him to be titled as a landscape contractor in the State of North Carolina upon payment of the initial certification fee as outlined in subsection (c).

(c) All certificates granted and issued by the Board under the provisions of this Chapter shall expire annually on December 31. Renewal of such certificates may be effected at any time during the month preceding the expiration date of such certificates upon proper application to the Board accompanied by the payment to the secretary-treasurer of the Board of a renewal fee, as set by the Board, of not more than seventy-five dollars ($75.00). The fee for an initial certificate shall be the same as for a renewal certificate and is in addition to the application fee. All certificates reinstated after expiration date thereof shall be subject to a late filing fee of twenty-five dollars ($25.00). In the event a registrant fails to obtain a reinstatement of such certificate within 12 months from the date of expiration thereof, the Board may, in its discretion, consider such registrant subject to the provisions of this Chapter relating to the issuance of an original certificate. Duplicate certificates may be issued by the Board upon payment of a fee not to exceed five dollars ($5.00) by the registrant. The Board may charge a fee not to exceed thirty-five dollars ($35.00) for issuance of a duplicate parchment certificate. (1975, c. 741, s. 5; 1983, c. 108, ss. 2, 3; 1991, c. 180, s. 1; 2007-426, s. 1; 2014-103, s. 3(a).)

§ 89D-6. (Repealed effective August 1, 2015) Registers of applicants and certificate holders.

(a) The secretary-treasurer of the Board shall keep a register of all applicants for certificates of title. The register shall include the date of application, name, place of business, place of residence, and indicate whether the certificate of title was granted or refused.

(b) The secretary-treasurer of the Board shall also keep a current roster showing the names and places of business of all registered titled landscape contractors. The roster shall be kept on file in the office of the Board and be open to public inspection.

(c) On or before the first day of September of each year, the Board shall file with the Secretary of State a copy of the roster of landscape contractors holding certificates of title. At the same time the Board shall file with the Secretary of State a report containing a complete statement of receipts and disbursements of the Board for the preceding fiscal year ending June 30. Such statement shall be attested by the secretary-treasurer of the Board. (1975, c. 741, s. 6; 2014-103, s. 3(a).)

§ 89D-7. (Repealed effective August 1, 2015) Denial, revocation or suspension of certificate.

(a) The Board shall have power to revoke or suspend certificates of title herein provided. The Board may upon its own motion or upon a verified complaint in writing hold a hearing as hereinafter provided to investigate the actions of any titled landscape contractor. The Board shall have the power to suspend or revoke any certificate of title issued under the provisions of this Chapter if the registrant has by false or fraudulent representations obtained a certificate; if the registrant has been convicted or has entered a plea of nolo contendere to any crime involving moral turpitude in any court, State or federal; if the registrant is found to have committed any act which constitutes improper, fraudulent or dishonest dealing; or if the registrant violates any rule or regulation duly promulgated by the Board.

(b) Chapter 150B of the General Statutes applies to proceedings under this section to deny, revoke, or suspend a certificate. (1975, c. 741, s. 7; 1987, c. 827, s. 74; 2014-103, s. 3(a).)

§ 89D-8. (Repealed effective August 1, 2015) Out-of-state applicants.

An applicant from another state which offers registration privileges to residents of North Carolina may be registered by conforming to all the provisions of this Chapter and, in the discretion of the Board, such other terms and conditions as are required of North Carolina residents applying for a certificate in such other state. The Board may exempt from the examination prescribed in this Chapter a landscape contractor duly registered in another state if a similar exemption is extended to registered landscape contractors from North Carolina. (1975, c. 741, s. 8; 2014-103, s. 3(a).)

§ 89D-9. (Repealed effective August 1, 2015) Persons in practice prior to July 1, 1976.

Before July 1, 1976, any person, partnership, corporation or other legal entity submitting an application, application fee and evidence satisfactory to the Board that he has actively engaged in the practice of landscape contracting for one year prior to July 1, 1976, shall be issued a certificate of title without the requirement of examination. (1975, c. 741, s. 10; 2014-103, s. 3(a).)

§ 89D-10. (Repealed effective August 1, 2015) Injunctions for violation of Chapter.

The Board shall have authority to petition for, and the superior courts of the State shall have authority to issue, temporary restraining orders, and preliminary and permanent injunctions for violations of this Chapter. (1975, c. 741, s. 11; 2014-103, s. 3(a).)

§ 89D-11. (Effective August 1, 2015) Definitions.

The following definitions apply in this Chapter:

(1) Board. The North Carolina Landscape Contractors' Licensing Board.

(2) Landscape construction or contracting. The act of providing services as a landscape contractor, as defined in this section, for compensation or other consideration.

(3) Landscape contractor. Any person who, for compensation or other consideration, does any of the following:

a. Engages in the business requiring the art, experience, ability, knowledge, science, and skill to prepare contracts and bid for the performance of landscape services, including installing, planting, repairing, and managing gardens, lawns, shrubs, vines, trees, or other decorative vegetation, including the finish grading and preparation of plots and areas of land for decorative utilitarian treatment and arrangement.

b. Practices the act of horticulture consultation or planting design for employment purposes.

c. Constructs, installs, or maintains landscape drainage systems and cisterns; provided the landscaping contractor makes no connection to pipes, fixtures, apparatus, or appurtenances installed upon the premises, or in a building, to supply water thereto or convey sewage or other waste there from as defined in G.S. 87-21.

d. Designs, installs, or maintains low-voltage landscape lighting systems, provided (i) the work does not exceed the scope of the exception set forth in G.S. 87-43.1(7) and (ii) the low-voltage lighting systems do not exceed 50 volts and constitute a Class II or Class III cord and plug connected power system.

e. Engages in the construction of garden pools, retaining walls, walks, patios, or other decorative landscape features.

(4) Person. An individual, firm, partnership, association, corporation, or other legal entity. (2014-103, s. 3(b).)

§ 89D-12. (Effective August 1, 2015) License required; use of seal; posting license.

(a) Except as otherwise provided in this Chapter, no person shall engage in the practice of landscape construction or contracting, use the designation "landscape contractor," or advertise using any title or description that implies licensure as a landscape contractor unless the person is licensed as a landscape contractor as provided by this Chapter. All landscape construction or contracting performed by a partnership, association, corporation, firm, or other group shall be performed under an individual who is readily available to exercise supervision over the landscape construction and contracting work and who is licensed by the Board under this Chapter.

(b) Nothing in this Chapter shall be construed to authorize a landscape contractor to engage in any of the following:

(1) The practice of landscape architecture, as defined in G.S. 89A-1.

(2) The practice of engineering, as defined in G.S. 89C-3.

(3) Practice as a well contractor certified under Article 7A of Chapter 87 of the General Statutes.

(4) The practice of irrigation contracting, as defined in G.S. 89G-1.

(5) The practice of architecture, as defined in G.S. 83A-1.

(6) The practice of plumbing, heating group number one, heating group number two, heating group number three, fire sprinkler, or fuel piping contracting, as defined in G.S. 87-21, provided the landscaping contractor may install piping, fittings, valves, and associated components for the purpose of landscape contracting that is downstream of a potable water source, groundwater source, or grey water source, and downstream of a backflow prevention assembly.

(7) The practice of electrical contracting, as defined in G.S. 87-43.

(c) A landscape contractor licensed under this Chapter is not required to be licensed as a general contractor under Article 1 of Chapter 87 of the General Statutes if the licensed landscape contractor is performing landscape construction or contracting work valued at an amount greater than thirty thousand dollars ($30,000).

(d) Upon licensure by the Board, each landscape contractor shall obtain a seal of the design authorized by the Board and bearing the name of the licensee, the number of the license, and the legend "N.C. Licensed Landscape Contractor." A landscape contractor may use the seal only while the license is valid.

(e) Every landscape contractor issued a license under this Chapter shall display the license conspicuously in the landscape contractor's place of business. Every landscape contractor shall display the license number issued to the contractor by the Board on all business cards, contracts, and vehicles used by the contractor in the landscape contracting business. (2014-103, s. 3(b).)

§ 89D-13. (Effective August 1, 2015) Exemptions.

The provisions of this Chapter shall not apply to the following:

(1) Any federal, State, or local governmental agency performing landscaping on public property.

(2) The North Carolina Department of Transportation (NCDOT). However, for landscape installations or establishment periods for any project

that exceeds the current contract amount requiring performance and payment bonds according to State law, NCDOT shall require a licensed landscape contractor to perform the work. NCDOT, at its discretion, may require a licensed landscape contractor for landscape projects of any cost.

(3) Any property owner performing landscape work on his or her own property.

(4) Any person or business owning or operating a golf course.

(5) Any landscaping work where the price of all contracts for labor, material, and other items for a given job site during any consecutive 12-month period is less than thirty thousand dollars ($30,000). A local governmental unit shall not enact a local ordinance or regulation requiring licensure for landscaping work performed pursuant to this subdivision.

(6) A general contractor licensed under Article 1 of Chapter 87 of the General Statutes who possesses a classification under G.S. 87-10(b) as a building contractor, a residential contractor, or a public utilities contractor.

(7) Any person or business licensed as an electrical contractor under Article 4 of Chapter 87 of the General Statutes who is designing, installing, or maintaining any electric work, wiring, devices, appliances, or equipment.

(8) Any person or business licensed as a plumbing contractor under Article 2 of Chapter 87 of the General Statutes who is installing pipes, fixtures, apparatus, or appurtenances to supply water thereto or convey sewage or other waste there from, including the installation, repair, or maintenance of water mains, water taps, services lines, water meters, or backflow prevention assemblies supplying water for irrigation systems or repairs to an irrigation system.

(9) A professional engineer licensed pursuant to Chapter 89C of the General Statutes.

(10) A professional landscape architect licensed under Chapter 89A of the General Statutes.

(11) An individual or a business engaged in any of the following activities while performing that activity:

a. Clearing and grading plots and areas of land.

b. Erosion control.

c. Arboriculture, including consultations on pruning and removal of trees.

d. The installation of sod, seed, or plugs by sod producers certified by the Plant Industry Division of the North Carolina Department of Agriculture and Consumer Services.

e. Landscape construction performed by utilities contractors for the purpose of grading and erosion control.

f. Lawn mowing, turf edging, and debris removal services.

g. Turf management or lawn care services only, including fertilization, aeration, weed control, or other turf management or lawn care practices other than mowing or edging.

h. Design, installation, and maintenance of on-site wastewater disposal or reuse systems within the on-site wastewater permit specifications.

(12) Any person performing landscaping work on a farm for use in agriculture production, farming, or ranching. (2014-103, s. 3(b).)

§ 89D-14. (Effective August 1, 2015) The North Carolina Landscape Contractors' Licensing Board.

(a) There is created the North Carolina Landscape Contractors' Licensing Board. The Board shall consist of nine members appointed as follows:

(1) One member appointed by the Governor who is a member of the general public.

(2) One member appointed by the Commissioner of Agriculture pursuant to recommendations from The North Carolina Green Industry Council.

(3) One member appointed by the Board of Directors of the North Carolina Nursery and Landscape Association, Inc., who is a practicing nurseryman operating a nursery certified by the North Carolina Department of Agriculture and Consumer Services Plant Industry Division.

(4) Four members who are licensed landscape contractors in the business of landscape construction or contracting. One of the four members shall be appointed by the General Assembly upon the recommendation of the Speaker of the House of Representatives pursuant to recommendations from The North Carolina Green Industry Council; one shall be appointed by the General Assembly upon the recommendation of the President Pro Tempore of the Senate pursuant to recommendations from the Carolinas Irrigation Association, who is also a licensed irrigation contractor; and two shall be appointed by the Board of Directors of the North Carolina Nursery and Landscape Association, Inc.

(5) One member appointed by the Board of Directors of the North Carolina Chapter of the American Society of Landscape Architects who is a registered landscape architect.

(6) One member appointed by the President of The University of North Carolina from within the land grant university community who is knowledgeable in landscaping methods and practices.

(b) All appointments shall be for three-year terms. No member shall serve more than two complete consecutive terms.

(c) A vacancy on the Board created by death, resignation, or otherwise shall be filled in the same manner as the original appointment, except that all unexpired terms of Board members appointed by the General Assembly shall be filled in accordance with G.S. 120-122. Appointees to fill vacancies shall serve the remainder of the unexpired term and until their successors are appointed and qualified.

(d) The Board shall elect annually a chair and other officers as it deems necessary to carry out the purposes of this Chapter and shall hold meetings at least twice a year. A majority of the Board shall constitute a quorum.

(e) Each member of the Board may receive per diem and reimbursement for travel and subsistence as set forth in G.S. 93B-5.

(f) The Board shall be entitled to the services of the Attorney General in connection with the affairs of the Board or may, in its discretion, employ an attorney to assist or represent it in the enforcement of this Chapter. (2014-103, s. 3(b).)

§ 89D-15. (Effective August 1, 2015) Powers and duties.

The Board shall have the following powers and duties:

(1) Administer and enforce the provisions of this Chapter.

(2) Adopt, amend, or repeal rules to carry out the provisions of this Chapter.

(3) Examine and determine the qualifications and fitness of applicants for licensure and licensure renewal.

(4) Issue, renew, deny, restrict, suspend, or revoke licenses.

(5) Reprimand or otherwise discipline licensees under this Chapter.

(6) Receive and investigate complaints from members of the public.

(7) Conduct investigations to determine whether violations of this Chapter exist or constitute grounds for disciplinary action against licensees under this Chapter.

(8) Conduct administrative hearings in accordance with Article 3A of Chapter 150B of the General Statutes.

(9) Seek injunctive relief through any court of competent jurisdiction for violations of this Chapter.

(10) Collect fees required by G.S. 89D-21 and any other moneys permitted by law to be paid to the Board.

(11) Require licensees to file and maintain an adequate surety bond.

(12) Establish and approve continuing education requirements for persons licensed under this Chapter.

(13) Employ a secretary-treasurer and any other clerical personnel the Board deems necessary to carry out the provisions of this Chapter and to fix compensation for employees.

(14) Maintain a record of all proceedings conducted by the Board and make available to licensees and other concerned parties an annual report of all Board action.

(15) Adopt and publish a code of professional conduct for all persons licensed under this Chapter.

(16) Adopt and publish a code of minimum practice standards for landscape construction and contracting.

(17) Adopt a seal containing the name of the Board for use on licenses and official reports issued by the Board. (2014-103, s. 3(b).)

§ 89D-16. (Effective August 1, 2015) Application for license; qualifications; examination; issuance.

(a) Upon application to the Board and payment of the required fees, an applicant for licensure as a landscape contractor may sit for the examination if the applicant submits evidence demonstrating the applicant's qualifications for licensure under this Chapter as prescribed in rules adopted by the Board and meets all of the following qualifications:

(1) Is at least 18 years of age.

(2) Is of good moral character as determined by the Board.

(3) Provides evidence of business identification as required by the Board.

(4) Files with the Board and maintains a corporate surety bond executed by a company authorized to do business in this State or an irrevocable letter of credit issued by an insured institution. The surety bond or the letter of credit

shall be in the amount of ten thousand dollars ($10,000). The surety bond or letter of credit shall be approved by the Board as to form and shall be conditioned upon the obligor faithfully conforming to and abiding by the provisions of this Chapter. Any person claiming to be injured by an act of a licensed landscape contractor that constitutes a violation of this Chapter may institute an action to recover against the licensee and the surety.

(b) If the applicant meets all the qualifications in subsection (a) of this section, the applicant shall be required to pass an examination administered by the Board before the Board may issue the license. The Board shall establish the scope and subject matter of the examination to be administered. The Board shall administer examinations at least twice a year at a time and place to be determined by the Board.

(c) When the Board determines that an applicant has met all the qualifications for licensure, submitted the required fee, and passed the examination, the Board shall issue a license to the applicant. (2014-103, s. 3(b).)

§ 89D-17. (Effective August 1, 2015) Corporations; partnerships; persons doing business under trade name.

(a) The Board may issue a license in the name of a corporation if the corporation complies with the following:

(1) One or more officers or full-time employees, or both, empowered to act for the corporation are individuals licensed under this Chapter.

(2) Only the officers or employees described in subdivision (1) of this subsection execute contracts for landscape construction or contracting in the name of a corporation and are readily available to exercise supervision over the work performed pursuant to the contract.

(b) The Board may issue a license in the name of a limited liability company if the company complies with the following:

(1) One or more managers, as defined in G.S. 57D-1-03, executives, or full-time employees, or a combination thereof, are individuals licensed under this Chapter.

(2) Only the managers, executives, or employees described in subdivision (1) of this subsection execute contracts for landscape construction or contracting in the name of the limited liability company and are readily available to exercise supervision over the work performed pursuant to the contract.

(c) The Board may issue a license in the name of a partnership if the partnership complies with the following:

(1) One or more general partners or full-time employees empowered to act for the partnership are individuals licensed under this Chapter.

(2) Only the partners or employees described in subdivision (1) of this subsection execute contracts for landscape construction or contracting in the name of the partnership and are readily available to exercise supervision over the work performed pursuant to the contract.

(d) The Board may issue a license in an assumed or designated trade name if the owner of the business complies with the following:

(1) The owner or one or more full-time employees empowered to act for the owner is an individual licensed under this Chapter.

(2) Only the persons described in subdivision (1) of this subsection execute contracts for landscape

construction or contracting in the assumed or designated trade name of the business and are readily available to exercise supervision over the work performed pursuant to the contract.

(e) When the Board issues a license under this section, the Board shall indicate on the license the name and license number of the individual licensee connected to the corporation, partnership, or business conducted under an assumed or designated trade name.

(f) A person licensed pursuant to this section shall be readily available to exercise supervision over a contract for landscape construction or contracting until the contract is completed.

(g) When a licensee executes a contract for landscape construction or contracting in any capacity other than as a sole proprietor contracting on the licensee's own behalf, the person on whose behalf the licensee is executing the contract shall be licensed under this section.

(h) A corporation, partnership, or person doing business under an assumed or designated trade name shall notify the Board in accordance with rules adopted by the Board if an individual licensee who is indicated in the license issued under this section ceases to be an officer, partner, owner, or employee of the corporation, partnership, or person doing business under the assumed or designated trade name. If the corporation, partnership, or person no longer has an officer, general partner, owner, or employee described in subdivision (1) of subsection (a), subdivision (1) of subsection (b), or subdivision (1) of subsection (c) of this section, the corporation, partnership, or person shall have 120 days from the date the officer, general partner, owner, or employee ceases the relationship with the corporation, partnership, or person to satisfy the requirements described in subdivision (1) of subsection (a), subdivision (1) of subsection (b), or subdivision (1) of subsection (c) of this section. The Board may, in its discretion, grant the corporation, partnership, or person a period greater than 120 days to satisfy the requirements described in subdivision (1) of subsection (a), subdivision (1) of subsection (b), or subdivision (1) of subsection (c) of this section as it deems appropriate. After 120 days, or a time period greater than 120 days as approved by the Board, if the corporation, partnership, or person does not have an officer, general partner, owner, or employee as described in subdivision (1) of subsection (a), subdivision (1) of subsection (b), or subdivision (1) of subsection (c) of this section, the license issued under this section is automatically suspended and the corporation, partnership, or person shall cease practicing landscape construction or contracting. (2014-103, s. 3(b).)

§ 89D-18. (Effective August 1, 2015) Licensing of nonresidents.

(a) Definitions. The following definitions apply in this section:

(1) Delinquent income tax debt. The amount of income tax due as stated in a final notice of assessment issued to a taxpayer by the Secretary of Revenue when the taxpayer no longer has the right to contest the amount.

(2) Foreign corporation. A corporation as defined in G.S. 55-1-40.

(3) Foreign entity. A foreign corporation, a foreign limited liability company, or a foreign partnership.

(4) Foreign limited liability company. A company as defined in G.S. 57D-1-03.

(5) Foreign partnership. One of the following that does not have a permanent place of business in this State:

a. A foreign limited partnership as defined in G.S. 59-102.

b. A general partnership formed under the laws of a jurisdiction other than this State.

(b) Licensing. Except as provided in this section, the Board may issue a license to a nonresident individual or a foreign entity that meets the requirements for licensure under this Chapter.

(c) Certificate of Authority Required. The Board shall not issue a license for a foreign corporation unless the corporation has obtained a certificate of authority from the Secretary of State pursuant to Article 15 of Chapter 55 of the General Statutes. The Board shall not issue a license for a foreign limited liability company unless the company has obtained a certificate of authority from the Secretary of State pursuant to Article 7 of Chapter 57D of the General Statutes.

(d) Information. The Board, upon request, shall provide the Secretary of Revenue the name, address, and tax identification number of every nonresident individual and foreign entity licensed by the Board. The information to be provided under this section shall be in a form required by the Secretary of Revenue.

(e) Delinquents. If the Secretary of Revenue determines that any nonresident individual or foreign entity licensed by the Board owes a delinquent income tax debt, the Secretary of Revenue may notify the Board of the nonresident individual or foreign entity and instruct the Board not to renew the nonresident individual or foreign entity's license. The Board shall not renew the license of a nonresident individual or foreign entity identified by the Secretary of Revenue unless the Board receives a written statement from the Secretary that (i) the debt has been paid or (ii) the debt is being paid pursuant to an installment agreement. (2014-103, s. 3(b).)

§ 89D-19. (Effective August 1, 2015) Reciprocity.

The Board may issue a license, without examination, to any person who is a landscape contractor licensed, certified, or registered in another state or country if the requirements for licensure, certification, or registration in the other state or country are substantially equivalent to the requirements for licensure in this State. (2014-103, s. 3(b).)

§ 89D-20. (Effective August 1, 2015) License renewal and continuing education.

(a) Every license issued under this Chapter shall be renewed on or before the first day of August of each year. Any person who desires to continue to practice shall apply for a license renewal and shall submit the required fee. Licenses that are not renewed shall be automatically revoked. A license may be renewed at any time within one year after its expiration if (i) the applicant pays the required renewal fee and late renewal fee, (ii) the Board finds that the applicant has not used the license in a manner inconsistent with the provisions of this Chapter or engaged in the practice of landscape construction or contracting after notice of revocation, and (iii) the applicant is otherwise eligible for licensure under the provisions of this Chapter. When necessary, the Board may require licensees to demonstrate continued competence as a condition of license renewal.

(b) As a condition of license renewal, a licensee shall meet the continuing education requirements set by the Board. Each licensee shall complete seven continuing education units per year. The Board may suspend a licensee's license for 30 days for failure to obtain continuing education units required by this subsection. Upon payment of a reinstatement fee, submission to the Board of proof of the continuing education units required by this subsection, and payment of the license renewal fee and late renewal fee, the licensee's license shall be reinstated. Failure to request a reinstatement of the license and failure to pay the reinstatement fee, renewal fee, and late renewal fee shall result in the forfeiture of a license. Upon forfeiture, a person shall be required to submit a new application and retake the examination as provided in this Chapter. (2014-103, s. 3(b).)

§ 89D-21. (Effective August 1, 2015) Expenses and fees.

(a) The Board may impose the following fees not to exceed the amounts listed below:

(1) Application fee	$100.00
(2) Examination fee	250.00
(3) Individual license fee and individual license renewal	100.00
(4) Initial corporate, limited liability company, partnership, or trade name license	100.00
(5) Corporate, limited liability company, partnership, or trade name license renewal	100.00
(6) Late renewal fee	50.00
(7) Reinstatement fee	250.00
(8) License by reciprocity	250.00
(9) Duplicate license	25.00

(b) When the Board uses a testing service for the preparation, administration, or grading of examinations, the Board may charge the applicant the actual cost of the examination services and a prorated portion of the examination fee. (2014-103, s. 3(b).)

§ 89D-22. (Effective August 1, 2015) Disciplinary action.

(a) The Board may deny, restrict, suspend, or revoke a license or refuse to issue or renew a license if a licensee or applicant does any of the following:

(1) Employs the use of fraud, deceit, or misrepresentation in obtaining or attempting to obtain a license or the renewal of a license.

(2) Practices or attempts to practice landscape construction or contracting by fraudulent misrepresentation.

(3) Commits an act of gross malpractice or incompetence as determined by the Board.

(4) Has been convicted of or pled guilty or no contest to a crime that indicates that the person is unfit or incompetent to practice as a landscape contractor or that indicates that the person has deceived or defrauded the public.

(5) Has been declared incompetent by a court of competent jurisdiction.

(6) Has willfully violated any provision in this Chapter or any rules adopted by the Board.

(7) Uses or attempts to use the seal in a fraudulent or unauthorized manner.

(8) Fails to file the required surety bond or letter of credit or to keep the bond or letter of credit in force.

(b) The Board may assess costs, including reasonable attorneys' fees and investigatory costs, in a proceeding under this section against an applicant or licensee found to be in violation of this Chapter. (2014-103, s. 3(b).)

§ 89D-23. (Effective August 1, 2015) Civil penalties.

(a) In addition to taking any of the actions permitted under G.S. 89D-22, the Board may assess a civil penalty not in excess of two thousand dollars ($2,000) for each violation of any section of this Chapter or the violation of any rules adopted by the

Board. The clear proceeds of any civil penalty assessed under this section shall be remitted to the Civil Penalty and Forfeiture Fund in accordance with G.S. 115C-457.2.

(b) Before imposing and assessing a civil penalty and fixing the amount of the penalty, the Board shall, as a part of its deliberations, take into consideration the following factors:

(1) The nature, gravity, and persistence of the particular violation.

(2) The appropriateness of the imposition of a civil penalty when considered alone or in combination with other punishment.

(3) Whether the violation was willful and malicious.

(4) Any other factors that would tend to mitigate or aggravate the violations found to exist. (2014-103, s. 3(b).)

§ 89D-24. (Effective August 1, 2015) Injunction to prevent violation; notification of complaints.

(a) If the Board finds that a person who does not have a license issued under this Chapter is engaging in the practice of landscape construction or contracting, the Board may appear in its own name in superior court in actions for injunctive relief to prevent any person from violating the provisions of this Chapter or the rules adopted by the Board.

(b) A licensed landscape contractor shall notify the Board of any written complaints filed against the landscape contractor not resolved within 30 days from the date the complaint was filed by registered mail to the Board. (2014-103, s. 3(b).)

About the Author

David Sauter is an educator with more than 30 years of teaching, administrative, and practical experience. He has served on the faculties of Foothill College in Los Altos Hills, California, and Kirkwood Community College in Cedar Rapids, Iowa, and worked as a Landscape Architect in the Midwest and on the West Coast. He has taught coursework in landscape design, landscape construction, computer-aided design, computer applications in horticulture, and business management.

David Sauter completed his BS in Landscape Architecture at Iowa State University and received an MA in Higher Education from the University of Iowa. He has presented seminars for the nursery industry, master gardeners, extension service, and public service organizations. He is a registered landscape architect and has practiced in Iowa, Minnesota and California. He has participated in the design and construction of landscape projects of all sizes. Mr. Sauter has additional experience in plant maintenance, plant installation, landscape construction, masonry, carpentry, paving, and landscape management.

ACKNOWLEDGMENTS

The author wishes to express his appreciation to the following people, businesses, and organizations for their assistance in the preparation of this text:

North Carolina Landscape Contractor Licensing Board
NCSU Cooperative Extension Service
NCSU Department of Horticultural Science
Chris Mitchell
Scott Makey
Fred Adams
Scott Myatt
Robert Harrison IV
Bob Shields
Mark Peters
Robert Peter
Frank Niccoli
Dwight Hughes, Jr.
Foothill College Landscape Construction and Plant Installation and Maintenance classes.
FX Luminaire
Mike Diefenbach
Jessie Klinker
Iowa City Landscaping
Pleasant Valley Nursery and Garden Center
Peck's Garden Center
Peck's Green Thumb Landscaping
Kirkwood Community College
Margaret Sauter
Gary Pribyl
Iowa Nursery and Landscape Association
Iowa One Call
Paul Dykstra
Lucy Hershberger
Interlocking Concrete Paving Institute
Spring Valley Nursery
Ed Sauter
Kirkwood Hort Construction I class, 1997
Kirkwood Hort Construction II class, 1997
Kirkwood grounds crew
Forevergreen Landscaping
Foothill Advanced Construction Class, 2003
Lyngso Building Materials
California Landscape Contractors Association
California Association of Nurseries and Garden Centers
California Chapter, Association of Professional Landscape Designers

The author and Delmar Publishers would also like to thank those individuals who reviewed the manuscript and offered suggestions, feedback, and assistance. Their work is greatly appreciated.

Glenn Herold
Illinois Central College
East Peoria, Illinois
Jack Ingels
Suny-Cobleskill
Cobleskill, New York
Cameron R. J. Man
Mississippi State University
Mississippi State, Mississippi
David B. Nichols
University of Georgia
Athens, Georgia
Glenn Petrick
Milwaukee Area Technical College
North Campus Center, Wisconsin
Daniel Robinson
Cal Poly Pomona
Pomona, California

GLOSSARY

A

Acid etch. A concrete finish created by rinsing the surface with an acid and water mixture.

ADA (Americans with Disabilities Act). A federal law mandating that the needs of persons with differing abilities be considered in the design of spaces.

Addenda. Official notifications of changes in the project, typically revisions to the construction plans or specifications, that occur prior to bid opening.

Air vent. An irrigation valve that supplies air when draining a system. **Alternating current (AC).** Alternating current. High-voltage electrical current. **Amps.** The "flow rate" of electricity in a circuit.

Anchor. A structural piece used to hold items to a footing or support.

Angle of repose. Angle formed when materials are piled and allowed to slump naturally.

Arc. Part of a circle; a curve.

As-built drawings. Drawings prepared by a land surveyor and marked to show the actual location of improvements. They typically highlight alterations in the original construction plans.

Ashlar. Random stone pattern composed of cut squares and rectangles of varying dimensions.

Asphalt. A mixture of petrochemicals, sand, and aggregate used to pave surfaces.

Assignable overhead. Nonlabor and nonmaterial costs that are directly attributed to a project.

Auger. A digging tool with a spiral or clam-shaped blade that is turned into the ground to remove soil.

B

Backdrain. A valve and housing that allows water to be drained out of an irrigation system.

Backsite. Measurement taken from survey instrument back to a benchmark.

Balled and burlapped. A plant that has been grown in the ground, dug out, and had the root-ball wrapped in burlap in preparation for transplanting.

Baluster. Narrow vertical post used for railing surfacing.

Bare-root. A plant that has had the soil removed from the roots in order to prepare it for transplanting.

Base. Layer of material below the paving. Provides support for paving.

Baseline. Layout technique that locates objects using measurements made at right angles at calculated points along a straight line.

Base material. Crushed stone used as support material for most paving material. Also referred to as *aggregate, gravel, roadstone,* and other regional names.

Base screed. Tool used to level base material. Typically a straight 2 × 4, with handles on top, slightly shorter than the width of the forms.

Batter. Backward lean of a retaining wall for stability.

Batterboards. L-shaped wooden framework used to mark corners, edges, and elevations of projects.

Beam. A large dimensioned wood structural member often placed on edge to support joists.

Benchmark. Fixed reference elevation.

Bender board. Thin strips of wood bound together that can be used as edge restraint. Thin strips allow the material to be bent into radii.

Bentonite. Finely ground clay material that expands upon contact with water.

Berm. Mounded and shaped soil.

BFM. Bonded fiber mulch. Hydromulch with materials chemically bonded.

Bidding. A pricing process in which contractors compete against each other by calculating their price and submitting their sealed bids to the owner.

Bioswale. A gradually sloped drainage channel with shallow sides that is lined with plant material and, in certain situations, rip-rap. Also called *swales.*

Blocking. Solid wood blocks placed between joists or rafters to maintain spacing.

Blue topping. Placing of project hub stakes, which are blue, to manipulate soil to the desired finish grade.

Bollard. Short post used to separate traffic or protect important site elements. **Bonding.** A document that ensures the financial surety of a company or a person. **Bracing.** Supports placed in the structural framework.

Breaker bar. A long, heavy, pointed metal bar used to break up hard compacted soil.

Brick (paving brick, pavers). Rectangular fired **clay** brick with typical dimensions of 4 inches × 8 inches × 2.5 inches thick. Available in a range of colors, paving bricks have no mortar holes and an average strength of approximately 5,000 PSI.

Bridging. Diagonal wood braces placed between joists or rafters to maintain spacing.

Building paper (roofing felt). Tar-impregnated paper used to waterproof roofs.

Bull float. Wide, flat metal (usually aluminum) tool with a long handle used to smooth the concrete surface after it has been screeded.

Bush hammered. A concrete finish created by scouring the surface with a gridded head mounted on a power hammer.

Buttering. Placing mortar on the end of a masonry unit.

Butt joint. Joint formed by placing the square ends of lumber end to end. **Butt stair.** Stairs that have tread material that butts up against cheek walls. **Buttress.** A support placed in front of or outside an object.

C

CADD (computer aided drafting and design). Drawings prepared with the aid of a computer drafting program.

Canopy. Top vegetative portion of a plant, including trunk, branches, and foliage.

Cantilever. Overhang of a deck beyond outside supports.

Carriage. Structural support member for stairs.

Cartesian coordinates. A measurement and layout system that locates an object using measurements off two baselines set up at right angles to each other.

Cascade. Water feature in which water spills gently from one level to the next. **Cast-in-place concrete.** Concrete that is custom formed and poured on the site. **Catch basin.** Concrete structure with a sump into which water runoff flows.

Chainsaw. A saw with a sharp chain blade and powered by a gas or electric motor.

Chalk line. Tool composed of a housing holding chalk and string. String is pulled out and snapped, leaving a chalk line used to mark locations.

Change orders. Revisions to the project that occur after the contracts have been signed.

Chasing a bond. Layout of masonry units before installing them to check for fit.

Cheek wall. Side wall that runs perpendicular to the face of a retaining wall. Stairs butt or are interlocked into the cheek wall.

Chord. A line segment that joins two points on a curve.

Circuit. A complete path of electrical current.

Circular saw. Hand-operated power saw using a round blade.

Cladding. Covering the sides of a post or column with a decorative surfacing material.

Clamshell digger. A posthole excavator composed of two rounded blades connected to handles.

Cleat. Small wood blocks used to support surfacing materials.

Clinometer (also called inclinometer or tilt sensor). A tool used to measure the degree of slope by aiming the tool up or down a slope and reading an angle measurement in a window.

Closed French drain. A short, shallow trench drain filled with loose stone. Used for water storage in low areas. No outlet is provided.

Coaxial. Cable used for TV with conducting wire in center and conducting mesh wrapped around outside of center conductor.

Cobbled concrete. A concrete slab with large rounded stone set into its surface.

Codes (building, plumbing, electrical). A set of guidelines and rules for proper installation of building improvements.

Colored, impressioned concrete. Concrete surface that has been colored and stamped to look like brick, stone, or other decorative surfaces.

Column. Decorative post.

Composting. Technique for piling and turning of vegetative waste that allows decomposition of waste into usable organic matter.

Concave corners. Wall corners where the radius is measured on the inside. Inside corners.

Concrete. Mixture of cement, sand, water, and aggregate (stone) that hardens to create a solid paving surface. Typical landscape concrete is ordered as 4,000 PSI.

Concrete broom. Stiff-bristled shop broom used to put a texture on concrete.

Concrete pumping. Delivering concrete to a remote location using a special truck that pumps concrete through a series of tubes.

Conduit. Plastic or metal piping in which wiring is placed.

Construction drawings. *See* contract documents.

Construction joint. Joint placed at the end of a concrete pour where work is stopped with plans to continue later. This joint can be a straight edge, an edge with rebar sticking out, or an edge with a keyway.

Container plant. A tree, shrub, perennial or other plant that has been grown in the nursery in a container.

Contour lines. A line on a drawing that connects points of the same elevation.

Contract. A legally binding agreement between two parties that outlines the exchange of services or products for a fee.

Contract documents. Plans, specifications, and related documents used to guide the construction of a project.

Contraction or control joint. Joint in concrete used to control the cracking that happens when concrete dries. These shallow joints are tooled into the concrete while it is still wet or are sawed in after the concrete dries.

Controllers. Automatic switches that turn a DC circuit on and off based on time or light.

Convex corners. Wall corners where the radius is measured on the outside. Outside corners.

Coping material. Flat pieces of edging placed around pools to cover the top edge of the pool.

Cor-ten® steel. Type of steel that has an oxidized (rusted) finish appearance.

Cost plus fixed fee bid. A bid format that lists the time and materials required for the project and includes the profit as a fixed line item.

Countersink. Driving a fastener slightly below the surface of the material being fastened.

Cover crop. Fast-germinating plant material seeded on a site to reduce erosion.

Crimping. Deforming the surface of a material.

Critical path method (CPM). Scheduling technique that identifies project tasks according to their completion time and their order of completion, identifying those tasks that are critical to the timely completion of a project.

Cross section. A side view that cuts vertically through an object.

Curb. A short linear concrete barrier used for directing drainage and delineating planting beds.

Curb inlet. Concrete drainage structure built into a curb into which water runoff flows.

Curing. The process of concrete drying.

Cut and fill. The process of removing and adding soil to a site to achieve desired grades.

Cutoff saw. A gas-powered saw with a circular blade.

D

Darby float. Long, wood hand float with handle on top, used to level concrete after placement.

Dash bond. A thin coating composed of cement, sand, and water that is put on a wall to improve stucco adhesion.

Deadman. Anchor that is connected to the wall face and buried into a hill behind the wall for stabilization.

Deep watering. A post-planting care technique where a large volume of water is injected into the backfill zone of a newly installed plant in order to remove air pockets.

Demolition (site). Removal of existing site improvements that are not part of the finished product.

Design professional. A registered design professional such as a landscape architect, architect, engineer, or land surveyor.

Detail. A drawing that shows the specific materials and dimensions of a landscape element.

Detail key. A symbol found on any plan, indicating the sheet number on which the detail is located and the detail number.

Detention. Holding back of storm water.

Direct current (DC). Direct current. Low-voltage electrical current.

Direct procurement. The acquisition of contracts for services directly from a client.

Drip edge. Metal flashing engineered to keep water from flowing under shingles.

Drip line. Line on the ground directly below the farthest extent of a plant's canopy.

Drip systems. Low-pressure irrigation systems that precisely distribute water directly to the root zone of plants.

Dry-laid stone. Stone pieces that are laid without mortar joints.

Dry well. See Closed French drain. A short, shallow trench drain filled with loose stone. Used for water storage in low areas. No outlet is provided.

Dumpy level. A tripod-mounted telescope that can be leveled and used to measure elevations.

E

ECB (erosion control blanket). Fibers or other mulch-like materials sandwiched between layers of thin nylon netting. Also called *erosion mats.*

Edger. Short tool with a handle on top, flat surface on the bottom, and a ¼-inch lip projecting down along the edge of the tool. Used along concrete forms to create rounded edges.

Edging (edge restraint). Material used along an edge to hold paving materials in place. Used with unit pavers and granular material, edgers can be concrete, stone, brick, wood, metal, or plastic. Edgers are typically anchored into the subgrade with pins or stakes. Also refers to materials placed to separate turf from planting beds.

Elevation. 1. A drawing that shows two dimensions, vertical and horizontal, and shows the surface of an object. 2. The vertical measurement of an object.

Ell (elbow). A pipe fitting that is right angled, or L shaped, and has openings for pipe at each end.

Emitters. Small irrigation heads that distribute

water at rates of 1/2 to 5 gallons per hour. Also called drip heads due to the water being emitted in a slow drip.

End posts. Larger diameter posts used at corners and gates in chain-link fencing installations.

Erosion. Removal of soil particles through the action of water and wind.

Erosion mat. *See* ECB (erosion control blanket).

Expanding bolt. Bolt that anchors itself by expanding when the stem is turned.

Expansion joint. Joint placed where concrete intersects with a stable, permanent object. This joint protects the stable object from being moved by the force of expanding concrete.

Expansion joint material. Plastic or fibrous strips that are placed between buildings and walks to protect both when concrete expands in hot weather.

Exposed aggregate. Concrete surface where decorative rock have been imbedded into the surface and rinsed to expose their surface.

Exterior grade plywood. Plywood manufactured with special glues and woods to resist delaminating in exterior applications.

F

Fascia. Material covering structural components.

Felled. Cutting down a tree.

Fibermesh. Concrete with minute fiberglass strands that act as reinforcement.

Fiber optic. Communications utility line composed of a fine glass strand encased in plastic housing.

Field finishing. Painting or touching up amenity finishes after installation.

Fieldstone. Irregular-sized rounded or angular shaped stone weathered by natural forces. Used in freestanding walls.

Finish coat. The final layer for a stucco application.

Finish floor elevation. The elevation of the finish level of a structure's floor. **Firepit.** An outdoor cauldron where a real or gas-fired flame can be maintained. **Fixtures.** Components such as lights that are attached to an electrical system.

Flagstone. Natural stone that is either cut into standard dimensions or broken into irregular pieces with a thickness of 1½–2½ inches.

Flashing. Metal sheeting installed between structural members to prevent moisture penetration.

Float. A broad, flat tool with a handle on top used to smooth concrete. Manufactured from wood, steel, or magnesium.

Floating and troweling. The laborious step of working the poured concrete surface with flat-bedded tools that push aggregate farther down into the pour and cause water and fine particles to move up to the surface.

Flowable fill. A thin concrete mixed with fly ash.

Footing. A structural support, often of concrete.

Foresite. Measurement taken of a paint to be surveyed from a survey instrument.

Form break compound. Liquid applied to forms to allow them to release easier after concrete hardens.

Form liners. Rubber or metal molds placed inside forms to leave a decorative surface.

Form nails. Special nails used in form construction that have two heads to make removal from the form easier.

Forms. Pieces and strips of wood or metal placed to shape concrete slabs. Forms are secured to the ground and tops are set at the desired height of the concrete.

Free-draining angular fill. Crushed stone without rounded edges or fine granular material used as fill behind a wall.

Free out (swale high point). Low point that allows water to pass out of a drainage area.

Frost depth (frost line). Average maximum depth at which frost penetrates the soil.

Frost footing. A footing that extends below frost depth.

G

Gabions. Wire baskets that are filled with stone and stacked to create a wall.

Gable. A roof form that has two angled surfaces.

Galvanized. Metal coated with zinc to reduce rusting.

Gannt chart. A scheduling technique that uses a matrix listing all tasks that must be completed on a vertical axis and the duration of the tasks on the horizontal axis. Horizontal bars indicate the starting date and the completion date of each task.

General contractor. Contractor responsible for coordinating work performed by subcontractors from several different trades (see also Prime Contractor).

Geogrid. Open-weave fabric used to stabilize retaining walls.

Geotextile. Interwoven structural fabric used to assist in stabilizing subgrades.

Geotextile sock. A textile covering wrapped around a tile to keep fine particles of soil from moving into the tile.

GFCI (ground-fault circuit interrupt). Circuit engineered to automatically shut off if a voltage change or short is detected.

Gilling. A piece of equipment towed behind a tractor and used to cultivate and smooth soil before seeding or sodding.

GPS (Global Positioning System). A method to locate positions on the ground using signals from satellites to triangulate the sender's position.

Grab beam. A beam that is two pieces of structural lumber, one placed on each side of a post.

Grade beam. A concrete footing on buried concrete piers used to bridge poor soils.

Grading. 1. Changing the slope or contour of the land. 2. Designating the quality of lumber pieces.

Granular base. Crushed stone material used to stabilize the bottom course of a wall. **Granular paving.** Paving materials that are broken into pieces typically ½ inch or less. **Grape stake.** Long, rounded, irregular-shaped stick used for fence surfacing.

Grommets. Round metal rings which protect the openings in fabric through which cords or rope are placed.

Grout. Weak mortar mix used to fill the center cavity of a masonry wall.

Gunnite®. Stiff concrete that is sprayed on a metal framework or surface and finished in place.

Gusset. The piece of dimensioned lumber that is bolted alongside the pieces being spliced to add additional stability.

Guying. A form of tree staking that uses three to four anchors placed on the ground with wires angled up and over branches halfway up the plant.

H

Halogen. An incandescent lamp with tungsten filament sealed into a bulb filled with an inert gas and a small amount of iodine or bromine halogen.

Hammer drill. A drill using a bit that rotates and vibrates to improve boring through hard surfaces such as masonry or concrete.

Hardwood. Deciduous, or broad-leafed, trees such as oak, maple, and walnut.

Haunching. The hand placed trench backfill that holds the pipe and fitting against movement.

Head. An irrigation component that distributes water to plants. Can use spray, flood, or drip methods to distribute water.

Header. 1. Brick course turned perpendicular to other courses. 2. A wood joint in a concrete slab.

Height of instrument. The benchmark elevation plus the backsite. Foresites are subtracted from this number to obtain the elevations of locations on a site.

Honeycombing. Voids or holes that occur when concrete is not properly vibrated or tamped.

Hose bibb. Threaded adapter placed on a hydrant that allows a hose to be attached.

Hydrant. Exterior water outlet, usually with a threaded connector for a hose.

Hydraulic splitter. Table-mounted masonry cleaving tool that exerts hydraulic pressure on a bar to split materials.

Hydromulching. Application of mulch by mixing it with water and a tackifier and spraying it onto a surface.

Hydroseeding. Seed application accomplished by mixing seed with water and spraying on a surface.

Hydrostatic pressure. Pressure caused by the buildup of water behind a retaining wall.

I

Inlet. Concrete or plastic structure into which water runoff flows.

Interceptor channel. A shallow swale lined with concrete or a heavy-grade vinyl liner that is placed along the site's perimeter on the high side.

Interlocking concrete paving block. Unit paving material composed of molded, cured concrete. Pavers come in a variety of shapes and colors, are 3.5 inches thick, and have a typical average strength of 8,000 PSI.

Interlocking stair. Stairs that have treads that interlock with cheek walls.

Irrigation. A system of piping, valves, and sprinkles designed to water plant material.

Itemized bid. A bid format that provides not only a total project price, but also a detailed listing of project materials or work tasks.

J

J bolt. A long metal bolt with a 90° turn at the end forming a J. Used to anchor items to a concrete footing.

Jointer. Similar to an edger, except the lip is located in the center and the tool is used to create contraction joints in a slab.

Joist. A large dimensioned wood structural member placed on edge that supports deck surfacing.

Joist hanger. Metal bracket used to connect joists to other structural elements.

Jumping jack. A handheld gas-powered compaction tool that compacts by bouncing up and ramming down.

Jurisdiction. Defined boundaries within which a person or an organization has control over activities.

K

Kerfing. Shallow cuts along the back of a board that allow the board to be bent.

Keying. Making grooves or indentations in one material so it will interlock with another material.

Keyway. An angled groove placed in concrete by a special form. Used to create a lip where two concrete slabs can be held together.

Kickplate. Vertical support running between posts at the bottom of a fence.

Kneeboard. A 24-inch × 24-inch sheet of ½-inch plywood board used to kneel on when finishing concrete.

L

Landscape architect. A registered (in states with title laws) design professional specializing in landscape projects.

Landscape designer. An individual who possesses special skills in arranging design elements.

Landscape fabric. A geotextile used specifically for preventing weed growth.

Landscape timber. Dimensioned lumber wall unit treated for contact with ground.

Laser plane level. A surveyor's instrument that indicates level using a rotating light beam picked up by a receiver.

Lateral line. A secondary irrigation line that carries water from valves to irrigation heads.

Lath. Thin, narrow piece of unfinished wood used for spacing and surface applications.

Lattice. Framework of lath or small-dimensioned lumber arranged in a decorative pattern.

Ledger. 1. Piece of dimensioned lumber attached to a structure that supports decks and roofs. 2. A ledge on which veneer is placed.

Level spreader. A level spreader diverts storm water from a channel and directs it into a holding pond, or forebay

Lifts. Layers of soil or granular base.

Light emitting diode (LED). A lamp that uses diodes to produce a light.

Light standard. Post to which a light fixture is connected.

Line posts. Small-diameter posts placed between larger posts in chain-link fencing installations.

Liner. Waterproof plastic or vinyl sheet used to line water features.

Lipped wall units. Precast wall units that use a lip cast at the back, bottom edge of the block to align and stabilize between courses. Lips also create a setback batter.

Low-voltage lighting. Lighting that uses electrical power reduced from a high level (110–120 volts) to a lower level (10–12 volts).

Lump sum bid. A bid format in which all project costs are provided to the client in a single number.

M

Mag (magnesium) float. Wide, flat tool with handle mounted on top used to smooth concrete surface. Made out of lightweight magnesium.

Main line. A primary irrigation line that carries water to valves.

Maintenance edge. Narrow strip of weed-proof material placed under the length of a fence to reduce trimming.

Masonry drill bit. Drill bit engineered to drill through concrete and masonry materials.

Material Safety and Data Sheets (MSDS). Printed instructions from manufacturers regarding the safe handling of materials they produce.

Mid rail. Bracing rail placed midway between the top and bottom of a panel of chain-link fence.

Mitered joint. Joint formed by placing angled edges of miter-cut lumber together.

Mortar. Mixture of cement, lime, sand, and water used to space masonry units.

Mortar bag. A vinyl or cloth bag used to squeeze mortar into small spaces.

Mulch. Organic or inorganic ground covering placed around plants to reduce weeds and retain moisture.

Multiplier. An addition to hourly costs to cover unassignable overhead.

Muriatic acid. Acid use for cleaning masonry and concrete.

N

Niche. Realignment of a wall to create a small space and/or additional stability.

Nipple. A short pipe connecting two irrigation components.

Nominal dimension. Dimensions of lumber used for ordering. Represents the actual dimensions before drying and planing.

Nonperforated tile. Plastic tile with no surface openings.

O

Ohm. The resistance between two points of a conductor.

Offset. A practice of placing stakes or lines for an improvement at a consistent, predetermined distance and direction from where the improvement is to be actually installed.

Open French drain. A short, shallow trench drain filled with loose stone with a tile at the bottom that runs to daylight. Used for water storage in low areas.

Ordinances (zoning, parking, sign, street tree). Laws that govern the type, size, and location of improvements on private property.

Orifice. Opening in a drainage grate surface.

OSB. Oriented strand board. Sheet lumber composed of chips or strands of lumber joined with special glues.

Overhead. Nonlabor or material costs of operating a business not specifically associated with a particular project.

P, Q

Pacing. A measuring technique that uses walking to obtain approximate dimensions.

Patio misters. Spray nozzles that distribute a fine mist under pressure to cool outdoor spaces.

Paving. 1. Applying a hard surface to an area. 2. The material used to apply a hard surface to an area.

PDF (Portable Document Format). A method of saving and transmitting drawings that allow them to be opened and read using a free program from Adobe® software.

Perforated tile. Plastic tile with small openings to allow water to enter.

Permeable pavement. Asphalt, concrete, or segmental pavers that are constructed with more open space between aggregate to allow water to percolate rather than run off the surface.

Personal protective equipment (PPE). Equipment such as latex gloves and CPR mouth pieces that protect workers from blood borne pathogens.

Phillips drive. Screw with an X pattern driving head.

Photocell. A device that allows a circuit to be turned off or on based on the amount of light present.

Pickets. Vertical boards used for fence surfacing.

Pier. Support for bridge platform.

Pier block. Precast concrete block used to support posts.

Pinned wall units. Precast wall units that use a metal or fiberglass pin to align and stabilize units between courses.

Planimeter. An engineering tool used to measure the area of random shapes.

Plan view. A two-dimensional drawing showing length and width, but not height.

Planting plans. Plans that indicate the location and type of plant material to be installed.

Plant schedule. A listing of plant material used in a design. Often located on the planting plan.

Platform framing. A method for structurally supporting a deck that does not use beams. Joist are "hung" between a framework of structural members.

Plug. A small circle or square of sod with roots, stems, leaves, and a small plug of soil.

Plumb. Placement of an object in true vertical position.

Plumb bob. A weighted tool suspended from a string. Used to determine plumb.

Poly pipe. Polyethlyene pipe.

Portland cement. Powdered blend of lime, coke, and other ingredients that forms the bonding agent in concrete, mortar, and stucco.

Post. A large dimensioned structural support that is set vertically.

Post and beam framing. A method for structurally supporting a deck that connects beams to posts. Joist are then placed on top of beams.

Post driver. A heavy, hollow metal tube with handles that is used to drive fenceposts into the ground.

Power driver. A hammer-like tool that uses a loaded charge to drive nails into concrete and other hard surfaces.

Precast concrete. Concrete that has been formed and hardened before being delivered to a site.

Pressure-treated wood. Wood that has had a preservative forced into the surface under high pressures.

Prime contractor. Contractor responsible for coordinating work performed by subcontractors from several different trades (see also Prime Contractor).

Privacy slatting. Plastic or metal materials inserted into chain-link fence to increase opaqueness of fence.

Program evaluation and review technique (PERT). Scheduling technique that uses charts showing the project tasks and their duration, identifying completion dates that are optimistic, pessimistic, and most likely.

PSI. Pounds per square inch. Strength measurement used for paving materials.

Pumping. Action of soil working up into aggregate through traffic compaction.

Punch. A small-diameter awl used for punching holes in tubes.

Purlin. Wood support that runs perpendicular to rafters and supports roofing materials.

PVC. Polyvinylchloride pipe.

R

Rafter. A large dimensioned wood structural member placed on edge that supports roof surfacing.

Rakes. The end overhang of a roof.

Rammed earth. A method of constructing walls by blending screened soil and a binder, then ramming it into forms.

Rammer (jumping jack). A handheld gas-powered compaction tool that compacts by bouncing up and ramming down.

Rebar. Durable steel or metal rods used in staking or for reinforcement.

Reciprocating saw. An electric-powered saw with a thin vertical blade that vibrates back and forth.

Recycled concrete. Concrete slabs and other surfaces that have been broken into pieces for reuse.

Record drawings. Drawings that show the way a project was actually build, including any adjustments made as a result of field conditions and change orders.

Reglet. Small groove under a waterfall that breaks surface tension of water.

Repetitive motion. An activity in which the same motion is repeated many times in the same manner.

Rerod (rebar). Heavy metal bar used to strengthen edges of concrete slabs. Sold in long lengths that are cut with saw or bolt cutters to length needed. Deformed rebars have a rough surface.

Reservoir basin. Water pool located at the bottom of a waterfall or cascade.

Resilient surfacing. Soft surfacing placed below play structures.

Retaining wall. A wall used to retain soil.

Return walls. Walls that run back from the wall face. Typically used to end a wall into a hillside.

Ridge plate. Dimensioned lumber structural member to which rafters are attached at the top.

Rim joist. A structural wood member that runs around the outside of a deck frame in the platform framing method.

Rip-rap. Large-diameter stone placed on embankments and in channels to reduce erosion.

Riser. 1. Vertical portion of a step. 2. The piping that connects an irrigation head to the lateral line.

Rock salt finish. A concrete finish created by sprinkling rock salt on the surface and then rinsing a few days later.

Rodding. Running a vertical screed board over a surface to which a first or second coat of stucco has been applied.

Roof pitch. The slope of a roof.

Root barrier. A plastic shield placed in the ground to direct root growth.

Root zone. The area under and around a plant where roots are located. A tree root zone can be over 1½ times the size of the canopy.

Rubble. A stone that has natural, untrimmed edges.

Rubble walls. Walls constructed of natural stone without mortar.

S

Sabre saw. A hand-powered saw with a thin vertical blade used for cutting curved and detailed shapes.

Safe surfacing. The surfacing under play equipment.

Scale. Instrument used to measure drawings. Also refers to the percent of reduction used to fit a full-sized site onto a sheet of paper.

Schedule 40. Thick-walled PVC pipe.

Scratch coat. The base coat for stucco.

Screed. Tool used to level concrete after it is placed. Typically a straight 2 × 4 longer than the width of the forms. Also term used for leveling of concrete after a pour.

Screening. Metal or fiberglass cloth used to keep out insects.

Sealer. Clear chemical coating that preserves wood or paving.

Section. A drawing that shows two dimensions, vertical and horizontal, and that cuts through an object.

Segmental precast concrete wall unit. Wall building material that is manufactured by casting concrete in a form.

Self-furring metal lath. A metal mesh with small openings and indentations on one side that hold the lath away from the surface. Commonly used in stucco applications.

Setback. The required distance between improvements and property lines, usually specified in zoning ordinances.

Setting bed. Approximately 1-inch thick layer of sand on which unit pavers are set.

Shank. The shaft of a nail or screw.

Sheathing. Sheeted wood material placed under wall and roof surfacing.

Shop drawings. Construction plans provided by the manufacturers of equipment and amenities, showing their interpretation of the designer's requirements.

Silt fence. Geotextile fabric suspended between posts used for erosion control.

Site furniture. Benches, trash receptacles, bike racks, tables, and other site amenities designed for exterior applications.

Skid-steer. A small multiwheeled tractor that turns by braking the wheels on one side.

Skimmers. Openings around the top edge of a pool designed to capture debris floating on the water surface.

Skirting. Screening placed under a deck to hide the structural framework.

Slab. A flat concrete surface.

Sleeper. Wood support for decking that is laid directly on the ground.

Slope. A percentage that represents the vertical difference between two points divided by the horizontal difference.

Slotted drive. Screw with a straight, grooved driving head.

Slump. A measure of the amount of water in concrete.

Sod. Grass that has been cut into strips, with a layer of soil below, for transplanting.

Soffit. Panel placed under the eave to cover structural work.

Softwood. Coniferous, or cone-bearing, trees such as pine, spruce, and fir.

Soil stabilizer. A material used to bind soil and granular materials.

Spacer. Block of wood used to maintain equal spacing between boards applied to a fence.

Spackle. Thin plaster applied over concrete pool surfaces.

Specifications. Written document that includes general information about a construction project and specific information about materials and installation techniques to be used.

Speed square. Small adjustable tool that can mark square and angled markings.

Spindle. Round or square railing post for porch.

Split rail. A horizontal board fence style where the horizontal pieces are split logs, or rails.

Spot elevations. Elevation of a single point on a site.

Sprig. A short section of turf grass stems with at least one or two nodes capable of rooting.

Square. Placement of two objects with a corner that forms a right angle. Also tool used to establish square.

Square-headed drive. Screw with a square pattern driving head.

Stadia. A process that uses the eyepiece crosshairs of a transit to measure both level and distance in one step.

Stain. Chemical coating that colors wood.

Static pool. Water feature that does not have flowing water.

Static roller. A drum-shaped roller compaction tool that is self-propelled or pulled by a tractor.

Step-back batter (stairstep batter). Batter technique in which the front of each higher course of a wall is set back slightly from the course below.

Stone set (brick set). Chisel-like tool used to cleave brick and stone.

Stretcher. Tool used to stretch chain-link fencing fabric.

Striking. Using a special tool to smooth the joints in a masonry installation.

Stringer. Horizontal structural support for fence and rail surfacing.

Stringline. Tool used to identify location and/or elevation of the edge of a project. **Stucco.** A cement and sand mixture applied in heavy coats to walls and vertical surfaces. **Subgrade.** Soil material below paving and base.

Sump. Recessed area at the bottom of an inlet that captures debris from runoff.

Surcharge. Water that is forced back out of an inlet.

Swale. Low ditch designed to occasionally carry water runoff. Swale high point. *See* free out.

Swing joint (swing ell). A riser that has four ells and a straight nipple that joins the laterial and the head.

T

T. A pipe fitting that is shaped like the letter *T* and has openings for pipe at the ends of each tee.

Tack. To temporarily nail objects together.

Tackifier. Sticky substance used to bind hydromulch or hydroseed materials to soil.

Take-off. The process of measuring a drawing to obtain material quantities.

Tangent. A straight line.

Tensile fabric structures (also called shade structures). Fabric stretched between supports to create a covering that can protect whatever it covers from the elements.

Tension wire. Wire used to anchor the bottom of chain-link fabric.

Terrace (Terracing). A series of retaining walls, each set back from the one below it.

Tie. A metal strand or wire that holds opposing forms together.

Ties. Aluminum wires wrapped around chain-link fabric to hold fabric next to posts.

Tile. Round tubing used to conduct drainage of water. Commonly manufactured of plastic, clay, or concrete.

Toe of slope. Low point of a slope.

Toenailing. Securing pieces of lumber by nailing at an angle.

Toggle bolt. A spring-loaded bolt that expands when inserted into a pilot hole and grips when the bolt is tightened.

Top of slope. Upper point of a slope.

Top rail. Top piping of a chain-link fence used to support top of fabric.

Tort. Illegal action that leads to damage of the property of another person.

Transformer. Electrical component engineered to reduce voltage in current.

Transit. Tripod-mounted level that can be used to measure elevations, distances, and horizontal angles on a project.

Tread. Horizontal portion of a step.

Treated woods. Woods that have been treated with preservatives to reduce the potential of decay.

Tree grate. Metal grid that allows water and air access to root systems of trees set in paved areas.

Tree guard. Metal cage placed around trunks of trees in urban areas to protect bark from damage.

Tree well. A retaining wall that keeps soil away from the root zone and trunk of a plant.

Tree spade. A large piece of equipment with hydraulically operated blades that cut through the soil and roots to remove a plant from where it is planted in order to transplant.

Trench drain. A formed/molded linear channel with a grate that sets in a frame on top of the channel.

Trisodium phosphate (TSP). A compound for cleaning masonry and concrete. **Trowel.** Wedge-shaped metal hand tool. Used to mix and place mortar and concrete. **Troweling.** Smoothing the surface of a material, usually concrete, using a trowel.

Truss. A premanufactured roof support composed of rafters and braces.

Turf. Grass areas.

U

Unassignable overhead. Costs of operating a business that cannot be directly attributed to a specific project.

Unit pavers. Bricks, paving block, or other manmade paving materials that are placed one at a time.

Utility. A wire or pipe that supplies basic services to a site (e.g., sewer, water, phone). **Utility plans.** Plans that show the location, type, size, and depth of proposed utilities. **V**

Valve. A mechanical device used to regulate the flow of water.

Veneer. A decorative vertical surfacing applied to an exterior wall. Typically brick or stone.

Verticals. Ties or timbers placed with the long dimension set vertically. Usually buried in front of a wall to prevent the wall from falling forward.

Vibrating roller. A drum-shaped roller compaction tool that is self-propelled or pulled by a tractor and vibrates as it rolls.

Vibratory plate compactor. Metal plate with a motor mounted on top and handle for steering. Vibrates and compacts base material as the machine moves.

Virtual design construction (VDC). Scheduling technique that uses computerized models to integrate the aspects of a building project, including the project itself, the organization working on the project, and the process used to implement the project.

Voltage. The electrical potential of a circuit, or the circuit's ability to do work.

Voltage drop. The loss of voltage.

W, X, Y, Z

Waterproof wire nut. A wire connector designed to protect the connection from water by surrounding it in a waterproof substance.

Watt. A measure of the amount of electricity being used.

Wattle. A tubular-shaped nylon netting filled with straw fibers or small sapling branches and used on slopes to control erosion.

Weepholes. Openings in the face of a retaining wall that allow water to drain from behind the wall.

Weep screed. Galvanized flashing.

Weir. An opening that regulates the amount of water flowing past a point.

Welded wire fencing. Panels of welding heavy gauge steel wire in a grid pattern.

Welded (woven) wire mesh (WWM). Metal wires welded together in a grid pattern used to reinforce concrete. Typically 10-gauge wire with 6-inch squares.

Wet masonry saw. Table-mounted circular saw that uses water to aid in cutting masonry materials.

Wet screed. A technique used when a screed is too short or a surface needs to be warped. Performed by resting one end of the screed on a form and holding the other end at a height that is approximately where the other form would be.

Wood float. Wide, flat wood tool with a handle mounted on top used to smooth concrete surfaces.

Wythe. Width of one masonry unit.

Xenon. A lamp that uses ionized xenon gas to produce light.

BIBLIOGRAPHY

Alth, Max. *Do It Yourself Plumbing.* New York: Sterling Publishing Co., Inc., 1987.

Aquascape Designs, Inc. *Professional Pond Kits.* Batavia, IL: Aquascape Designs, Inc., 2000.

Bruneau, Arthus, Miller, Grady, Peacock, Charles. *Carolina Lawns.* North Carolina Cooperative Extension Service, no date.

California Redwood Association. *Redwood Deck Construction.* Novato, CA: California Redwood Association, 2001.

Collier, Clifford W. Jr. *Tree Wells.* Morgantown, WV: Cooperative Extension Work in Agriculture and Home Economics, West Virginia University and the U.S. Department of Agriculture, 1973.

Construction Specification Institute. *CSINet website.* Alexandria, VA: Construction Specification Institute, 2003. http://www.csinet.org/.

DeCosse, Cy, ed. *Black and Decker Home Improvement Library, Landscape Design and Construction Projects.* Minnetonka, MN: Cy DeCosse Incorporated, 1992.

Everett, T. H. *Lawns and Landscaping.* New York: Grosser Good Life Books, 1976.

Feucht, James R., and Butler, Jack D. *Landscape Management.* New York: Van Nostrand Reinhold.

FX Luminaire. *Specification Guide.* San Diego, CA: 2009.

Gale Pacific Limited. *Coolaroo Installation Guide,* Victoria, Australia: 2009.

Glen-Gery Brickwork. *Exterior Paving with* Brickwork. Wyomissing, PA: Glen-Gery Corporation, 1992.

Greenfix America. *Technical Data, ECB Installation Guide* (www.greenfix.com). Calipatria, CA: Greenfix America, 2003.

Hinze, Jimmie. *Construction Planning and Scheduling.* Upper Saddle River, NJ: Prentice Hall, 1998.

Home How To Institute. *A Portfolio of Deck Ideas.* Minnetonka, MN: Cy DeCosse Incorporated, 1993.

Hughes, Dwight Jr. *Systems for Success.* Cedar Rapids, IA: Dwight Hughes Systems, Inc., 1996.

Ingels, Jack E. *Landscaping Principles and Practices,* 5th ed. Clifton Park, NY: Thomson Delmar Learning, 1997.

Interlocking Concrete Pavement Institute. *Tech Spec, # 2, #3, and #5,* Sterling, VA: Inter locking Concrete Pavement Institute, 1994, 1995, 1996.

International Society of Arboriculture. (Web site search terms: ISA). Champaign, IL: -ISA 2003.

Iowa One Call. *Professional Excavators Manual.* Des Moines, IA: Iowa One Call, 1995.

King's Materials. *Installation Instructions Data Sheet.* Cedar Rapids, IA: King's Materials, 1997.

Lewis, Gaspar. *Carpentry,* 2nd ed. Clifton Park, NY: Thomson Delmar Learning, 1994.

Maylon, Gary. *Walls and Ceilings. National Gypsum* Product *Information.* Troy, MI: Business News Publishing Co, 2003.

National Association of Home Builders Research Foundation. *Residential Concrete,* 2nd ed.

Washington, DC: Home Builder Press, 1994.

Naval Education and Training Command, and Buza, John. *Builder 3 and 2, Volume 1 and Volume 2, NAVEDTRA 12520 and 12521.* Philadelphia, PA: U.S. Navy, 1994.

Physiotherapy Associates. *Protect Your Back—Prevent Injury.* Cedar Rapids, IA: Work Injury Rehabilitation Center, 1995.

Pittenger, Dennis R. ed. *California Master Gardener Handbook.* Oakland, CA: Division of Agriculture and Natural Resources, University of California, 2002.

Portland Cement Association. *Design and Control of Concrete Mixtures,* 12th ed. Skokie, IL: Portland Cement Association, 1979.

Portland Cement Association. *The Homeowner's Guide to Building with Concrete, Brick & Stone.* Emmaus, PA: Rodale Press, 1988.

Portland Cement Association. *Portland Cement Plaster (*Stucco*)* (Web site search terms: stucco, Portland cement). Skokie, IL: Portland Cement Association, 2003. http://www.portcement.com/.

Presto Products Company. *Cellular Confinement System Installation Technical Guide.* Appleton, WI: Presto Products Company, 2003.

Rayner, Horace, and Schmidt, Milton. *Fundamentals of* Surveying. New York: Van Nostrand Reinhold Company, 1969.

Reid, Jeffrey. *How to Build Ponds and Waterfalls: The* Complete *Guide.* New York: Tetra Press, 1998.

Roocroft, Tony. *Complete Pond Solver Book,* 2003. http://www.pondprofessorfountains.com/admin/about_us.htm

Sherwood, Gerald, and Stroh, Robert. *Wood Frame House* Construction. New York: Sterling Publishing Co., Inc., 1992.

Spence, William Perkins. *Construction Methods, Materials, and Techniques.* Clifton Park, NY: Thomson Delmar Learning, 1998.

Stone Deck Incorporated. *Natural Stone Decking Installation Guide.* Concord, CA: 2007

Stone Products Corporation. Culture *Brick Installation Instructions* (Web site search terms: cultured stone products), Napa, CA: Author, 1996.

Stryker, Jess. *Jess Stryker's Landscape Sprinkler and Drip Irrigation Installation Tutorial.* Jess Stryker, 2001. http://www.irrigationtutorials.com/.

Sunset Books and Magazines. *Decks.* Menlo Park, CA: Lane Publishing Co., 1975.

Sunset Books and Magazines. *Fences and Gates.* Menlo Park, CA: Lane Publishing Co., 1975.

Sunset Books and Magazines. *Patio Roofs and Gazebos.* Menlo Park, CA: Lane Publishing Co., 1992.

Sunset Books and Magazines. *Walls, Walks, and Patio Floors.* Menlo Park, CA: Lane Publishing Co., 1975.

Tallahassee, Florida, City of. *A Mini-Directory of Tree Protection Techniques.* Tallahassee, FL: 2001.

Townsend, Karen, Ham, Donald, Miller, Ansel, and Chesnut, Timothy. *Soil Aeration Systems—Do They Really Improve Tree Root Zone Conditions Under Fill and Paving?*

Clemson, SC: Department of Forestry, Clemson University, 1997.

U.S. Concrete, Central Concrete Supply Co. Inc. *Pervious Concrete Sample Specification.*

Houston, TX, 2003.

U.S. Consumer Product Safety Commission. *Handbook for Public Playground Safety.* Washington, DC: Author, 1995.

U.S. Department of Agriculture, Forest Service. *Techline Durability: What's in That Pressure-Treated Wood?* Madison, WI: USDA Forest Service, 2000.

Vivian, John. *Building Stone Walls,* 2nd ed., North Adams, MA: Storey Books, 1978.

Wilson, Bruce. *Efficacy of Erosion-Control Blankets and Soil Stabilizer.* Minneapolis, MN: Regents of the University of Minnesota, 2002.

Wing, Charlie. *Visual Handbook of Building and Remodeling.* Emmaus, PA: Rodale Press, 1990.